Preface

In a rapidly expanding field such as plant physiology an author of a general text finds himself with the difficult task of summarizing and evaluating a vast abundance of material. Indeed, the ability to omit and condense becomes some of his most practiced talents. Despite considerable pruning, however, the fundamental principles as they apply to the various fields of study in plant physiology have been clearly stated and analyzed. Areas such as photosynthesis, mineral nutrition, and plant growth regulation have been given careful attention since advances in these areas in the last decade and a half can only be described as explosive.

The material presented in the book has been organized in such a manner as to make it applicable to a one or two semester course. Adequate coverage of the entire book can be accomplished in a full two semester academic year. However, with a certain amount of trimming and condensation, it can be used in a one semester course. It is suggested that before a student uses this book for a course in general plant physiology he should take general courses in botany and inorganic and organic chemistry. In our time one is "hard put" to distinguish between the fields of biochemistry and physiology, a situation that makes it almost mandatory for a student to be well grounded in certain chemical principles before he undertakes a course in plant physiology.

The book is divided into eight sections, each section covering a specific area of plant physiology. A professor using it can start at the beginning of any one section, depending upon the background of his students. In other words, lecture units can conveniently be associated with sections in the book. This allows for closer ties between lecture and text, something of a rarity in today's college classroom.

The author recognizes the value of an illustration as an aid to the presentation of difficult or complex material. For this reason the book is extensively illustrated. Many of the illustrations have been taken from professional papers and, as is customary, specific acknowledgments have been given in the captions. For the more inquisitive student there are numerous references at the end of most of the chapters suggesting sources of more detailed information. Most of the references listed are from original papers and if used by a student should help him become acquainted with the literature in his field of particular interest. Finally, the extensive use of references helps bring a student into contact with those men who contribute most to plant physiology.

I wish to asknowledge the aid given by Drs. M. Arif Hayat, Robert L. Burgess, and Earl A. Helgeson who gave encouragement when it was most needed. I also wish to thank my wife, Wanda T. Devlin, whose patience and cheerfulness made the writing of this book a less arduous task.

ROBERT M. DEVLIN

June, 1966

Thomas Julie

2-1

Reinhold books in the biological sciences

Consulting Editor: PROFESSOR PETER GRAY
Andrey Avinoff Distinguished Professor of Biology
University of Pittsburgh, Pittsburgh, Pennsylvania

The Encyclopedia of the Biological Sciences, edited by Peter Gray
The Biological Control of Insects, Pests, and Weeds, edited by Paul DeBach
Biophysics: Concepts and Mechanism, by E. J. Casey
Cell Function, by L. L. Langley
Chordate Morphology, by Malcolm Jollie
Concepts of Forest Entomology, by Kenneth Graham
Cytology, Second Edition, by G. B. Wilson and John H. Morrison
Ecology of Inland Waters and Estuaries, by George K. Reid
Environmental Measurement and Interpretation, by Robert B. Platt and John F. Griffiths
Evolution: Process and Product, Revised Edition, by Edward O. Dobson
Experimental Biology: Measurement and Analysis, by R. H. Kay
Experimental Entomology, by Kenneth W. Cummins, Lee D. Miller, Ned A. Smith, and Richard M. Fox
General Zoology, by Clarence J. Goodnight, Marie L. Goodnight, and Peter Gray
Human Genetics and Its Foundations, by Maurice Whittinghill
Introduction to Comparative Entomology, by Richard M. Fox and Jean Walker Fox
Introduction to Microbiology, by Stanley E. Wedberg
Macromolecular Structure of Ribonucleic Acids, by A. S. Spirin
Management of Artificial Lakes and Ponds, by George W. Bennett
Manual of Insect Morphology, by E. Melville DuPorte
Natural History, Richard A. Pimentel
Paramedical Microbiology, by Stanley E. Wedberg
Physiology of Man, Third Edition, by L. L. Langley and E. Cheraskin
The Plant Community, by Herbert C. Hanson and Ethan D. Churchill
Principles in Mammalogy, by David E. Davis and Frank B. Golley

Selected Topics in Modern Biology

Developmental Genetics, by Frederick J. Gottlieb

Functional Organelles, by John H. Morrison

The Gene Concept, by Natalie Barish

Homeostasis, by L. L. Langley

Introduction to Cell Differentiation, by Nelson T. Spratt, Jr.

The Origin of Life, by John Keosian

Selected Topics in Modern Chemistry

Acids, Bases, and the Chemistry of the Covalent Bond, by Calvin A. Vander-Werf

Basic Concepts of Nuclear Chemistry, by Ralph T. Overman

Chemical Bonding and the Geometry of Molecules, by George Ryschkewitsch

Chemical Energy, by Laurence E. Strong and Wilmer J. Stratton

The Chemistry of the Lanthanides, by Therald Moeller

Chemistry in Non-Aqueous Solvents, by Harry H. Sisler

The Chemistry of Some Life Processes, by Vernon H. Cheldelin and Robert W. Newburgh

Colloid Chemistry, by Robert D. Vold and Marjorie J. Vold

Electronic Structure, Properties, and the Periodic Law, by Harry H. Sisler

Inorganic Complex Compounds, by R. Kent Murmann

An Introduction to Molecular Kinetic Theory, by Joel Hildebrand

Modern Chemical Kinetics, by Henry Eyring and Edward M. Eyring

The Mole Concept in Chemistry, by William F. Kieffer

The Nature and Chemistry of High Polymers, by Kenneth F. O'Driscoll

Organometallic Chemistry, by Eugene G. Rochow

Physical Methods for Determining Molecular Geometry, by Wallace Brey

Principles of Chemical Equilibrium, by Kelso Morris

Consulting editor's statement

A book on plant physiology is a specialized work in a generalized field. An introductory book on this subject therefore presents the author with the difficult problem of making sure that the student is as aware of the wood as he is of the trees. Professor Devlin has achieved this by devoting his first eight chapters to the fundamental processes of physiology, illustrating his remarks with examples drawn from the plant kingdom without at any time narrowing the breadth of approach necessary to fundamental understanding. A chapter on the translocation of sugars then forms a natural bridge to three chapters on the photosynthetic process and photosynthetic structures, in which the author presents an unusually clear account of contemporary theory well documented by references to the literature. This is followed by an extensive treatment of mineral metabolism, nitrogen metabolism, and hormones, with chapters on photoperiodism, vernalization, and dormancy.

The treatment is throughout both scholarly and clear, and the extensive bibliography which terminates each chapter gives ample opportunity for reading assignments or the organization of seminars. In fact, Professor Devlin's book not only fills, but fills admirably, a gap in the series of Reinhold Books in the Biological Sciences.

Peter Gray

Plant

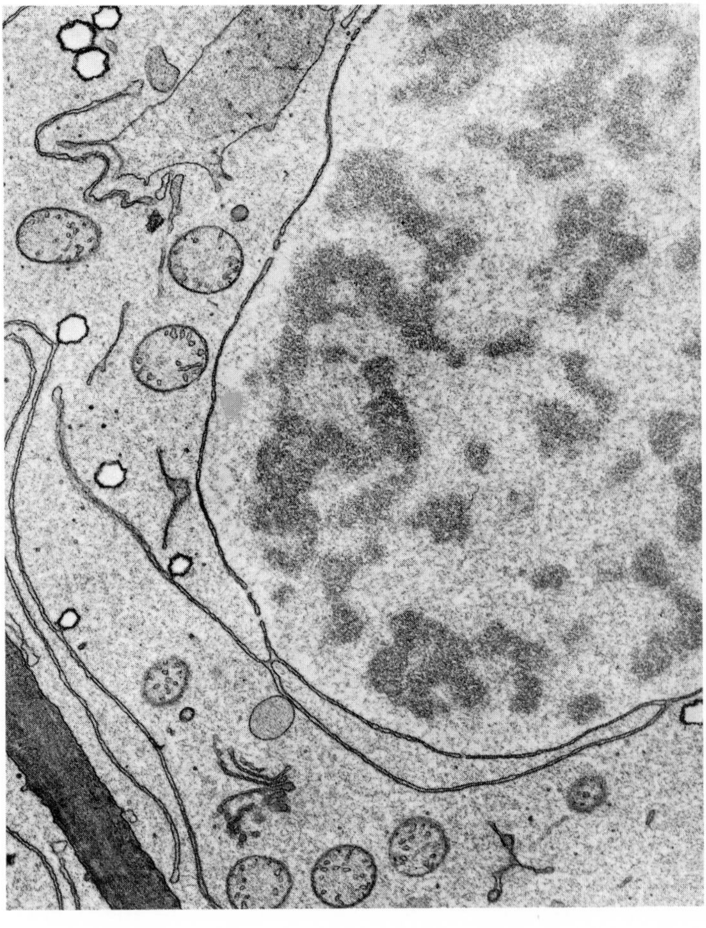

physiology

ROBERT M. DEVLIN
University of Massachusetts
East Wareham, Massachusetts

Reinhold Publishing Corporation New York

Library of Congress Catalog Card Number: 66-25438
Printed in the United States of America

The photograph on the title page is an electron micrograph of a portion of a meristematic rootcap cell of maize. (From W. Whaley et al. 1960. Am. J. Botany 47:401.)

Contents

Part ONE

Introduction

1

The plant cell—structure and function of its parts

INTRODUCTION

Although appearing relatively homogeneous in structure, the plant can actually be thought of as a community of microscopic structures or units called cells. In a most amazing and not as yet completely understood manner, these small units work harmoniously together to give life to the multicellular plant. In the unicellular plant, such as found in the lower forms of plant life (bacteria and algae), the cell is a living individual unit capable of existing in the absence of other cells.

We are on pretty safe ground when we say the cell is the basic unit of life. That is, it is the smallest structure in the universe capable of growth and reproduction. Viruses, considered living units by some, are considerably smaller than cells. No virus, however, has yet been observed that was not associated with a living cell and completely dependent upon it for reproduction. The viruses, then, lacking this important characteristic of self-replication, cannot be called basic units of life.

The size and shape of a plant is due largely to the number, morphology, and arrangement of its cells. For example, succeeding chapters will show how the conductive tissues of a plant are made up of cells structurally equipped for the rapid transport of large amounts of water and nutrients. Also in later chapters a definite relationship between cellular structure and function in the leaves and roots of a plant will be given. Indeed, it is the purpose of this book to study the physiology of the plant, a study that begins with the plant cell and its parts.

Figure 1-1 shows a diagrammatic representation of the typical plant cell.

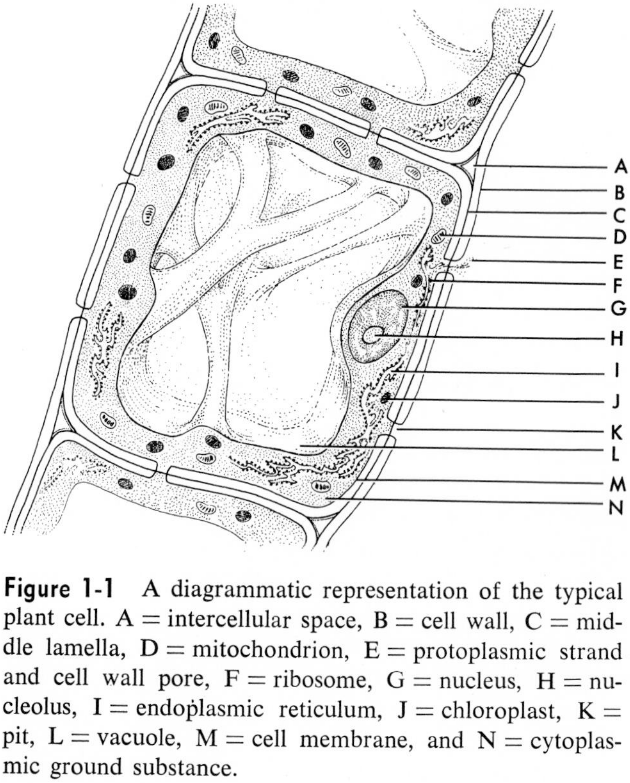

Figure 1-1 A diagrammatic representation of the typical plant cell. A = intercellular space, B = cell wall, C = middle lamella, D = mitochondrion, E = protoplasmic strand and cell wall pore, F = ribosome, G = nucleus, H = nucleolus, I = endoplasmic reticulum, J = chloroplast, K = pit, L = vacuole, M = cell membrane, and N = cytoplasmic ground substance.

CELL WALL

With only a few exceptions, all organisms must have mechanical support of some kind in order to maintain a definite form. In the animal world, this support is either an exoskeleton within which other cells are confined or an endoskeleton to which the other cells cling. In the plant world, however, each individual cell is enclosed in a relatively rigid structure called the *cell wall,* which is lacking in the animal cell. The cell wall is generally thought of as a nonliving part of the cell, which is secreted and maintained by the living portion of the cell called the *protoplast.* However, the designation of nonliving and living properties to different parts of the cell is not entirely correct since its component parts cannot exist apart from each other.

By far the chief structural component of the cell wall is *cellulose,* a compound formed by the stringing together of many thousands of sugar units produced by photosynthesis. A more complete picture of the chemical aspects of cell wall synthesis has been left to a later chapter. In addition to cellulose, pectic compounds, hemicelluloses, lignin, suberin, and cutin represent the chief compounds found in the cell wall.

Cell wall formation

Cell wall formation is initiated during the most advanced stage of mitosis called the telophase (Figure 1-2). Note in Figure 1-2 that tubular fragments of the endoplasmic reticulum appear to have migrated to the equatorial region during telophase. It is thought by many investigators that these fragments participate in the formation of the *cell plate* or *middle lamella.* We may think of the middle lamella as the cementing substance between adjoining cells. One compound in particular, calcium pectate (calcium salt of pectic acid), is most abundant in the middle lamella and acts as an important cementing material between cells. Indeed, the characteristic softening of fruit during the ripening process is caused to a large extent by the pectic substances of the middle lamella becoming more soluble. That is, these substances lose their binding properties through the mediation of pectolytic enzymes, which increase in activity as a fruit matures.

Primary wall. The primary wall borders the middle lamella and is the first product of cell wall synthesis by the protoplast. While the cell is enlarging, the primary wall stays relatively thin and elastic, thickening and becoming rigid only after the completion of cell enlargement.

Early investigators believed that the primary wall contained pectic substances, hemicelluloses, and cellulose, with the pectic substances being present in abundance and having a dominant role in the behavior of the wall during cell growth. For example, Kerr (13) has pointed out that the flexibility of the primary wall during cell elongation suggests the presence and importance of pectic substances. However, an analysis of the primary walls of *Avena coleoptile* cells by Bishop et al. (5) showed that hemi-

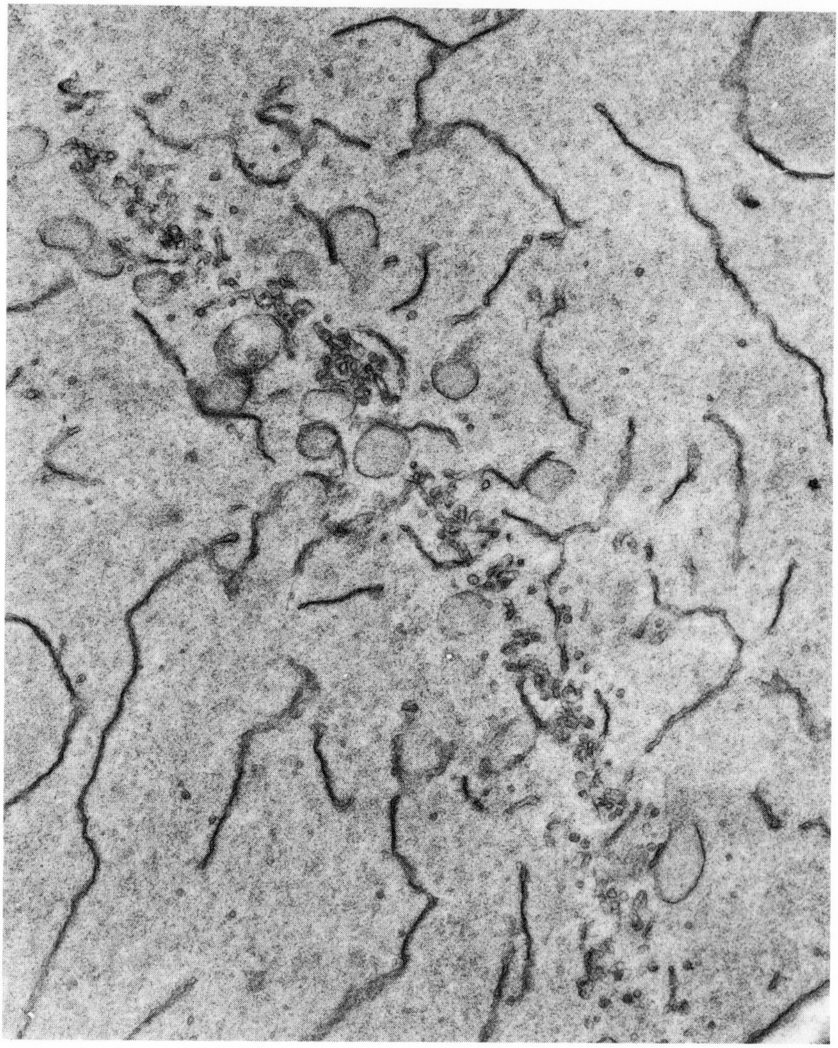

Figure 1-2 Electron micrograph showing early state of cell plate formation in telophase of dividing onion root tip cell. A small portion of each telophase nucleus is seen at the upper right and lower left. The developing cell plate extends diagonally from lower right to upper left. Membrane elements of the endoplasmic reticulum with evidence of branching are present on both sides of the cell plate. In the immediate vicinity of the cell plate the elements of the endoplasmic reticulum are shorter and form a reticulation composed of a close lattice of tubules along the midline between the two cells. (After K. Porter and R. Machado. 1960. Biophys. Biochem. Cytol. 7:167.)

celluloses were present in much greater concentration than pectic substances. Similarly, Ray (20) and Albersheim (1) have demonstrated that primary walls are low in pectic substances. This information suggests that hemicelluloses and other components of the primary wall play a more important role in the initial stages of cell growth than previously thought.

In a study of the wall composition of onion root tip cells, Jensen (12) found that although cell walls of provascular cells were high in pectic substances and hemicelluloses, the cell walls of the cortex and protoderm were low in these compounds. It appears that although all of the common constituents of the cell wall are present in the primary wall, their relative concentrations vary in accordance with the type of cell under investigation.

Secondary wall. As the cell matures, the cell wall thickens as layers of cellulose are laid down by the cytoplasm. The wall becomes much less flexible and, finally, almost inelastic. It is understandable, then, why cell elongation ceases with the onset of secondary wall formation. It is the secondary wall that gives the plant cell its structural independence.

By far the most conspicuous constituent of the secondary wall is cellulose. Cell wall layers laid down toward the latter stages of cell growth are, in many cases, almost pure cellulose. A familiar example is the cotton fiber where more than 90% of the wall dry weight is pure cellulose.

Molecular and macromolecular arrangement of cellulose in the cell wall. The cell wall may be thought of as a finely interwoven network of cellulose strands of varying complexity and size. The association of molecular cellulose chains has recently been reviewed by Siegel (24) and are as follows. The smallest structural units of the cell wall are the *elementary fibrils* or *micelles*. These so-called micelles are composed of approximately 100 individual cellulose chains and have a cross-sectional area of about 3000 Å^2. The next largest cellulose strand is the *microfibril,* which is thought to be composed of about 20 micelles and to have a cross-sectional area of about 62,500 Å^2 (Figure 1-3). Although the individual cellulose molecular chains cannot be observed even with the electron microscope, the micelles and microfibrils are clearly discernible under the electron microscope. An aggregation of about 250 microfibrils will compose a microscopic *fibril* with a cross-sectional area of 0.16 μ^2. A cotton fiber, which is visible to the naked eye, may have as many as 1500 fibrils. A little multiplication will show that there are as many as 7.5×10^8 individual molecular cellulose chains in one macroscopic cotton fiber.

The physical organization of the microfibrils in the primary and secondary wall is quite different. In the primary wall the microfibrils run roughly transverse to the cell axis, but do show a longitudinal orientation at the cell corners. Three distinct layers have been distinguished in the secondary wall, each one having a different microfibril arrangement (Figure 1-4).

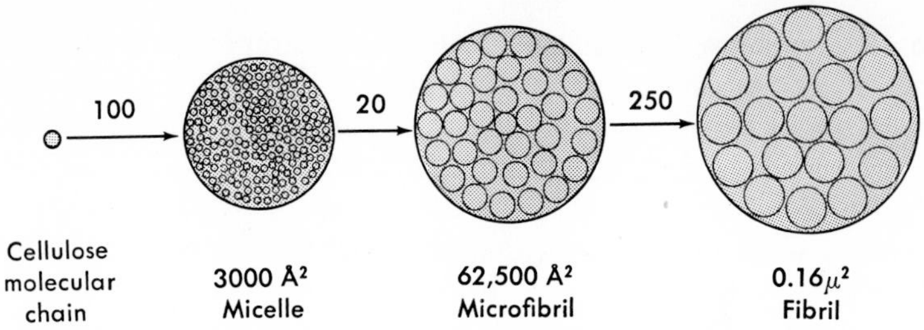

Figure 1-3 Diagrammatic representation of the association of molecular cellulose strands showing the approximate cross-sectional area.

For example, in the conifer tracheid wall one can distinguish five layers—the middle lamella, a thin primary wall, and a three-layered secondary wall. We can account, then, for nine layers of wall separating the cell cavities of two adjacent tracheids.

In Figure 1-4 two spirals of microfibrils may be seen in the outer layer

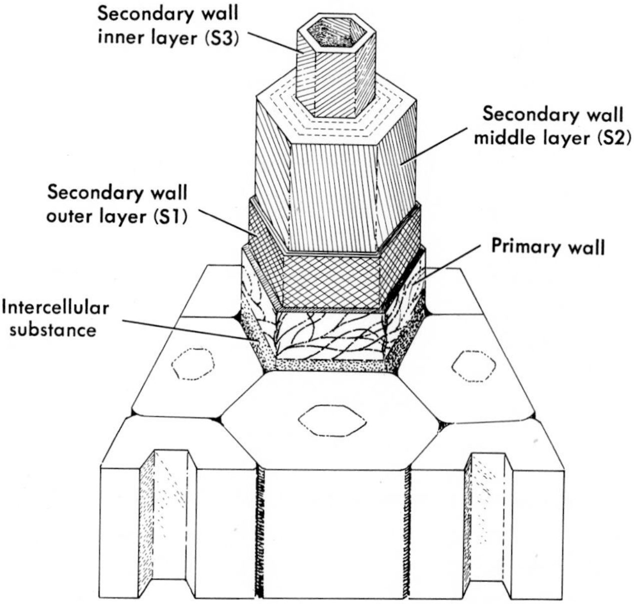

Figure 1-4 A cutaway view of the different layers of the cell wall showing the different arrangement of cellulose microfibrils in each layer. (After A. Wardrop and D. Bland. 1959. Proc. 4th Intl. Congr. of Biochem. Pergamon Press, New York. 2:76.)

of the secondary wall forming a rather large angle with the cell axis. In the middle section a steep spiral in addition to concentric rings of microfibrils can be observed. The inner layer is thought to have a flat helical arrangement (see review by Wardrop and Bland (26)).

Site of synthesis. Early investigators believed that wall synthesis took place at a distinct cytoplasm-wall interface. However, with the advent of the electron microscope, the consensus of opinion was that the cytoplasm actually penetrated the wall at different localities along the cytoplasm-wall interface (19, 31). Wall synthesis, it was postulated, takes place in these isolated areas. Other investigators adopted a somewhat modified version of the above concept, that wall synthesis takes place where *plasmadesmata* (cytoplasmic strands) penetrate the wall (25, 23). Still other investigators believe that the synthesis of microfibrils can take place throughout the wall at areas separate from the cytoplasmic surface (3). Apparently, all the precursors necessary for wall synthesis would move to these areas of wall synthesis, most likely through the mediation of plasmadesmata. Whaley et al. (29) have pointed out the probable importance of the extension of the endoplasmic reticulum to the surface of the protoplast in this respect.

Thus, it is apparent that we can no longer accept the idea of a precise cytoplasm-wall interface. There is no doubt that the wall is penetrated in numerous places by the cytoplasm, and these places, in all likelihood, are areas of wall synthesis.

CELL MEMBRANE

Although the cell wall to some extent separates the cell from its environment, it does a very inefficient job in this respect. Most materials in the immediate environment of the cell have no trouble passing through the cell wall. If the cell possessed no other barrier to the entrance of unwanted materials into its interior, life for the cell would indeed be hazardous. In fact, the living cell, as such, could not exist. However, directly adjacent to the interior wall and surrounding the protoplast is a thin, delicate, flexible structure called the *cell membrane* or *plasmalema.* The importance of this structure to the living cell cannot be overemphasized. Since the membrane encloses the cytoplasm and cytoplasmic inclusions, we can say the membrane contains the living system and in a very real sense protects it.

The cell membrane performs the vital role of regulating the passage of materials in and out of the cell. In other words, the cell membrane is *differentially permeable,* allowing certain materials to pass into the cell but excluding others. In addition, the cell membrane provides only a one-way passage for certain materials into the cell and blocks their passage out. For example, certain essential mineral elements must be accumulated in the cell in higher concentrations than they are found in the cell's immediate environment. Also of major importance to the cell, the membrane blocks to a great extent the penetration of most toxic compounds into the cytoplasm.

Because of the color similarity between the cell membrane and its cytoplasm, it is very difficult to separately distinguish the two under the light microscope. However, the cell membrane is very clearly shown as a structure separate from the cytoplasm by the electron microscope.

Chemical and physical analyses of the cell membrane suggest that it is a lipoprotein structure, having a bimolecular lipid center sandwiched between monomolecular layers of protein. Robertson (21) has postulated that the total thickness of the membrane should be about 75 Å. A molecular model representing the cell membrane is given in Figure 1-5.

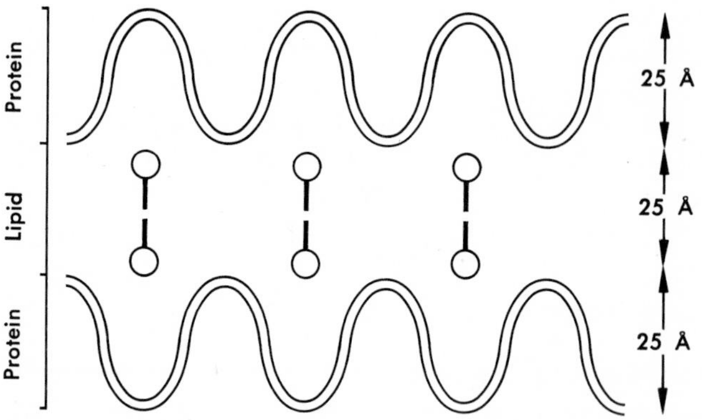

Figure 1-5 A molecular model of the cell membrane showing a bimolecular lipid center bordered by monomolecular layers of protein. (After J. Robertson. 1962. Sci. Am. 206(4):64.)

INCLUSIONS OF THE CYTOPLASM

Endoplasmic reticulum

The cytoplasm of the meristematic cell is interlaced by an elaborate membrane-bound vesicular system called the *endoplasmic reticulum* or *ergastoplasm*. The membranes bounding this system are thought to have a lipoprotein structure somewhat analogous to that of the cell membrane. Although maintaining its general appearance, the endoplasmic reticulum may become modified during development and during certain activities of the cell.

According to several observations, the endoplasmic reticulum is continuous with the nuclear membrane and extends to the cell surface (27, 30). In fact, membranes of this system have been found in the primary walls of some cells and even extending to neighboring cells (29, 30). Whaley et al. (29) have pointed out that the inclusion of the nuclear membrane with the endoplasmic reticulum provides for extensive surface contact between nuclear material and the cell cytoplasm. Where some strands of the endoplasmic reticulum extend from one cell to the next, the nuclei of both cells may be said to be in direct contact with each other.

A three-dimensional view of the cell will show that the endoplasmic reticulum divides the cytoplasm into numerous small cavities. This compartmentalization of the cytoplasm has drawn a great deal of attention in recent years. Within these compartments certain enzymes and metabolites may be accumulated or excluded—a circumstance, perhaps, of vital importance to the cell. We will see in a later chapter, for example, that a reaction can be forced to move in a certain direction by overloading the system with a certain metabolite and excluding another. Although not completely explored by any stretch of the imagination, the importance of the endoplasmic reticulum to the general functioning of the cell has been fully appreciated.

Mitochondrion

With the possible exception of the nucleus, the *mitochondrion* has been the most studied component of the cell. As a result, our knowledge of the morphology and function of this cytoplasmic inclusion is quite extensive. We will concern ourselves at this time more with the morphology of the mitochondrion than with its function, which is covered in detail in the chapter on respiration.

Energy transfer in mitochondria. Because a great deal of the cell's usable energy is provided by the mitochondrion, it is often referred to as the "powerhouse" of the cell. As might be expected, where cellular activity is high, mitochondria tend to accumulate. An example would be the meristematic cell where mitochondria are found in abundance. What is meant when we say mitochondria provide the cell with usable energy? When biological oxidations of proteins, fats, and carbohydrates occur in the cell, energy is released. This is somewhat analogous to the burning of paper or wood where energy is released in the form of heat. However, in the cell, and particularly in mitochondria, much of the energy released is conserved in the form of high-energy phosphate bonds. The most important compound in this respect is adenosine triphosphate (ATP). The advantage of storing energy in this compound is that it can be released and utilized quite readily to drive the energy-consuming reactions of the cell. ATP, then, is synthesized in mitochondria from where it is dispersed throughout the cell to energy-consuming areas. The mitochondrion is indeed the "powerhouse" of the cell.

Mitochondria morphology. Let us now consider the structure of the mitochondrion, an area of study where the electron microscope has been a dominant factor. These pleomorphic (many forms) bodies are bounded by a double membrane, which encloses an inner matrix, and range in size from about 0.2 to 3.0 μ. Numerous folds, which project deep into the

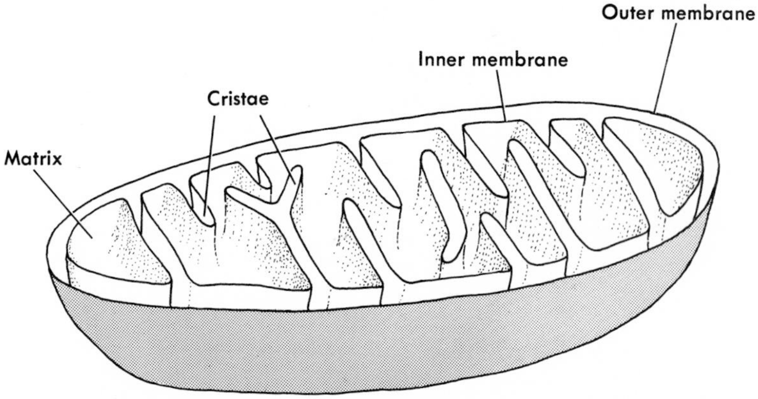

Figure 1-6 A diagrammatic representation of a longitudinal section of a mitochondrion. Note the double membrane and the projecting folds or cristae of the inner membrane.

matrix, occur in the inner membrane. Some of these folds have been observed completely bridging the interior of the mitochondrion and connecting with the inner membrane on the opposite side. These projecting folds of the inner membrane are collectively called the *cristae* (Figure 1-6).

The cristae of mitochondria have attracted a great deal of attention because of their close resemblance to the lamellar system found in chloroplasts (see Chapter 10). Perhaps these two cytoplasmic inclusions have a common origin.

Importance of structural organization. Because of the complex structural organization found in mitochondria and because of the similarity of organization in mitochondria from a large variety of species, one can only assume a close relation between form and function. For example, oxidative phosphorylation (synthesis of ATP) ceases on loss of the double membrane structure. Also, it appears that reactions of the Krebs cycle, which occur in mitochondria, are dependent upon the double membrane structure (32) although the enzymes involved in these reactions can easily be extracted from the soluble matrix. It is interesting to note that fragments of mitochondria are capable of carrying out some, but not all, of the oxidations of the Krebs cycle (8, 9).

Origin of mitochondria. Although numerous studies have been made, the origin of mitochondria has not satisfactorily been elucidated. However, several theories as to their origin have been expressed. Whaley et al. (30) have stated the opinion that mitochondria probably can both fuse and divide. Small, dense, cytoplasmic inclusions called "microbodies" have been implicated as precursors of mitochondria (22). The Golgi apparatus (7) and even the nucleus (11, 12) have been suspected of giving rise to mitochondria. Finally, the suggestion that mitochondria may arise from the cell membrane has been offered by Ben Geren and Schmidt (4).

Chloroplast

The structure and function of the chloroplast has been thoroughly covered in the three chapters on photosynthesis.

Golgi apparatus

Before the advent of the electron microscope, the existence of the *Golgi apparatus,* or *Golgi complex* as it is sometimes called, was a controversial subject. However, electron micrographs leave no doubt as to its existence (Figure 1-7).

Structure of Golgi apparatus. The *Golgi apparatus* as seen in electron micrographs is composed of two distinct structures, a stack of flattened membrane-bound *cisternae* and several small spherical *vesicles,* which appear to group around the edges of the cisternae. According to Whaley et al. (29), the Golgi vesicles evolve from the edge of the Golgi cisternae. The probable assumption here is that the vesicles "pinch off" from the surface of the cisternae membrane.

The membranes of the Golgi apparatus somewhat resemble those of the endoplasmic reticulum. Indeed, some investigators (10) believe that some fusion between the Golgi cisternae and the endoplasmic reticulum may take place. These investigators suggest also that the small vesicles associated with the Golgi cisternae may fuse with these cisternae or fuse with each other to form cisternae.

Function of the Golgi apparatus. As yet the Golgi apparatus has not

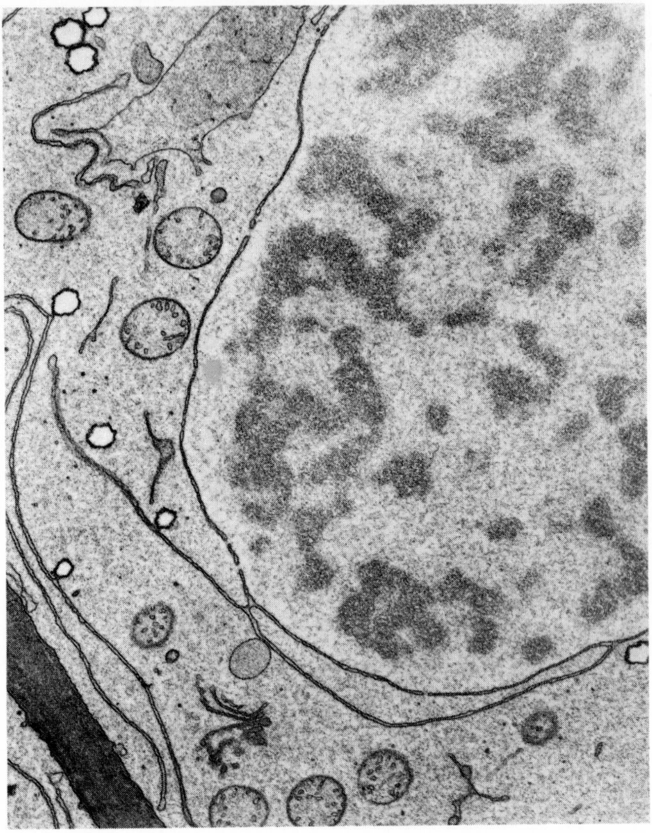

Figure 1-7 Electron micrograph of portion of a meristematic rootcap cell of maize, showing a double-layered nuclear membrane with distinct pores. Note the continuity of the outer membrane of the nuclear membrane with double membrane elements of the endoplasmic reticulum. Mitochondria, a Golgi apparatus (lower left in figure) and unidentified cytoplasmic inclusions are shown. (After W. Whaley et al. 1960. Am. J. Botany 47:401.)

been isolated in the pure state, so we can only speculate on its function. Since it is most readily observed in secretory cells, the most popular theory is that it may be involved in some sort of cellular synthesis. Golgi apparatuses have been observed to concentrate in the region of cell plate formation (30), suggesting some function in this process.

Microsome (ribosome)

Associated with the endoplasmic reticulum and floating free in the cytoplasm are submicroscopic particles called *microsomes* or *ribosomes.* According to Whaley et al. (30), microsomal fractions of the cytoplasm may contain as high as 40–50% of the cell ribonucleic acid (RNA), 15% of the cell protein, and about 50% of the cell phospholipid. The microsome, then, can be termed a "phospholipid-ribonucleo-protein complex." RNA is a nucleic acid that functions primarily in the synthesis of protein, a fact which led investigators to assume that microsomes have an important function in protein synthesis. This assumption was proven correct when protein synthesis was demonstrated with microsomes isolated from the cell.

Vacuole

In young immature cells, such as found in meristematic regions, the cell generally is filled with a dense cytoplasm. Scattered throughout the cytoplasm are relatively clear droplets resembling in many respects air bubbles in water. These little droplets are called *vacuoles.* As the cell matures and enlarges, the small vacuoles fuse together to form one large vacuole which usually fills almost the entire cavity of the cell. In this case the cytoplasm is pressed up against the cell wall, forming just a thin layer around the vacuole (Figure 1-1).

The vacuole is bounded on the outside by a single lipoprotein membrane, which encloses water containing numerous materials in solution and suspension referred to collectively as the *cell sap.* As with the cell membrane, the vacuolar membrane is differentially permeable.

In higher plant tissues, the primary function of the vacuole is the maintenance of turgor so necessary for support and the control of water movement. Since the cell sap contains such substances as sugars, organic acids, mineral salts, gases, pigments, fats, etc., it is obvious that the vacuole also acts as a "sink" for metabolic products or substrates.

Nucleus

Ever since its discovery by Robert Brown in 1835, the *nucleus* of the cell has attracted the interest and curiosity of thousands of investigators. It is, indeed, an interesting subject for study, being the controlling influence in the heredity and activity of the cell. For example, the nucleus controls or directs the synthesis of the enzymes that catalyze most, if not all, of the metabolic reactions of the cell. In other words, the nucleus has a controlling influence on the physiology of the cell.

In the immature cell the nucleus appears as a spherical body centrally located in the cytoplasm of the cell. However, in the mature living cell the nucleus is generally located to one side of the cell as a result of the cytoplasm being pressed up against the cell wall by the vacuole. Generally, the nucleus appears slightly flattened under these conditions.

Nuclear membrane. As with all of the cytoplasmic inclusions, the nucleus is bounded by a double membrane of lipoprotein composition. The *nuclear membrane* separates the cytoplasm from the granular substance (nucleoplasm) of the nucleus. The electron microscope has revealed two very interesting features of the nuclear membrane. First, the membrane is continuous with the endoplasmic reticulum, and second, the nuclear membrane contains relatively large pores in its structure (Figure 1-7).

The importance of these two structural features has not yet been fully appreciated, but it is obvious that direct communication between cytoplasm and nucleoplasm is a definite possibility.

Nucleoplasm. The *nucleoplasm* appears to be composed of a structural and a structureless phase. The structural phase consists of a tangle of threads called the *chromatin network.* This phase of the nucleoplasm appears as a network or as distinct chromosomes, depending upon the mitotic stage of the cell. The structureless phase of the nucleoplasm appears as a granular substance, similar to but a little denser than the ground substance of the cytoplasm. This phase is generally referred to as the nuclear sap.

Our knowledge of the chemical composition of the nucleoplasm is limited. This is primarily because of the difficulty of isolating the nucleoplasm from its formed constituents. However, substantial amounts of lipids, phospholipids, and, particularly, proteins have been found. According to Brachet (6), several hydrolytic enzymes, such as ribonuclease, dipeptidase, and phosphatase, are present in the nucleus and may be specific components of the nucleoplasm.

Nucleolus. The interphase nucleus contains one or more *nucleoli,* the number present depending upon the species being observed (e.g., the onion cell nucleus generally contains four nucleoli). It is presently thought that the nucleolus is formed during the telophase stage of mitosis as a result of the activity of certain areas on specific chromosomes. These chromosomes are sometimes referred to as "nucleolar chromosomes" (Figure 1-8).

Chemical analysis of the nucleolus shows that it is primarily composed of RNA and protein. No membrane has yet been detected for the nucleolus.

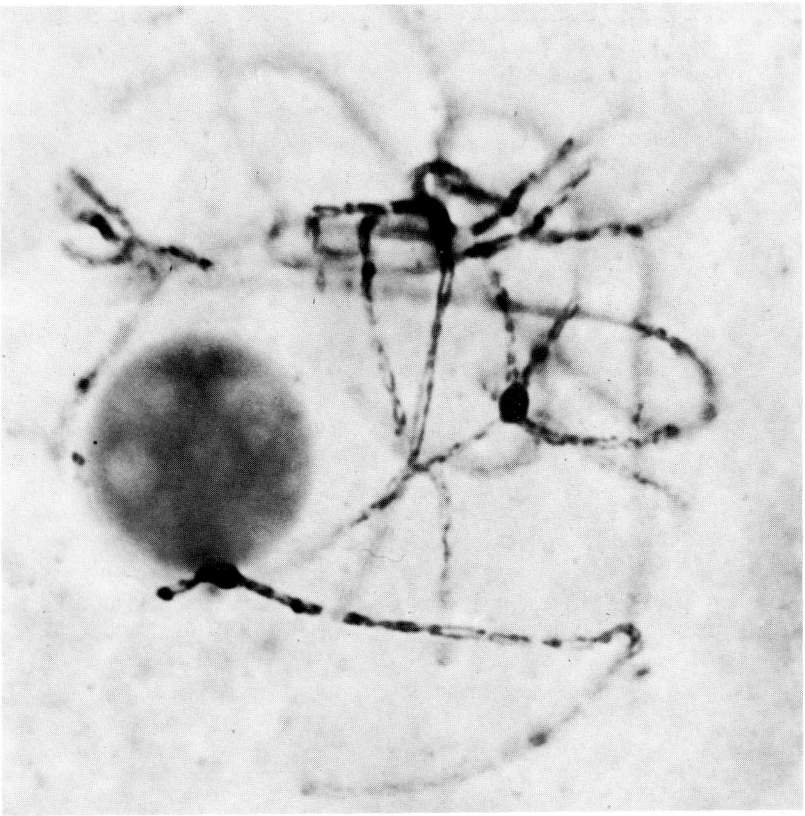

Figure 1-8 Photomicrograph of microsporocyte of *Zea mays* in the mid-prophase of the first meiotic division. The nucleolus is shown in close association with the dark-staining nucleolar-organizing body of chromosomes 6. Both chromosomes are in close opposition along their length and possess a terminal satellite, which is separated from the nucleolar-organizing body by a thin, faint-staining thread. (After B. McClintock. 1934. Z. Zellforsch. Mikroskop. Anat. 21:294.)

CYTOPLASMIC GROUND SUBSTANCE

The *ground substance* is the matrix surrounding the formed components (mitochondria plastids, nucleus, etc.) of the cytoplasm. Although the ground substance is structureless, it is still a very important feature in the physiological activity of the cell. For example, the enzymes necessary for the degradation of carbohydrates to pyruvate (glycolysis), as well as the enzymes of the hexose monophosphate shunt, are present in the ground substance. Finally, the ground substance is considered to be an important site for fatty acid synthesis.

Remember also that the formed components (cytoplasmic inclusions) are bathed by the ground substance and depend upon certain of its metabolites for their own physiological activity.

BIBLIOGRAPHY

1. Albersheim, P. 1958. Recent developments in the chemistry of cell walls. Plant Physiol. 33 (Suppl.): XIVi–XIVii.
2. Barton, A., and G. Causey. 1958. Electron microscopic study of the superior cervical ganglion. J. Anat. 92: 399.
3. Beer, M., and G. Setterfield. 1958. Fine structure in thickened primary walls of collenchyma cells of celery petioles. Am. J. Botany 45: 571.
4. Ben Geren, B., and F. Schmidt. 1954. The structure of the Schwann cell and its relation to the axon in certain invertebrate nerve fibers. Proc. Nat. Acad. Sci. 40: 863.
5. Bishop, C., S. Bayley, and G. Setterfield. 1958. Chemical constitution of the primary cell walls of *Avena* coleoptiles. Plant Physiol. 33: 283.
6. Brachet, J. 1957. Biochemical cytology. Academic Press, New York.
7. Dempsey, E. 1956. Variations in the structure of mitochondria. J. Biophys. Biochem. Cytol. 2 (Suppl.): 305.
8. Green, D. 1959. Electron transport and oxidation phosphorylation. Adv. Enzymol. 21: 73.
9. Green, D. 1959. Mitochondrial structure and function. *In* T. Hayashi (ed.), Subcellular particles. Ronald Press, New York. 84.
10. Hodge, A., J. McLean, and F. Mercer. 1956. A possible mechanism for the morphogenesis of lamellar systems in plant cells. J. Biophys. Biochem. Cytol. 2: 597.
11. Hoffman, H., and G. Grigg. 1958. An electron microscopic study of mitochondria formation. Expertl. Cell Res. 15: 118.
12. Jensen, W. 1960. The composition of the developing primary wall in onion root tip cells, II. Cytochemical localization. Am. J. Botany 47: 287.
13. Kerr, T. 1951. Growth and structure of the primary wall. *In* F. Skoog (ed.), Plant growth substances. University of Wisconsin Press, Madison, Wisc.
14. Loewy, A., and P. Siekevitz. 1963. Cell structure and function. Holt, Rinehart & Winston, New York.
15. McClintock, B. 1934. The relation of a particular chromosomal element in the development of the nucleoli in *Zea mays*. Z. Zellforsch. Mikroskop. Anat. 21: 294.
16. Porter, K., and R. Machado. 1960. Studies on the endoplasmic reticulum.

IV. Its form and distribution during mitosis in cells of onion root tip. J. Biophys. Biochem. Cytol. 7: 167.
17. Preston, R. 1955. Microscopic structures of plant cell walls. *In* W. Ruhland (ed.), The encyclopedia of plant physiology. 1: 722.
18. Preston, R. 1955. The submicroscopic structure of plant cell walls. *In* W. Ruhland (ed.), The encyclopedia of plant physiology. 1: 731.
19. Preston, R. 1955. Mechanical properties of the cell wall. *In* W. Ruhland (ed.), The encyclopedia of plant physiology. 1: 745.
20. Ray, P. 1958. Composition of cell walls of *Avena* coleoptiles. Plant Physiol. 33 (Suppl.): XIVii.
21. Robertson, J. 1962. The membranes of the living cell. Sci. Am. 206(4): 64.
22. Rouiller, C., and W. Bernhard. 1956. "Microbodies" and the problem of mitochondrial regeneration in liver cells. J. Biophys. Biochem. Cytol. 2 (Suppl.): 355.
23. Scott, F., K. Hamner, E. Baker, and E. Bowler. 1956. Electron microscope studies of cell wall growth in the onion root. Am. J. Botany 43: 313.
24. Siegel, S. 1962. The plant cell wall. The Macmillan Company, New York.
25. Wardrop, A. 1958. The organization of the primary wall in differentiating conifer tracheids. Australian J. Botany 6: 299.
26. Wardrop, A., and D. Bland. 1959. The process of lignification in woody plants. Proc. 4th Intl. Congr. of Biochem. Pergamon Press, New York. 2: 76.
27. Watson, M. 1959. Further observations on the nuclear envelope of the animal cell. J. Biophys. Biochem. Cytol. 6: 147.
28. Whaley, W., J. Kephart, and H. Mollenhauer. 1959. Developmental changes in the Golgi-apparatus of maize root cells. Am. J. Botany 46: 743.
29. Whaley, W., H. Mollenhauer, and J. Kephart. 1959. The endoplasmic reticulum and the Golgi structures in maize root cells. J. Biophys. Biochem. Cytol. 5: 501.
30. Whaley, W., H. Mollenhauer, and J. Leech. 1960. The ultrastructure of the meristematic cell. Am. J. Botany 47: 401.
31. Williams, W., R. Preston, and G. Ripley. 1955. A biophysical study of etiolated broad bean internodes. J. Expertl. Botany 6: 451.
32. Ziegler, D., A. Linnane, and D. Green. 1958. Studies on the electron transport system. XI. Correlation of the morphology and enzymic properties of mitochondrial and sub-mitochondrial particles. Biochem. Biophys. Acta 28: 524.

2

Properties of solutions, suspensions and colloidal systems

INTRODUCTION

In order to understand with some sophistication the different physiological processes to be discussed in succeeding chapters, we must first equip ourselves with a working knowledge of solutions, suspensions, and colloidal systems. A study of the living cell and its parts will convince anyone that life exists in, and is dependent upon, a watery medium. Therefore, when one discusses the chemistry of living systems he must, as a matter of course, include first an analysis of the different physical and chemical states of water in the cell. Indeed, physiological processes operate in dilute aqueous solutions and suspensions, therefore placing the reactions involved under the control of the physical and chemical laws governing dilute solutions and suspensions.

THE NATURE OF SOLUTIONS

When a spoonful of sucrose (common table sugar) is stirred into a glass of water, the sugar disappears and a clear *solution* of sugar in water results. The sucrose is said to have *dissolved* in water. We can distinguish two components in the above system, a *solute* (sucrose) and a *solvent* (water), the solute being dissolved in the solvent. In this and any other solution the molecules of the solute are evenly dispersed throughout the solvent, resulting in a homogeneous mixture of solute and solvent molecules. Although the molecules of the solute and the solvent are constantly in motion, their movement is random, thus resulting in a homogeneous mixture in any area of the solution. The solute does not settle out, no matter how long the solution stands, but remains evenly dispersed.

When only a small amount of solute is added to a solvent, a *dilute* solution results. In order to make the solution more *concentrated,* we add more solute. At a given temperature and pressure only a certain amount of solute can be made to form a solution with a given amount of solvent. When this amount of solute is present, the solution is said to be *saturated.*

Now suppose we stir a small amount of an ionic substance, such as sodium chloride (common table salt), in water. Although a solution is formed, it occurs in a slightly different way than the sucrose in water solution. Sucrose is a *nonionic* substance and therefore remains intact in water. Sodium chloride (NaCl), on the other hand, is an *ionic* substance and undergoes ionization when placed in water. That is, the sodium chloride molecule breaks down to form sodium and chloride *ions.* These ions are evenly distributed throughout the water, forming a stable, homogeneous mixture—a true solution (Figure 2-1).

TYPES OF SOLUTIONS

When the layman—even the scientist—thinks of a solution, he is generally thinking of some solid dissolved in water. This is understandable since water is used as a solvent in a countless number of ways. For this reason, water is sometimes referred to as the universal solvent. However, water has its limits as a solvent as anyone who has tried to use it to remove a grease spot can testify. Now if carbon tetrachloride or acetone were used, the grease spot could be removed with ease, proving that where grease and oils are concerned, more efficient solvents than water exist.

So far, we have mentioned only liquids as solvents. It may come as a surprise to many students that any one of the three states of matter, liquids, solids, and gases, may act as a solvent for any other liquid, solid, or gas. Theoretically, then, there are nine different solutions: solids in

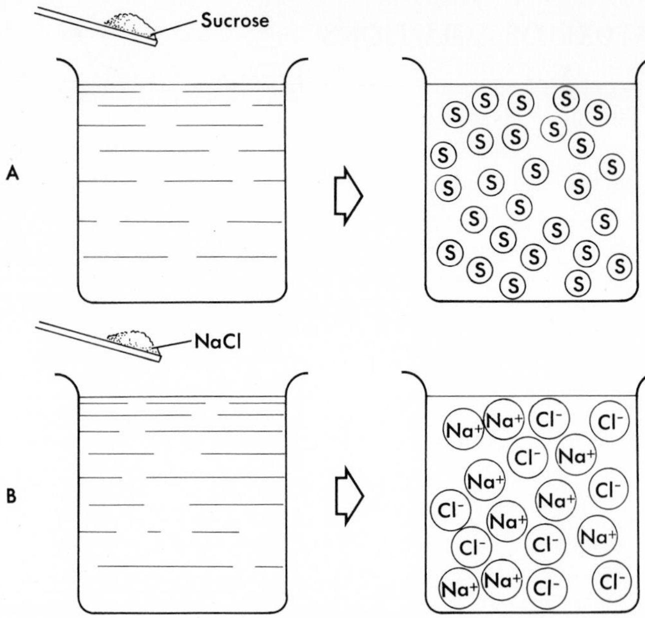

Figure 2-1 Molecules and ions are evenly distributed when in solution. A. Sucrose, a nonionic substance, in solution. B. Sodium chloride, an ionic substance in solution.

liquids, solids, and gases; liquids in liquids, solids, and gases; and gases in liquids, solids, and gases. Let us look at some examples.

Solutions of gases in liquids

Effect of temperature. The solubility of a solid in a liquid increases with increases in temperature. That is, more solute can be added if the temperature of the solvent is increased. Exactly the opposite applies in the relationship *between* gas solubility in liquids and temperature. The solubility of gases in liquids *decreases* with increase in temperature. For example, at 760 mm pressure, 0.04889 liters of oxygen will dissolve in 1 liter of water at 0°C, 0.03891 liters at 10°C, 0.03102 liters at 20°C, 0.02608 liters at 30°C, and 0.01761 liters at 80°C. Indeed, one common laboratory practice for the removal of gases from a liquid is to boil them off.

Effect of pressure. With the exception of very soluble gases, the solubility of gases in liquids *increases* with an increase in pressure. This property of gases is the basis of Henry's law, that *"the mass of a slightly soluble gas that dissolves in a definite mass of a liquid at a given temperature* *is very nearly directly proportional to the partial pressure of that gas.*" Henry's law *is not* true for those gases that unite chemically with the solvent (i.e., the very soluble gases). What Henry's law states is that if 1 gram of a gas dissolves in 1 liter of water at 1 atm of pressure (760 mm Hg), then 5 grams of that gas will dissolve in 1 liter of water at 5 atm of pressure (3800 mm Hg).

A practical application of Henry's law may be found in the carbonated beverage business. The dissolution of carbon dioxide in the beverage is accomplished under a pressure of about 5 atm and then capped. When the cap is removed, the pressure above the solution drops to 1 atm, and the gas escapes in the form of bubbles from the now supersaturated solution. The release of bubbles of gas from a liquid is known as *effervescence*.

Nature of the gas and solvent. The extreme solubility of some gases in water makes them exception to Henry's law. The reason for their extreme solubility is that the gas and water react to form some product. This is easily detected by noting the large evolution of energy in the form of heat, indicating a chemical reaction has taken place. Ammonia (NH_3) and sulfur dioxide (SO_2) are examples of very soluble gases. Let us look at what happens when these gases enter into a reaction with water.

$$NH_3 + H_2O \rightleftharpoons NH_4OH$$

$$SO_2 + H_2O \rightleftharpoons H_2SO_3$$

With ammonia and water the product formed is ammonium hydroxide (NH_4OH), and with sulfur dioxide and water the product formed is sulfurous acid (H_2SO_3). Since a good deal of water is removed by chemical reaction, it is easy to see why Henry's law does not apply to the very soluble gases. In the case of ammonia and water, almost half of the water enters into reaction, and what is left is actually a concentrated solution of ammonium hydroxide.

Solution of liquids in liquids

In the laboratory one encounters hundreds of pure and mixed liquids. Water, alcohol, benzene, glycerin, acetone, and chloroform are some of the pure liquids found, and gasoline and kerosene are examples of mixed liquids. Some of the above liquids will mix with water in all proportions; that is, they are perfectly *miscible* with water. Alcohol, glycerin, and many acids, such as nitric (HNO_3), sulfuric (H_2SO_4), and phosphoric (H_3PO_4), are good examples. Gasoline and kerosene are good examples of liquids that *do not* mix with water in any proportion and, so, are said to be *immiscible* with it.

The terms solvent and solute, with liquid-in-liquid solution where the components are perfectly miscible, are not precisely defined. Generally, the component present in greatest amount is called the solvent.

Sometimes two liquids are only partially soluble in each other. If two partially miscible liquids are placed together in the same container, shaken thoroughly, and then allowed to stand, two distinct layers will form. Each layer will be a solution of one liquid in the other. In the case of ether and water, the top layer will be a dilute solution of water in ether and the bottom layer will be a dilute solution of ether in water.

Supersaturated solutions

If more solute is added to a saturated solution, it will settle on the bottom of the containing vessel and not dissolve. However, if a saturated solution (with no additional undissolved solute present) prepared at an elevated temperature is allowed to cool, the excess solute, instead of crystallizing out of solution, will remain in solution. The solution will actually hold more solute in solution than normally can be held at the lower temperature. This solution is said to be *supersaturated.* If a small amount of solute is added to a supersaturated solution or it is agitated, the excess solute will crystallize out, leaving merely a saturated solution.

CONCENTRATION OF SOLUTIONS

The *gram molecular weight* of a substance is the weight of that substance in grams equal in number to the weight of the substance in atomic weight units. For example, the atomic weight of glucose is 180.16 and the gram molecular weight of glucose is 180.16 grams. The gram molecular weight of any substance contains 6.02×10^{23} molecules of that substance. This number is referred to as *Avogadro's number* and is very helpful, as we shall see, to scientists in expressing the concentration of solutions.

Molar solutions

If a gram molecular weight of a water-soluble substance is added to enough water to make a *liter of solution,* the result is a *molar* (M) *solution* of that substance. The molar solution contains Avogadro's number of molecules of the dissolved solute. If 180.16 grams of glucose, for example, were dissolved in enough water to make a liter of solution, the result would be a $1M$ solution of glucose. If twice as many grams of glucose were dissolved in water to make a liter of solution, we would have a $2M$ solution, etc. A $1M$ solution of glucose contains Avogadro's number of glucose molecules, and a $2M$ solution would have twice that many.

A molar solution of sucrose contains 342.3 grams of sucrose dissolved in a liter of solution. As in the 1*M* glucose solution, the 1*M* sucrose solution contains Avogadro's number of molecules of dissolved solute. In other words, equal volumes of different solutions of the same molarity contain the same number of solute molecules, but different numbers of solvent molecules. Dilution of a molar solution can be accomplished with relative ease. For example, if a 0.5*M* solution is wanted, one merely has to add an equal volume of water to a 1*M* solution. If a 0.1*M* solution is desired, one can dilute a given volume of a molar solution with 9 volumes of water.

Molal solutions

Sometimes it may be convenient to keep the number of solvent molecules constant instead of the number of solute molecules. If such is the case, we want to deal with *molal* solutions. A molal solution contains a gram molecular weight of a substance dissolved in 1 liter of water. The final volume of the solution is generally greater than 1 liter. Since the volume in excess of 1 liter varies depending on the solute used, we *cannot* say that equal volumes of molal solutions contain the same number of solute molecules. However, we can say that equal volumes of molal solutions contain the same number of solvent molecules.

Percent solutions

If we add 5 grams of NaCl to 95 grams of water, we have a 5% solution of sodium chloride. In this system the concentration is expressed as the percent composition by weight. Although percent solutions are used quite frequently in the laboratory, for precise work they are generally found inadequate.

ACIDS, BASES, AND SALTS

Acidic and basic solutions are unquestionably vital aspects of the living system. A great variety of substances that may be considered either acids or bases are produced during the metabolic history of the cell. Amino acids, fatty acids, and Krebs cycle intermediates are good examples of acids occurring in the living system. Purines and pyrimidines, organic bases that are quite common in the cell, play important roles in the synthesis of nucleic acids.

Acids and bases in solution may be distinguished in a variety of ways. Acids have a sour taste. Lemons are sour because of their high content of citric acid, and milk turns sour because of the lactic acid produced in it by bacteria. Certain natural dyes change color from blue to red when treated with an acid, and certain metals, such as zinc, release hydrogen on contact with an acid. Finally, an acid can neutralize a base (see later), forming in the process water and a salt.

Bases have a bitter taste and can cause color changes in certain natural dyes. Bases in solution feel soapy to the touch. A base can neutralize an acid and as a result form water and a salt.

However, these distinguishing features do not tell us anything about the chemistry of acids and bases. We are still faced with the question, what are acids and bases?

Nature of acids, bases, and salts

An acid is any molecule or ion that can donate a proton (H^+) *to any other molecule or ion.* If an acid is dissolved in water, it reacts with the water, and *ionization* takes place. Ionization may be defined as a reaction between a solute and a solvent resulting in the formation of *ions*.

$$HA \rightleftharpoons H^+ + A^-$$

In this equation the acid (HA) undergoes ionization to form positive (H^+) and negative (A^-) ions. Ions are atoms or groups of atoms that are electrically charged. Ions carrying a positive charge are called *cations,* and ions carrying a negative charge are called *anions*. In an aqueous solution cations will migrate toward a negative electrode (cathode), and anions will migrate toward a positive electrode (anode). The hydrogen ion (H^+) is called a *proton*. When one is referring to acids and bases, the term *dissociation* is generally used in place of ionization.

A base is any molecule or ion that will accept a proton. If a base is dissolved in water, ionization takes place.

$$BOH \rightleftharpoons B^+ + OH^-$$

In this equation the base (BOH) undergoes ionization to form positive (B^+) and negative (OH^-) ions.

Electrolytes and nonelectrolytes. *Electrolytes* are substances that can conduct an electric current when dissolved in water. The passage of an electric current through an aqueous solution of an electrolyte results in the decomposition of the electrolyte. This process is called *electrolysis*. For example, if an electric current is allowed to pass through an aqueous solution of hydrochloric acid, hydrogen gas will be released at the cathode and chlorine gas at the anode. Acids, bases, and salts are electrolytes. Their ability to conduct electricity results from the fact that electrically charged ions are formed when they are dissolved in water. Sugars and alcohols do not undergo ionization when dissolved in water and, therefore, are termed *nonelectrolytes*.

Strength of acids or bases. The ease with which an acid will yield a proton is a measure of its strength. Strong acids will yield protons quite readily, while weak acids yield protons reluctantly. Strong bases are compounds that accept protons quite readily, while weak bases have only a very weak affinity. Almost complete ionization takes place when either a strong acid or a strong base is dissolved in water. On the other hand, only slight ionization takes place when either weak acids or weak bases are dissolved in water. A list of acids and bases of varying strength is given in Table 2-1.

Table 2-1 The strength of some common acids and bases.

Acid	*Formula*	*Ions*	*Strength*
hydrochloric	HCl	$H^+ + Cl^-$	strong
sulfuric	H_2SO_4	$H^+ + HSO_4^-$	strong
nitric	HNO_3	$H^+ + NO_3^-$	strong
acetic	CH_3COOH	$H^+ + CH_3COO^-$	weak
sulfurous	H_2SO_3	$H^+ + HSO_3^-$	weak
Base	*Formula*	*Ions*	*Strength*
sodium hydroxide	$NaOH$	$Na^+ + OH^-$	strong
potassium hydroxide	KOH	$K^+ + OH^-$	strong
ammonium hydroxide	NH_4OH	$NH_4^+ + OH^-$	weak

Amphiprotic compounds. Water can act either as a weak acid or a weak base; that is, it can either donate or accept a proton. Amino acids, components of the protein molecule, are also good examples of compounds that can act as weak acids or weak bases. Compounds that can act both as an acid and as a base are said to be *amphiprotic*. An example of water acting as a base in the presence of HCl and as an acid in the presence of NH_3 is given below:

Water as a base $\quad H_2O + HCl \rightleftharpoons H_3O^+ + Cl^-$

Water as an acid $\quad H_2O + NH_3 \rightleftharpoons NH_4^+ + OH^-$

Water in the presence of a strong acid such as HCl acts as a base and accepts a proton to form a hydronium ion (H_3O^+), while water in the presence of ammonia, a base, acts as an acid and donates a proton.

Neutralization. If equivalent amounts of aqueous solutions of HCl and

NaOH are added one to the other, acidic and basic properties are lost. *Neutralization* is said to have taken place. The loss of acidic and basic properties occurs because free hydrogen ions, which give a solution its acidic character, have reacted with free hydroxyl ions, which give a solution its basic character, to form water. The free sodium and chlorine ions do not enter into the reaction.

$$H^+ + Cl^- + Na^+ + OH^- \rightleftharpoons H_2O + Cl^- + Na^+$$

Now if the water of the resulting solution is evaporated, crystals of sodium chloride salt are left. In other words, a salt is formed when acid and base solutions are brought together. For example, when a solution of NaOH is added to an acetic acid solution, the salt, sodium acetate, is formed. Some acid-base neutralizations are given in Table 2-2.

Table 2-2 A few common acid-base neutralizations and the name and formula of the salt formed.

Reaction	*Name of salt*	*Formula*
HCl + NaOH	sodium chloride	NaCl
HCL + KOH	potassium chloride	KCl
H_2SO_4 + 2KOH	potassium sulfate	K_2SO_4
2HCl + $Ca(OH)_2$	calcium chloride	$CaCl_2$
CH_3COOH + NaOH	sodium acetate	CH_3COONa

Normal solutions. The dissolution of a *gram equivalent weight* of a substance in 1 liter of solution results in a *normal* solution of that substance. The dissolution of 2 gram equivalent weights in a liter of solution will give a two normal ($2N$) solution, etc. Before we go further, let us define a gram equivalent weight. The gram equivalent weight of an element is the weight in grams of the element that combines with or is otherwise equivalent to 1.008 grams of hydrogen. The gram equivalent weight of a compound is the weight of the compound that will interact with one equivalent weight of an element. It is more convenient to express the concentrations of acid and base solutions in terms of normality than molarity. The gram equivalent weight of an acid or base is the quantity that will release or neutralize 1 mole of hydrogen ion. Thus, a $1M$ solution of HCl is also a $1N$ solution of the acid. However, a $1M$ solution of H_2SO_4 is, when expressed in terms of normality, $2N$. This is because H_2SO_4 is capable of releasing 2 moles of hydrogen ion. A $1M$ solution of NaOH is also $1N$ since the mole of hydroxide ion released in solution can neutralize 1 mole of hydrogen ion. On the other hand, a $1M$ solution of barium hydroxide

[$Ba(OH)_2$] is $2N$ since in solution the 2 moles of hydroxide ion released are capable of neutralizing 2 moles of hydrogen ion.

After reading the above discussion, one should be aware that it would take 10 ml of a $1N$ solution of HCl to completely neutralize 10 ml of a $1N$ solution of NaOH. What quantity of a $1N$ solution of H_2SO_4 would be needed to neutralize the same quantity and strength of NaOH expressed in the previous sentence?

Hydrogen ion concentration. The acidity or basicity of a solution is determined by its hydrogen ion concentration. Conventionally, the hydrogen ion concentration of a solution is expressed as its negative logarithm or pH value.

$$pH = -\log [H^+]$$

The term pH may be defined, therefore, as the *negative logarithm of the hydrogen ion concentration.* Actually, the term pH stands for "potential of hydrogen."

The pH scale covers a range of values from 0 to 14. The hydrogen ion concentration in a liter of pure water is 0.0000001 or 10^{-7}. Since pH is equal to the negative logarithm of the hydrogen ion concentration, then

$$pH = -\log 10^{-7}$$

$$pH = \log \frac{1}{10^{-7}} = 7$$

Pure water, with a pH of 7, is considered neutral. Any pH values below 7 represent acid solutions, and any pH values above 7 represent basic solutions.

A solution with a pH of 8 has a hydrogen ion concentration ten times less than a solution with a pH of 7. That is, its hydrogen ion concentration is 0.00000001 or 10^{-8}. We can see that pH values differ by a factor of ten and that solutions with low pH values are strongly acidic and solutions with high pH values are strongly basic. A chart of pH values is given in Table 2-3.

Buffer solutions. A solution that contains a weak acid and its salt (e.g., acetic acid and sodium acetate) or a weak base and its salt will resist changes in hydrogen ion concentration when small amounts of a strong acid or base are added to it. These solutions are called *buffer solutions.*

Let us use the common buffer pair, acetic acid and sodium acetate, to explain buffer action. Remember that acetic acid is a weak acid and, therefore, only slightly ionizes in solution. Now, if we add a small amount of NaOH, the hydroxyl ions released in solution are neutralized by the free hydrogen ions in the buffer solution. This causes some more of the acetic acid to ionize, thus restoring the original hydrogen ion concentration. As

Table 2-3 pH scale.

Hydrogen ion concentration in terms of normality		*pH value*
1	10^{0}	0
0.1	10^{-1}	1
0.01	10^{-2}	2
0.001	10^{-3}	3
0.0001	10^{-4}	4
0.00001	10^{-5}	5
0.000001	10^{-6}	6
0.0000001	10^{-7}	7
0.00000001	10^{-8}	8
0.000000001	10^{-9}	9
0.0000000001	10^{-10}	10
0.00000000001	10^{-11}	11
0.000000000001	10^{-12}	12
0.0000000000001	10^{-13}	13
0.00000000000001	10^{-14}	14

more NaOH is added, more acetic acid ionizes until all of the acetic acid in solution is ionized. At this point, any further addition of NaOH will cause an abrupt rise in pH. If a small amount of hydrochloric acid is added to the acetic acid-sodium acetate buffer, the hydrogen ions that are released rapidly unite with free acetate ions to form undissociated acetic acid. Therefore, there is no change in hydrogen ion concentration. Remember, sodium acetate exists in solution as free sodium and acetate ions. As more of the HCl acid is added, more of the free acetate ions are converted to acetic acid until finally all of the acetate ions have been converted. When this happens, any further addition of HCl will cause an abrupt drop in pH.

Buffer solutions are universally present in living plant cells and play vital roles in their existence. Enzymes, the organic catalysts of life, generally function within narrow pH ranges. A deviation of any magnitude impairs or completely inhibits their function. Obviously, the living system cannot tolerate any large increases or decreases in hydrogen ion concentration.

COLLOIDAL SYSTEMS

If a spoonful of ordinary clay soil is placed in a glass of water and agitated thoroughly, a murky liquid, which appears uniformly brown in color, results. If we allow this mixture to stand, it starts to clear rapidly, the larger particles of soil settling out first, followed by smaller and smaller particles. However, after a considerable length of time, it becomes evident that not all of the soil is going to settle out. Some of it remains indefinitely in suspension. The stable heterogenous mixture that results is called a *colloidal suspension*—in this case composed of very minute soil particles called clay micelles suspended in water. The suspended phase is termed the *dispersed phase,* and the medium in which dispersion takes place is called the *dispersion medium.*

The use of the term *colloid* was first suggested by Thomas Graham in 1861. It is derived from the two Greek words *kolla,* which means glue, and *eidos,* meaning like. Apparently, Graham used the term to describe gluelike preparations, such as solutions of certain proteins, and liquid preparations of vegetable gums, such as gum arabic. However, today the term colloid has much more general use, and there are many colloidal suspensions known today that are far from gluelike.

We have discussed so far the dispersion of a solid in a liquid. However, colloidal suspensions are not limited to this category. For example, the dispersion medium may be a liquid, gas or solid. Smoke is composed of a solid dispersed in gas. Milk and mayonnaise are examples of a liquid dispersed in a liquid. Pumice stone is an example of a gas dispersed in a solid. In this discussion we will be primarily interested in two general types of colloidal suspension: *sols,* colloidal systems with the property of fluidity, and *gels,* colloidal systems without the property of fluidity.

Colloidal dimensions

Particles of colloidal dimension range in size from 1 to 200 millimicrons ($m\mu$). A millimicron is one-thousandth of a micron (μ) or one-millionth of a millimeter. Small as this may seem, however, it does not approach with any stretch of the imagination the minute size of most molecules. Colloidal particles are too small to be seen with the light microscope, but are large enough to scatter light. Because of this ability to scatter light, the presence of colloidal particles may be detected with the ultramicroscope. Today, particles of colloidal dimension can be detected quite readily with the electron microscope. We can arbitrarily state that the size of colloidal particles is somewhere between the size of particles forming true solutions and the size of particles found in *unstable* suspensions.

Different colloidal systems

The different types of colloidal dispersions in liquids may be divided into two general classes called *lyophilic* and *lyophobic* systems. In the lyophilic system the disperse phase and the liquid dispersion medium are attracted to each other, while in the lyophobic system the two phases actually repel each other. If the dispersion medium is water, then the terms *hydrophilic* (water-loving) and *hydrophobic* (water-hating) are used. On addition of such solids as starch, gelatin, or agar to hot water, large quantities of water are taken up to form a hydrophilic colloidal sol. Sols of this type are formed rather easily, and no special method of preparation is employed. The dispersed particles of the hydrophilic sol are "hydrated"; that is, water molecules are adsorbed to the surfaces of these particles. Water molecules nearest to the surface of the particles are adsorbed very tightly, while those farther and farther away are less and less tightly adsorbed.

Hydrophobic colloids are generally composed of compounds of an inorganic nature and in most cases are more difficult to prepare than hydrophilic colloids. Condensation methods are frequently employed in the formation of this type of sol. These methods involve the formation of colloidal particles by inducing smaller particles to aggregate and generally employ chemical reactions. For example, if a concentrated solution of ferric chloride is mixed with hot water, a dark red colloidal suspension of ferric hydroxide results. What happens is that the $FeCl_3$ ionizes, and hydrolysis of the ferric ion takes place to form ferric hydroxide $Fe(OH)_3$. The same reaction would take place in cold water, but is considerably speeded up by using hot water. Aggregation of the $Fe(OH)_3$ molecules form the colloidal particles of the disperse phase.

$$Fe^{3+} + 3Cl^- + 3H_2O \rightarrow Fe(OH)_3 + 3(H^+ + Cl^-)$$

In much the same manner a colloidal suspension of arsenic sulfide is prepared by bubbling H_2S gas into a solution of arsenic oxide.

$$As_2O_3 + 3H_2S \rightarrow As_2S_3 + 3H_2O$$

Emulsions

An unstable *emulsion* may be prepared by vigorously shaking two immiscible liquids together. Small droplets (disperse phase) of one of the liquids will be dispersed throughout the other (dispersion medium). However, these small droplets have a tendency to coalesce, forming larger and larger droplets until eventually two distinct layers are formed and the two liquids are again separated.

An emulsion can be made stable by the addition of an *emulsifying agent*. These substances generally function in either of two ways: (1) they may decrease the surface tensions of the liquids, which reduces the tendency of the small droplets to combine, and (2) they may form a protective layer or film around the droplets making it impossible for them to combine with each other. Milk, a very common emulsion, is composed of butter fat dispersed in water with casein as an emulsifying agent.

Properties of colloidal suspensions

Tyndall effect. If a powerful narrow beam of light is passed through a darkened room and viewed at right angles, it is visible because some of the light is scattered in the direction of the observer. This scattering of light is due to the presence of dust particles of colloidal dimension floating in the air. If the air is cleared of these dust particles, the beam of light can no longer be seen. This phenomenon is known as the *Tyndall effect* after its original discoverer, John Tyndall.

If a narrow beam of light is passed through a true solution, its path cannot be observed. On the other hand, if the light is passed through a colloidal suspension, it is readily observed. The particles of the dispersed phase are large enough to noticeably scatter light, while the particles of true solutions are not. Employment of the Tyndall effect, therefore, is one way of distinguishing a colloidal suspension from a true solution. Note, however, that we are not actually able to see the colloidal particles—we are only detecting their presence by their ability to scatter some of the light that falls upon them (Figure 2-2).

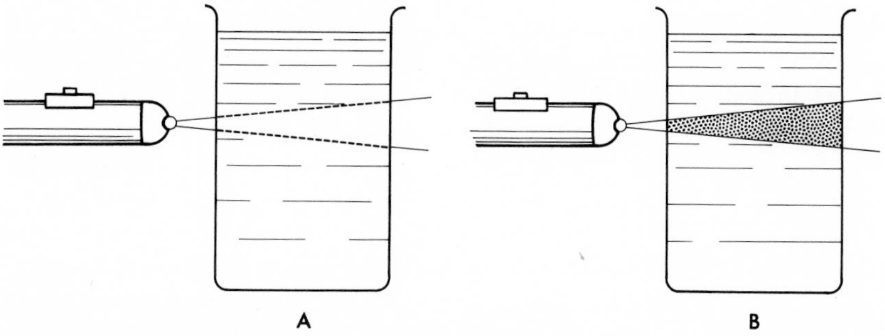

Figure 2-2 Representation of the Tyndall effect. A. True solution. B. Colloidal suspension.

Brownian movement. The Tyndall effect can be utilized with the ultramicroscope to study some of the properties of colloidal suspensions. The principle involved here is *dark-field illumination.* Dark-field illumination is achieved with a microscope through the use of a special condenser that focuses converging beams of light, which strike the stage at too oblique an angle to enter the objective. Because of the fact that no light enters the objective, a clean glass slide will appear completely black. However, if the converging beams of light are allowed to pass through a colloidal suspension, the tiny colloidal particles will scatter some of the light that falls upon them. Some of the scattered light enters the objective, allowing the colloidal particles to be detected as bright points of light against a black background. These bright points of light appear to move in an irregular random fashion, outlining the path of the colloidal particle in suspension. This random motion is caused by the uneven bombardment of the colloidal particles by molecules of the dispersion medium. The colloidal particles are small enough to be moved by the molecules in the direction of least resistance, a direction which is changing constantly. This random motion of very small particles in suspension is called *Brownian movement* after the botanist, Robert Brown, who first described it.

Brownian movement cannot be observed in a true solution, thus giving another way of distinguishing colloidal suspensions from true solutions.

Filtration. Although the disperse phase cannot be separated from the dispersion medium with ordinary filter paper, colloidal particles can be separated from the dispersion medium with *ultrafilters.* Ultrafilters composed of biologically inert cellulose esters (Millipore filters) have been constructed with pore sizes ranging from 10 mμ to 5 μ. Since colloidal particles range in size from 1 to 200 mμ, it is easy to see that separation of the two phases of a colloidal suspension could be accomplished in most cases by the use of these filters. The components of true solutions, however, cannot be separated in this manner.

Adsorption. The tendency of molecules or ions to adhere to the surface of certain solids or liquids is known as *adsorption.* Since it is a surface phenomenon, the capacity for adsorption is dependent upon the amount of surface exposed as well as the chemical nature of the constituents involved. It is not surprising, therefore, that the adsorptive capacity of a colloidal suspension is extremely high for a given weight of colloidal particles. For example, the amount of surface exposed by a solid 1 cm on edge is 6 cm^2. If this cube should be divided into cubes 0.1 μ on edge, the amount of surface area exposed would be 6×10^5 or 600,000 cm^2, an increase of 100,000 times over the original area. Undoubtedly, most of the important functions of colloidal systems found in the living cell are dependent upon their immense adsorptive capacity.

Electrical properties of colloidal systems. Colloidal particles generally carry an electric charge. The charge may be either positive or negative, but for any one colloidal system it is the same on all particles. For example, the particles of a ferric hydroxide colloidal suspension all carry a positive charge, while the particles of a colloidal suspension of arsenic sulfide all carry a negative charge.

The charges found on colloidal particles result from the adsorption of free ions in the dispersion medium. The preferential adsorption of positive ions by a colloidal particle will give it a positive charge, while the preferential adsorption of negative ions results in a negatively charged colloidal particle. In the ferric hydroxide colloidal suspension all of the particles have a positive charge because the ferric ion (Fe^{3+}), released in the ionization of $FeCl_3$, is preferentially adsorbed. The free chlorine ions (Cl^-) are attracted to the positive charge on the particles and also accumulate secondarily around the particles forming what is known as an *electrical double layer*. In the arsenic sulfide system, sulfide ions (S^{2-}) are preferentially adsorbed by the arsenic sulfide particles. Hydrogen ions, released in the ionization of H_2S, are secondarily adsorbed by the negatively charged particles (Figure 2-3).

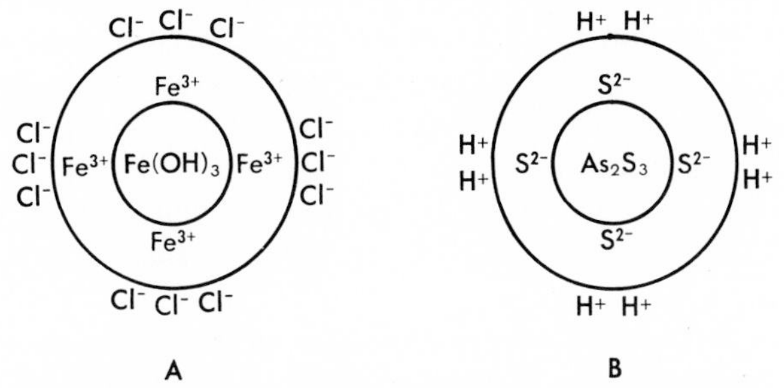

Figure 2-3 Diagrammatic representation of the electric double layer surrounding colloidal particles in suspension. A. Colloidal particle in a colloidal suspension of ferric hydroxide. B. Colloidal particles in a colloidal suspension of arsenic sulfide.

One way of determining the electric charge on the particles of a colloidal suspension is to observe their direction of migration in an electric field. Under the influence of a direct current, all of the particles of a colloidal suspension will move in one direction. Where the disperse phase has a positive charge, the particles will collect at the cathode, and where the charge is negative, they will collect at the anode. This phenomenon was first called cataphoresis, but the term *electrophoresis* has now found more general usage.

The fact that colloidal particles carry an electric charge and that all the particles of any one suspension carry the same charge is mainly responsible for the stability of colloidal suspensions. Units of like charge repel each other. If it were not for this, the colloidal particles would collide and aggregate and eventually precipitate out of suspension.

Precipitation. Destruction or removal of the electric double layer will cause the dispersed particles of a colloidal suspension to collide, aggregate, and finally to precipitate out of suspension. This may be accomplished by the addition of a certain amount of an electrolyte. For example, the addition of HCl to a colloidal suspension of arsenic sulfide will cause precipitation. Hydrogen ion concentration is increased by the addition of HCl to the extent that it causes H_2S to form ($2H^+ + S^{2-} \rightarrow H_2S$). The removal of the negative charges on the sulfide ions causes the particles to be neutralized. The extent to which an ion will cause precipitation when added to a colloidal suspension depends on its valence. The monovalent sodium ion, for example, is less efficient than the divalent barium ion, and it in turn is much less efficient than the trivalent aluminum ion.

An interesting effect of ions on colloidal suspensions is observed at the mouth of rivers as they enter the ocean. The charged ions of ocean water cause the negatively charged clay micelles of river water to lose their charge and settle out. This leads eventually to the formation of the deltas always found at the mouths of rivers.

Sometimes a colloid can be *protected* from precipitation by the presence of another colloid. Apparently, one colloid forms a protective film around the particles of the other colloid. The two colloids gelatin and gum arabic are the most widely used in this capacity. For example, the colloidal dispersion of silver halides on photographic plates is protected by the gelatin on these plates.

Gels. One of the properties of certain lyophilic sols is their ability under certain conditions to form an extremely viscous solidlike mass. Thus, hot aqueous gelatin or agar sols will *set* when cooled to form a jellylike mass called a *gel.* The conversion of a sol to a gel is called *gelation.* If a gel of agar or gelatin is again heated, it will convert back to a sol, a process known as *solation.* The addition of dilute hydrochloric acid to sodium silicate will form a silica gel—a colloidal dispersion of hydrated silicon dioxide.

The living cell and the colloidal state

The protoplasm of the cell is not a true solution. Although there are many materials that are truly dissolved, much of the particulate phase of the protoplasm is colloidal in nature. Indeed, the protoplasm is usually referred to as a colloidal complex and exhibits many of the properties attributed to colloidal systems. The cell membrane and wall may be thought of as gel-like, and, in fact, some investigators believe that some of the particulate structures of the cell, such as the centrosomes and chromosomes, are so constructed.

A good deal, if not all, of the colloidal character of the protoplasm is due to the proteins present there. Proteins are very large complex molecules, which sometimes reach colloidal dimension. They are dispersed throughout the ground substance of the protoplasm where they are involved in such cell activities as respiration, digestion, secretion, etc. Undoubtedly, the immense surface area provided by protein enzymes dispersed in the protoplasm is of extreme importance to the many enzyme-substrate reactions upon which all life depends. Without doubt the colloidal system is an essential feature of living matter.

Part TWO

Water relations

3

Diffusion, osmosis, and imbibition

INTRODUCTION

Water, a substance which may justifiably be called the fluid of life, makes up the greater part of our globe. All life depends on water and may literally be said to swim in it. In many instances, water composes over 90% of an organism and is a participant indirectly or directly in all of its metabolic reactions.

Despite its commonness, water is a most unusual compound, which, due to certain physical and chemical characteristics, is possessed of a number of unique properties. For example, water has a *high specific heat,* which is the reason that living tissues experience considerable heat absorption or loss with only small changes in temperature. Also, water's *high heat of vaporization* (evaporates slowly when heated) causes relatively large amounts of energy to be dissipated under conditions favoring evaporation —a cooling process of considerable magnitude. Another one of the unusual properties of water is that it is *less dense* as a solid than as a liquid. That is, water as a solid will float on water as a liquid. This property is of obvious advantage to aquatic life in temperate and cold climates where lakes and rivers form ice from the top down, thus allowing life to continue in a liquid medium at lower depths. The adverse consequence of the expansion of water when freezing in living cells is obvious.

Water molecules cling to each other and to many different surfaces; these properties are called *cohesion* and *adhesion,* respectively. Both cohesion and adhesion have major consequences in the rise of water in plants. This subject will be covered in more detail in a later chapter.

The above properties are chiefly due to the configuration of the water molecule, which lends itself to *hydrogen bonding.* The water molecule is composed of two hydrogen atoms covalently bonded to one side of an oxygen atom, the angle between them being about 105° (Figure 3-1). From

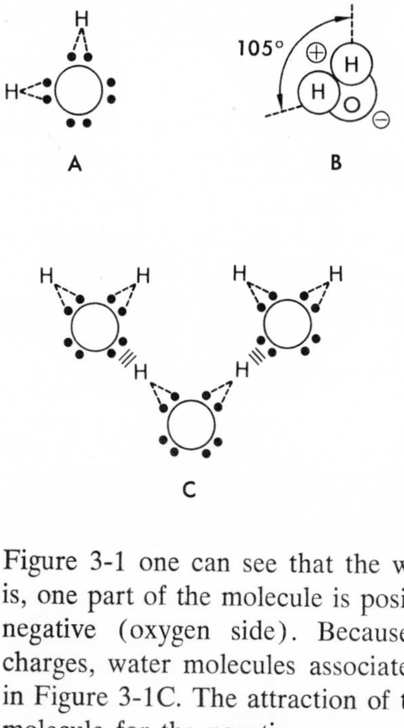

Figure 3-1 Structure of the water molecule. A. Schematic representation of the water molecule showing the arrangement of the hydrogen atoms to one side of the oxygen atom. B. Distribution of charges and angle between hydrogen and oxygen bonds is shown. C. Association between three water molecules through hydrogen bonding.

Figure 3-1 one can see that the water molecule is a polar molecule; that is, one part of the molecule is positive (hydrogen side) and the other part negative (oxygen side). Because of the asymmetrical distribution of charges, water molecules associate with each other (cohesion) as shown in Figure 3-1C. The attraction of the positive hydrogen atom of one water molecule for the negative oxygen atom of another water molecule results in what is called a *hydrogen bond* or *bridge.* Although the hydrogen bond is stronger than the van der Waals forces that draw molecules together, it is considerably weaker than the covalent or electrovalent type of bond. There is no limit to the number of water molecules that can become attached to each other in this manner. To use a fanciful example, a lake may be thought of as a loosely held together gigantic molecule, rather than as an accumulation of an astronomical number of discrete water molecules.

The presence of hydrogen bonds is directly responsible for the high heat of fusion, high specific heat, and high heat of vaporization of water. That is, the energy required to break hydrogen bonds for the melting of ice, the heating of water, and the evaporation of water is considerably more than the energy needed to overcome van der Waals forces, which are normally found in the grouping of molecules such as methane, ether, benzene, etc.

As far as life is concerned, the most important property of water is its solvent action. Because of its ability to enter into solution with a vast array of compounds, water is sometimes referred to as the "universal solvent." The solvent action of water is due to its ability to form hydrogen bonds and the fact that there is an asymmetrical distribution of charges on the water molecule. For example, compounds such as sugars, alcohols, amino acids, etc., which contain oxygen atoms, hydroxyl groups (—OH), or amino groups ($—NH_2$), are held in water solution by hydrogen bonding. On the other hand, the polar nature of water molecules causes various salts to be held in solution through charge interaction. Therefore, salts can exist in water in the form of ions.

The solvent action of water is of obvious advantage to the plant. The various essential elements necessary for normal plant growth, the compounds necessary for energy transfer and storage, and the components of structural compounds all require water as a translocation medium. These materials are dissolved in the water of the plant and, in this manner, distributed throughout the plant. The processes of diffusion, osmosis, and imbibition are intimately associated with the essential function of the translocation of water and solutes from site of origin to site of activity.

DIFFUSION

We have all experienced the phenomenon of diffusion in one way or another. When we put sugar in a liquid, such as coffee or tea, the sugar molecules diffuse throughout the liquid, giving it a uniformly sweet taste. The fragrance from an opened bottle of perfume reaches us through the process of diffusion—the molecules of perfume diffusing through the molecules of air. However, to fully understand the process of diffusion, we must first focus our attention on the kinetic nature of matter.

Kinetic nature of matter

At temperatures above absolute zero ($-273°K$), all components of matter are in motion; that is, they possess a certain amount of kinetic energy. This motion is random, the molecules or atoms moving in all directions and, in many cases, colliding with one another. Take, for example, the air that we live in. It is composed primarily of nitrogen, oxygen, and carbon dioxide gases. The nitrogen, oxygen, and carbon dioxide molecules are, therefore, present in a uniform mixture that composes air. These molecules are constantly moving in a random manner and occasionally collide with one another. In air nitrogen molecules are present in much more abundance than oxygen and, especially, carbon dioxide molecules. However, all three types of molecules are uniformly mixed.

Now, if we were to open a bottle of perfume, the perfume molecules evaporating off the surface of the liquid perfume would diffuse out among the molecules of air and eventually become uniformly mixed with the molecules of air. The perfume molecules are able to do this because they, too, are in constant motion. After complete evaporation of the perfume and complete dispersal of the perfume molecules among the air molecules, a dynamic system exists, composed of randomly moving nitrogen, oxygen, carbon dioxide, and perfume molecules.

Diffusion of gases

Of the three different states of matter, the gases offer the least resistance to diffusing molecules. At normal pressures and temperatures, gas molecules are widely separated, thus limiting the number of collisions that would interfere with the diffusion of one gas into another. This fact is easily appreciated when one considers the extent to which gas can be compressed. For example, the air filling a classroom could easily be compressed into a test tube and still remain in a gaseous state.

Perhaps a better understanding of gas diffusion may be found in a description of a common chemistry laboratory demonstration. If a vial of bromine is broken under a bell jar that has been partially evacuated of air, molecules of bromine gas almost immediately fill the space under the jar. This can easily be observed, due to the red-brown color of bromine gas. However, if the bell jar has not been evacuated of air, the diffusion of bromine gas is considerably slowed down and can actually be observed slowly penetrating the space under the jar. Consideration of these two conditions, diffusion in a partial vacuum and diffusion in air, brings to focus the importance of the concentration of gas molecules in diffusion. Obviously, the diffusion of bromine gas molecules is impeded by the presence of air molecules. When these are absent, diffusion occurs much more rapidly.

Diffusion pressure. One of the most common demonstrations of gas pressure is found in the barometer, an instrument for measuring atmospheric pressure. If a glass tube is filled with mercury and then inverted with the open end under the surface of mercury contained in a shallow dish, the mercury in the tube will fall to a certain height (Figure 3-2). The height at which a column of mercury will stand in a glass tube at sea level is 760 mm. That is, the weight of gas over the surface of the mercury in the dish shown in Figure 3-2 is sufficient to push a column of mercury up a glass tube to a height of 760 mm. The average pressure at sea level is known as the standard atmospheric pressure and is expressed as 760 mm of mercury or as 1 atm.

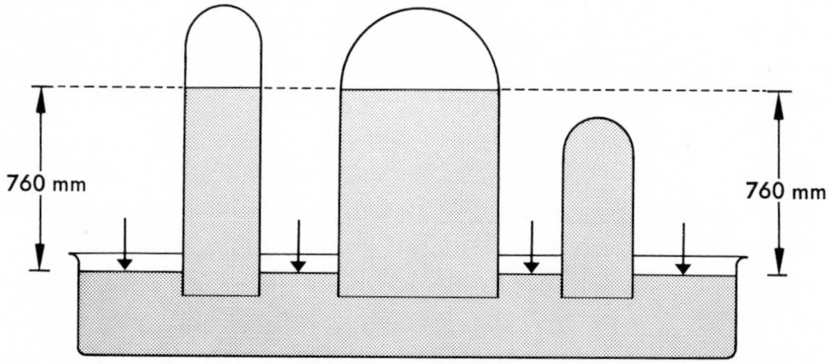

Figure 3-2 The average height of a column of mercury in a barometer at sea level is 760 mm. Note that the height of the column does not depend on the diameter of the glass tube. Note also that the short tube on the right is not long enough to allow any mercury to run out. The arrows signify the pressure exerted by the atmosphere on the mercury surface.

A good example of actual pressure being exerted by confined gas may be observed in an inflated balloon. The rubber membrane of the balloon is only slightly permeable to nitrogen and oxygen, the gases most prominent in air. When a balloon is inflated, the air molecules become more concentrated, resulting in an increase in pressure. A pressure exerted by a gas in a closed container is the sum of the pressures exerted by a great number of molecules as they hit the walls of the container simultaneously. An increase in the concentration of the gas in the container will mean that many more of the gas molecules will collide with the walls at any one time. Obviously, this results in an increase in pressure. The walls of the balloon will stretch in order to compensate for the increase in pressure, giving visual evidence of the ability of a gas to exert a pressure.

We have been given two examples of gas pressure that can actually be observed. How is this related to diffusion pressure? Actually, *diffusion pressure* is a hypothetical term describing the potential ability of a gas, liquid, or solid to diffuse from an area of its greatest concentration to an area of lesser concentration. For example, the confined gas in the balloon has a greater diffusion pressure than the air that surrounds it. Therefore, if the balloon were broken, the confined gas, having a greater diffusion pressure, would diffuse out into the surrounding air.

Independent diffusion. The direction of diffusion of a substance is determined entirely by the differences in diffusion pressure of that substance and is completely independent of the diffusion pressures of surrounding substances. Let us again use the rubber balloon to illustrate this important principle. Suppose a balloon is inflated with nitrogen gas. Since the rubber walls of the balloon are relatively impermeable to nitrogen, the confined nitrogen in the balloon will have a relatively high diffusion pressure. Carbon dioxide, unlike nitrogen, can readily pass through a rubber membrane. If the balloon filled with nitrogen is allowed to stand in air, the carbon dioxide of the air will diffuse into the balloon until an equilibrium is established. Carbon dioxide diffuses into the balloon because its diffusion pressure in air is higher than its diffusion pressure in the balloon (which was zero). The inward diffusion of carbon dioxide occurs even though the diffusion pressure of the nitrogen gas confined in the balloon was considerably higher than the diffusion pressure of the carbon dioxide in the air. The importance of independent diffusion to the plant will become more apparent in the succeeding chapters.

Factors affecting the rate of diffusion of gases

1. Temperature. The rate at which a gas will diffuse increases with increase in temperature. An increase in temperature increases the kinetic energy of the gas molecules; that is, a rise in temperature is accompanied by an increase in the velocity at which the gas molecules move.
2. Density of the diffusing molecules. The rates at which gases diffuse under constant conditions vary widely with different gases. The reason for this is related to the density of the gas. Graham's law of diffusion summarizes this principle: "the rates of diffusion of gases are inversely proportional to the square roots of their densities." On the basis of this law, the following relationship can be written:

$$\frac{r_1}{r_2} = \frac{\sqrt{d_2}}{\sqrt{d_1}}$$

where r_1 and r_2 are the diffusion rates of gases that have the densities d_1 and d_2, respectively. If we apply this equation to the gases hydrogen and oxygen, we find:

$$\frac{r_H}{r_O} = \frac{\sqrt{d_O}}{\sqrt{d_H}} = \frac{\sqrt{16}}{\sqrt{1}} = \frac{4}{1}$$

Since the density of oxygen is 16 times that of hydrogen, the rate of diffusion of hydrogen is 4 times that of oxygen.

The above law can be illustrated easily in the laboratory. If a glass tube is plugged at both ends with cotton and the cotton plugs are soaked simultaneously with ammonium hydroxide (NH_4OH) and hydrochloric acid (HCl), we will have a system in which two gases (NH_3 and HCl) are diffusing toward each other at rates dependent upon the mass of their molecules. The spot where the two gases meet is indicated by a white ring of solid ammonium chloride (NH_4Cl) (Figure 3-3). As indicated in Figure

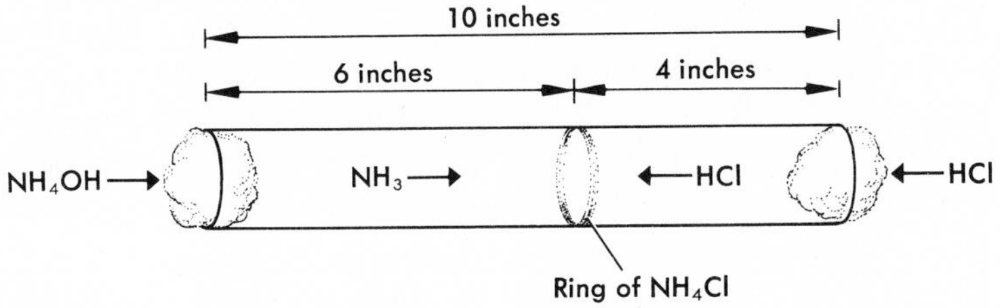

Figure 3-3 A method of illustrating Graham's law. Ammonium hydroxide is added to the cotton plug at one end of the tube while hydrochloric acid is added to the cotton plug at the other end. The ring of ammonium chloride represents the point where the two gases, HCl and NH_3, met after diffusing from their respective cotton plugs.

3-3, the ammonium chloride ring is closer to the HCl end of the tube. One would anticipate this result since the density of HCl is almost twice that of NH_3.

3. Medium in which diffusion occurs. The more concentrated a medium is, the slower molecules will diffuse through it. This is well illustrated in the example mentioned earlier, describing bromine gas diffusing in air and in a partial vacuum.
4. Diffusion pressure gradient. In general, the steeper the diffusion pressure gradient, the faster is the rate of diffusion. The steepness of the gradient is controlled by the difference in concentrations of the diffusing substance between one area and another and the connecting distance between these two areas through which diffusion will occur.

The factors controlling the rates of diffusion of gases, in general, control the rates of diffusion of liquids and solids. In addition to temperature, molecular density, diffusion medium, and diffusion pressure gradient, the diffusion of solutes in solvents, liquids in liquids, and gases in liquids is influenced by the size and solubility of the diffusing molecule.

OSMOSIS

Osmosis may be thought of as a special type of diffusion, which involves the movement of water through a differentially permeable membrane from an area where it is in high concentration to an area where it is in low concentration. Although we can include solvents other than water within the general phenomenon of osmosis, the important concern here is the osmosis of water in plants.

The osmotic process can be demonstrated by a very simple procedure. Tie a piece of material, such as pig bladder, over the wide end of a thistle tube. The pig bladder is differentially permeable, allowing water but not dissolved solutes, such as sucrose, to pass through. A solution of sucrose is placed inside the thistle tube, and the membrane end of the tube submerged in a beaker of pure water (Figure 3-4). Since the membrane

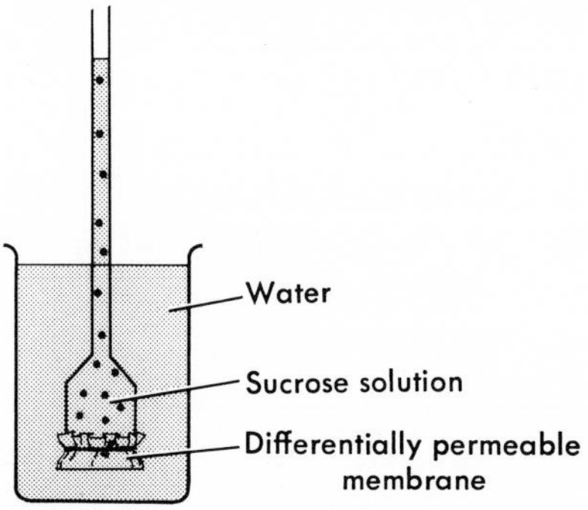

Figure 3-4 A method of illustrating osmosis. Water moves into the thistle tube through the differentially permeable membrane from its high concentration to its low concentration.

fastened over the mouth of the thistle tube is permeable to water, water will move both in and out of the tube. However, the rate of movement of water moving into the tube will be higher than that of water moving out. This is because the concentration of water in the beaker is higher than the concentration of water in the tube. Under these circumstances, water will accumulate in the thistle tube, and a column of water will rise in the tube. The greatest difference in water concentration exists at the moment the tube is submerged in water. At this time, the highest rate of water moving into the tube and the lowest rate of water moving out of the tube occurs. As water accumulates in the thistle tube, the sucrose solution becomes more and more diluted, and the rate of water moving into the tube slows down accordingly. That is, there is less and less difference between the concentration of water in the beaker and in the tube. Yet if no other factors were involved, the amount of water moving into the tube would always be greater than the amount moving out. However, as the column of water builds up in the tube, it exerts a pressure, which causes a continually greater amount of water to move out of the tube. Eventually, an equilibrium is reached where the forces controlling the movement of water into the tube balance those controlling the movement of water out of the tube.

Clearly, osmosis is very similar to diffusion, the only distinguishing factor being the presence of a differentially permeable membrane.

Osmotic pressure

Osmotic pressure is a term often used in discussions on water relations of plants. Because of the difficulty in demonstrating this pressure and because it can only be measured indirectly, the term osmotic pressure is a hard one for the student to grasp. We can define osmotic pressure as that pressure needed to prevent the passage of pure water into an aqueous solution through a differentially permeable membrane, thereby preventing an increase in the volume of the solution.

This definition implies that the solution is confined by a perfectly inelastic structure that is permeable to water but not to solutes. However, an unconfined solution is also said to have an osmotic pressure. Osmotic pressure is one of the colligative properties of a solution; that is, it is directly proportional to the number of solute molecules in a given amount of solvent. Therefore, a 1 molal solution of an undissociated substance at 0°C has a *theoretical* osmotic pressure of 22.4 atm. Since osmotic pressure is directly proportional to the number of solute molecules per solvent molecules, a 0.5 molal solution would have a theoretical osmotic pressure of 11.2 atm.

Although we speak of an unconfined solution as having an osmotic pressure, pressure in the literal sense of the word is not evident. Only when a solution is confined by a differentially permeable membrane, does a pressure become evident. Perhaps the terms osmotic potential or osmotic value are more applicable when speaking of unconfined solutions.

Turgor pressure

As mentioned in Chapter 1, the cell cytoplasm and organelles are enclosed by a differentially permeable membrane called the plasmalema or simply the cell membrane. Unlike the animal cell, the plant cell and its cell membrane is enclosed by a rigid relatively inelastic structure called the cell wall. This unique property of the plant cell allows it to exist in a relatively wide range of osmotic concentrations. In contrast, the animal cell can only exist in solutions where the osmotic concentrations are identical or nearly identical to its own cell contents.

The plant cell, when placed in pure water, swells only to a small extent and does not burst. Because of the higher osmotic pressure of the cell contents, water will move into the cell, resulting in the cell membrane being pressed up against the cell wall. The actual pressure that develops (i.e., the pressure responsible for pushing the cell membrane against the cell wall) is called *turgor pressure*. The cell wall, being rigid, exerts an equal and opposite pressure, which we will call *wall pressure*. As a result of this interplay of forces, the plant cell under these conditions is said to be turgid. One of the first easily observed signs of a water deficit in a plant is a loss of turgor by its leaf cells, which results in a wilted appearance of the leaves.

Diffusion pressure deficit

The diffusion pressure of pure water is theoretically 1236 atm. If some substance, such as sugar or salt, is dissolved in pure water, the resulting solution has a diffusion pressure lower than that of pure water. If both the solution and pure water are subjected to the same pressure, then the difference in diffusion pressures between the two systems is exactly equal to the osmotic pressure of the solution. That is, if the solution has an osmotic pressure of 8 atm, then the *diffusion pressure deficit* of that solution is 8 atm. We may define diffusion pressure deficit, therefore, as the difference in diffusion pressures between a solution and pure solvent when both are subjected to the same atmospheric pressure (1).

Perhaps an example equating the terms osmotic pressure, turgor pressure, and diffusion pressure deficit will help clarify the above discussion. A solution with an osmotic pressure of 30 atm is enclosed by an inelastic membrane permeable only to water. This system is submerged in a solution with an osmotic pressure of 10 atm (Figure 3-5). Water will move from the external into the internal solution. This may also be expressed as water moving from a solution of lower to a solution of higher osmotic pressure or from a solution of lower to a solution of higher diffusion pressure deficit. Another way to express the movement of water in this example is to say that water is moving from a solution of high to a solution of low diffusion pressure.

Since the internal solution is enclosed in an inelastic membrane, an equilibrium will be reached between the two systems with the entrance of only a small amount of water into the internal solution. The actual pressure or turgor pressure developed in the internal solution will amount to 20 atm. The wall pressure at this point will also be 20 atm. Since the diffusion pressure of a solution is increased by the amount of pressure it is subjected to, the diffusion pressure of the internal solution should increase by 20 atm, thus equaling the diffusion pressure of the external solution. The dif-

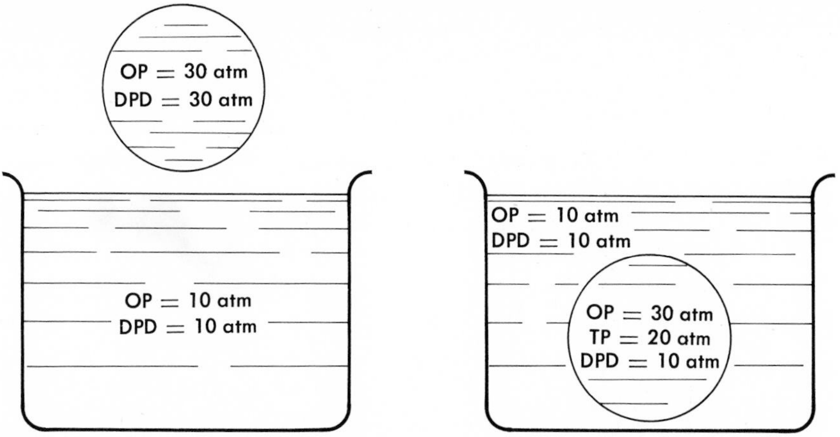

Figure 3-5 An example equating the terms osmotic pressure, turgor pressure, and diffusion pressure deficit. A turgor pressure develops when a solution confined in an inelastic membrane permeable only to water is submerged in a solution of lower concentration. Note that the diffusion pressure deficits of both solutions at equilibrium are equal.

fusion pressure deficits of both solutions at equilibrium will therefore be equal to 10 atm. Here we can make the general statement that when two aqueous solutions of different osmotic pressure are separated by a membrane permeable only to water, their diffusion pressure deficits and not their osmotic pressures will tend to equate. With the above discussion in mind, we can write the expression:

$$\text{DPD} = \text{OP} - \text{TP}$$

From this expression, we can see that when the turgor pressure (TP) equals the osmotic pressure (OP) of a solution, the diffusion pressure deficit (DPD) of that solution equals zero. If an aqueous solution with an osmotic pressure of 10 atm is enclosed in an inelastic membrane and submerged in pure water (DPD = 0), a turgor pressure of 10 atm will be reached in the internal solution when the two systems reach equilibrium. That is, at equilibrium, the diffusion pressure deficit of the internal solution will be zero.

Start	$10 = 10 - 0$
	$\text{DPD} = \text{OP} - \text{TP}$
Equilibrium	$0 = 10 - 10$

In the examples so far, we have been using hypothetical situations where the solution is enclosed by an inelastic membrane. However, the cell wall of the plant cell is elastic to some degree, and a certain increase

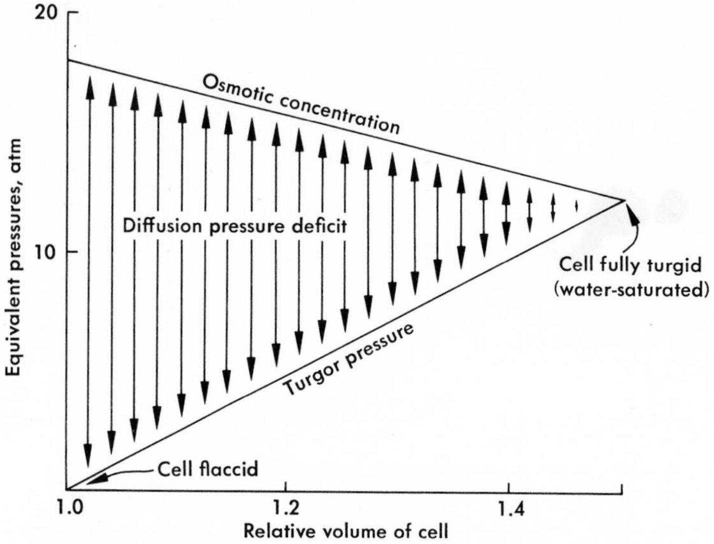

Figure 3-6 Changes that occur when a plant cell takes up water. Note that when osmotic pressure (osmotic concentration) and tur- of the cell sap is zero. (After *Principles of Plant Physiology* by gor pressure are equal in magnitude, the diffusion pressure deficit James Bonner and Arthur W. Galston. Copyright 1952. W. H. Freeman and Company.)

in volume is realized when a flaccid cell becomes fully turgid. With an increase in volume, there is a dilution of the cell sap, thus lowering the osmotic pressure of the sap. However, the expression DPD = OP − TP is still accurate, and there still is an equating of diffusion pressure deficits. The changes that occur when a plant cell takes up water are expressed in Figure 3-6. In a flaccid cell (TP = 0), the osmotic pressure of the cell sap is equal to its diffusion pressure deficit. If this cell is placed in pure water, there is a movement of water into the cell causing a turgor pressure to develop and a certain amount of elastic stretching of the cell wall to occur. With an increase in cell volume (caused by stretching of the cell wall), there is a dilution and consequent decrease in the osmotic pressure of the cell sap. At the point where the osmotic pressure equals the turgor pressure and the diffusion pressure deficit equals zero, the cell is said to be fully turgid. There is no further increase in volume of the cell at this point.

Plasmolysis

When a living plant cell is placed in a solution with an osmotic pressure indentical to its own cell sap (an isotonic solution), the appearance of the cell remains normal in every respect. However, if the cell is placed in a solution of lower (hypotonic) or higher (hypertonic) osmotic pressure than its own cell sap, several easily observed changes in cell appearance may be seen. If epidermal tissue from the leaves of *Rhoeo* or *Zebrina* are immersed in a hypertonic solution of sucrose, the cell membrane may be observed pulling away from the cell wall. This is easily seen because of the pigmentation of the vacuolar contents of the leaf cells of these plants. Let us examine what happens in this situation in a little more detail. First, the cell is immersed in a hypertonic solution, which means the concentration of water in the cell is higher than the concentration of water in the external solution. Secondly, the cell membrane and vacuolar membrane are practically impermeable to sucrose, but readily permeable to water. Thirdly, the cell wall will allow the passage of both sucrose and water. The water in the cell vacuole will move out of the cell into the external solution (i.e., from its high concentration to its low concentration). This results in a loss of turgor, a shrinking of the vacuole and a pulling away of the cell membrane from the cell wall. A cell in this condition is said to be *plasmolyzed.*

A different situation develops if a living plant cell is placed in a hypotonic solution. In this situation, water moving from its high concentration (external solution) to its low concentration (cell sap), will enter the cell, causing it to become more turgid. Since the cell wall is elastic to some degree, there will be a slight increase in cell volume. There will also, of course, be an increase in the turgor pressure of the cell. It is difficult to observe any differences in appearance between a plant cell in an isotonic solution and a plant cell in a hypotonic solution. The slight increase in volume of the cell in a hypotonic solution is generally very small.

Plasmolyzed cells usually can be *deplasmolyzed.* That is, if a cell that has been plasmolyzed is placed in a hypotonic solution, it will regain its turgidity. Plasmolysis and deplasmolysis may be observed in one demonstration if the plant cell is placed in a hypertonic solution containing a solute that can slowly diffuse across the cell and vacuolar membranes. At first, plasmolysis will be observed because of the much faster diffusion of water across the two membranes. However, with time enough solute will diffuse into the cell so that the osmotic concentration of the cell sap will equal that of the external solution and the cell will appear normal again.

Measurement of osmotic pressure

The *boiling point* of an aqueous solution is higher than that of pure water; the *vapor pressure* of the water in a solution is lower than that of pure water, and a solution freezes at a lower temperature (*freezing point depression*) than pure water. These factors, called the *colligative properties* of solutions, are interrelated and the extent to which each factor is affected is directly proportional to the number of dissolved particles (molecules or ions). Thus, a measure of any one of these factors is an indirect measure of osmotic pressure. We have already mentioned that osmotic pressure is one of the colligative properties of solutions. Vapor pressure depression and boiling point elevation are generally not used to measure the osmotic pressure of cell contents. However, freezing point depression of expressed plant juices may be measured with a considerable degree of accuracy. The theoretical freezing point depression of a 1 molal solution of an unionized substance is 1.86°C (compared to pure water), and a 1 molal solution has a theoretical osmotic pressure of 22.4 atm. An equation relating these two factors, freezing point depression and osmotic pressure, is easily arrived at and may be used to determine the osmotic pressure of a solution of unknown concentration.

$$OP = \frac{22.4 \times \Delta}{1.86}$$

In this equation, Δ stands for the observed freezing point depression of the unknown solution. If, for example, some plant juice is expressed and found to have a freezing point depression of 1.395, the osmotic pressure of this solution would be:

$$OP = \frac{22.4 \times 1.395}{1.86} = 16.8 \text{ atm}$$

The determination of a solution's osmotic pressure by determination of its freezing point depression is termed *cryoscopy,* and the technique is referred to as the *cryoscopic method.*

A less strenuous method of determining the osmotic pressure of cell contents employs the plasmolytic phenomenon. A graded series of solutions are prepared covering a certain range of osmotic pressures, which, presumably, bridge the osmotic pressure of the contents of the cells to be treated. Strips of tissue from some plant are placed in the different solutions and after a time examined under the microscope. Sucrose solutions are generally used in this technique. Microscopic examination of the strips of tissue from the different solutions will show some in which all of the cells are turgid, some in which nearly all of the cells are plasmolyzed, and some in which about 50% of the cells are just beginning to show signs of plasmolysis (incipient plasmolysis). At incipient plasmolysis, the turgor pressure of the cell is zero and the osmotic pressure of the cell contents is equal to the osmotic pressure of the external solution.

IMBIBITION

Still another process is available to the plant for the uptake of water, a process known as *imbibition.* As with osmosis, imbibition may be considered a special type of diffusion, since the net movement of water is along a diffusion gradient. If dry plant material is placed in water, a noticeable swelling will take place, sometimes amounting to a considerable increase in volume. Anyone who has experienced a sticking wooden door or window frame during a prolonged period of humid weather has had an encounter with the imbibition phenomenon. Dry wood is a particularly good imbibant.

Tremendous pressures can develop if an imbibant is confined and then allowed to imbibe water. For example, dry wooden stakes driven into a small crack in a rock and then soaked, can develop enough pressure to split the rock. Indeed, this form of quarrying has been used to some advantage by many people.

Conditions necessary for imbibition

Two conditions appear to be requisite in order for imbibition to occur:

1. A diffusion pressure gradient must exist between the imbibant and the substance imbibed.
2. A certain affinity must exist between components of the imbibant and the imbibed substance.

The diffusion pressure of dry plant materials capable of imbibition is practically zero. Therefore, when this material is placed in pure water, a steep diffusion pressure gradient is established, and water moves rapidly into the imbibant. As water continues to move into the imbibant, the diffusion pressure of the water in the imbibant rises until it finally equals that of the external water. At this point an equilibrium is established, imbibition ceases, and water moving in is equal to the water moving out of the imbibant.

An imbibant does not necessarily imbibe all kinds of liquids. For example, dry plant materials immersed in ether do not swell appreciably. However, rubber does imbibe ether and will swell appreciably if submerged in it. On the other hand, rubber will not imbibe water. The obvious implication is that certain attractive forces exist between components of the imbibant and the imbibed substance.

A considerable amount of colloidal material is present in both living and dead plant cells. Proteins and polypeptides are hydrophilic colloids, which have a strong attraction for water. In addition, plant cells possess a considerable amount of carbohydrate in the form of cellulose and starch to which water is strongly attracted. The adsorption of water to the surfaces of these hydrophilic colloids is of major importance to the imbibition process. Seeds, which are particularly high in colloidal material, are very good imbibants. Indeed, the main source of water to the germinating seed is through the process of imbibition.

Imbibition pressure

Imbibition pressure is analogous to osmotic pressure in that it represents the potential maximum pressure that an imbibant will develop if submerged in pure water (1). The actual pressure that develops when water is imbibed may be thought of as turgor pressure. With the above considerations in mind, the expression

$$\text{DPD} = \text{IP} - \text{TP}$$

may be used. This expression, of course, is similar to the one used for osmotic systems where diffusion pressure deficit is equal to osmotic pressure minus turgor pressure. No turgor pressure develops in an unconfined imbibant, and the above expression under these conditions simplifies to

$$\text{DPD} = \text{IP}$$

The imbibition pressure of air-dried seeds, such as cocklebur, may approach 1000 atm (2). If seeds such as these are immersed in pure water, the diffusion pressure deficit of the very small amount of water in the dry seeds would be nearly 1000 atm. After imbibition ceases, the diffusion pressure deficit of the external and internal water is zero. On the other hand, if seeds containing water with a diffusion pressure deficit of 500 atm are submerged in a solution of NaCl with an osmotic pressure of 50 atm (DPD = 50 atm), the diffusion pressure deficit of the seed water at equilibrium will be 50 atm. As in osmotic systems, the diffusion pressure deficits equate.

Factors affecting the rate and extent of imbibition

The rate and extent of imbibition is affected primarily by temperature and the osmotic pressure of the substance to be imbibed. Temperature does not affect the amount of water taken up by an imbibant, but has a definite effect on the rate of imbibition. An increase in temperature increases the rate of imbibition (Figure 3-7).

Both the amount of water imbibed and the rate of imbibition are affected by the osmotic pressure of the substance to be imbibed. The addi-

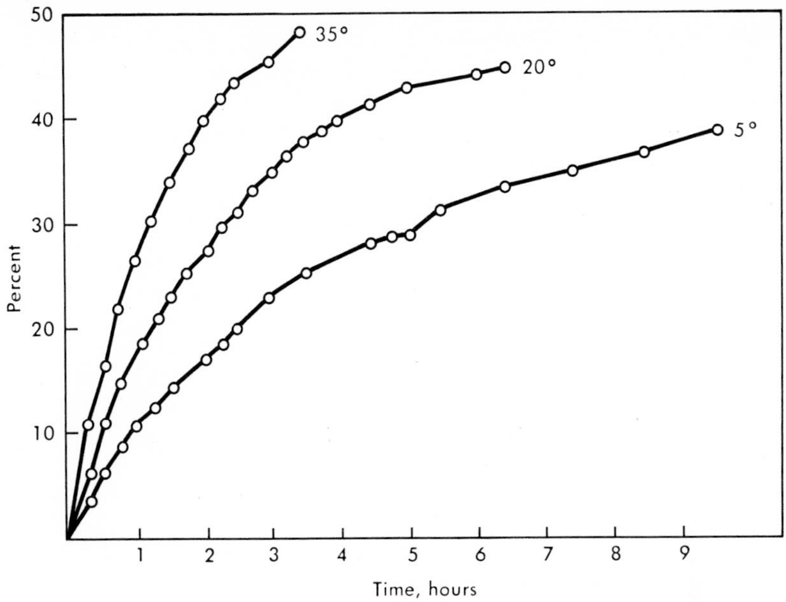

Figure 3-7 Rate of imbibition by *Xanthium* seeds at different temperatures (C°). (After C. A. Shull. 1920. Botan. Gaz. 69:361.)

tion of a solute to pure water lowers the diffusion pressure of the water. This has the effect of producing a diffusion pressure gradient between the solution water and an imbibant that is less steep than the diffusion pressure gradient that would exist if the same imbibant were submerged in pure water. A decrease in the diffusion pressure gradient will decrease the rate at which water is imbibed and the amount of water taken up. Some data by Shull (2) on the effects of osmotic pressure on the imbibition of air-dried cocklebur seeds are shown in Table 3-1.

Volume and energy changes

We have already mentioned that the volume of an imbibant increases as a result of imbibition. However, the total volume of the system, the volume of the water in which the imbibant is submerged plus the volume of the imbibant, is always less after imbibition than before imbibition starts. This is easily demonstrated by placing a certain number of air-dried seeds in a graduated cylinder containing water, reading the initial volume, and comparing it with the volume of the system after imbibition ceases. The reason for this is that water molecules adsorbed to the surfaces of colloidal material present in the imbibant are held relatively tight and as a consequence

Table 3-1 Imbibition by *Xanthium* seeds as affected by different osmotic pressures.[a]

Molar concentration	*Water imbibed after 48 hrs, % of dry wt*	*Osmotic pressure, atm*
H_2O	51.58	0.0
0.1*M* NaCl	46.33	3.8
0.2*M* NaCl	45.52	7.6
0.3*M* NaCl	42.05	11.4
0.4*M* NaCl	40.27	15.2
0.5*M* NaCl	38.98	19.0
0.6*M* NaCl	35.18	22.8
0.7*M* NaCl	32.85	26.6
0.8*M* NaCl	31.12	30.4
0.9*M* NaCl	29.79	34.2
1.0*M* NaCl	26.73	38.0
2.0*M* NaCl	18.55	72.0
4.0*M* NaCl	11.76	130.0
Sat. NaCl	6.35	375.0
Sat. LiCl	−0.29	965.0

[a] After C. A. Schull. 1916. Botan. Gaz. 62:1.

are packed closer together. The result is a decrease in volume of the system.

As a result of the tight adsorption of the water molecules, some of the kinetic energy possessed by these molecules is lost. This energy loss shows up in the system as heat. Therefore, there is always an increase in temperature as a result of imbibition.

BIBLIOGRAPHY

1. Meyer, B. S. 1938. The water relations of plant cells. Botan. Rev. 4: 531.
2. Shull, C. A. 1916. Measurement of the surface forces in soils. Botan. Gaz. 62: 1.
3. Shull, C. A. 1920. Temperature and rate of moisture intake in seeds. Botan. Gaz. 69: 361.

FOR FURTHER REFERENCE

Bennet-Clark, T. A. 1959. Water relations of cells. *In* F. C. Steward (ed.), Plant physiology. Academic Press, New York. 2: 105.

Dainty, J. 1963. Water relations of plant cells. *In* R. D. Preston (ed.), Advances in botanical research. Academic Press, New York. 1: 279.

Kozlowski, T. T. 1964. Water metabolism in plants. Harper and Row, New York.

Ray, P. M. 1960. On the theory of osmotic water movement. Plant Physiol. 35: 783.

4
Transpiration

INTRODUCTION

We have already mentioned that water is the most abundant constituent of plant tissues. Nevertheless, a plant retains but a small portion of the water absorbed and passed through it during its life cycle. Large amounts of water are continuously being absorbed from the soil, translocated through the plant, and passed off into the atmosphere without ever being involved in any apparent function. One of the curiosities of nature is the terrible inefficiency in the water economy of plants. Although plants need water in relatively large amounts to exist, the anatomical features of their leaf structure are such that large amounts of water are continuously lost.

TRANSPIRATION

Water is primarily lost from a plant in the form of vapor through a process known as *transpiration*. On absorption from the soil by roots, water is translocated via the xylem tissue to the mesophyll cells of the leaves. The loose arrangement of these living thin-walled cells, resulting in an abundance of intercellular space, provides ideal conditions for the evaporation of water from cell surfaces. Part of the epidermal surface of the leaf is made up of a great number of microscopic pores, called *stomata.* The stomatal pores open into the intercellular spaces of the leaf, providing an uninterrupted path from the interior of the leaf to the external environment. One can visualize the transpiration stream as an unbroken chain of water being pulled from the soil, through the roots, up the xylem ducts, out of the mesophyll cells, and through the stomatal pores.

In addition to *stomatal transpiration,* water is lost, also as a vapor, directly from the surfaces of leaves and herbaceous stems and through *lenticels,* small openings in the corky tissue covering stems and twigs. The former is called *cuticular transpiration* and the latter *lenticular transpiration.* Cuticular transpiration is so named because it involves diffusion of water vapor directly through the *cuticle,* a waxlike layer of cutin covering the surfaces of leaves. This layer greatly retards water loss, and without it any water retention by the plant would be almost impossible. The cuticle, although retarding water loss, is permeable to a certain degree to water vapor. The extent of cuticular transpiration varies to a great degree among different species of plants. In plants with leaves possessing a thick cutin layer, this form of transpiration is insignificant. However, in plants where the cutin layer is thin, severe water deficits may be suffered when conditions favoring high transpiration are prevalent. Generally, the cutin layer is thicker in sun leaves and plants of dry habitats as compared to shade leaves and plants of moist habitats.

The magnitude of water lost through cuticular and lenticular transpiration is insignificant when compared to the amount of water lost through stomatal transpiration. Only under very dry conditions, when the stomates are closed, can water loss through the cuticle and lenticels be considered important. However, lenticular transpiration may cause some desiccation in those trees that shed their leaves at the onset of winter. During a cold winter, water absorption by roots is at a minimum, thus increasing the importance of lenticular transpiration.

Magnitude of transpiration

As already mentioned, the amount of water actually used by a plant is small, compared to the large quantities transpired. Indeed, transpiration rates of some herbaceous plants are of such a magnitude that under favorable conditions, the entire volume of water in a plant may be replaced in the course of a single day (32). For example, it has been estimated that a single corn plant may transpire up to 54 gallons of water in one growing season. At this rate, a single acre of corn could transpire the equivalent of 15 inches of water during one growing season. The amount of water lost varies to some extent from one species to the next as the data in Table 4-1 show.

Table 4-1 Water loss by transpiration per single plant for five kinds of plants during the growing season.[a]

Kind of plant	*Transpiration during growing season, gal*
cowpea	13
irish potato	25
winter wheat	25
tomato	34
corn	54

[a] Reprinted with permission of The Macmillan Company from *Fundamentals of Plant Physiology*, by J. F. Ferry and H S. Ward. Copyright © 1957, The Macmillan Company.

In a recent discussion of water loss by plants, Kozlowski (24) has cited data from several papers, which dramatically emphasize the tremendous amounts of water that are lost by trees and forests. For example, an average forest in southern United States may lose as much as 8000 gallons of water per acre per day (34). Cummings (6) has estimated that a single 48-foot high open-grown silver maple tree may transpire as much as 58 gallons per hour.

With the above figures in mind, one becomes well aware of the importance of good water management in agricultural practices. Economic losses caused by crop failures sometimes reach tremendous proportions during prolonged periods of drought. In a hungry world, this matter is of considerable importance.

Measurement of transpiration

Several methods have been employed in measuring transpiration. These methods usually involve either a measure of the water absorbed or a measure of the water vapor transpired by a plant. The first approach takes advantage of the fact that the rate of absorption and transpiration are in accord with each other under a number of conditions. However, there are several exceptions to this rule.

Weighing methods. Perhaps the simplest way to measure transpiration is to merely weigh a potted plant at the beginning and at the end of a prescribed period of time. The soil surface should be covered and the pot wrapped with some water repellent material, such as aluminum foil, to retard evaporation from surfaces other than the plant. The loss of weight by the plant over a short period of time will be almost completely due to transpiration. Gain or loss of weight due to photosynthesis or respiration is insignificant. When using this method, one is restricted to small plants, which can be conveniently grown in a pot.

The transpiration of excised parts of plants, such as leaves, fruits, branches, etc., have been measured. A plant part is excised, immediately weighed, and then, after a short period of time, weighed again. Although relative rates of transpiration may be compared in this manner, transpiration of an excised organ frequently deviates from the normal transpiration of the intact plant. In the initial stages, the rate of transpiration of an excised organ may exceed normal rates, probably because of the release of tensions in the xylem ducts. After a short period of time, however, transpiration rates will fall off, because of a decrease in the water content of the tissue, stomatal closure, permeability changes, etc.

Potometer method. The potometer method takes advantage of the fact that, generally, the rate of water absorption is very nearly equal to the rate of transpiration. A shoot of coleus, geranium, or some other suitable plant is sealed in a water-filled glass vessel. The glass vessel has two other outlets, a graduated capillary tube and a water reservoir (Figure 4-1). Before the rate of transpiration (or more exactly the rate of absorption) can be measured, the entire apparatus is filled with water so that no air spaces are present. This may be accomplished by manipulating the stopcock, which controls the flow of water into the vessel from the reservoir. An air bubble is introduced into the capillary tube. As transpiration proceeds, the air bubble will move along the capillary tube, giving a measure of the rate of transpiration. The potometer method is ideal for observing the effects of different environmental factors (temperature, light, air movement) on transpiration rates. However, the method suffers from the fact that it actually measures water absorption rather than transpiration, and under certain circumstances, the two can vary considerably.

Cobalt chloride method. In this method, transpiration is indicated by a change in color, rather than a change in weight. Filter paper disks are impregnated with a slightly acetic 3% solution of cobalt chloride and thoroughly dried. When dry, the color of the paper impregnated in this manner will be blue. When exposed to humid air, the blue color will gradually change to pink. Likewise, when exposed to a transpiring leaf surface, the color of the cobalt chloride-treated paper will gradually change

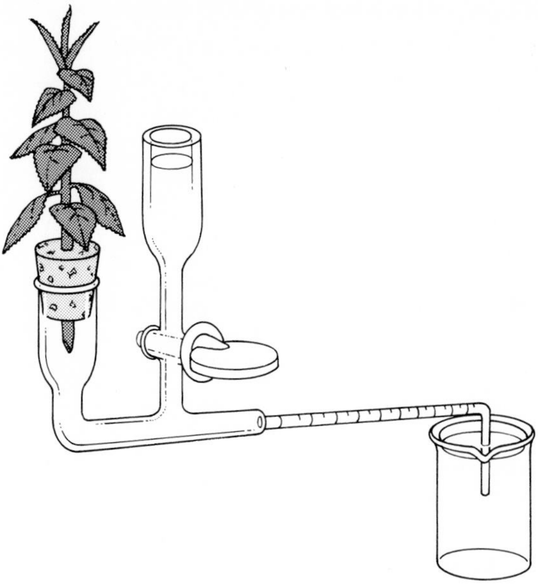

Figure 4-1 Potometer.

from blue to pink. The rate of color change is indicative of the rate of transpiration.

The cobalt chloride method can only be used for measuring the relative rates of transpiration of different plants. Due to modifications of different environmental conditions, transpiration rates determined by this method may deviate considerably from the actual transpiration rates. The surface of the leaf covered by the paper is subjected to practically no air movement, a reduction in light, and a steeper vapor pressure gradient.

A comparison of transpiration rates measured by the weighing and cobalt chloride methods is shown in Figure 4-2. Note in Figure 4-2 that in a few cases there was some agreement, but generally the two methods produced entirely different results.

Method of collecting and weighing water vapor lost in transpiration. This method entails the enclosure of the plant in a glass container so that water vapor can be trapped and weighed (Figure 4-3). Air of known moisture content is passed over the plant through an opening in the glass container and passed out over some preweighed water-absorbing material, such as anhydrous calcium chloride. The continuous stream of air passing over the plant keeps the moisture content of the enclosed air approximately equal to that of the surrounding atmosphere. The moisture content of the air passed over the plant is measured by passing it through the same

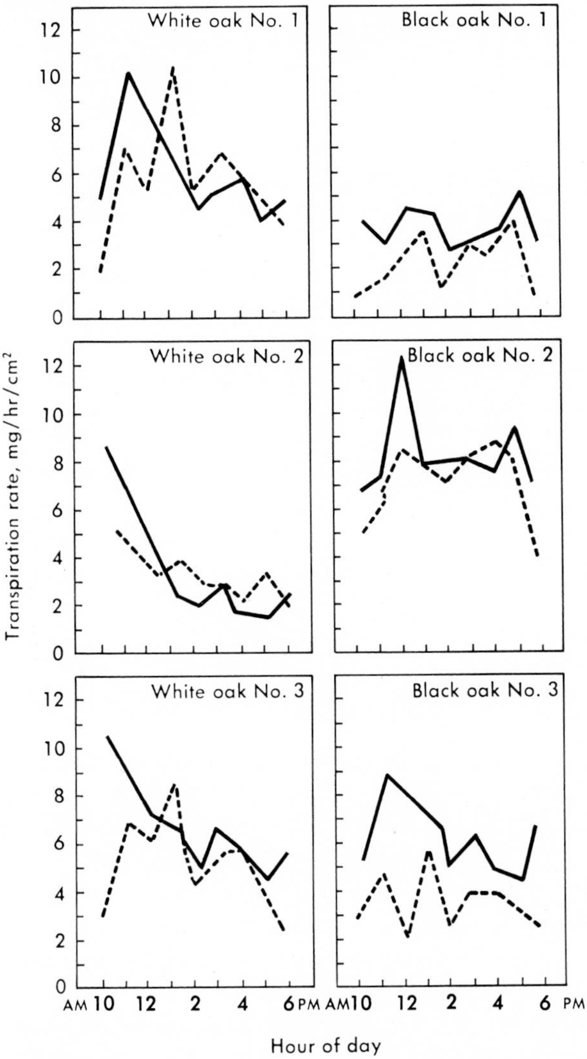

Figure 4-2 Comparison of the weighing and cobalt chloride methods as measures of transpiration in three different white oak and black oak plants. Broken line represents the weighing method and the solid line the cobalt chloride method. (After L. F. Bailey et al. 1952. Plant Physiol. 27:563.)

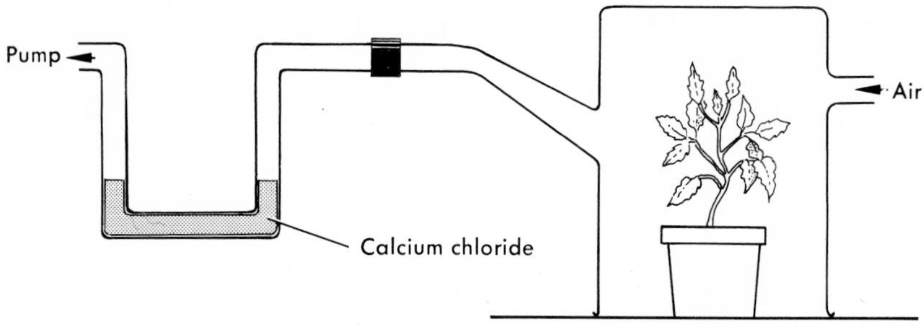

Figure 4-3 Apparatus for the measurement of transpiration. Air of a known moisture content is drawn over a transpiring plant and through the water-absorbing calcium chloride. An explanation of how transpiration is calculated using this apparatus is given in the text.

apparatus minus the plant. The difference in weight between the calcium chloride before and after air is passed through it is a measure of the moisture content of the air. The difference in weight between the calcium chloride receiving air passed over the plant and calcium chloride receiving air passed through the apparatus without the plant is a measure of transpiration.

THE STOMATAL MECHANISM

The epidermal surface of a leaf exhibits a great number of pores called *stomata.* The stomata are microscopic and are bordered by two specialized epidermal cells called *guard cells,* which control the opening and closing of the stomata. When fully opened, the stomatal pore may measure from 3 to 12 μ across and from 10 to 40 μ in length (26). The surface of a leaf, depending upon the species, may contain anywhere from 1000 to 60,000 stomates per square centimeter. As large as these figures are, the stomatal pores are so small that they occupy, when fully opened, only 1 to 2% of the total leaf surface. Stomates are more frequently found on the under surface of leaves, but occur with many species on both surfaces (Table 4-2).

With the exception of a few aquatic types, stomates are possessed by all angiosperms and gymnosperms (10). Functional stomates have been found among the cycads (41), ferns (55), horsetails (14), liverworts, and mosses (13). Apparently, stomates are widespread in the plant kingdom, the algae and fungi being the only groups lacking them. In addition, Guttenberg (13) has pointed out that all stomates are basically similar in structure, regardless of the species.

Table 4-2 Number of stomates per square centimeter of leaf surface.[a]

Plant	*Upper epidermis*	*Lower epidermis*
apple (*Pyrus malus*)	none	38,760
bean (*Phaseolus vulgaris*)	4,031	24,806
corn (*Zea mays*)	6,047	9,922
oak (*Quercus relutina*)	none	58,140
orange (*Citrus sinensis*)	none	44,961
pumpkin (*Cucurbita pepo*)	2,791	27,132
sunflower (*Helianthus annuus*)	8,527	15,504

[a] After C. L. Wilson and W. E. Loomis 1962. Botany. Holt, Rinehart & Winston, New York.

Stomatal movement

The mechanism by which the opening and closing of the stomatal pore is accomplished has been the subject of numerous investigations. It is generally understood that stomatal movement is a direct response to increases or decreases in the osmotic contents of the guard cells. The changes in diffusion pressure deficits, which result from these osmotic changes, cause water to move in or out of the guard cells, causing them to either expand (become turgid) or to go flaccid. When the guard cells are turgid, the stomate is open; when flaccid, the stomate is closed. To accomplish this movement of water, an exchange must take place between the guard cells and the surrounding mesophyll and epidermal cells. An increase in the osmotic contents of the guard cells would cause a diffusion pressure deficit gradient to develop between the guard cells and their neighboring cells. Water would diffuse into the guard cells, causing them to become more turgid. A drop in the osmotic contents of the guard cells would, of course, cause a diffusion pressure deficit gradient to develop in the opposite direction, and water would flow out of the guard cells into the neighboring cells. The factors causing the fluctuation of the osmotic contents of the cell will be discussed later in this chapter.

Anatomy and cytology of the stomate. Although changes in turgor provide the motive force for the opening and closing of stomates, an unusual feature of the wall of the guard cell causes the stomates to open in the manner that they do. The cell wall adjacent to the stomatal pore is thicker and more inelastic than the wall adjacent to the surrounding epidermal cells. An increase in turgor pressure will cause the more elastic part of the guard cell wall to stretch considerably, while the relatively inelastic thicker part of the wall bordering the pore is stretched only to a small extent.

This results in the formation of an elliptical aperture between two guard cells (Figure 4-4).

The appearance of the guard cells characteristically differs from the surrounding epidermal cells. In addition, the guard cells of some plant species are accompanied by epidermal cells whose appearance, like the guard cells, differs from the rest of the epidermal cells. These cells are variously called *companion cells, subsidiary cells,* or *accessory cells.*

One other distinguishing feature of the guard cell is its possession of chloroplasts. Epidermal cells characteristically do not possess chloroplasts. Microspectrophotometrically obtained absorption spectra taken from individual guard cell chloroplasts are similar to those obtained for mesophyll

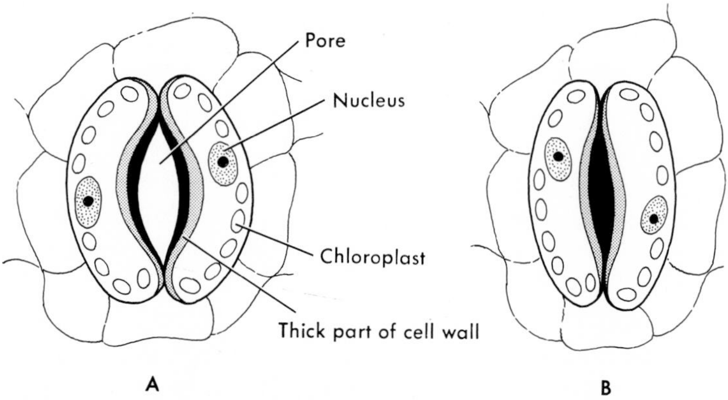

Figure 4-4 A. Opened stomate. B. Closed stomate. Note that the cell wall bordering the stomatal pore is thicker than that next to the surrounding cells and that the guard cells contain chloroplasts.

chloroplasts, indicating the presence of both chlorophyll a and b (56). The evidence is strong that photosynthesis takes place in the guard cell, but at a reduced rate (43, 42, 9). Later in this chapter, we will discuss the significance of guard cell photosynthesis, as it relates to stomatal opening and closing.

Diffusive capacity of the stomata. The stomatal pores may be thought of as ports of exchange between the external environment and the interior of the leaf. Therefore, the physical factors influencing the diffusion of water vapor through these pores is important in the study of transpiration. We should, at first, consider the striking efficiency of the diffusion of water vapor through the stomatal pores. Although, when opened, the combined pore area only represents 1–2% of the total leaf area, the diffusion of water vapor through the pores often exceeds 50% of that evaporating from a free water surface (26). One extreme example is cited by Stålfelt (45), who claims that a leaf of birch (*Betula pubescens*) under ideal conditions may have a transpiration rate exceeding 60% of that evaporating from a free water surface of the same area.

The initial investigations of Brown and Escombe (4) on the diffusion of CO_2 through isolated circular pores gave the first hint as to why diffusion through small pores is much more efficient than evaporation from an open surface. They found that diffusion through a small circular pore *is more nearly proportional to the perimeter or diameter of the pore than to its area.* This general rule has since been supported by the investigations of several workers (39, 50, 47). Data from work by Sayre (39) on this subject are shown in Table 4-3. An analysis of the data present in Table 4-3 strongly supports the observations of Brown and Escombe. The area of the smallest pore (0.01) is 1% of the largest pore (1.00), and the perimeter of the smallest pore (0.13) is 13% of the largest pore. The amount of water lost by the smallest pore is 14% of that lost by the largest pore.

Table 4-3 Diffusion of water vapor through small openings under uniform conditions.[a]

Diameter of pores, mm	*Loss of water vapor, g*	*Relative amounts of water lost*	*Relative areas of pores*	*Relative perimeters of pores*
2.64	2.655	1.00	1.00	1.00
1.60	1.583	0.59	0.37	0.61
0.95	0.928	0.35	0.13	0.36
0.81	0.762	0.29	0.09	0.31
0.48	0.455	0.17	0.03	0.18
0.35	0.364	0.14	0.01	0.13

[a] After J. D. Sayre. 1926. Ohio J. Sci. 26: 233.

Why is the diffusion of water vapor much more rapid through small pores per unit area than diffusion from a large free water surface? In both circumstances, water vapor becomes increasingly more concentrated over the evaporating surface, decreasing the vapor pressure gradient. This, in turn, has the effect of decreasing the rate of diffusion. However, over a large free water surface, water vapor would collect in the form of several overlapping diffusion "shells" or "caps" (Figure 4-5). Under these circumstances, a heavy blanket of water vapor will eventually cover the water surface, lowering the vapor pressure gradient over the whole area. The only appreciable diffusion that will take place will be around the perimeter

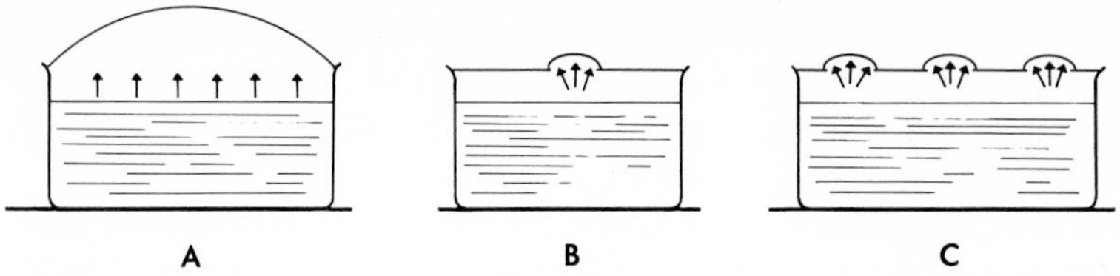

Figure 4-5 Diffusion of water vapor. A. Off a large free water surface. B. Through a small isolated pore. C. Through several small pores.

where the least resistance from water vapor in the air will be encountered. However, the magnitude of this "perimeter diffusion," when compared with diffusion from the complete surface, is relatively insignificant. Water vapor diffusing through a small isolated pore will also form a diffusion shell and lower the vapor pressure gradient (Figure 4-5). However, in this case, "perimeter diffusion" is much more significant since the perimeter of an enclosed surface becomes larger in relation to the area of the surface as that surface becomes smaller. Therefore, the smaller a pore becomes, the more nearly diffusion through it becomes proportional to its perimeter.

Now, suppose we take a water surface that is covered by a membrane containing numerous small pores. Let us say, also, that these pores are spaced far enough apart so that their diffusion shells do not interfere with one another (Figure 4-5). It is conceivable, under these conditions, that the amount of water vapor diffusing through a multiperforate septa, whose pore area represents only a small portion of the area of water surface covered, would be equal to the amount of water vapor diffusing from the same surface of water if uncovered. This hypothetical situation is analogous to that of water diffusing through the stomata of a leaf. It is obvious that stomates, when opened, do not present a barrier to the diffusion of water vapor from the interior of the leaf into the atmosphere.

Factors affecting stomatal movement

Those environmental factors having the greatest influence on the opening and closing of stomates are light, water, and temperature.

Light. Generally, the stomates of a leaf open when exposed to light and remain opened under continuous light unless some other factor becomes limiting. On return to darkness, the stomates will close. The amount of light necessary to achieve maximal stomatal opening varies with the species, but usually is considerably less than that needed for maximal photosynthetic activity. For example, a light intensity of 250 foot candles is all that is necessary to achieve maximal stomatal opening in tobacco leaf tissue (58). A much higher light intensity would be needed to obtain even an average rate of photosynthesis in this species. Indeed, the stomata of some plant species may be induced to open by bright moonlight (28).

A study of the effect of different wavelengths of light on the opening of tobacco leaf stomates suggests that some wavelengths are much more effective than others. Zelitch and Kuiper (reported by Zelitch, (59)) found that no opening occurred when stomates were exposed to either far red or ultraviolet irradiation. Good stomatal opening was obtained in the red and blue regions of the spectrum, but no opening in the green region. Essentially, the same results were obtained with *Senecio*. It is interesting to note that the response of stomates to the different wavelengths bears a resemblance to the action spectrum for adenosine triphosphate (ATP) synthesis in isolated chloroplasts (3). As we shall see later, ATP may be intimately involved in the opening and closing of stomates.

How is the effect of light on stomates accomplished? Early workers approached the problem in what appeared to be a logical manner. They assumed that guard cells, when exposed to light and warmth, increased their output of osmotically active substances through the process of photosynthesis. The resulting increase in osmotic pressure and turgor resulted in the opening of the stomate. However, as mentioned earlier, photosynthesis occurs in the guard cell only at a reduced rate and certainly could not account for the amount of osmotically active substances needed to cause the response of stomates to light.

Several workers have observed that the starch content of guard cells is high in the dark and low in light (27, 28, 39). This is rather a strange behavior, since in the other epidermal cells and the mesophyll cells exactly the opposite effect is observed (16).

Sayre (39), in his work with *Rumex patientia,* also noted that the opening and closing of stomates is sensitive to changes in pH. Generally, a high pH favors opening and a low pH closure of the stomates. Subsequently, it was observed that illumination of the guard cells in many species results in an increase in pH—return to darkness causes a lowering of pH in the guard cells (40, 44). A high pH is accompanied by a decrease in starch and an increase in reducing sugars (osmotically active), resulting in an increase in turgor. The converse responses were noted when the pH was lowered. The problem appeared to be solved when Yin and Tung (57) obtained evidence of the presence of the enzyme *phosphorylase* in chloroplasts. This enzyme catalyzes the reaction

$$\text{Starch} + \text{iP} \underset{\text{pH 5}}{\overset{\text{pH 7}\atop\text{Phosphorylase}}{\rightleftharpoons}} \text{Glucose-1-phosphate}$$

The point of equilibrium in this reaction depends upon the pH in which the reaction is occurring. At the higher pH (pH 7) and in the presence of inorganic phosphate (iP), the hydrolysis of starch is favored and glucose-1-phosphate is formed. At the lower pH (pH 5), the synthesis of starch from glucose-1-phosphate is favored. Since starch is osmotically inactive and glucose-1-phosphate is osmotically active, the above reaction has been considered an explanation for the pH effect on stomates.

However, the above scheme has been criticized by Steward (46), who has pointed out that unless glucose-1-phosphate is further converted to glucose and inorganic phosphate, no appreciable change in osmotic pressure can be obtained. Inorganic phosphate on the left side of the above equation is just as osmotically active as glucose-1-phosphate on the right. Steward has offered the following scheme (Figure 4-6).

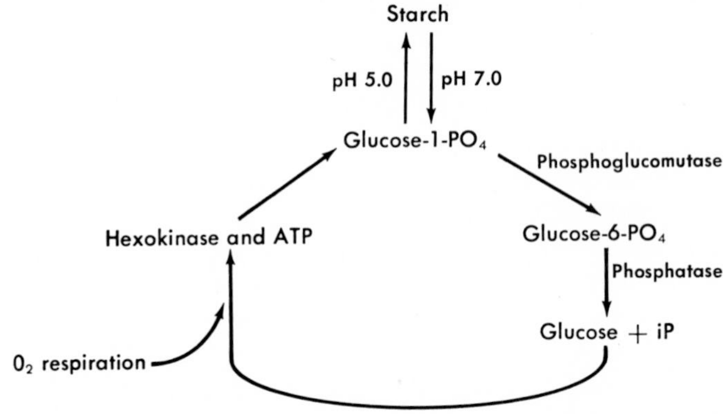

Figure 4-6 Metabolic reactions involved in the opening and closing of stomates. Note that reactions leading to closure require O_2 and energy, while reactions leading to opening do not. (After F. C. Steward. 1964. Plants at work. Addison-Wesley, Reading, Mass.)

In Steward's scheme, metabolic energy in the form of ATP would be necessary for stomatal closure. This necessitates the presence of O_2. However, in wheat, at least, stomatal closure is facilitated by anaerobic conditions (17).

The pH changes in the guard cell effected by light were thought to occur as a result of photosynthesis. The reduction of CO_2 (an acid) concentration in the guard cells and surrounding tissues that results from its utilization in photosynthesis causes a rise in pH. On return to darkness, photosynthesis stops, and the concentration of CO_2 rises as a result of respiration. This results in a decrease in pH.

Whether or not the effect of light on the opening and closing of stomates can be explained as simply as the above discussion implies, we do not know. Other more complex explanations have been offered, but the above hypothesis has obtained the largest following.

Water deficit and stomatal movement. Whenever the rate of transpiration exceeds the rate of absorption for any period of time, a water deficit is created in the plant. This may take place even under conditions favoring good water absorption and usually results in a condition termed *incipient wilting*—although wilting of the leaves has set in, it is not visible to the eye. The development of an internal water deficit in a plant causes a diffusion pressure deficit gradient between the guard cells and the mesophyll and epidermal cells surrounding the guard cells. This gradient favors the movement of water out of the guard cells, the reduced turgor causing the stomate to partially or completely close.

It appears that the development of a water deficit in a plant can cause chemical changes in the guard cells. The work of Yemm and Willis (56) demonstrates this rather nicely. They subjected *Chrysanthemum maximum,* grown outdoors, to different degrees of water deficit, and noted that stomates, which had opened with the early morning light, closed due to the water deficits. The greater the degree of water deficit, the sooner the stomates closed. Most important, however, was their finding that under conditions causing an internal water deficit, *the starch content of the guard cells increased.* It is significant to note here that under the same circumstances (wilting), the starch of the mesophyll cells is rapidly hydrolyzed (19). This increases their diffusion pressure deficit, thus enabling them to draw water from the nearby guard cells.

There is some evidence that under conditions of water deficit, stomates become more sensitive to other factors affecting their movement. For example, application of dry air to a *Pelargonium* leaf accelerates stomatal closure due to CO_2 (15) and darkness (15, 51). On the other hand, opening induced by light or CO_2-free air also is accelerated (15, 51).

Temperature and stomatal movement. When all other factors are equal, there is evidence that an increase in temperature causes an increase in stomatal opening. Wilson (52) demonstrated that the stomates of *Camellia,* privet, and cotton remain closed under continuous light when temperatures are lower than 0°C. As temperatures are increased, stomatal opening in all three plants increases. However, in cotton at least, there is a decline in stomatal opening at temperatures exceeding 30°C (Figure 4-7).

FACTORS AFFECTING THE RATE OF TRANSPIRATION

In the preceding section, we discussed those factors that influence stomatal movement and, as a consequence, the rate of transpiration. However, other

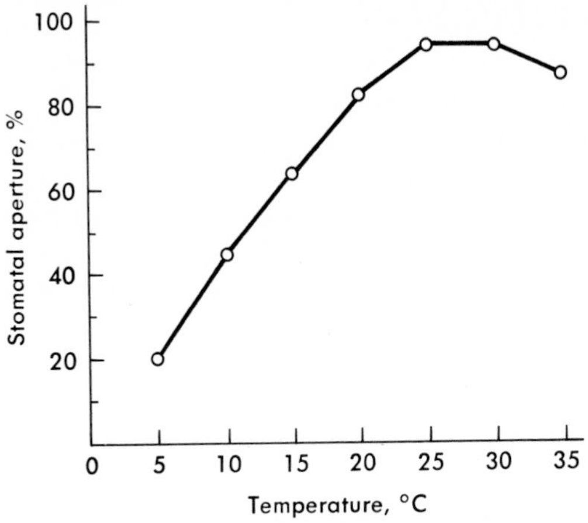

Figure 4-7 Effect of temperature on the opening of cotton leaf stomates under constant light. (After C. C. Wilson. 1948. Plant Physiol. 23:5.)

features of the plant are known to affect the rate of transpiration. The root-shoot ratio and the area and structure of the leaf have considerable influence on the loss of water from plants. Any environmental factor affecting the steepness of the vapor pressure gradient between the internal and external atmosphere of the leaf will, of course, affect the rate of transpiration. Finally, the extent to which water is available in the soil will influence transpiration.

Plant factors

Root-shoot ratio. In a situation where all of the conditions for good transpiration are present, the efficiency of the absorbing surface (root surface) and evaporating surface (leaf surface) controls the rate of transpiration. As mentioned before, if water absorption lags behind transpiration, a water deficit will occur in the plant which, in turn, will reduce transpiration. Parker (35) and Bialoglowski (2) found that transpiration increases with increase in root-shoot ratio (Figure 4-8). Sorghum, typically, transpires at a higher rate per unit of leaf surface than corn. Miller (33) has pointed out that secondary root development is much more advanced in sorghum, compared to corn, and that this may be the dominating reason for the different transpiration rates in these two plants. In other words, the sorghum root system provides more water to the shoot than the corn root system.

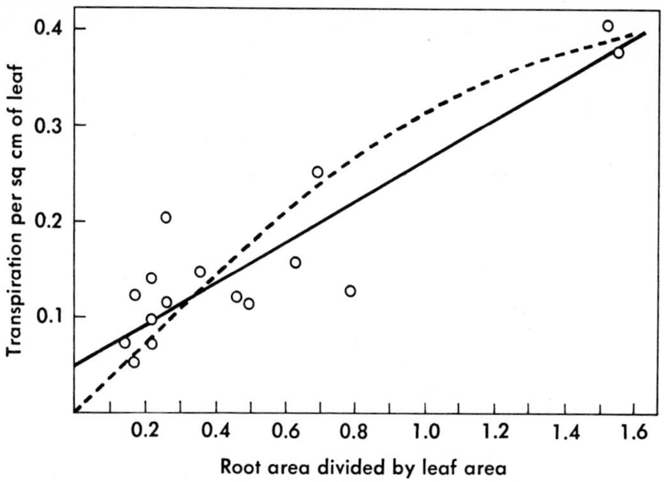

Figure 4-8 Grams of water lost per square centimeter of leaf area of loblolly pine per day is plotted over root area divided by leaf area in square centimeters. The broken line represents what might be theoretically expected under these circumstances. The solid line represents the data actually collected. (After J. Parker. 1949. Plant Physiol. 24:739.)

Leaf area. It appears perfectly logical to assume that the greater the leaf area, the greater will be the magnitude of water loss. This assumption is correct, although proportional agreement between leaf area and water loss is absent (26). On a per unit area basis, smaller plants often transpire at a greater rate than larger plants. A good illustration is presented from data given by Miller in Table 4-4. Note in Table 4-4 that although the greater

Table 4-4 Total water loss during a 6 hour period and water loss per square meter per hour by two different strains of corn.[a]

Plant	*Leaf surface, cm²*	*Total H_2O lost over 6 hr period, g*	*Transpiration rate per m² per hr, g*
Pride of Saline corn	14,568	918	629
Sherrod White Dent corn	12,989	784	723

[a] After *Plant Physiology*, 1938 edition, by E. C. Miller. Copyright 1938. McGraw-Hill Book Company. Used by permission.

amount of water was lost by the larger plant, the amount of water loss per unit area was greater in the smaller plant.

The removal of leaves (decreasing leaf area) from a plant may increase the rate of transpiration per unit leaf area of that plant. Thus, investigations by Cullinan (5) and Kelley (21) showed that the pruning of various fruit trees increases their transpiration rates per unit of leaf area, but the total water loss is greater in the unpruned trees. Presumably, this situation arises from the fact that the root system of the pruned trees is providing a greater amount of water to a smaller number of leaves, thus increasing transpiration efficiency.

Leaf structure. Plants native to dry habitats generally exhibit a number of structural modifications, particularly in their leaves. Thus, leaves of xerophytic plants may possess a thick cuticle, thick cell walls, well-developed palisade parenchyma, sunken stomates, a covering of dead epidermal hairs, etc. That these features affect water loss may be easily shown by allowing detached xerophytic and mesophytic leaves to dry together under the same conditions. Visible wilting will be observed in the mesophytic leaves long before it is observed in the xerophytic leaves. The resistance of xerophytic leaves to water loss and wilting is primarily a function of cutin layer thickness and efficiency. Under dry conditions, the stomates are closed and cuticular transpiration becomes the main avenue for water loss.

Many investigators have observed that with adequate water supply, the rates of transpiration of xerophytic species may be *higher* than those of mesophytic species. This may be due, in part, to the higher number of stomates per unit area and the more extensive venation of xerophytic leaves as compared to mesophytic leaves. This difference in stomatal frequency and venation may even be observed in the same plant species grown under moist and dry conditions. Another factor that may result in higher rates of transpiration by xerophytic leaves is their greater internal evaporating surface (48, 49). That is, more cell wall surface is exposed to the internal atmosphere than is generally found in mesophytic leaves.

Remember, however, that the higher rates of transpiration found in xerophytic plants as compared to mesophytic plants are found only under those conditions where stomates are opened. Perhaps it would be more correct to say that the rate of *stomatal transpiration* of xerophytes exceeds that of mesophytes.

Environmental factors

The rate of transpiration is influenced to a great extent by several different environmental factors. The most important of these are light, humidity of the air, temperature, wind, and availability of soil water. The following discussion will cover the individual effects of each one of these factors. However, transpiration by the plant in its natural habitat is generally under the influence of several of these factors at any one time. Whereas one factor may augment the effect of another factor, in another instance, it may negate this effect.

Light. Light occupies a prominent position among those factors influencing transpiration, since it has a dominating effect on stomatal movement. The stomates of a plant exposed to light are opened, allowing transpiration to proceed. In the dark, stomates are closed and transpiration essentially ceases. The effect of other environmental factors are, therefore, dependent upon the presence of light.

Humidity of the air. Before covering the effect of humidity on transpiration, we should discuss some of the terms used to express the moisture content of the air. Most of us are familiar with the term *relative humidity*. Since a direct proportionality exists between vapor pressure and the concentration of water vapor in the atmosphere, relative humidity is an expression of the ratio of the actual vapor pressure to the vapor pressure of the atmosphere when saturated at the same temperature. For example, the atmosphere at 20°C is saturated at a vapor pressure of 17.54 mm Hg and has a relative humidity of 100%. If the relative humidity at 20°C is 50%, then the vapor pressure would be 8.77 mm Hg, and at 10% relative humidity it would be 1.754 mm Hg.

For our purposes, it is more convenient to use the term *vapor pressure* instead of relative humidity, since it more precisely defines the situation. For example, at 50% relative humidity the vapor pressure of the atmosphere may have any of a number of values, depending upon the temperature (Table 4-5). The vapor pressure at 50% relative humidity and at

Table 4-5 Relation between vapor pressure and relative humidity at different temperatures.

Temperature, °C	*Vapor pressure, mm Hg, at different values of relative humidity*										
	0	10%	20%	30%	40%	50%	60%	70%	80%	90%	100%
0	0	0.46	0.92	1.37	1.83	2.29	2.75	3.21	3.66	4.12	4.58
10	0	0.92	1.84	2.76	3.68	4.60	5.53	6.45	7.37	8.29	9.21
20	0	1.75	3.51	5.26	7.02	8.77	10.52	12.28	14.03	15.79	17.54
30	0	3.18	6.36	9.55	12.73	15.91	19.09	22.27	25.46	28.64	31.82
40	0	5.53	11.06	16.60	22.13	27.66	33.19	38.72	44.25	49.79	55.32

40°C is 27.66 mm Hg, whereas at 0°C, it is 2.29 mm Hg. This amounts to a difference in pressure of 25.37 mm Hg. If we relate these figures to the rate of evaporation from a moist surface into surrounding air at 50% relative humidity, it is easy to see that evaporation would take place much more rapidly at 40°C than at 0°C. The *vapor pressure gradient* would be much steeper at 40°C (55.32–27.66 mm Hg) than at 0°C (4.58–2.29 mm Hg).

A change in temperature or vapor pressure can change the relative humidity. A rise or fall in temperature with no change in vapor pressure will cause a drop or rise, respectively, in relative humidity. A rise or fall in vapor pressure with no change in temperature will be accompanied by a rise or fall, respectively, in relative humidity.

Generally, the internal atmosphere of a leaf is considered to be saturated, or nearly so. The external atmosphere, on the other hand, is usually in an unsaturated condition. A vapor pressure gradient exists, therefore, between the internal and external atmospheres, and water vapor will diffuse through the stomates from the area of high vapor pressure to the area of low vapor pressure. The steeper the vapor pressure gradient, the more rapidly transpiration will proceed. If the vapor pressure of the external atmosphere is kept constant, the steepness of the vapor pressure gradient may be increased or lowered by increasing or lowering, respectively, the temperature of the atmosphere. In other words, the external atmosphere can hold more water vapor at a higher temperature and less at a lower temperature. However, the water content of the internal atmosphere of the leaf will remain at or near the point of saturation at both the high and low temperatures. Therefore when the water content or vapor pressure of the external atmosphere remains constant, an increase in temperature increases the vapor pressure gradient.

Assume that the external atmosphere has a vapor pressure of 8.77 mm Hg. This would be equivalent to 50% relative humidity at 20°C. At 20°C, the internal atmosphere has a vapor pressure of 17.54 mm Hg. Now, if we increase the temperature to 30°C and keep the vapor pressure of the external environment constant at 8.77 mm Hg, the difference in vapor pressure between the internal and external atmospheres increases. By lowering the temperature to 10°C and again keeping the vapor pressure of the external atmosphere constant, we can decrease the difference between the two, as shown in Table 4-6.

If the temperature remains constant, the vapor pressure gradient between the internal and external atmosphere may be increased or lowered

Table 4-6

temperature, °C (internal and external)	10	20	30
internal atmosphere, mm Hg, (100% RH)	9.21	17.54	31.82
external atmosphere, mm Hg, (VP = 8.77 mm Hg)	8.77	8.77	8.77
difference, mm Hg, (measure of VP gradient)	0.44	8.77	23.05

by lowering or increasing, respectively, the vapor pressure of the external atmosphere. Of course, if the vapor pressures of the internal and external atmospheres are the same, no transpiration will take place.

Temperature. If all other factors are constant, an increase in temperature within a certain physiological range almost always increases the rate of transpiration. This is due to the effect of temperature on stomatal movements and vapor pressure gradients. As mentioned previously, stomates generally close at temperatures approaching 0°C and increase in aperture with increase in temperature up to about 30°C (see Figure 4-7).

In addition to its effect on the opening of stomates, an increase in temperature steepens the vapor pressure gradient between the internal atmosphere of the leaf and the surrounding atmosphere.

In the discussion so far, we have assumed that the temperature of the leaf and air is the same. However, this is not always true. Fleshy or relatively thick plant structures, such as fruits, stems, thick leaves, etc., when exposed to sunlight, often reach temperatures above that of the surrounding air (26). This would have the effect of steepening the vapor pressure gradient between the plant structure and the external atmosphere.

Wind. Air in the immediate area of a transpiring leaf becomes more and more concentrated with water vapor. From the discussion above, we know that under these circumstances the vapor pressure gradient is lowered and the rate of transpiration decreases. However, if the water vapor concentrating in the area of the leaf is dispersed by wind, transpiration will again increase.

Increase in transpiration as a result of wind is not proportional to the wind velocity (38) (Figure 4-9). Several investigators (30, 12, 37) have

Figure 4-9 Effect of wind velocity on the transpiration rate of *Chamaecyparis obtusa.* (After Taisitiroo Satoo, "Wind, Transpiration, and Tree Growth" in *Tree Growth,* edited by Theodore T. Kozlowski. Copyright © 1962. The Ronald Press Company.)

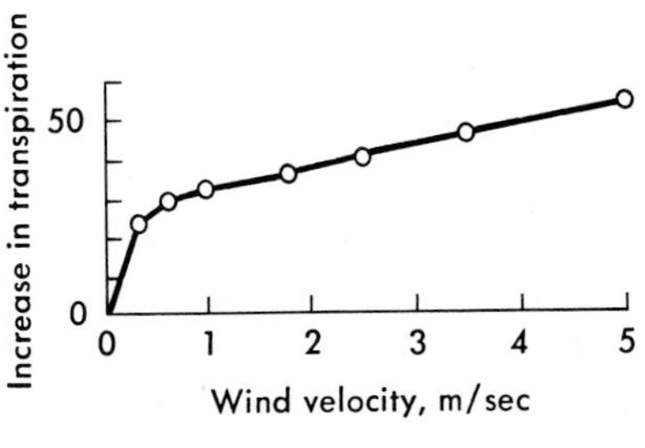

shown that when plants are suddenly exposed to wind, there is a sharp increase in the rate of transpiration, followed by a gradual falling off of this increase, which illustrates that the effect of wind on transpiration may be rather complex.

It should be realized that wind blowing over an evaporating surface would have a significant cooling effect, a circumstance which would lower the vapor pressure gradient and thus, the rate of transpiration. In addition, winds of high velocity may possibly cause stomatal closure. It appears, therefore, that the increase in transpiration caused by wind is actually the sum total of positive and negative influences.

Availability of soil water. Absorption of water by the plant may lag behind its release via transpiration for a short period of time without noticeably affecting the plant. If this condition is prolonged, however, a water deficit will develop, and the plant will appear wilted. It is apparent, therefore, that the availability of soil water to the roots of a plant and the efficiency of its absorption have a profound influence on the rate of transpiration.

The environmental and plant factors involved in the availability and absorption of soil water will be discussed in detail in the following chapter.

SIGNIFICANCE OF TRANSPIRATION

Cooling effect

The value or lack of value of transpiration to the plant has been a subject of debate among plant physiologists for quite some time. Some have argued that the cooling effect of transpiration keeps the plant from being overheated. However, plants growing under conditions where transpiration is negligible do not overheat, suggesting that the cooling effect of transpiration is of no real significance in the dissipation of heat as far as the plant is concerned.

Effect on growth and development

Some indirect evidence indicating that transpiration may have an influence on the growth of some plants has been obtained by Winneberger (54). He observed that buds of the Hardy pear cease to grow under conditions of high humidity and that under the same conditions, growth of sunflower plants is reduced to about half of the normal. Since under conditions of high humidity transpiration is negligible, Winneberger concluded that transpiration is a necessary factor in the normal growth of these two plants.

We have mentioned earlier in this chapter that when the rate of transpiration exceeds that of absorption, a water deficit may occur and wilting may take place. This, of course, is detrimental to the plant and, if carried to extreme, may result in the death of the plant. Injury due to desiccation may occur to plants in temperate climates that retain their leaves through the winter months. On some winter and early spring days, air temperatures may be high enough to support a considerable amount of transpiration.

However, the soil is usually frozen, or nearly so, under these conditions, and water is not absorbed (22, 23). The results may be particularly damaging to conifers.

Effect on mineral salt absorption

Because of the presence of mineral salts and water together in the soil, and because both are absorbed by roots, early plant physiologists naturally assumed that salt absorption and transport took place as a consequence of transpiration. Numerous studies in the 1930's, however, clearly established that salt absorption is predominately an active process (requires metabolic energy) and that only a small amount of salt is absorbed passively as a result of water uptake (see Chapter 14). Once the absorbed salts have been "dumped" into the xylum ducts of the root, transpiration definitely influences their translocation and distribution in the plant. In this respect, the transpiration stream provides an efficient means of transport and distribution once salts have been absorbed by the roots.

Some authors have maintained that a significant amount of salt absorption does take place passively and is under the influence of transpiration "pull." In other words, investigators such as Hylmö (18), Kramer (25), Pettersson (36), and Lopushinsky (29) have demonstrated some correlation between the absorption of ions and the rate of transpiration. It is generally accepted at this time that, although active absorption of salts predominates, some passive absorption also takes place and that this is under the influence of the transpiration "pull."

GUTTATION

Plants growing in a moist, warm soil and under humid conditions will often exhibit droplets of water along the margin of their leaves. The loss of water in a liquid form in this manner is called *guttation*. A discerning student will note that the conditions described above favor the absorption of water, but do not favor its transpiration. In other words, under these conditions water absorption greatly exceeds transpiration—water is literally "pushed" up the xylem ducts and out through specialized structures called *hydathodes* (Figure 4-10). When water uptake exceeds water loss, a hydrostatic pressure is built up in the xylem ducts, and water must escape by whatever path is available. Hydathodes are generally found at the tip of veins of leaves and therefore represent excellent ports of exit for water being "pushed" up from the roots.

Water that exudes from a hydathode does so as a result of hydrostatic pressure developed in the sap of the xylem ducts and not as a result of any

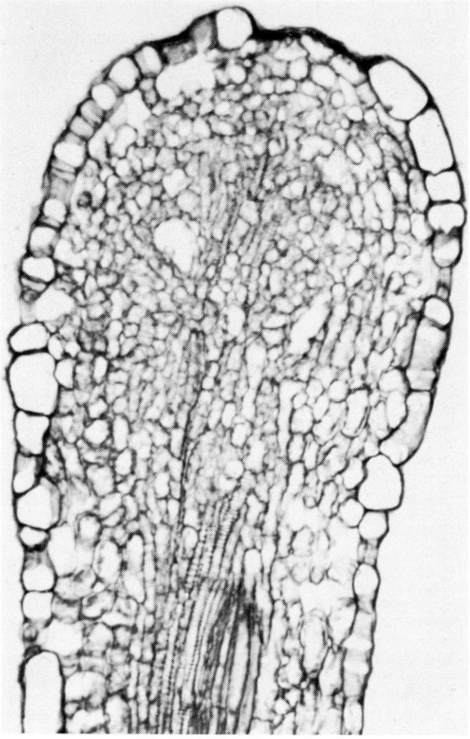

Figure 4-10 Leaf of Brassica showing hydathode. Note pore at the very tip of the leaf and nearby terminal tracheids.

local activity on the part of the hydathode or surrounding tissues. However, there are openings in various organs of plants through which water is actively secreted. That is, the cells surrounding the pore actively participate in pushing water through the pore. These are sometimes called *water glands* and sometimes called *active hydathodes*.

We speak of the liquid escaping through hydathodes as water. However, guttation liquid is not pure water, but a solution containing a great number of dissolved substances (Table 4-7). When guttation water is evaporated rapidly, the dissolved materials may sometime be seen as precipitates on the surface of the leaf. Sometimes the salts precipitated on the leaf surface are redissolved and taken into the interior of the leaf. Generally, the salt concentration is very high under these circumstances and may cause injury to the leaf (7, 20).

Table 4-7 Chemical analysis of the composition of guttation liquid from various plants. The chemical content is given in parts per million (ppm).[a]

	Squash	*Tomato*	*Cucumber*	*Cabbage*
pH	6.5	6.75	6.0	6.08
nitrite nitrogen	—	1.5	1.0	—
nitrate nitrogen	250.0	1.0	3.0	4.0
ammonia nitrogen	5.0	7.5	4.0	2.0
phosphorus	75.0	2.0	8.0	4.0
potassium	75.0	40.0	15.0	15.0
calcium	750.0	125.0	100.0	100.0
magnesium	50.0	8.0	6.0	5.0
aluminum	—	0.3	0.3	0.3
manganese	—	1.0	Trace	1.0
chlorine	—	25.0	50.0	35.0
sulphate sulfur	—	30.0	25.0	25.0
sodium	—	Trace	Trace	—
zinc	—	—	—	—
copper	—	—	—	—
total solids	2500.0	600.0	—	600.0
organic matter	1100.0	275.0	—	250.0

[a] After L. C. Curtis. 1944. Phytopathology 34: 196.

BIBLIOGRAPHY

1. Bailey, L. F., J. S. Rothacher, and W. H. Cummings. 1952. A critical study of the cobalt chloride method of measuring transpiration. Plant. Physiol. 27: 563.
2. Bialoglowski, J. 1936. Effect of extent and temperature of roots on transpiration of rooted lemon cuttings. Proc. Am. Soc. Hort. Sci., 34: 96.
3. Black, C. C., J. F. Turner, M. Gibbs, D. W. Krogmann, and S. A. Gordon. 1962. Studies on photosynthetic processes. II. Action spectra and quantum requirement for triphosphopyridine nucleotide reduction and the formation of adenosine triphosphate by spinach chloroplasts. J. Biol. Chem. 237: 580.
4. Brown, H. T., and F. Escombe. 1900. Static diffusion of gases and liquids in relation to the assimilation of carbon and translocation of plants. Phil. Trans. Roy. Soc. (London), B, 193: 223.
5. Cullinan, F. P. 1920. Transpiration studies with the apple. Proc. Am. Soc. Hort. Sci. 17: 232.
6. Cummings, W. H. A. 1941. A method for sampling the foliage of a silver maple tree. J. Forestry 39: 382.
7. Curtis, L. C. 1943. Deleterious effects of guttated fluids on foliage. Am. J. Botany 30: 778.

8. Curtis, L. C. 1944. The influence of guttation fluid on pesticides. Phytopathology 34: 196.
9. Dyar, M. T. 1953. Studies on the reduction of a tetrazolium salt by green plant tissue. Am. J. Botany 40: 20.
10. Esau, K. 1953. Plant anatomy. John Wiley & Sons, New York.
11. Ferry, J. F., and H. S. Ward. 1959. Fundamentals of plant physiology. The Macmillan Company, New York.
12. Griep, W. 1940. Über den Einfluss von Aussenfaktoren auf die Wirkung des Windes auf die transpiration der Pflanzen. Z. Botan. 35: 1.
13. Guttenberg, H. 1959. Die physiologische Anatomie der Spaltöffnungen. W. Ruhland (ed.), Encyclopedia of plant physiology. 17 part 1: 399.
14. Hauke, R. L. 1957. The stomatal apparatus of equisetum. Bull. Torrey Botan. Club 84: 178.
15. Heath, O. V. S. 1950. Studies in stomatal behaviour. V. The role of carbon dioxide in the light response of stomata. Part 1. Investigation of the cause of abnormally wide stomatal opening within porometer cups. J. Exptl. Botany 1: 29.
16. Heath, O. V. S. 1959. The water relations of stomatal cells and the mechanisms of stomatal movement. *In* F. C. Steward (ed.), Plant physiology. Academic Press, New York, 2: 193.
17. Heath, O. V. S., and B. Orchard. 1956. Studies in stomatal behaviour. VIII. Effects of anaerobic conditions upon stomatal movement—a test of Williams' hypothesis of stomatal mechanism. J. Exptl. Botany 7: 313.
18. Hylmö, B. 1955. Passive components in the ion absorption of the plant. I. The zonal ion and water absorption in Brouwer's experiments. Physiol. Plant. 8: 433.
19. Iljin, W. S. 1930. Der Einfluss des Welkens auf den Ab- und Aufbau der Stärke in der Pflanze. Planta 10: 170.
20. Ivanoff, S. S. 1944. Guttation-salt injury on leaves of cantaloupe, pepper, and onion. Phytopathology 34: 436.
21. Kelley, V. W. 1932. The effect of pruning of excised shoots on the transpiration rate of some deciduous fruit species. Proc. Am. Soc. Hort. Sci. 29: 71.
22. Kozlowski, T. T. 1955. Tree growth, action and interaction of soil and other factors. J. Forestry 53: 508.
23. Kozlowski, T. T. 1958. Water relations and growth of trees. J. Forestry 56: 498.
24. Kozlowski, T. T. 1964. Water metabolism in plants. Harper and Row, New York.
25. Kramer, P. J. 1957. Outer space in plants. Science 125: 633.
26. Kramer, P. J. 1959. Transpiration and the water economy of plants. *In* F. C. Steward (ed.), Plant physiology. Academic Press, New York. 2: 607.
27. Lloyd, F. E. 1908. The physiology of stomata. Carnegie Inst. Wash. Publ. 82: 1.
28. Loftfield, J. V. G. 1921. The behavior of stomata. Carnegie Inst. Wash. Publ. 314: 1.

29. Lopushinsky, W. 1964. Effect of water movement on ion movement into the xylem of tomato roots. Plant Physiol. 39: 494.
30. Martin, E. V., and F. E. Clements. 1935. Studies of the effect of artificial wind on growth and transpiration in *Helianthus annuus.* Plant Physiol. 10: 613.
31. Maximov, N. A. 1928. The plant in relation to water. English translation by R. H. Yapp. George Allen & Unwin, London.
32. Meyer, B. S. 1956. The hydrodynamic system. *In* W. Ruhland (ed.), Encyclopedia of plant physiology. 3: 596.
33. Miller, E. C. 1938. Plant physiology. McGraw-Hill Book Co. New York.
34. Möller, C. M. 1947. The effect of thinning, age, and site of foliage, increment, and loss of dry matter. J. Forestry 45: 393.
35. Parker, J. 1949. Effects of variations in the root-leaf ratio on transpiration rate. Plant Physiol. 24: 739.
36. Pettersson, S. 1960. Ion absorption in young sunflower plants. I. Uptake and transport mechanisms for sulphate. 13: 133.
37. Satoo, T. 1955. The influence of wind on transpiration of some conifers. Bull. Tokyo Univ. Forests 50: 27.
38. Satoo, T. 1962. Wind, transpiration, and tree growth. *In* T. T. Kozlowski (ed.), Tree growth. Ronald Press, New York. 299.
39. Sayre, J. D. 1926. Physiology of the stomata of *Rumex patientia.* Ohio J. Sci. 26: 233.
40. Scarth, G. W. 1932. Mechanism of the action of light and other factors on stomatal movement. Plant Physiol. 7: 481.
41. Shapiro, S. 1951. Stomata on the ovules of *Zamia floridana.* Am. J. Botany 38: 47.
42. Shaw, M. 1954. Chloroplasts in the stomata of *Allium cepa L.* New Phytologist 53: 344.
43. Shaw, M., and G. A. Maclachlan. 1954. The physiology of stomata. I. Carbon dioxide fixation in guard cells. Can. J. Botany 32: 784.
44. Small, J., M. I. Clarke, and J. Crosbie-Baird. 1942. pH phenomena in relation to stomatal opening. II.–V. Proc. Roy. Soc. (Edinburgh), B, 61: 233.
45. Stålfelt, M. G. 1932. Die stomatäre Regulator in der pflanzlichen Transpiration. Planta 17: 22.
46. Steward, F. C. 1964. Plants at work. Addison-Wesley Publishing Co., Reading, Mass.
47. Ting, I. P., and W. E. Loomis. 1963. Diffusion through stomates. Am. J. Botany 50: 866.
48. Turrell, F. M. 1936. The area of the internal exposed surface of dicotyledon leaves. Am. J. Botany 23: 255.
49. Turrell, F. M. 1944. Correlation between internal surface and transpiration rate in mesomorphic and xeromorphic leaves grown under artificial light. Botan. Gaz. 105: 413.
50. Verduin, J. 1949. Diffusion through multiperforate septa. *In* J. Franck

and W. E. Loomis (eds.), Photosynthesis in plants. Iowa State College Press, Ames, Iowa. 95.

51. Williams, W. T. 1950. Studies in stomatal behaviour. IV. The water-relations of the epidermis. J. Exptl. Botany 1: 114.
52. Wilson, C. C. 1948. The effect of some environmental factors on the movements of guard cells. Plant Physiol. 23: 5.
53. Wilson, C. L., and W. E. Loomis. 1962. Botany. Holt, Rinehart & Winston, New York.
54. Winneberger, J. H. 1958. Transpiration as a requirement for growth of land plants. Physiol. Plant. 11: 56.
55. Wylie, R. B. 1948. The dominant role of the epidermis in leaves of adiatum. Plant Physiol. 35: 465.
56. Yemm, E. W., and A. J. Willis. 1954. Stomatal movements and changes of carbohydrates in leaves of *Chrysanthemum maximum*. New Phytologist 53: 373.
57. Yin, H. C., and Y. T. Tung. 1948. Phosphorylase in guard cells. Science 108: 87.
58. Zelitch, I. 1961. Biochemical control of stomatal opening in leaves. Proc. Natl. Acad. Sci. U.S. 47: 1423.
59. Zelitch, I. 1963. The control and mechanisms of stomatal movement. *In* I. Zelitch (ed.), Stomata and water relations in plants. Connecticut Agri. Exptl. Sta., New Haven, Conn. 664: 18.

FOR FURTHER REFERENCE

Kozlowski, T. T. 1964. Water metabolism in plants. Harper and Row, New York.

Kramer, P. J. 1959. Transpiration and the water economy of plants. *In* F. C. Steward (ed.), Plant physiology. Academic Press, New York. 2: 607.

Stålfelt, M. G. 1956. Die cuticuläre Transpiration. *In* W. Ruhland (ed.), Encyclopedia of plant physiology. 3: 342.

Stålfelt, M. G. 1956. Die stomatäre Transpiration und die Physiologie der Spaltöffnungen. *In* W. Ruhland (ed.), Encyclopedia of plant physiology. 3: 351.

Stocking, C. R. 1956. Guttation and bleeding. *In* W. Ruhland (ed.), Encyclopedia of plant physiology. 3: 489.

5

Absorption and translocation of water

INTRODUCTION

As explained in the last two chapters, water and its movement through the plant are necessary factors in the plant's existence. We have also mentioned that during the plant's life cycle, enormous amounts of water are moved only to be lost through the process of transpiration. Some scientists have argued that the movement of water in such a fashion has a beneficial function. Others have claimed that the whole process of water movement is uneconomical and more detrimental than beneficial to the plant.

In this chapter we will concern ourselves with the absorption and translocation of water within the plant system, a problem that has baffled scientists for literally hundreds of years. Although there are several theories that may account for the rise of water in plants, none have been shown to be unequivocally correct. While it is relatively simple to account for the rise of water in the shorter herbaceous and shrubby plants, the problem becomes much more complex when we try to explain how water can reach the tips of our tallest trees, some of which reach heights approaching 400 feet.

The student of botany knows that the movement, or to use a better term, *translocation,* of water takes place in the xylem tissue. A logical introduction to a discussion on water translocation, then, would be to review what is known about the xylem tissue.

ANATOMY OF THE XYLEM TISSUE

That xylem is the tissue most involved in water translocation has been recognized for well over 100 years. Several different types of cells, living and nonliving, may be observed in the xylem tissue. Of these, the tracheary elements are the most characteristic, and it is through these cells that practically all water translocation takes place. Also found in the xylem tissue are xylem fibers and living parenchyma cells.

Cell types and functions

Tracheary elements. The *vessel elements* and *tracheids* constitute the tracheary elements of the xylem and are the cells most concerned with water translocation in the plant. Both are more or less elongated, have lignified secondary walls, and are dead when mature and functional. Since vessel elements and tracheids are dead at maturity, there is no interfering protoplast in the lumina of the cells—a situation that allows for the efficient translocation of relatively large amounts of water. Perforated end walls are characteristic of both vessel elements and tracheids. In the more advanced vessel elements, the end walls may be entirely missing, thus leaving nothing to obstruct the passage of water through the cell.

If we took a large number of vessel elements and stacked them end-on-end, we would have a long tubelike structure. This is exactly what one finds in the arrangement of vessel elements in the plant. The long tubelike structure resulting from a series of vessel elements being attached to one another by their end walls is called a *vessel* or *xylem duct.* The vessels of the xylem tissue form a network of ducts that extends to all areas of the plant, giving all living cells an easily accessible supply of water. This is of primary importance to the plant not only for the maintenance of turgor, but also for the translocation of other substances that may be carried from cell to cell by the moving water (e.g., essential mineral elements).

The vessel system is the principal pathway by which water is translocated in the angiosperms. However, vessels are not present in the conifers, and in this group the tracheids form the principal pathway for water translocation. Tracheids are long spindle-shaped cells with sharply inclined, perforated end walls. The end walls of the tracheids overlap each other providing a continuous pathway for the movement of water. Obviously, the movement of water in a group of tracheids, as compared to a vessel system, is much less direct and meets with more resistance. It is interesting to note, however, that most of our taller trees are conifers, which are completely devoid of vessels.

Although vessels and tracheids, with respect to their long axis, are oriented in the plant in a vertical direction and water movement is predominantly in this direction, some lateral movement does take place. The side walls of vessel elements and tracheids are perforated by numerous *pits,* through which water may pass. Generally, where cells lie alongside each other, pits occur in pairs and are called, appropriately, *pit pairs*. Thus where pits lie adjacent each other, the lateral movement of water from cell to cell may be accomplished. Since pit pairs may occur between two vessel elements, two tracheids, a tracheid and a vessel element, a tracheid or vessel element and living parenchyma cells, etc., water can be easily distributed throughout all the tissues of a plant. Different types of vessel elements, tracheids, and xylem fibers may be seen in Figure 5-1.

Xylem fibers. The xylem fiber is a long, thin, tapering cell with a very thick lignified cell wall and is dead at maturity. The primary function of the xylem fiber is support, and it is doubtful if any significant amount of water is moved through this cell. Nevertheless, it is possible for some water to pass through xylem fibers, since they are in association with each other and with the tracheids and vessel elements via pit pairs.

Xylem parenchyma. Living parenchyma cells may be found interspersed in the wood xylem or as components of the xylem rays. These cells are generally referred to as wood and ray parenchyma, respectively. One obvious function of xylem parenchyma is the storage of food. Starch is accumulated toward the end of the growing season and then is depleted during the cambial activity of the following growing season (15). It also appears possible that the lateral transport of both water and nutrients would be greatly facilitated by the xylem ray parenchyma.

It has been suggested that the living parenchyma cells of the xylem may have a vital role in the translocation of water. In a later section of this chapter, we will discuss this interesting suggestion in more detail.

ABSORPTION OF WATER

Under natural conditions, practically all water absorption by rooted plants takes place through the root system. The area of the root where most

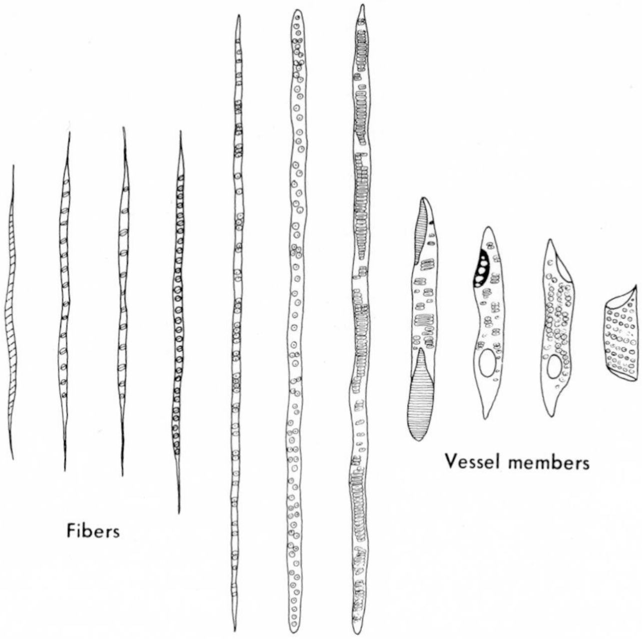

Figure 5-1 Different types of vessel elements, tracheids, and xylem fibers found in the xylem tissue. (After Esau. 1958. Plant anatomy. Wiley, New York.)

absorption takes place is in the root hair zone (Figure 5-2). Water diffuses into the root hair and, to a lesser degree, other root epidermal cells as a result of a *diffusion pressure deficit gradient.* As long as the diffusion pressure deficit of the root cell sap is greater than that of the soil solution, more water will enter the cell than leaves it. An increase in the solute concentration of a cell or a decrease in its turgor pressure will increase the diffusion pressure deficit of its cell sap and, as a result, increase the uptake of water. It appears, then, that most water absorption occurs through the mediation of osmotic mechanisms; that is, water is taken up passively.

Some investigators believe that active, nonosmotic uptake of water also occurs and that metabolic energy is expanded in the process (3, 40, 4).

Passive absorption

In a rapidly transpiring plant, the xylem vessels and tracheids are generally in a state of *negative tension* or reduced pressure. Although the rate of transpiration often is similar to the rate of absorption (Figure 5-3),

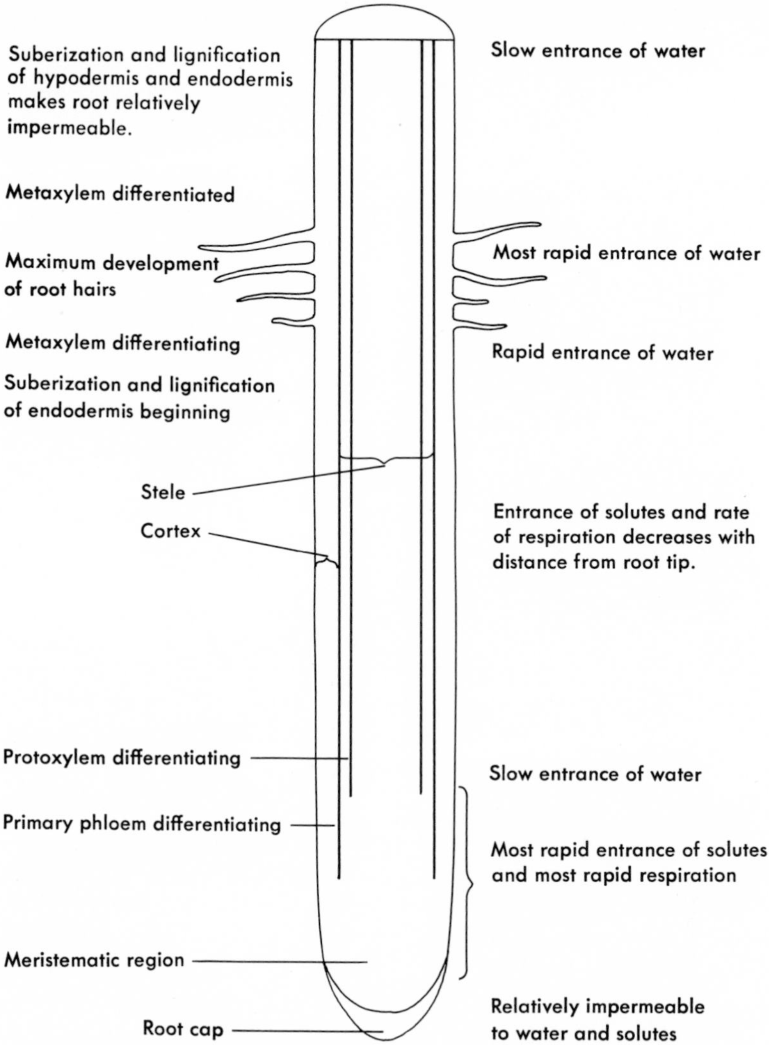

Figure 5-2 Schematic representation of those areas of the root involved in the absorption and translocation of water. (From *Plant and Soil Relationships* by P. J. Kramer. Copyright 1949. McGraw-Hill Book Company. Used by permission.)

under a variety of circumstances transpiration can and does exceed absorption. The suction force created by the rapidly moving columns of water is transmitted to the root, and water is literally "pulled" into the root from the soil. The diffusion pressure deficit of a cell sap is increased by the

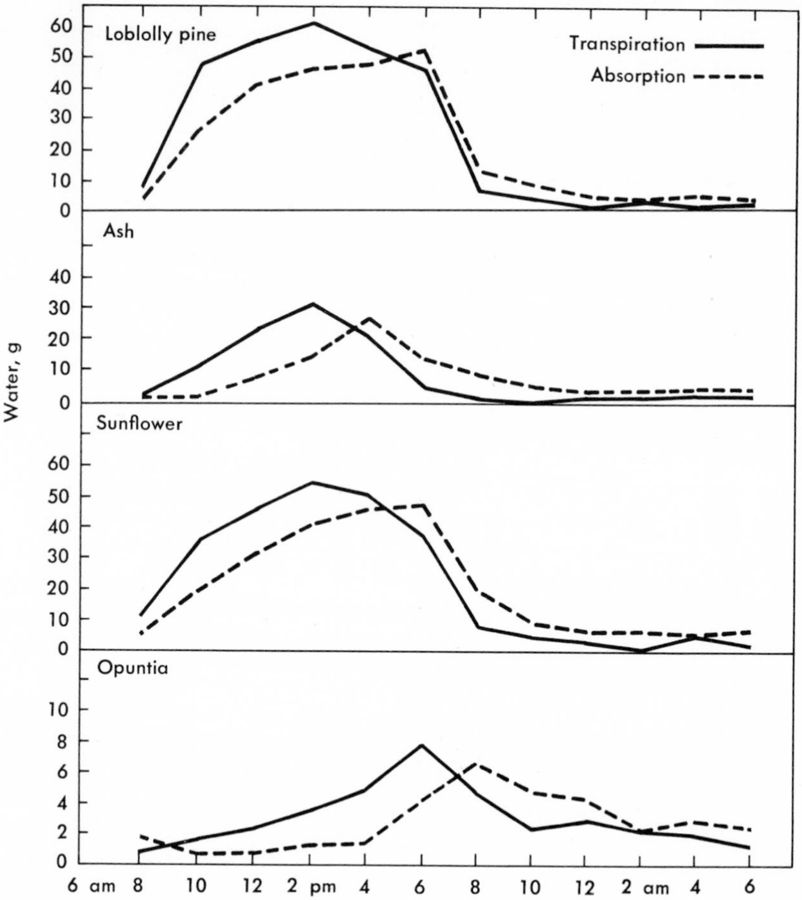

Figure 5-3 Rates of transpiration and absorption (grams/plant) in loblolly pine, ash, sunflower, and *Opuntia* on a clear, hot summer day (After P. J. Kramer. 1937. Am. J. Botany 24:10.)

amount of negative tension it is subjected to. This may be expressed in the equation:

$$DPD = OP - (-TP)$$

The natural consequence of increased diffusion pressure deficit is an increased water uptake.

It must be understood that water uptake in the manner described occurs as a result of activity in the shoot (transpiration). The root merely acts as an absorbing surface; that is, the absorption of water in this manner is passive. This is clearly supported by the fact that the shoot can absorb water through dead roots and may, in fact, take it up at a faster rate (see review by Kramer (27)). Kramer (27) has suggested that the resistance to water uptake by living roots may be due to the living cells of the root.

Active absorption

Although active mechanisms do not account for any appreciable amount of water being absorbed, they are of immense academic interest to plant physiologists. When we speak of water being absorbed actively, we mean that water is being absorbed through an expenditure of metabolic energy. Active absorption occurs as a result of activities in the root and does not concern the shoot. Generally, it is thought that the active absorption of water may occur in one of two ways—as a result of the active absorption and accumulation of salt or through nonosmotic mechanisms.

Active absorption through osmotic mechanisms. Actually, water absorbed by osmotic means does not *directly* require an expenditure of energy. Water is thought to move from the soil to the interior of the root along an increasing osmotic pressure gradient. That is, water moves through the root epidermis, cortex, and into the xylem ducts because of increasing solute concentrations as it passes from the exterior to the interior cells of the root.

We may ask the question, why is the salt content of the interior cells higher than that of the exterior root cells? The absorption and accumulation of salt by root cells requires metabolic energy (see Chapter 14). A theory by Crafts and Broyer (10) suggests that there is a decreasing O_2 and increasing CO_2 gradient from the cortex to the stele. Metabolic activity would be at a minimum, then, in the interior cells in the immediate area of the xylem ducts. Since energy is required to accumulate and hold salt against a concentration gradient, the stele cells, in contrast to the cortex cells, favor the loss of salt. Since diffusion back through the impervious *Casparian strip* is impossible, there is a unidirectional loss of salt into the lumina of the xylem vessel. Water would also follow this unidirectional path, diffusing from the low osmotic pressure of the soil solution to the higher osmotic pressure of the sap in the xylem ducts of the stele.

Root pressure developed by the accumulation of salt in the xylem ducts appears to be affected by a variety of factors, which also affect respiration. Kozlowski (22) has listed these as oxygen tension, narcotics, auxin, and respiration inhibitors. It is interesting to note that several investigators (19, 20, 32, 42) have observed an autonomic diurnal fluctuation in exuda-

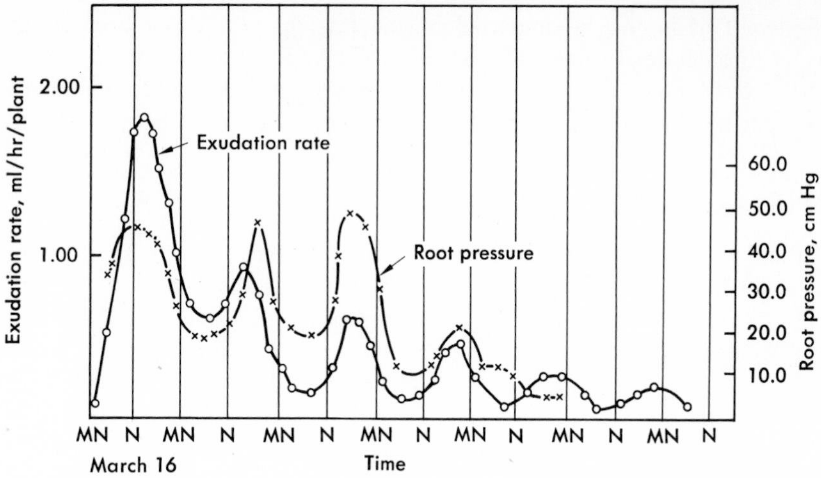

Figure 5-4 Autonomic diurnal fluctuation in exudation rate and root pressure of decapitated sunflower plants. (After Y. Vaadia. 1960. Physiol. Plant. 13:701.)

tions caused by root pressure. An example of the rhythmic nature of root pressure exudations is given in Figure 5-4. Note in Figure 5-4 the close agreement between the periodicity of root pressure and exudation rate.

Detopped tomato plants with their root systems immersed in solutions of different salt concentrations exhibit different exudation rates (2). Lower exudation rates result when roots are immersed in solutions of lower salt concentration. Vaadia (42) has suggested that the diurnal fluctuation of exudation rates is caused by a periodicity of salt transfer into the xylem. Obviously, this would cause a periodicity in the magnitude of the osmotic pressure of the xylem ducts, which would have the effect of changing the rate of water absorption in accordance with the changing osmotic pressure gradients.

We should stress again that water absorbed in this manner does not *directly* require an expenditure of energy. The energy is expended in the absorption and accumulation of salts. However, osmotic pressure is the driving force, and this is a passive process.

Nonosmotic absorption of water. What we mean by the nonosmotic movement of water is that water is moving against a concentration gradient or at an accelerated rate (27). Presumably, this requires an expenditure of metabolic energy. Although numerous able workers have studied the possibility of nonosmotic absorption of water, none have been able to unequivocally prove that metabolic energy is *directly* involved in the uptake of water.

Factors affecting the absorption of water

There are several factors that affect water absorption by roots. Most important are the soil factors, such as temperature, osmotic pressure of the soil solution, aeration, and availability of the soil water. Although atmospheric conditions also may affect absorption, conditions in the soil are generally the limiting factors in the absorption of water by roots.

Temperature of the soil. Temperature of the soil has a profound influence on the rate of water absorption. That low soil temperatures reduce water absorption has been known for over 200 years, but only within relatively recent years has this effect been explained. Apparently, the inhibitory influence of low temperature on water absorption is manifested in a variety of ways. First of all, water is more viscous at lower temperatures, a factor which reduces its mobility. Protoplasm is less permeable at low temperatures (36), and root growth is inhibited. The combined effect of these factors causes a reduction in water absorption at low temperatures.

One can demonstrate the inhibitory effect of low temperature on water absorption quite readily in the greenhouse. If a layer of crushed ice is placed on the surface of soil in which a vigorous coleus plant is growing and conditions are good for transpiration, the plant will appear thoroughly wilted in a couple of hours. If the ice is then removed, the plant will again regain its turgidity in a short period of time.

Concentration of the soil solution. Since, as we have already discussed, water is absorbed because a diffusion pressure deficit gradient exists between the soil solution and the cell sap of the interior root cells, it is easy to understand why the salt concentration of the soil solution is an important factor in water absorption. Indeed, if the osmotic pressure of the soil solution is greater than that of the cell sap of the root cells, water will be drawn out of the plant instead of being absorbed.

Some plants (halophytes) have a greater tolerance than others for high salt concentrations in the soil solution. It is significant to note that the osmotic pressure of the cell sap of these plants is a good deal higher than that found in others.

Aeration of soil. If a tobacco field is saturated by a heavy rainfall and then exposed later to bright sunlight, the leaves of the tobacco plants, in many instances, will appear severely wilted in a short period of time (25). This is often termed "flopping" by tobacco growers, and is most severe under conditions of poor drainage. The "flopping" or wilting of the tobacco leaves is caused by a retardation of water absorption as a result of water replacing the soil atmosphere, leaving the roots poorly aerated. When transpiration occurs at a rapid rate in the bright sunlight, the combined effect of accelerated water loss with retarded water absorption results in the development of a water deficit in the plant.

There are several reasons for poor aeration having a retarding effect on water absorption. Root growth and metabolism are definitely retarded under conditions of low oxygen tension. Although under conditions of prolonged periods of poor aeration inhibited root growth would have a significant effect on water absorption, immediate effects would be insignificant. However, the slowing down of the metabolism of the root and, thus, its ability to take up and accumulate salt would seriously affect the water-absorbing ability of the root. An adverse direct effect of lowered oxygen tensions on water absorption is also probable, although to the author's knowledge this has not, as yet, been proven.

The accumulation of CO_2 in the soil appears to have a greater inhibitory effect on water absorption than lowered oxygen tensions. Apparently, an increase in CO_2 increases the viscosity of protoplasm and decreases permeability (16, 31), both of which would retard water absorption. Kramer and Jackson (25) found that sunflower and tomato plants wilted more rapidly when soil air was replaced by CO_2 than when the soil air was replaced by nitrogen.

Although increased CO_2 concentration in the soil atmosphere has a detrimental effect on water absorption, it should not be emphasized too strongly. Toxic amounts of CO_2 in the soil atmosphere under field conditions is an unlikely event (27).

Availability of soil water. Not all of the water in the soil is available to the plant. As the soil in the immediate area of the root system is depleted of its water supply, the absorption of water by the plant becomes more and more difficult. Eventually, those physical factors that hold water to the soil become stronger than the physical factors involved in the uptake of water by the plant.

Before we can discuss soil water-plant relationships, we should become familiar with the terms *field capacity*, *permanent wilting percentage* (PWP), and *total soil moisture stress* (TSMS). Kramer (27) defines field capacity as the water content of a soil after it has been thoroughly wetted and then allowed to drain until capillary movement of the water has essentially ceased. Permanent wilting percentage is the percentage of soil water left when the leaves of a plant growing in the soil first exhibit the symptoms of permanent wilting. That is, the leaves will not regain turgor when placed in a saturated atmosphere. Wadleigh and Ayers (43) introduced the term "total soil moisture stress." They defined TSMS as the sum of the osmotic pressure of the soil solution and *soil moisture tension*. By soil moisture tension, we mean those gravitational, adsorptive, and hydrostatic forces that hold water to the soil.

Work done in the early part of the twentieth century established the fact that field capacity and PWP differ with the type of soil tested. Contrasting two widely different types of soil, we find, for example, that clay has a much higher field capacity and PWP than sand. However, field capacity and PWP were also thought to be soil-moisture constants for any particular type of soil. This, undoubtedly, is true for field capacity, but is questionable as far as PWP is concerned. The PWP of a soil appears to differ, depending upon the test plant used. Slatyer (34) has indicated that the PWP of a soil is determined by plant osmotic factors rather than soil factors. A mesophytic leaf may have an osmotic pressure of less than 20 atm, while the osmotic pressure of the leaves of some halophytes may exceed 200 atm (22). This large difference in osmotic pressures is indicative of the differences in ability of different plants to "draw" water from the soil. In other words, the PWP of a soil is dependent upon the ability of the plant to "draw" water from the soil and is not, as earlier thought, a soil-moisture constant.

Let us examine the progressive changes that occur in both plant and soil as the soil moves toward a PWP. The sequence of events has been outlined by Slatyer (34) and is diagrammatically shown in Figure 5-5.

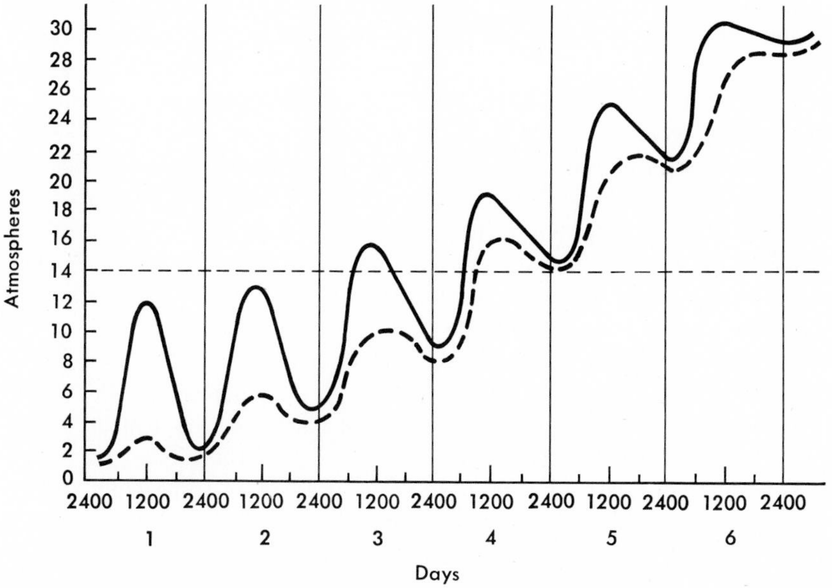

Figure 5-5 Diagrammatic representation of diurnal changes in DPD (continuous line) and TSMS (broken line) as soil is dried progressively from field capacity. (After R. O. Slatyer. 1957. Botan. Rev. 23:585.)

During the day, as the soil in the near vicinity of the root surface is depleted of water, its TSMS increases. This decreases during the night (night recovery) as water moves from the remaining soil mass to the surface of the root. The diffusion pressure deficit (DPD) of the plant follows the same pattern, but always remains at a greater magnitude than the TSMS. This is essential if water is to be drawn into instead of out of a plant. As the soil dries a little more each day, the TSMS and DPD increase progressively. As these events proceed, the gradient from soil to plant is always a little less steep, and night recovery for both TSMS and DPD is always a little slower.

As might be surmised, the daily increase in DPD, coupled with progressively slower night recovery, leads to an increasingly apparent loss of turgor by the leaves. Finally, a point will be reached where the TSMS attains a level equal in magnitude to the osmotic pressure of the test plant leaves (we will assume this to be 14 atm). Recovery of turgor at this level is impossible because the DPD-TSMS equilibrium established at night is at a DPD that allows for only zero turgor pressure. The PWP is obtained at this point. We can redefine PWP, then, as the soil water content present when the plant DPD and the soil TSMS are at equilibrium and the turgor pressure of the test plant leaves is zero (34).

Although water is not readily available to the plant at levels above field capacity and at levels below the PWP, some water may be taken up under these circumstances (33, 34, 21). However, growth of a plant has essentially ceased at the level of the PWP and death through desiccation will occur unless water is added to the soil (which would lower the TSMS).

Characteristics of the root system affecting water absorption. Since the root systems of different plants sometimes vary a great deal in appearance and extent of soil penetration, there is no doubt that their water-absorbing capacity also differs. Some root systems penetrate deep into the soil, while others form a dense network of branch roots that do not penetrate deep but cover a large area of soil at a shallow depth.

We have already mentioned that the root hair zone is the area of the root where most water absorption takes place. In other words, this is the area of greatest permeability. However, root hairs are very delicate structures and commonly last for only a short period of time. Root hairs that persist, although relatively rare, have been observed on some plant species (9). These root hairs, however, become thick walled and to a certain degree lignified and suberized, extensively limiting their ability to absorb water.

In a growing root system, there are a large number of root tips through which absorption takes place. The root tips represent the growing area of the root. In the older tissues of the root, a short distance back from the tip, secondary thickening takes place, and a periderm layer of highly suberized cells develops. The permeability of the root is greatly impeded by this layer. Obviously, most of a plant's root system does not absorb water very efficiently.

Although, by far, the most efficient water absorption takes place at the unsuberized root tip, under certain circumstances a significant amount of water may also be taken up by suberized areas of the root (26). Many investigators have noted that only a very small percentage of the root system of certain trees is unsuberized, making it necessary for water to be taken up by suberized tissues in order to adequately supply the tree with water (see review by Kramer (26)). Addoms (1) observed that the suberized roots of yellow poplar (*Liriodendron tulipifera* L), sweet gum (*Liquidambar styraciflua* L.), and shortleaf pine (*Pinus echinata* Mill.) were capable of absorbing a dye solution. She pointed out that there are three ports of entry for water through suberized roots: (1) lenticels, (2) breaks around branch roots, and (3) wounds. It is quite possible, then, that the capacity for water absorption by suberized root areas of different plants is related to the extent to which their anatomy allows for the development of these "avenues of entrance."

Absorption of water by the aerial parts of the plant

The absorption of water in both liquid and vapor form occurs to a small extent through the aerial parts of most, if not all, plants. According to Gessner (18), the extent to which this occurs is dependent upon the diffusion pressure deficit of the leaf cells and the permeability of the cutin layer. For example, Roberts et al. (30) found that the cutin layer on the leaves of the McIntosh apple was not continuous, but existed in lamellae parallel to the outer epidermal walls. Interspersed with the parallel layers of cutin, they found parallel layers of pectinaceous material of good water-absorbing capacity. Not only was this material present with the cutin layer at the surface of the leaf, but it extended vertically to the vein extensions within the interior of the leaf. It thus formed a continuous path for water from the surface to the vascular tissue. Obviously, the permeability of the cutin layer of the McIntosh leaf is rather good.

Some investigators believe that water absorbed by the leaves can travel in a "negative" direction through the plant and actually diffuse through the roots into the soil. Studies by Breazeale et al. (5, 6, 7) and Breazeale and McGeorge (8) demonstrated that both tomato and corn plants are capable of moving water absorbed by the leaves back into the soil. This, of course, occurs along diffusion pressure gradients favoring movement in this direction.

MECHANISMS INVOLVED IN THE TRANSLOCATION OF WATER

In previous pages, we discussed how water is transpired and absorbed by the plant. The distances separating the absorbing and transpiring organs are, in many instances, of considerable magnitude. The verticle translocation of water from roots to leaves over distances in excess of 200 feet is a relatively common occurrence in some of our larger forests. Indeed, some of our tallest trees (e.g., redwood) approach heights of 400 feet. In the succeeding pages, we will discuss the various theories which attempt to explain how water can be raised to such heights in plants.

Root pressure

The stump of a recently felled tree or a detopped herbaceous plant will often give visual evidence of root pressure. Xylem sap under pressure may be observed exuding out of the cut end of the stump. If a well-watered tomato plant is detopped and the stump attached with a rubber sleeve to a glass tube containing some water, the manifestation of this pressure can be observed (Figure 5-6). Figure 5-6 shows that water is actually "pushed" up the glass tube.

Stocking (37) defines root pressure "as a pressure developing in the tracheary elements of the xylem as a result of the metabolic activities of roots." Root pressure is therefore referred to as an active process. It

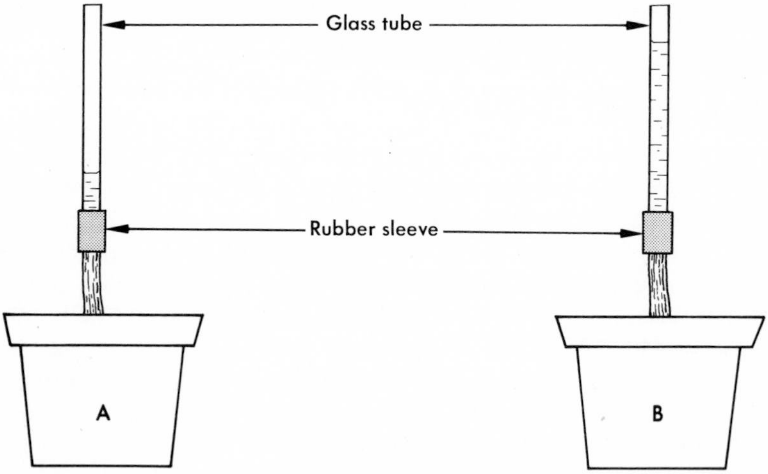

Figure 5-6 A method of demonstrating root pressure. A. Tomato plant just after decapitation. B. Tomato plant some time after decapitation. Note the rise of water in the glass tube.

should be clearly understood, however, that the movement of water up the stem as a result of root pressure is due to osmotic mechanisms (passive), which are created as a result of the active absorption of salt by the roots (see p. 94). We can refer to root pressure as being an active process in the sense that living roots are essential for it to occur.

Some workers have attempted to explain the rise of water in plants as occurring primarily as a result of root pressure. There are several reasons why this probably is not so. First of all, the magnitude of pressure developed is too small to "push" water up to the heights reached by most trees. Although values higher than 6 atm have been observed (44), root pressures in excess of 2 atm are seldom obtained. Indeed, root pressures of any magnitude are conspicuously absent from most conifers, which are among the tallest of trees. In addition, most estimates of the ability of root pressure to raise water to appreciable heights do not take into account the friction encountered in the passage of water through the xylem ducts. Another reason root pressure probably is not a major factor in the rise of water in plants is that exudation rates are generally much slower than normal transpiration rates. Finally, xylem sap under normal conditions is generally under tension instead of pressure, an observation which supports the argument that root pressure is not an important factor in water translocation. We should mention here, however, that when conditions for transpiration are poor, root pressure may be a significant factor in the movement of water. A good example would be guttation, a phenomenon that is caused by root pressure and is most noticeable under conditions poor for transpiration.

Vital theories

Many early investigators believed that the ascent of water in plants was under the control of "vital activities" in the stem. This belief was most likely stimulated by the fact that living cells are present in the xylem tissue (xylem parenchyma and xylem ray cells). Experiments by Strasburger (38, 39) and many others, however, have caused the vital theories on water translocation to be strongly doubted by modern botanists. Strasburger, for example, demonstrated that stems in which the living cells have been killed by the uptake of poisons, are still capable of water translocation. Proponents of the vital theory have pointed out that leaves soon wither and die on stems that have been killed, thus supporting their thesis that living cells in the stem are necessary for water translocation. However, critics of the vital theory claim that since the leaves remain turgid for at least a few days, the reason for leaf wilting is probably due to secondary causes, such as the blockage of vessels (11, 12, 29).

It appears quite probable that living cells of the stem have little to do with the movement of water. However, this has not been proven beyond doubt and still remains a small but important unanswered question in the water relations of plants.

Cohesion-tension theory

Imagine, if you will, a long hollow glass tube, one end of which is submerged in a beaker of water. The tube is filled with water so that there is an unbroken connection between the water in the beaker and in the tube. If a thoroughly soaked sponge is placed at the other end of the tube so that a connection is made between the water held by the sponge and the water in the tube, an unbroken column of water can be "pulled up" from the beaker. This may be speeded up by using a fan to move dry air over the sponge and by increasing the temperature of the area immediately surrounding the sponge with a heat lamp. The rate at which the water moves up the tube is directly related to its rate of evaporation from the sponge. As water is evaporated from the sponge, it is replaced by water in the tube which, in turn, is replaced by water from the beaker (Figure 5-7).

How is it possible to pull a column of water up a tube without having the column break? Why doesn't the column of water, when under tension

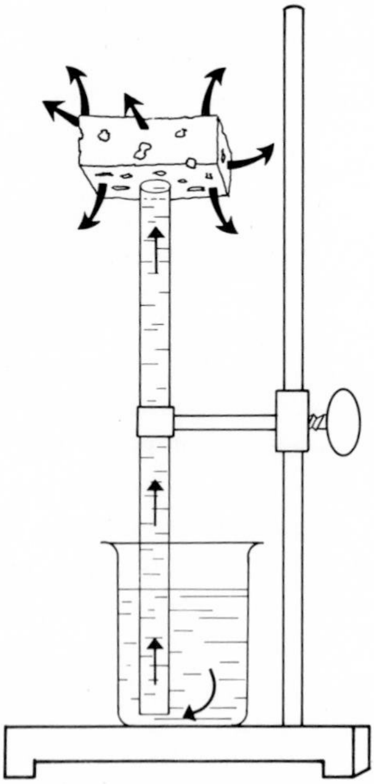

Figure 5-7 A physical system for demonstrating the cohesion-tension theory. Water evaporating off the surface of the sponge will be replaced by the water in the glass tube which in turn will be replaced by the water in the beaker.

(being pulled), pull away from the glass wall of the tube? In Chapter 4, we learned about the cohesive and adhesive properties of water, both of which are demonstrated in the process described in Figure 5-7. The water molecules cohere to each other and, at the same time, adhere to the glass wall of the tube. Therefore, the water column will not break until its cohesive and adhesive strength is overcome by gravitational pull on the column.

Let us now compare this physical example with a plant growing in soil in a natural habitat. The water in the beaker could be compared with the soil water. The glass tube is somewhat analogous to the tracheary tissue of the plant, the vessels more closely fitting this analogy. The evaporating surface of the sponge is similar to the evaporating surface of the leaf mesophyll. If we presume that an unbroken column of water exists between the soil water and the water of the leaf tissue, we can see how water could be pulled up from the soil. As water evaporates from the leaf mesophyll cells, it causes an increase in the diffusion pressure deficit of those cells in direct contact with the air spaces of the leaf. The water lost by the surface cell is replaced by water moving from cells deeper in the interior of the leaf. In an attempt to equate diffusion pressure deficits, the leaf cells ultimately have to draw water from the veins of the leaf, thus putting water in the xylem tissue in a state of tension (negative pressure). This state of tension is transmitted through unbroken columns of water reaching from the top of the plant to its root system.

Do we have any evidence that the contents of xylem vessels are, in fact, under tension in a normal transpiring plant? Direct evidence is lacking, since direct measurement of tension with known methods would disrupt the continuity of the water columns, thus eliminating any tension that might be present. However, indirect evidence that the xylem contents of a transpiring plant are in a state of tension is plentiful. Thut (41) demonstrated that a leafy shoot cut under water and sealed to a mercury manometer could support a column of mercury above barometric level. The column of water attached to the mercury in the manometer would have to be in a state of tension under the above circumstances. If a woody twig of a rapidly transpiring plant is cut, the water in the xylem elements "snaps" away from the area of the cut (28), indicating that it is under tension. Perhaps the most striking demonstration that water is under tension in transpiring plants may be found in dendrographic measurements of diameter variations in tree trunks. When water in the xylem elements is under tension, it will, because of its adhesive properties, cause a shrinkage in the diameters of these cells. Although this decrease in diameter is insignificant and unmeasurable for the individual xylem element, the total effect can be recorded by means of a dendrograph. This instrument gives a continuous record of changes in the diameter of a trunk over a period of time. As might be expected, there is a decrease in diameter during periods of high transpiration and an increase in periods of low transpiration. An example is given in Figure 5-8.

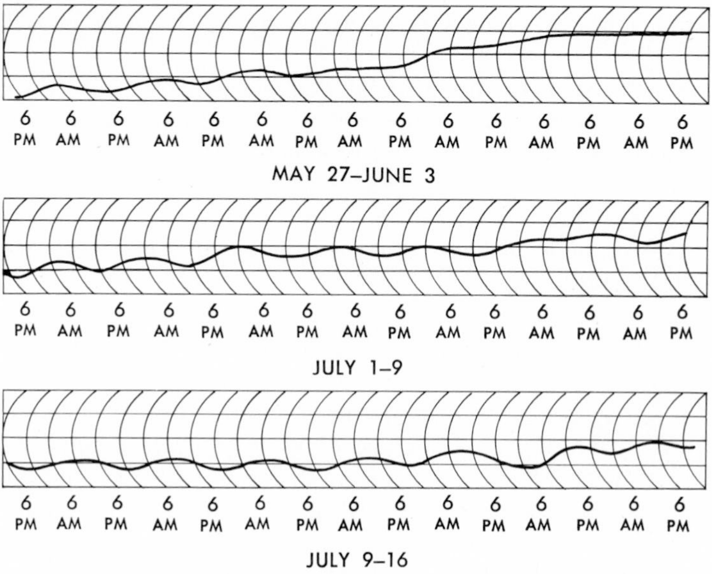

Figure 5-8 Increase and decrease in the relative diameter of an American beech (*Fagus grandifolia* Ehrh.) as measured by a dendrograph. Data were collected for three one-week periods. (After H. C. Fritts. 1958. Ecology. 39:705.)

Note in Figure 5-8 that when transpiration was relatively low in late May and early June, only slight variation in trunk diameter may be observed. However, in July, when temperatures and transpiration increased, variations in trunk diameter were obvious (17).

Assuming that we are convinced that water—due to its cohesive and adhesive properties and to the anatomy of the xylem tissue—can be "pulled" up in an unbroken chain through the plant, our next question should be "can the tensile strength of water support the column of water that would be necessary to reach the tops of our highest trees?" The answer to this question is yes. Measurements of the tensile strength of water have exceeded 300 atm. To raise water to the top of a 400 foot tree would require a difference in pressure of about 13 atm between the top and bottom. In the above statement, we neglected to mention the friction water would encounter moving through the xylem tissue. Although this is considerable, it is obvious that the tensile strength of water is sufficient to overcome the frictional and gravitational forces encountered in its vertical rise in a plant.

The cohesion-tension theory, first introduced by Dixon (13, 14), is the most popular explanation today of the translocation of water in plants. Root pressure is capable of moving water upward in a plant, but not in the quantity and to the heights necessary for most plants. Probably the

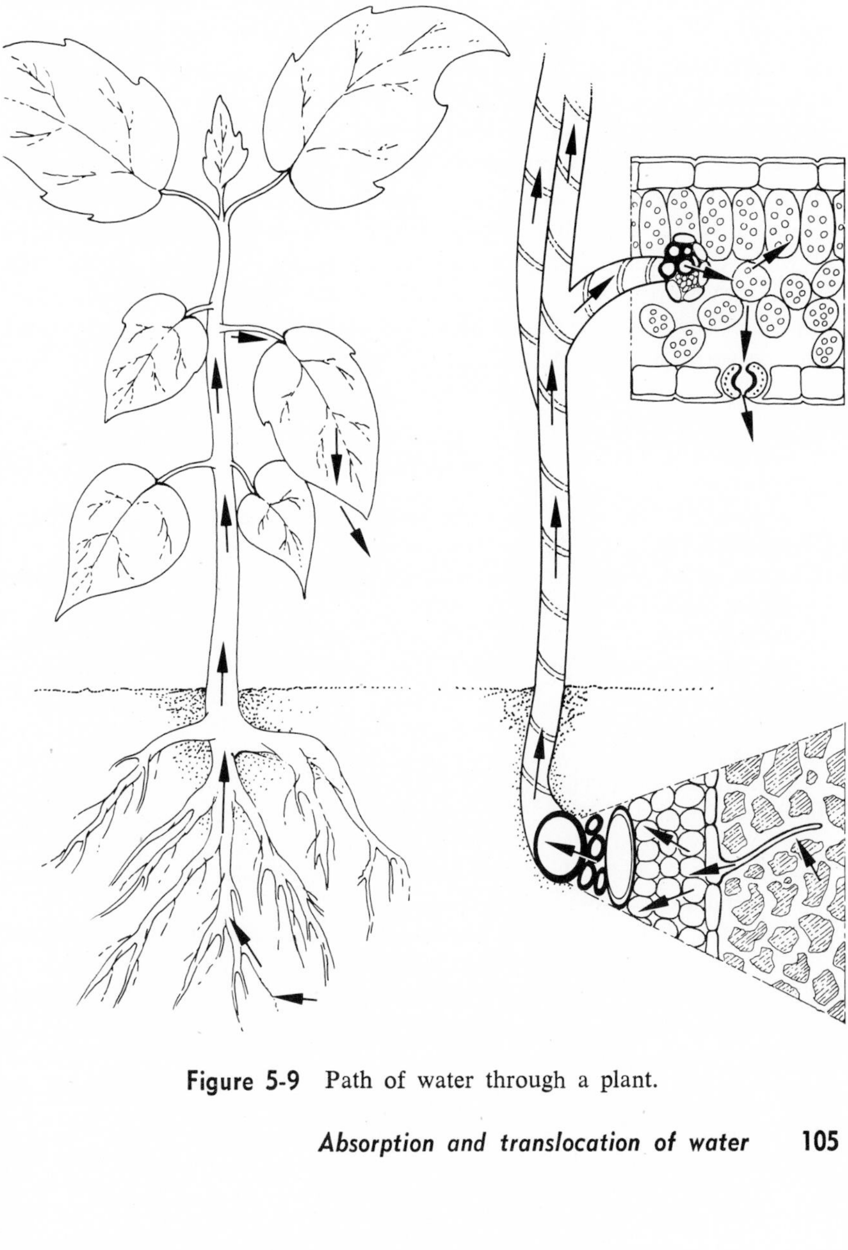

Figure 5-9 Path of water through a plant.

strongest argument for the cohesion-tension theory is that it is the only theory that can account for the quantity and the rate of water movement in a vigorously transpiring plant.

PATH OF WATER

We should by now be familiar with the tissues encountered by water moving from the soil to the leaves of a plant. In Figure 5-9 the path of water through a plant is diagrammatically shown. Water is first absorbed from the soil by *root hairs* and other epidermal cells in or near the root hair zone. Water then moves through the *cortex tissue* and across the *endodermis* and *pericycle* and finally into the *xylem ducts*. The xylem tissue of the roots connects directly with the xylem tissue of the stem, thus allowing water to move out of the root and into the stem. The xylem of the stem is divided and subdivided many times to form a complex network of water-conducting tissues, finally ending in the fine veins of the leaf. Water moves from the leaf veins into the *mesophyll cells,* is evaporated from their surfaces, and finally moves as water vapor through the *stomates* into the surrounding atmosphere.

BIBLIOGRAPHY

1. Addoms, R. M. 1946. Entrance of water into suberized roots of trees. Plant Physiol. 21: 109.
2. Anlel, O. M. van. 1953. The influence of salts on the exudation of tomato plants. Acta Botan. Neerl. 2: 445.
3. Bennet-Clark, T. A., A. D. Greenwood, and J. W. Barker. 1936. Water relations of osmotic pressures of plant cells. New Phytologist 35: 277.
4. Bogen, H. J., and H. Prell. 1953. Messung nichtosmotischer Wasseraufnahme an plasmolysierten Protoplasten. Planta 41: 459.
5. Breazeale, E. L. 1950. Moisture absorption by plants from an atmosphere of high humidity. Plant Physiol. 25: 413.
6. Breazeale, E. L., W. T. McGeorge, and J. F. Breazeale. 1951. Movement of water vapor in soils. Soil Sci. 71: 181.
7. Breazeale, E. L., W. T. McGeorge, and J. F. Breazeale. 1951. Water absorption and transpiration by leaves. Soil Sci. 72: 239.
8. Breazeale, J. F., and W. T. McGeorge. 1953. Exudation pressure in roots of tomato plants under humid conditions. Soil Sci. 75: 293.
9. Cormack, R. G. H. 1949. The development of root hairs in angiosperms. Botan. Rev. 15: 583.
10. Crafts, A. S., and T. C. Broyer. 1938. Migration of salts and water into xylem of the roots of higher plants. Am. J. Botan. 25: 529.

11. Dixon, H. H. 1909. Vitality and the transmission of water through the stems of plants. Notes Botany School Trinity College, Dublin, 2: 5; Sci. Proc. Roy. Dublin Soc. 12: 21.
12. Dixon, H. H. 1910. Transpiration and the ascent of sap. Progressus Rei Botanicae 3: 1.
13. Dixon, H. H. 1914. Transpiration and the ascent of sap in plants. The Macmillan Company, London.
14. Dixon, H. H. 1924. The transpiration stream. University of London Press, London.
15. Esau, K. 1958. Plant anatomy. John Wiley & Sons, New York.
16. Fox, D. G. 1933. Carbon dioxide narcosis. J. Cell. Comp. Physiol. 3: 75.
17. Fritts, H. C. 1958. An analysis of radial growth of beech in a central Ohio forest during 1954–1955. Ecology 39: 705.
18. Gessner, F. 1956. Die Wasseraufnahme durch Blätter und Samen. *In* W. Ruhland (ed.), Encyclopedia of plant physiology. 3: 215.
19. Grossenbacher, K. A. 1938. Diurnal fluctuation in root pressure. Plant Physiol. 13: 669.
20. Grossenbacher, K. A. 1939. Autonomic cycle of rate of exudation of plants. Am. J. Botany 26: 107.
21. Haise, H. R., H. J. Haas, and L. R. Jensen. 1955. Soil moisture studies of some Great Plains soils. II. Field capacity as related to $\frac{1}{3}$ atmosphere percentage and "Minimum Point" as related to 15- and 26-atmosphere percentages. Proc. Soil Sci. Soc. Am. 10: 20.
22. Kozlowski, T. T. 1964. Water metabolism in plants. Harper and Row, New York.
23. Kramer, P. J. 1937. The relation between rate of transpiration and rate of absorption of water in plants. Am. J. Botany 24: 10.
24. Kramer, P. J. 1949. Plant and soil water relationships. McGraw-Hill Book Company, New York.
25. Kramer, P. J., and W. T. Jackson. 1954. Causes of injury to flooded tobacco plants. Plant Physiol. 29: 241.
26. Kramer, P. J. 1956. Roots as absorbing organs. *In* W. Ruhland (ed.), Encyclopedia of plant physiology. 3: 188.
27. Kramer, P. J. 1959. Transpiration and the water economy of plants. *In* F. C. Steward (ed.), Plant physiology. Academic Press, New York. 2: 607.
28. McDermott, J. J. 1941. The effect of the method of cutting on the moisture content of samples from tree branches. Am. J. Botany 28: 506.
29. Overton, J. B. 1911. Studies on the relation of the living cells to the transpiration and sap-flow in *Cyperus*. II. Botan. Gaz. 51: 102.
30. Roberts, E. A., M. D. Southwick, and D. H. Palmiter. 1948. A microchemical examination of McIntosh apple leaves showing relationship of cell wall constituents to penetration of spray solutions. Plant Physiol. 23: 557.
31. Seifriz, W. 1942. Some physical properties of protoplasm and their bearing on structure. The structure of protoplasm. Iowa State College Press, Ames, Iowa. 245.
32. Skoog, F., T. C. Broyer, and K. A. Grossenbacher. 1938. Effect of auxin

on rates, periodicity, and osmotic relations in exudation. Am. J. Botany 25: 749.
33. Slatyer, R. O. 1955. Studies of the water relations of crop plants grown under natural rainfall in northern Australia. Australian J. Agr. Research 6: 365.
34. Slatyer, R. O. 1957. The significance of the permanent wilting percentage in studies of plant and soil water relations. Botan. Rev. 23: 585.
35. Slatyer, R. O. 1957. The influence of progressive increases in total soil moistures stress on transpiration, growth and internal water relationships of plants. Australian J. Biol. Sci. 10: 320.
36. Stiles, W. 1924. Permeability. Wheldon & Wesley, London.
37. Stocking, C. R. 1956. Root pressure. *In* W. Ruhland (ed.), Encyclopedia of plant physiology. 3: 583.
38. Strasburger, E. 1891. Über den Bau und die Verrichtungen der Leitungsbahnen in den Pflanzen. Hist. Beitr. Jena 3: 609.
39. Strasburger, E. 1893. Über das Saftsteigen. Hist. Beitr. Jena 5: 1.
40. Thimann, K. V. 1951. Studies on the physiology of cell enlargement. Growth Symposium 10: 5.
41. Thut, H. F. 1932. Demonstrating the lifting power of transpiration. Am. J. Botany 19: 358.
42. Vaadia, Y. 1960. Autonomic diurnal fluctuations in rate of exudation and root pressure of decapitated sunflower plants. Physiol. Plant. 13: 701.
43. Wadleigh, C. H., and A. D. Ayers. 1945. Growth and biochemical composition of bean plants as conditioned by soil moisture tension and salt concentration. Plant Physiol. 20: 106.
44. White, P. R. 1938. "Root pressure"—an unappreciated force in sap movement. Am. J. Botany 25: 223.

Part THREE

Carbohydrate metabolism

6
Enzymes

INTRODUCTION

The dynamic state of the biochemistry of living systems is for the most part under the regulation of organic catalysts called *enzymes*. An enzyme is a protein (thus of biological origin), which can tremendously increase the efficiency of a biochemical reaction and is generally specific for that reaction. As with inorganic catalysts, the final products of the reaction are not affected by the enzyme. Although a biochemical reaction will proceed to completion in the absence of an enzyme, the process would be extremely slow—so slow, in fact, as to make life as we know it impossible. Indeed, one could go so far as to say that with enzymes and life there is a marriage that is inseparable.

The use of enzymes by man for practical purposes can be traced back to the ancient Greeks, who used the action of enzymes in the process of fermentation to produce wine. Other practices in which the activity of enzymes is a necessary feature and which have a long history are the making of cheese, the production of vinegar, and the leavening of bread. During the drive to improve the quality and production of these products (especially wine), much indirect knowledge of enzyme activity was learned, leading, eventually, to the recognition of living cells as essential participants. Much of the credit for this work must be given to Louis Pasteur, the great French scientist. In all of this early work, living intact cells were held responsible, not enzymes per se, for the activity observed. However, a significant breakthrough in the study of enzymes was made when it was discovered by Buchner in 1897 that the juice of ground and pressed yeast cells could ferment sugar. In other words, Buchner observed that living yeast cells contributed some factor(s), which was (were) able to catalyze the fermentation of sugar in a cell-free environment.

The next significant breakthrough in the study of enzymes was the isolation of the enzyme urease and the recognition that enzymes are proteins by Sumner in 1926. The observation that enzymes are proteins was greeted with much skepticism. But, with the isolation of several other enzymes, which were shown unequivocally to be protein in nature, this skepticism died, and it is now universally accepted that enzymes are proteins.

NATURE OF ENZYMES

Enzymes, being organic catalysts, have many of the properties of inorganic catalysts and thus can be characterized as follows:

(1) Enzymes are active in extremely small amounts. That is, in a biochemical reaction only a small amount of enzyme is necessary to convert a large amount of substrate to product. The two terms *substrate* and *product* signify the starting and ending material of a reaction. The number of moles of substrate converted per minute by 1 mole of enzyme is called the *turnover number* of the enzyme. A dramatic example of the variance among the activities of enzymes in different biochemical reactions can be seen in a comparison of their turnover numbers. This number may vary from 100 to over 3,000,000.

(2) True catalysts remain unaffected by the reaction which they catalyze. This property of the ideal catalyst is approached very closely by enzymes under stable conditions. Because of the protein nature of enzymes, however, their activities are confined to narrow ranges of temperature, pH, etc. Under conditions other than those considered optimum, an enzyme is a relatively unstable compound and may be affected by the reaction it catalyzes.

(3) Although an enzyme considerably hastens the completion of a reaction, it will not affect the equilibrium of that reaction. The reversible reactions usually present in the living system would proceed toward equilibrium at a very slow rate in the absence of enzymes. However, an enzyme will speed a reaction in either direction, that is, will bring about the equilibrium of that reaction at a much faster rate.

(4) Catalytic action is specific. Enzymes exhibit specificity for the reactions they catalyze. That is, an enzyme that will catalyze one reaction may not catalyze another. This specificity is very strong for some enzymes and rather general in others. Nevertheless, the property of specificity remains one of the most important properties of enzymes.

(5) How does an enzyme catalyst speed up a reaction? Perhaps this question can best be answered by describing what happens when substance A is spontaneously converted to substance B, first in the absence of an enzyme and then in the presence of an enzyme. In a given number of molecules of substance A at a specific temperature, there is a certain average kinetic energy. Although the majority of molecules possess the average kinetic energy, a few of the molecules possess higher and lower than average kinetic energy because of collisions. These are referred to as "energy-rich" or "energy-poor" molecules. Since the reaction we are describing ($A \rightarrow B$) is spontaneous, the average kinetic energy of the A molecules is higher than the average kinetic energy of the B molecules. However, only the energy-rich A molecules are able to react and thus be converted to B molecules. Therefore, only a few molecules at any one time, as a result of molecular collisions, can reach the level of energy necessary to react. The energy above average that is required for A to react and be converted to B is called the *activation energy* of the reaction. B may also be converted to A, but its activation energy for the reaction $B \rightarrow A$ is higher because of the lower energy status of B compared to A.

An enzyme will lower the activation energy of a reaction. It is thought that an enzyme will react with the energy-rich and the energy-poor molecules alike to form an *intermediate complex*. This complex, in turn, will react to release the enzyme and yield the products of the reactions. Now, if the activation energy for the formation and decomposition of this complex is low, many more of the A molecules can participate in the reaction than if the enzyme were absent. It should be noted that when the activation energy of a reaction is lowered, it is lowered for the backward as well as the forward reaction. In other words, an enzyme will speed a reaction to its equilibrium. These principles are diagrammatically shown in Figure 6-1.

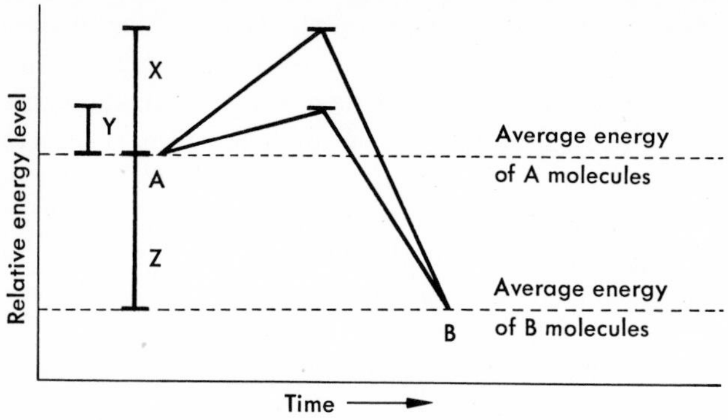

Figure 6-1 A diagrammatic description of the energy requirements of the reaction A → B in the absence and in the presence of an enzyme. The symbol X represents the activation energy of the reaction in the absence of an enzyme; Y represents the activation energy in the presence of an enzyme; Z represents the energy released in the reaction.

NOMENCLATURE AND SPECIFICITY

Enzymes are generally named according to the substrate they attack or the type of reaction they catalyze. The usual practice is to add the suffix *-ase* to the name of the substrate attacked. Thus, the enzymes arginase and tyrosinase attack the substrates arginine and tyrosine, respectively. Enzymes also may be grouped under a more general term describing a certain group of compounds they attack. Thus, we have lipases, proteinases, carbohydrases, etc. Finally, enzymes may be named according to the type of reaction they catalyze. Some examples are hydrolases, oxidases, carboxylases, and phosphorylases. Unfortunately, some of the older nomenclature still persists, and occasionally, one runs into a name of an enzyme in the literature that has no bearing to the reaction it catalyzes. However, this is more often the exception than the rule.

The specificity of an enzyme is an important feature of the metabolism of the living system. The catalytic property of an enzyme is confined to one or a group of related reactions. For example, the enzyme urease is highly specific for the substrate urea.

$$\text{Urea} + H_2O \xrightleftharpoons{\text{Urease}} \text{Carbon dioxide} + \text{Ammonia}$$

In contrast, some enzymes are less restricted and their specificity may be confined to a certain chemical linkage. Thus, some esterases can act on the ester link between different fatty acids and alcohols without any great distinction between any of the ester linkages. Nevertheless, esterases are specific in the sense that they catalyze the hydrolytic cleavage of only ester links. That is, they do not catalyze the hydrolysis of other types of chemical linkages nor do they catalyze oxidation reactions, decarboxylation reactions, etc.

CLASSIFICATION

The inadequacy of present systems of enzyme classification is evident to any student of cellular metabolism. It is most probable that a major part of this is due to our very sketchy knowledge of protein structure and, hence, enzyme structure. However, in order to work with the enormous number of enzymes active in metabolism, one needs some system of classification, whatever its shortcomings. We will attempt here only a very simple classification, based on the type of chemical reaction catalyzed. For the most part, this will suffice for the discussions on plant metabolism which follow this chapter.

Hydrolytic enzymes

Hydrolytic enzymes catalyze the addition of the elements of water to a specific bond of the substrate. The classification of this type of enzyme as hydrolytic is an arbitrary one. Since most hydrolytic reactions are reversible, the hydrolytic enzyme could just as well be called a condensation or synthetic enzyme.

$$\text{RCO—OR}' \xrightleftharpoons{\text{HOH}} \text{RCOOH} + \text{R}'\text{OH}$$

Some examples of hydrolytic enzymes are esterases, carbohydrases, and proteases.

Oxidation-reduction enzymes

Oxidation-reduction enzymes catalyze the removal or addition of hydrogen, oxygen, or electrons from or to the substrate, which is oxidized or reduced in the process.

$$RH_2 + A \rightarrow R + AH_2 \quad \text{(removal of hydrogen)}$$

$$RO + \tfrac{1}{2}O_2 \rightarrow RO_2 \quad \text{(addition of oxygen)}$$

$$R^{2+} \longrightarrow R^{3+} + e^- \quad \text{(removal of electron)}$$

These enzymes occupy a major position in cellular metabolism. Because of their importance, their function in metabolism will be covered in more detail in a later chapter. Examples of oxidation-reduction enzymes are the dehydrogenases and oxidases.

Phosphorylases

The phosphorylases catalyze the reversible phosphorolytic cleavage of a specific bond on a substrate. The best known phosphorylases are those which catalyze the addition of the elements of phosphoric acid to the $\alpha(1 \rightarrow 4)$ glycosidic linkages of starch and glycogen.

$$\text{Starch} + \text{Phosphate} \rightleftharpoons \text{Glucose-1-phosphate}$$

The activity of these enzymes is somewhat analogous to that of the hydrolytic enzymes, except that the elements of phosphoric acid are added instead of water.

Transferases

Transferases catalyze the transfer of a group from a donor molecule to an acceptor molecule. This is a very large group and includes such enzymes as transglycosidases, transpeptidases, transaminases, transmethylases, and transacylases. Probably the best known example of a transferase is the enzyme glutamic-aspartic transaminase. This enzyme catalyzes the transfer of an amino group from glutamic acid to oxaloacetic acid to form aspartic acid.

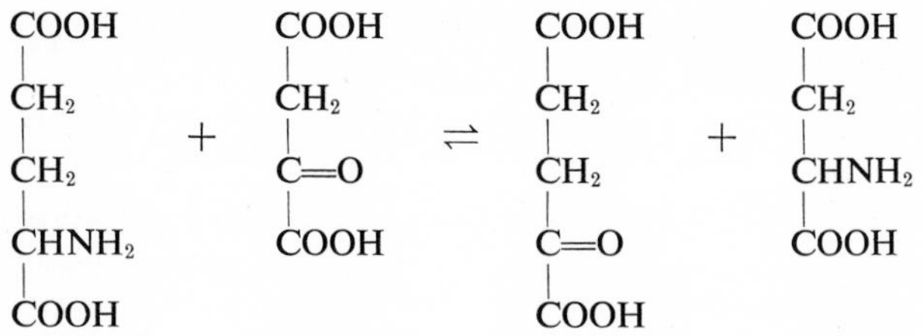

$$
\begin{array}{cccc}
\text{COOH} & \text{COOH} & \text{COOH} & \text{COOH} \\
| & | & | & | \\
\text{CH}_2 & \text{CH}_2 & \text{CH}_2 & \text{CH}_2 \\
| \quad + & | \quad \rightleftharpoons & | \quad + & | \\
\text{CH}_2 & \text{C}{=}\text{O} & \text{CH}_2 & \text{CHNH}_2 \\
| & | & | & | \\
\text{CHNH}_2 & \text{COOH} & \text{C}{=}\text{O} & \text{COOH} \\
| & & | & \\
\text{COOH} & & \text{COOH} & \\
\text{Glutamic} & \text{Oxaloacetic} & \alpha\text{-Ketoglutaric} & \text{Aspartic} \\
\text{acid} & \text{acid} & \text{acid} & \text{acid}
\end{array}
$$

Carboxylases

The carboxylases catalyze the removal or addition of carbon dioxide. An example of an enzyme that removes CO_2 would be glutamic decarboxylase. This enzyme catalyzes the removal of CO_2 from glutamic acid to yield γ-aminobutyric acid.

$$\text{Glutamic acid} \rightleftharpoons \gamma\text{-Aminobutyric acid} + CO_2$$

An example of an enzyme that catalyzes the addition of CO_2 would be carboxydismutase. This enzyme is important in photosynthesis where it catalyzes the carboxylation of ribulose-1,5-diphosphate. This reaction will be discussed in more detail in a later chapter on photosynthesis.

Isomerases

Isomerases catalyze the interconversion of aldose and ketose sugars. For example, the interconversion of glucose-6-phosphate with fructose-6-phosphate is catalyzed by the enzyme phosphoglucoisomerase.

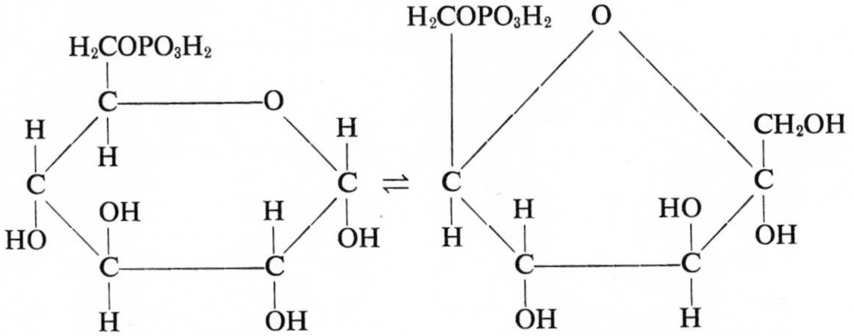

Glucose-6-phosphate   Fructose-6-phosphate

ENZYME-SUBSTRATE COMPLEX

Studies on the kinetics of enzyme action are consistent with the concept that enzymes combine with their substrates before yielding the products of the reactions they catalyze. In other words, the enzyme and substrate form an *intermediate complex* before decomposition of the substrate can occur.

$$E + S \rightleftharpoons ES \rightarrow E + P$$

Enzymes are thought to have active sites with which a substrate molecule can form an intimate association. There may be and probably are many of these sites on the very large enzyme molecule. If we visualize an enzyme with several active sites surrounded by numerous substrate molecules, which are very small by comparison, we can see immediately that random collisions play an important part in enzyme substrate reactions. Since the major portion of the enzyme molecule is devoid of active sites, many collisions between substrate and enzyme molecules would have to take place before the occurrence of an active collision. However, if enough substrate molecules are present, the active sites on an enzyme may become completely occupied, and the rate of the reaction will be at a maximum—all other factors being held constant.

In the preceding pages, we discussed the specificity of enzymes. The enzyme-substrate complex offers a good explanation of this specificity. Apparently, active sites are specifically shaped within the numerous folds of the enzyme molecules. Only specifically shaped substrate molecules can fit correctly into these active sites (Figure 6-2).

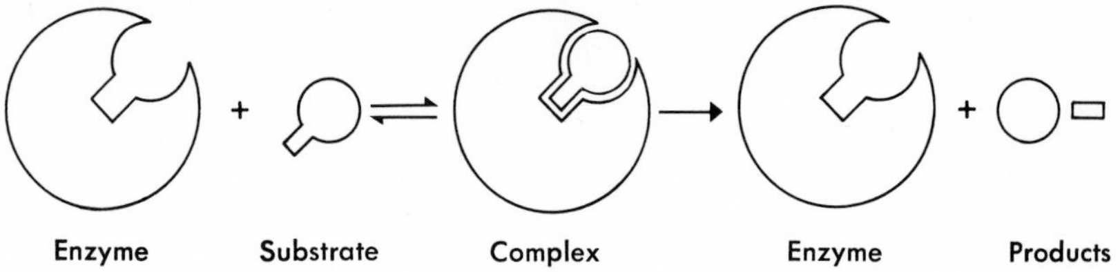

Figure 6-2 Diagrammatic representation of an enzyme-substrate reaction.

Indirect evidence supporting the validity of the enzyme-substrate complex theory can be found in a study of the action of inhibitors on enzyme activity. Structural analogs of a substrate molecule may, in some cases, occupy active sites on an enzyme that are normally occupied by the substrate. The new complex formed is reversible and inactive with respect to the formation of products. In other words, these structural analogs compete with the normal substrate molecules for active sites on the enzyme. Substances that act in this manner are called *competitive inhibitors,* and their inhibition of enzyme activity is called *competitive inhibition.*

$$E + I \rightleftharpoons EI$$

Competitive inhibition can be overcome by increasing the concentration of substrate until all the active sites are occupied by substrate molecules.

One of the classic examples of competitive inhibition is the inhibition by malonic acid of the enzyme succinic dehydrogenase, which catalyzes the conversion of succinic acid to fumaric acid. The inhibitor, malonic acid, closely resembles the normal substrate, succinic acid, in chemical structure and as a result is able to occupy active sites normally occupied by succinic acid. Malonic acid is a competitive inhibitor, since inhibition can be overcome by increasing the concentration of succinic acid. Competitive inhibition can be visualized in the manner shown in Figure 6-3.

PROSTHETIC GROUPS: ACTIVATORS, COFACTORS, AND COENZYMES

Many enzymes, in addition to their protein structure, have an attached nonprotein group. Proteins (in this case an enzyme) with attached nonprotein groups are called *conjugated proteins.* Proteins or enzymes of this type may be thought of as consisting of two parts, an *apoenzyme,* composed only of amino acids, and a nonamino acid *prosthetic group.* A good example of this type of complex may be observed in enzymes that require

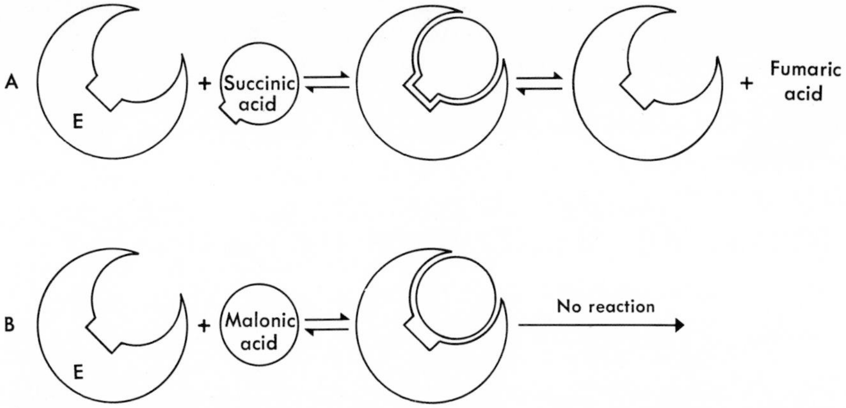

Figure 6-3 Diagrammatic representation of competitive inhibition. Malonic acid is very similar in structure to succinic acid and can occupy active sites on the enzyme.

a certain metal for activity. The metal is generally referred to as an *activator*. Definite correlations between the catalytic properties of some enzymes and their association with various metal components have been shown. Indeed, the separation of the enzyme from its metal component generally results in complete loss of activity. Restoration of the metal to the apoenzyme returns activity. Many investigators believe that the metal component of an enzyme may help in the binding of a substrate to its enzyme (2, 4, 3). Many of the enzymes associated with glycolysis require metal activators. Some metals known to be activators of enzyme systems are copper, iron, magnesium, manganese, zinc, calcium, potassium, and cobalt.

In contrast to the metal-requiring enzymes, some enzymes require a loose association with certain organic substances for activity. These organic prosthetic groups are called *cofactors* or *coenzymes*. Generally, the cofactor or coenzyme acts as a donor or acceptor of groups of atoms that have been added or removed from the substrate. The coenzyme can be easily separated from the protein portion of the enzyme, and when this happens, the catalytic properties of the enzyme are greatly reduced. Some of the coenzymes that have been identified are nicotinamide-adenine-dinucleotide (NAD),[1] nicotinamide-adenine-dinucleotide phosphate (NADP),[1] adenosine triphosphate (ATP), coenzyme A (CoA), flavin mononucleotide (FMN), and flavin adenine dinucleotide (FAD). These coenzymes form a very loose association with an enzyme and may become

[1] NAD was formerly called diphosphopyridine nucleotide (DPN) and NADP was formerly called triphosphopyridine nucleotide (TPN).

attached to several different proteins forming in the process different enzymes. It is interesting to note that some of the organic prosthetic groups or coenzymes of enzymes are *vitamins,* organic compounds that are not formed in mammals, but are synthesized in plants.

DISTRIBUTION OF ENZYMES IN THE PLANT

The development in relatively recent years of techniques enabling scientists to study enzyme systems outside of the living cell has given us a good picture of the distribution of enzymes within the architecture of the cell. The unicellular plants—such as the yeast, bacteria, and algae—because of their high protein content and less complex structures, have proved to be excellent sources for this type of study. Also, the physiological functions of certain parts of the cell are excellent guides to the location of enzymes involved in these functions. For example, ribosomes have been identified as cytoplasmic particles chiefly functioning in the process of protein synthesis. Thus, the enzymes catalyzing the formation of peptide chains should be located on the surface or in the very immediate vicinity of these particles.

Many of the enzymes of cellular metabolism are associated with the cytoplasmic particles of the cell. Perhaps the highest concentrations of enzymes may be found in the mitochondria and chloroplasts. All of the enzymes necessary for the complete oxidation of pyruvate in the Krebs cycle to CO_2 and H_2O are present in the mitochondria. This would include the enzymes necessary for the passage of electrons to oxygen for the formation of H_2O. The passage of electrons from the intermediates of the Krebs cycle to oxygen occurs via the cytochrome or electron transport system and results in the formation of ATP.

The chloroplast is even more remarkable for the diverse array of enzymes that are within it. The enzymes necessary for the dark reactions of photosynthesis (assimilation of CO_2) are present in the matrix of the chloroplast. Also, cytochrome enzymes have been located in this cell particle and, as in mitochondria, their activity leads to the production of ATP. In addition, the enzymes necessary for the synthesis of the pigments of the chloroplast (chlorophylls, carotenoids, etc.) are most likely present.

Very little work has been done on the enzymes confined within the nucleus. It is thought, however, that the enzyme deoxyribonuclease is located in the nucleus. This enzyme catalyzes the hydrolytic cleavage of deoxyribose nucleic acid (DNA). The ground phase of the cytoplasm (cytoplasm without formed particles), in contrast to the nucleus, abounds in enzymes. The enzymes of glycolysis and the hexosemonophosphate shunt are located in the cytoplasm. Also various hydrolytic enzymes and phosphorylases are present.

In addition to enzymes associated with specific areas of the cell, there are enzymes that may be considered extracellular. Although extracellular enzymes are rare in higher plants, they are abundantly found in bacteria and fungi. These enzymes function in the extracellular digestion and transport of nutrients into the cell. For example, some bacteria utilize proteins and polysaccharides as nutrients. These molecules are very large and complex and could not possibly penetrate the cell membrane. However, the bacteria excrete enzymes that reduce these large molecules to smaller molecules, which are able then to penetrate the cell.

It is obvious from this discussion that a certain degree of compartmentalization of enzymes takes place within the cell. In many cases, this affords a better association of enzyme and substrate, resulting in a more efficient system. The compartmentalization of enzymes reaches a high degree in the mitochondrion and the chloroplast. However, even the cytoplasm is thoroughly partitioned by the endoplasmic reticulum, suggesting that here also compartmentalization of enzymes and metabolites may take place.

FACTORS AFFECTING ENZYME ACTIVITY

Like all chemical reactions, an enzyme-catalyzed reaction is susceptible to external conditions. Because of their protein nature, however, enzymes are unusually sensitive to the fluctuating influences of their immediate environment. Thus, the substrate or enzyme concentration, temperature, and pH all affect the rate of an enzyme-catalyzed reaction.

Substrate concentration

If we first assume that the formation of an enzyme-substrate complex precedes decomposition of the substrate, then the effect of substrate concentration on the rate of an enzyme-catalyzed reaction can be clearly described. In the usual circumstance, the enzyme molecule is much larger than its substrate and is possessed of several active sites on its surface. Consider, then, a giant enzyme molecule surrounded by a relatively low concentration of substrate molecules, some near and some far from the active sites on the enzyme. In this situation, some of the active sites may not be occupied. In addition, occupied sites, when vacated, may experience a brief interval before being contacted by another substrate molecule. Obviously, under these conditions, the enzyme is not working at maximum efficiency. Increase in the substrate concentration will increase the number of molecules in the immediate vicinity of the enzyme's active sites and, as a result, increase the chance of a substrate molecule coming in contact with an active site. Therefore, at a constant enzyme concentration, an increase in substrate concentration will increase the rate of an enzyme-catalyzed reaction. When the substrate concentration is increased to the point of "swamping" the active sites, the enzyme is said to be working at maximum efficiency, all other factors being constant. Further increase in substrate will have no effect on the rate of reaction. These relationships are described in Figure 6-4.

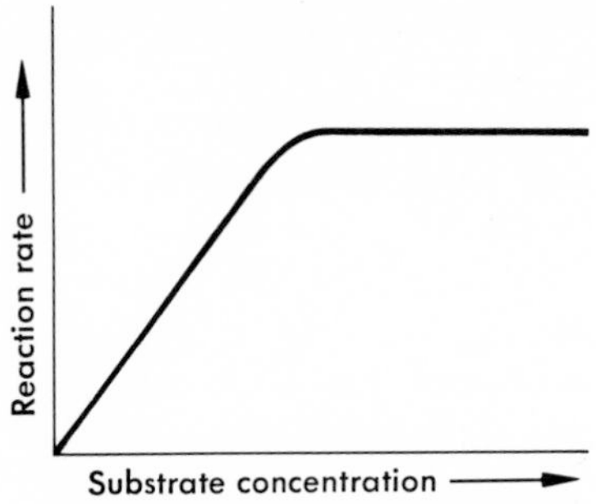

Figure 6-4 Typical effect of substrate concentration on the rate of an enzyme-catalyzed reaction.

Enzyme concentration

A consideration of the above discussion of the effect of substrate concentration on an enzyme-catalyzed reaction should clearly illustrate why an increase in enzyme concentration would increase the rate of reaction. Suppose at a specific enzyme concentration we have "swamped" the active sites with substrate molecules and no longer can effect an increase in the reaction rate by adding more substrate. Now, if we increase the enzyme concentration, we, in effect, increase the number of available active sites, thus increasing the chance of reactive contact between enzyme and substrate.

Generally, when measuring the activity of an enzyme, low concentrations of enzyme are used in high concentrations of substrate. Under these circumstances, enzyme activity would be maximum, no matter what enzyme concentration is used as long as it is sufficiently low for continuous contact between active sites and substrate molecules. In this situation, we can observe that the rate of reaction is directly proportional to enzyme concentration (Figure 6-5). We should not lose sight of the fact, however, that if the substrate concentration was relatively low, increasing enzyme concentration would cause the rate of reaction to increase to a point and then remain constant. In other words, increasing the enzyme concentration

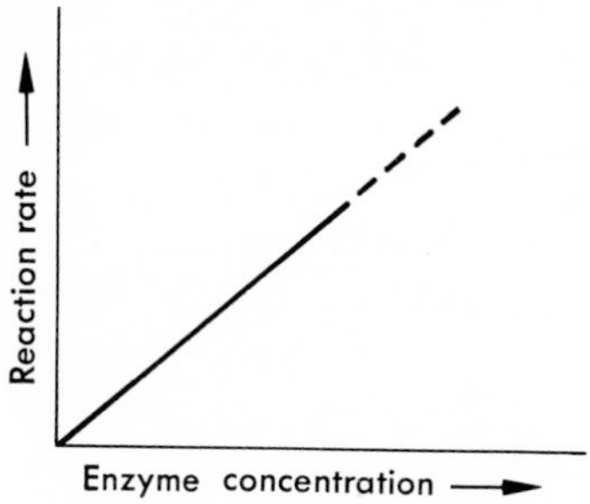

Figure 6-5 Typical effect of enzyme concentration on the rate of reaction. Substrate concentration is sufficiently high to allow for active sites being continuously occupied.

would have the same effect on the rate of reaction as increasing the substrate concentration (see Figure 6-4).

Temperature

As with any chemical reaction, an enzyme-catalyzed reaction is influenced by temperature. However, the protein nature of enzymes causes them to be particularly sensitive to temperature changes and confines their activity to a much narrower temperature range than would be encountered in most ordinary chemical reactions. At 0°C the rate of an enzyme-catalyzed reaction is practically zero. As the temperature increases, there is a more or less steady increase in the reaction rate. Generally, the reaction rate increases on the average 2.5 times for every 10°C increase in temperature up to 25°C. Two factors are involved here:

1. Increase in the kinetic energy of both the substrate and enzyme molecules.
2. Increase in the chance of collision between enzyme and substrate molecules as a result of their greater agitation by higher temperatures.

As 30°C is approached, however, factors leading to enzyme denaturation become more apparent. The complex molecular structure of an enzyme is an essential factor in its catalytic activity. This structure is held in its unique pattern by numerous weak links, called hydrogen bonds. Because of increased thermal activity, these bonds are stretched and finally broken as the temperature increases. Like the collapse of a house of cards, the rupture of one hydrogen bond makes it easier to rupture the next and the next and so on, until the integrity of the enzyme structure can no longer be maintained and catalytic properties are completely lost. Collapse of the enzyme structure caused by an increase in temperature or other factors is generally called *denaturation* (i.e., loss of natural properties). The loss of catalytic properties is rather abrupt and, in typical cases, begins at about 35°C and is complete as 60°C is approached (Figure 6-6).

We must also consider a time factor when discussing the effect of temperature on enzyme activity. In Figure 6-6 we can see that the reaction rate is approaching maximum at 45°C. However, at this temperature

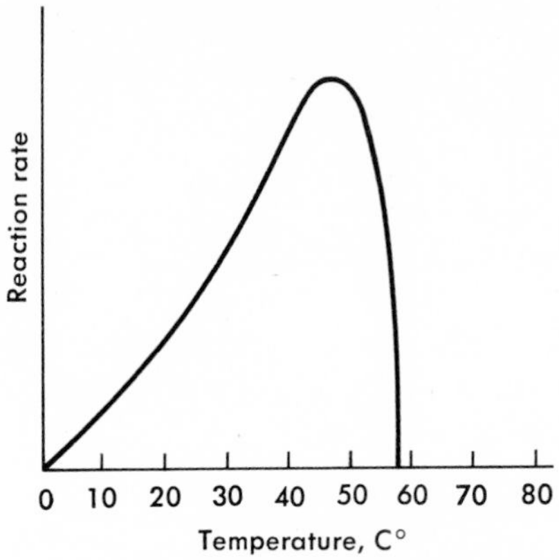

Figure 6-6 Typical effect of temperature on an enzyme-catalyzed reaction.

destruction of the essential structure of the enzyme molecule is also taking place. If the reaction occurs for any length of time at this temperature, there will be a gradual falling off of activity.

Hydrogen ion concentration (pH)

Changes in pH also can cause denaturation of the enzyme molecule, resulting in a falling off of activity. However, this does not appear to be the major effect of pH on enzyme-catalyzed reactions. Typically, an enzyme will have an optimum pH, a shift to the alkaline or acid side of the pH scale, causing a drop in activity. Characteristically, proteins possess many ionic groups, which may either be charged or uncharged, depending upon the hydrogen ion concentration of their immediate environment. If these ionic groups happen to be functional groups, say as part of an active site, and the formation of the enzyme-substrate complex is dependent upon their ionic state, it is easy to see why a change in pH can cause a change in enzyme activity. In addition, if the substrate is an electrolyte, as is often the case, then its ionic state is also affected by changes in pH. Thus, if the ionic state of the substrate is an important factor in the reaction, the reaction rate will be influenced by any change in the ionic state of the substrate caused by a change in pH. Other conditions being equal, the highest efficiency in an enzyme-catalyzed reaction can be expected at that pH that leaves the greatest number of molecules in the proper ionic state. From this statement, we can infer that different enzymes have different optimal pH's. This is shown in Figure 6-7.

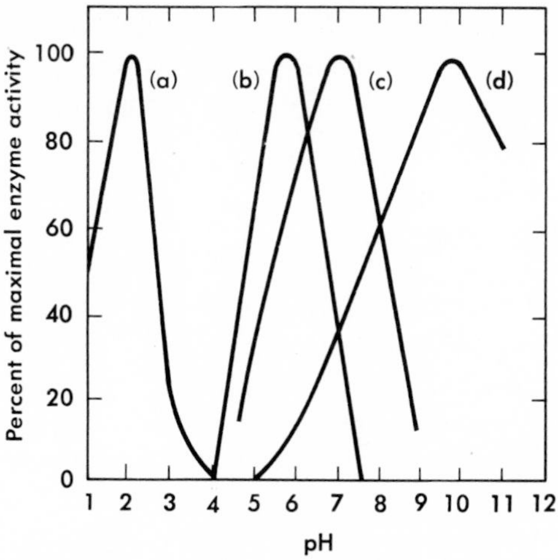

Figure 6-7 Effect of pH on the activity of (a) pepsin, (b) glutamic acid decarboxylase, (c) salivary amylase, and (d) arginase. (After J. S. Fruton and S. Simmonds. 1959. General biochemistry. Wiley, New York.)

Inhibitors

Since enzymes are proteins, they possess a variety of functional groups capable of interacting with numerous other compounds. Interaction of an enzyme with substances other than the normal substrate in many instances leads to an alteration of structure essential to catalytic activity. If this happens, there is a loss in catalytic efficiency or complete inactivation of the enzyme. Enzyme inhibitors may be divided into two general classes, *competitive* and *noncompetitive*. Competitive inhibition has already been discussed in a previous section of this chapter and so will not be dealt with here.

Noncompetitive inhibition. In contrast to competitive inhibitors, noncompetitive inhibitors do not compete with the substrate for active sites on the enzyme surface. As a result, noncompetitive inhibition *cannot* be overcome by the addition of more substrate. Generally, in noncompetitive inhibition, the inhibitor reacts with either parts of the enzyme not involved in catalytic activity or with the enzyme-substrate complex.

$$E + I \rightleftharpoons EI$$

or

$$E + S + I \rightleftharpoons ESI$$

In the former situation, inhibition is often caused by modification of enzyme structure, destroying the ability of the enzyme and substrate to interact. In the latter situation, the inhibitor renders the enzyme-substrate complex inactive.

SUMMARY

The organized and integrated complex of biochemical reactions that give a system the qualities of life is under the control and regulation of organic catalysts called enzymes. Enzymes are proteins and as such are sensitive to the same environmental influences that proteins are. Thus, changes in temperature and hydrogen ion concentration have profound effects on enzyme activity.

Although many enzymes are simple proteins, many also are conjugated proteins, their prosthetic groups often being essential for activity. The prosthetic groups may be inorganic (e.g., metals) or organic (e.g., NADP or NAD).

An important feature of enzyme-substrate interaction is the formation of a complex before decomposition of the substrate takes place. The ability of structural analogs of substrate molecules to compete for active sites on the enzyme surface may be taken as indirect proof of the complex concept.

In an organism, enzymes often are concentrated in areas where the reactions they catalyze take place. Thus, enzymes important in photosynthesis are found in the chloroplast and enzymes functioning in the oxidation of glucose to CO_2 and H_2O are found in the mitochondria.

BIBLIOGRAPHY

1. Fruton, J. S., and S. Simmonds. 1959. General biochemistry. John Wiley & Sons, New York.
2. Hellerman, L., and C. C. Stock. 1938. Activation of enzymes. V. J. Biol. Chem. 125: 771.
3. Klotz, I. M. 1954. Thermodynamic and molecular properties of some metal-protein complexes. *In* W. D. McElroy and H. B. Glass (eds.), Mechanism of enzyme action. John Hopkins Press, Baltimore, Md. 257.
4. Smith, E. L., N. C. Davis, A. Adams, and D. N. Spackman. 1954. The specificity and mode of action of two metal-peptidases. *In* W. D. McElroy and H. B. Glass (eds.), Mechanism of enzyme action. John Hopkins Press, Baltimore, Md. 291.
5. Sumner, J. B. 1926. The isolation and crystallization of the enzyme urease. J. Biol. Chem. 69: 435.

7
Carbohydrates

INTRODUCTION

As their name implies, the carbohydrates are a group of organic compounds containing the elements carbon, hydrogen, and oxygen generally in the ratio of 1:2:1. However, the above criteria for this group has been widened to include compounds containing nitrogen and sulfur and compounds that do not conform to a strict 1:2:1 ratio of carbon, hydrogen, and oxygen. Because of this, carbohydrates are no longer exclusively thought as "hydrates of carbon," but are grouped in a more general category as *polyhydroxyaldehydes* or *polyhydroxyketones* and their derivatives.

The carbohydrates are important to the plant in many ways. First and foremost, they represent a means for the storage of the energy trapped from light in the process of photosynthesis—a function of utmost importance to animals as well as plants. Secondly, the carbohydrates form the supporting tissues of the plant, enabling it to achieve erect growth sometimes as high as 400 feet. Finally, the carbohydrates provide the carbon skeletons for most if not all of the organic compounds that make up the plant.

CLASSIFICATION

The carbohydrates may be divided roughly into three large groups, the *monosaccharides,* the *oligosaccharides,* and the *polysaccharides.* The first group, the monosaccharides, are the least complex of the carbohydrates and do not yield simpler carbohydrates on hydrolysis. They are the building units for the more complex oligosaccharides and polysaccharides. The oligosaccharides are also relatively simple, being made up of two or more monosaccharides held together by glycosidic linkages. The polysaccharides, on the other hand, are complex molecules of high molecular weight composed of a large number of monosaccharides joined through glycosidic linkages. The border line between oligosaccharides and polysaccharides is rather wide. One may call a large oligosaccharide a polysaccharide or a small polysaccharide an oligosaccharide.

Monosaccharides

If we were to adhere to the original definition of carbohydrates (hydrates of carbon), then two carbon compounds such as formaldehyde and acetic acid would have to be considered among the carbohydrates. However, some of the chemical and physical factors associated with the carbohydrates are lacking in these compounds. The simplest carbohydrates are generally considered to be the three-carbon compounds *glyceraldehyde* and *dihydroxyacetone.*

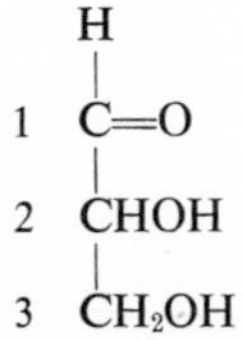
Glyceraldehyde

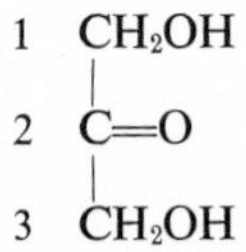
Dihydroxyacetone

A consideration of the above compounds will help us with the general terminology used to describe sugars. For example, the monosaccharides are classified in accordance with the number of carbons present. Thus, glyceraldehyde and dihydroxyacetone are called *trioses.* Note also that on these compounds one of the carbons bears a carbonyl oxygen, on the first carbon of glyceraldehyde to form an *aldehyde group,* and on the second carbon of dihydroxyacetone to form a *ketone group.* Thus, we can differentiate between the two trioses by calling glyceraldehyde an *aldose* and dihydroxyacetone a *ketose*. The aldehyde group and the ketone group are known as *reducing groups* because of their ready oxidation by certain compounds, which are themselves reduced in the reaction. Sugars possessing these groups are called *reducing sugars*.

As far as the plant is concerned, the most important monosaccharides are the *pentoses* (five carbon sugars) and the *hexoses* (six carbon sugars). We will therefore confine our discussion of the monosaccharides primarily to these two groups.

Hexoses. The four hexoses D-glucose, D-fructose, D-manose, and D-galactose are commonly found in most plants, either as a component of some more complex carbohydrate or dissolved in the cell. Generally, glucose and fructose are the only hexoses found dissolved in the free form.

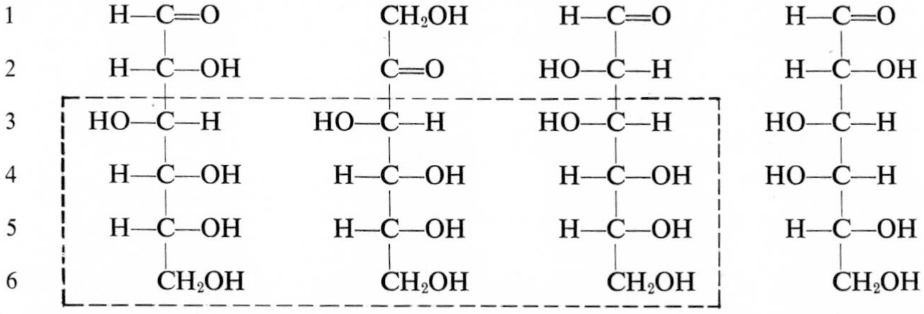

D-Glucose D-Fructose D-Mannose D-Galactose

One can see immediately that there appears to be very little difference in the structures of these sugars. In the first three, the only differences are on the first and second carbons. Fructose differs from both glucose and mannose in that it is a ketose and the other two are aldoses. However, the last four carbons are identical in these three compounds. Galactose differs from glucose only in the position of the hydroxyl group on carbon four.

The hexoses characteristically contain several *asymmetric* carbons (containing four different substituents), thus allowing for the existence of several diastereoisomers differing in physical, chemical, and biological properties and known by different names, such as glucose, mannose, galactose, etc. However, these sugars may also have mirror images, which are identical in all physical properties except optical rotation. We mean by optical rotation that a plane of polarized light transmitted by pure solutions of these mirror compounds will either be rotated to the left (levorotatory) or to the right (dextrorotatory) depending upon what mirror image is present. Conventionally, the italic letter *d* or the plus (+) sign is inserted before the name of a sugar for rotation to the right and the italic letter *l* or the minus (−) sign for rotation to the left. Thus, we have *d*(+)-glucose and *l*(−)-glucose.

Although the use of *d* or *l* (+ or −) tells something about the optical properties of sugars, it does not give any information on the configuration about the centers of asymmetry in the molecule. A system has been devised based on configurational rather than optical properties, and the key atom generally used in this system is the highest numbered asymmetric carbon. In the hexoses, this is carbon number 5 and the hydroxyl group of this carbon is said to be either in the D position or in the L position. When putting the structure of a sugar on paper, the hydroxyl of carbon 5 of a D-hexose is written to the right of the carbon chain. In an L-hexose, the hydroxyl is written to the left of the carbon chain, as shown in the formulas

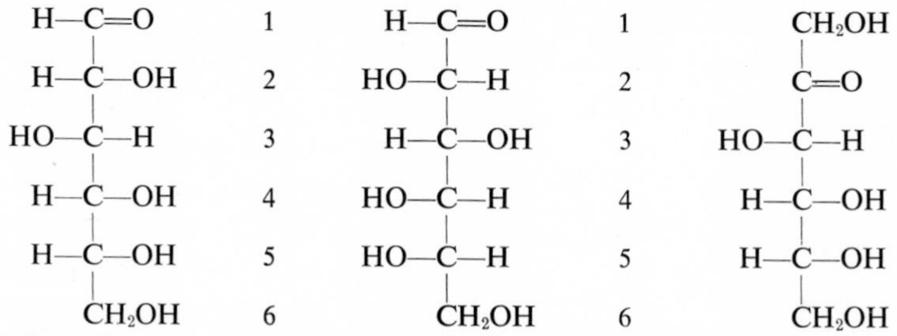

D(+)-Glucose L(−)-Glucose D(−)-Fructose

for glucose and fructose. Practically all of the sugars found in the plant are of the D configuration.

Pentoses. The pentoses are five-carbon sugars, which are rarely found dissolved in the free state in the cell cytoplasm. However, they are quite abundantly found as constituents of some of the more complex carbohydrates of the plant. Thus, D-*xylose* and L-*arabinose* occur in plants as constituents of *xylans* and *arabans,* respectively—large polysaccharides with a structural function in the cell wall.

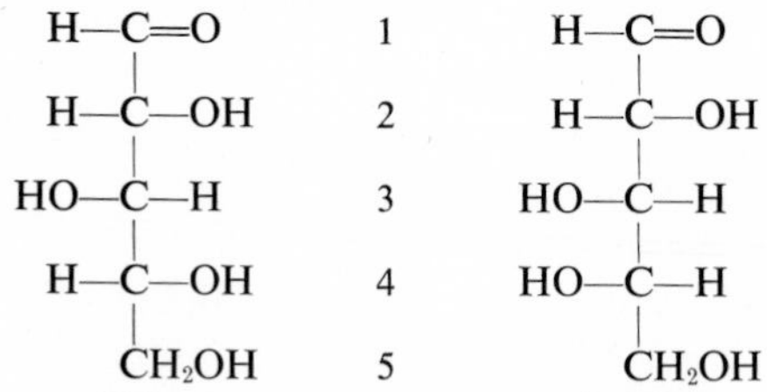

D-Xylose L-Arabinose

In addition to xylose and arabinose, the five-carbon sugars D-*ribose* and *2-deoxy*-D-*ribose* are also commonly found in plants as components of the nucleic acids. Certain coenzymes important in hydrogen and group transfer

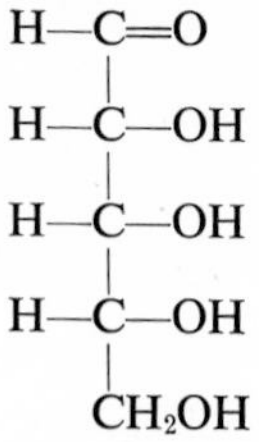

D-Ribose

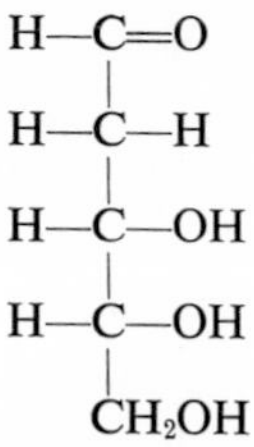

2-Deoxy-D-ribose

reactions have D-ribose as a component of their structure. Note the close similarity between ribose and 2-deoxyribose. These pentoses differ only in the substituents about the second carbon. In place of a hydroxyl group, 2-deoxyribose has a hydrogen atom. We will learn more about these two pentoses when respiration and the structure and function of nucleic acids are discussed in later chapters.

Ring structure. So far in our discussion of carbohydrates, we have considered sugars only as straight-chain carbon structures when, in fact, carbohydrates are largely found in *cyclic* or *ring* forms. In the carbon chain of glucose, there are *four* centers of asymmetry (carbons 2, 3, 4, 5). If carbons 1 and 5 come in close proximity of each other, however, as might occur in solution, an oxygen bridge may form between these carbons resulting in the formation of a hydroxyl group on carbon 1. This creates a new center of asymmetry around carbon 1, and the glucose molecule now has *five* instead of four asymmetrical carbons. The newly formed hydroxyl group may be in either the α or β position on carbon 1, thus adding another

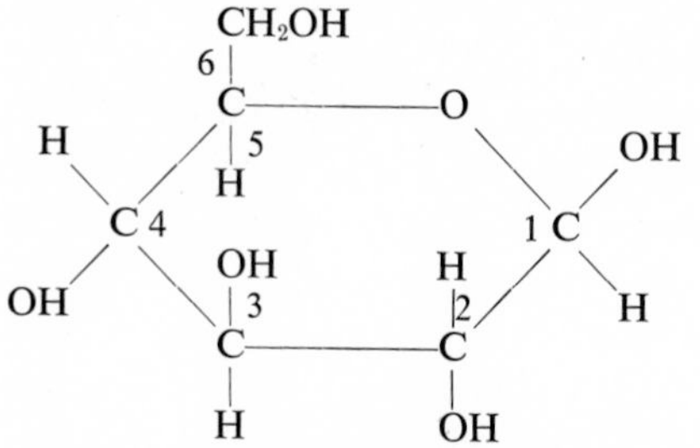

β-D-Glucose

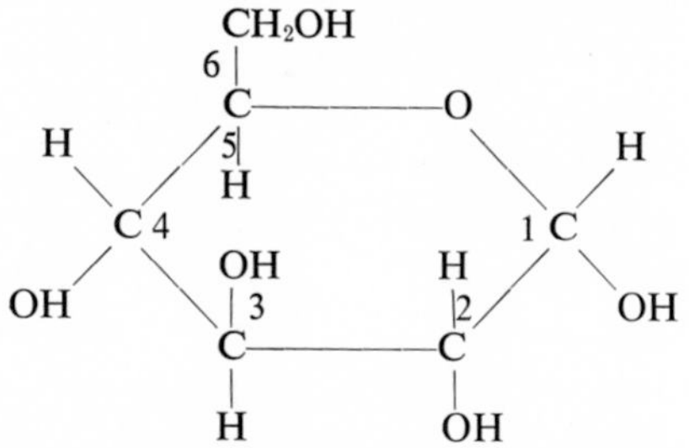

α-D-Glucose

feature to our classification of the carbohydrates. Although α- and β-D-glucose appear very similar in structure, they are quite different in their physical, chemical, and biological properties. For example, β-D-glucose units make up the structure of *cellulose,* a polysaccharide of the cell wall. Structural support is the obvious function here. On the other hand, α-D-glucose units make up the structure of the polysaccharide *starch*. Starch is the most common storage material of plants.

Oligosaccharides

The oligosaccharides are generally classified according to the number of monosaccharide units found in their structures. Therefore, if two monosaccharide units make up a sugar, it is called a disaccharide, if three, a trisaccharide, if four, a tetrasaccharide, etc. Generally, when the number of monosaccharide units reaches a cumbersome number, the structure is referred to as a polysaccharide.

The principal disaccharide of higher plants is *sucrose,* a condensation product of glucose and fructose. That is, in the formation of sucrose, glucose and fructose are linked together, resulting in the elimination of water. Since sucrose is the common table sugar we use every day, it is of commercial value to man. Thus, plants such as the sugar cane and the sugar beet, which produce large quantities of this sugar, are valued quite highly.

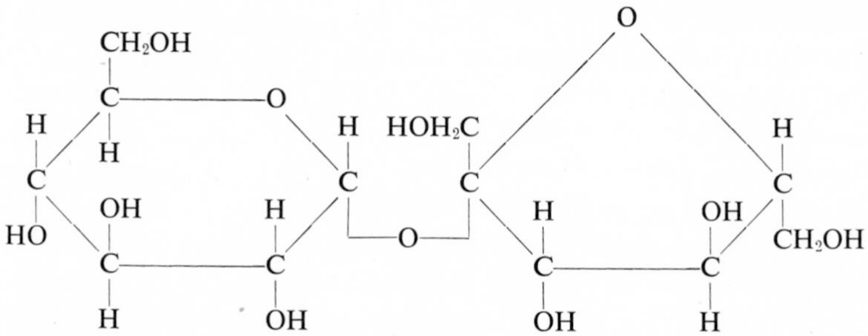

Sucrose

Although glucose and fructose, which make up the structure of sucrose, are reducing sugars, sucrose itself is not. This is because the reducing groups of both of the simple sugars are involved in the bond that links them together to form sucrose. That is, the oxygen bridge between the two monosaccharides occurs between carbon 1 of glucose and carbon 2 of fructose, resulting in the elimination of the free carbonyl groups of both these sugars. It should also be noted from the structure of sucrose that fructose occurs as a five-membered ring (furanose ring) as compared to glucose, which occurs as a six-membered ring (pyranose ring).

Sucrose is the principal form in which carbohydrates are transported in higher plants. In recent years, this fact has been clearly demonstrated with the use of radioactive materials. A plant undergoing photosynthesis in an atmosphere of radioactive carbon dioxide will show that translocation of this radioactive carbon out of the leaf after it has been assimilated will be primarily in the form of sucrose.

Other disaccharides of any importance are usually products of the partial degradation of polysaccharides, such as starch and cellulose. Therefore, a partial degradation of starch may yield the disaccharide *maltose,* a compound composed of two molecules of D-glucose joined together in an $\alpha(1 \rightarrow 4)$ link. The numbers refer to the carbons involved in the link between the two glucose molecules. Partial degradation of cellulose, on the other hand, may yield the disaccharide *cellobiose,* a compound composed of two D-glucose molecules joined together by a $\beta(1 \rightarrow 4)$link. In contrast to sucrose, both maltose and cellobiose are reducing sugars.

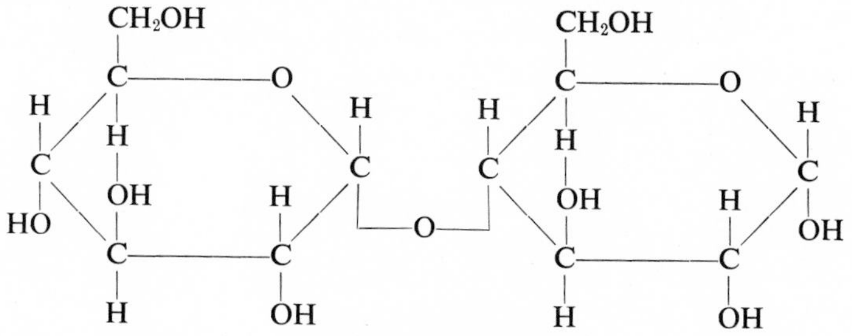

Maltose (α-1,4-link)

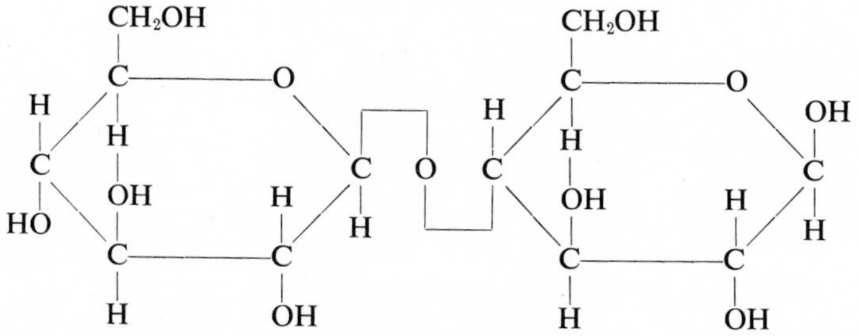

Cellobiose (β-1,4-link)

Naturally occurring trisaccharides, such as *gentianose* and *raffinose,* have been found in plants (12). On hydrolysis, gentianose yields two molecules of glucose and one of fructose. Hydrolysis of raffinose will yield glucose, fructose, and galactose. Both gentianose and raffinose are nonreducing sugars. The tetrasaccharide *stachyose* has been found in several tree species by Zimmermann (32, 33). On hydrolysis, stachyose yields glucose, fructose, and two molecules of galactose. Webb and Burley (29) have made the interesting observation that instead of sucrose, stachyose is the principal carbohydrate transported in *Fraxinus americana, Cucurbita pepo,* and *Verbascum thapsus.*

Polysaccharides

In many cases, the simple sugars produced by a plant are not utilized immediately, but are converted to polysaccharides. The two most common polysaccharides of plants are starch, a storage product of plants, and cellulose, a structural polysaccharide, which makes up the greater part of the plant cell wall. In the lower plants, such as the algae, bacteria, and fungi, other polysaccharides of structural and nutrient function are found in addition to cellulose and starch.

Starch is a compound of high molecular weight which, upon complete hydrolysis, yields only α-D-glucose molecules. Cellulose also has a high molecular weight and, upon complete hydrolysis, yields β-D-glucose molecules. Both of these compounds, and polysaccharides in general (with several exceptions), differ from monosaccharides and oligosaccharides in being insoluble in water and lacking sweetness. The molecular structures of starch and cellulose are as shown.

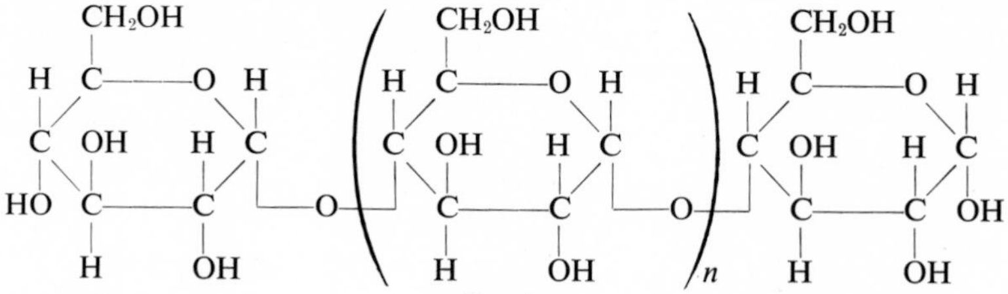

Starch

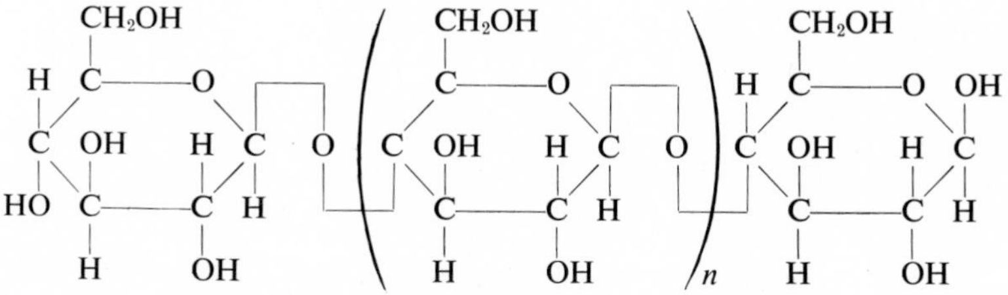

Cellulose

Starch. Much of the sugar produced in photosynthesis is converted to starch, which is deposited in the plant tissues as *starch grains*. Starch grains are very prevalent in storage organs, such as seeds, tubers, bulbs, etc., where they function as reserve nutriment for the growth and development of the plant. Starch grains differ in shape and size from plant to plant and are large enough to be distinguished microscopically.

Although starch is generally thought of as a straight chain polymer of glucose units, it is actually composed of two polysaccharides, *amylose* and *amylopectin*. Both of these polysaccharides yield α-D-glucose units on hydrolysis. However, amylose is a straight chain polymer of glucose units, while amylopectin is a branched molecule. Only $\alpha(1 \rightarrow 4)$ links are found in the amylose molecule. In contrast, amylopectin has, in addition to $\alpha(1 \rightarrow 4)$ links, $\alpha(1 \rightarrow 6)$ links. There is also some evidence that $\alpha(1 \rightarrow 3)$ links occur in amylopectin (31). Because of its more complex structure, amylopectin is less soluble in water than amylose. Because of this difference in solubility, these two components of starch may be separated partially by allowing starch to stand in water for prolonged periods of time. The blue-black color that occurs when iodine is added to starch is due to amylose. The amylopectins give a red to purple color with iodine. A representation of the amylopectin molecule is given, which shows the $\alpha(1 \rightarrow 4)$ and $\alpha(1 \rightarrow 6)$ linkages.

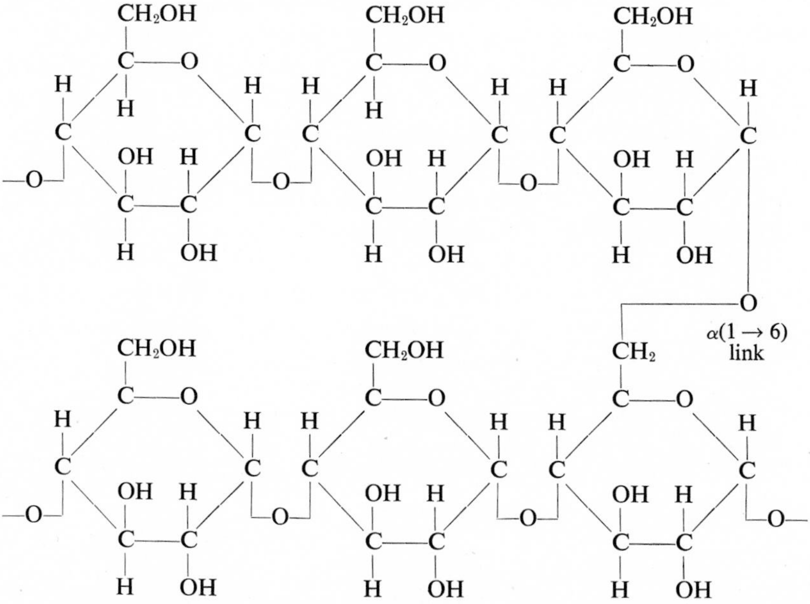

Amylopectin

Cellulose. Cellulose is a straight chain polymeric molecule of high molecular weight composed of D-glucose units bound together with $\beta(1 \rightarrow 4)$ links. It is a fundamental component of the cell wall and, as such, may be considered to be the most abundant organic compound in the world. When the primary wall is formed on new cells, it is composed almost exclusively of cellulose. However, as the cells mature and new wall material is deposited to form secondary walls, the cellulose may become impregnated with noncarbohydrate materials such as lignin, suberin, or cutin.

Cellulose is a relatively inert material, being completely degraded only under the most strenuous chemical treatment. For example, it may be hydrolyzed to glucose when treated with concentrated sulfuric or hydrochloric acid or with concentrated sodium hydroxide. Cellulose is insoluble in water, but may be dissolved in ammoniacal solutions of cupric salts. Because of the lack of chemical reactivity of cellulose, it has no nutritive value. However, these same characteristics endow cellulose with properties that are excellent for structural purposes. Although we generally think of the structural value of cellulose to the plant, we should also consider its structural value to man. Well before the "dawn of history" and ever since, the inert qualities of cellulose have served man in many ways—in the tools he has used, in the fences he has built, and most important in the structures he has built to shelter himself from his environment. Indeed, not only is cellulose the most abundant organic compound in the world, but it is also one of the most valued compounds.

Pectic compounds. Three general types of pectic substances have been observed in plants: *pectic acid* and two derivatives of pectic acid called *pectin* and *protopectin.* Pectic substances are found most abundantly in the middle lamella between cell walls, usually in the form of calcium or magnesium salts of pectic acid. However, pectin and protopectin are also present. Pure pectic acid is an unbranched molecule consisting of about 100 D-galacturonic acid residues bound together by $\alpha(1 \rightarrow 4)$ linkages. On complete hydrolysis, pectic acid releases galacturonic acid molecules. Galacturonic acid differs from galactose only in carbon 6, which is a carboxyl group (—COOH) rather than a carbinol group (—CH_2OH). Pectic acid is soluble in water and may be precipitated by calcium ions.

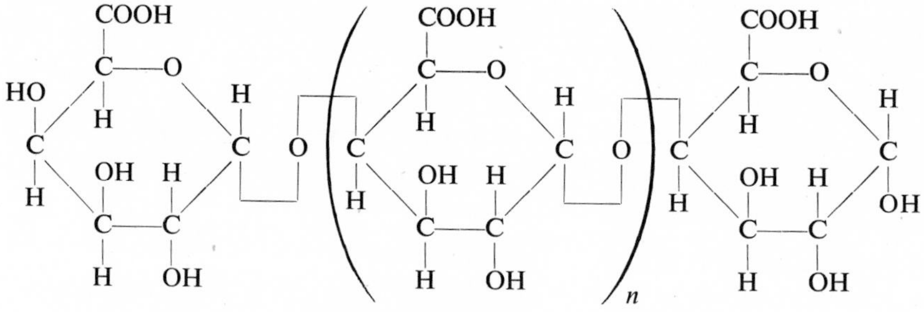

Pectic acid

Pectin very closely resembles pectic acid, the only difference being in the esterification of many of the carboxyl groups with methyl groups. Pectin will form a colloidal suspension in water that will "set" or form a gel on the addition of small concentrations of alcohol or high concentrations of sugar. The ability of pectin to form a gel makes it commercially valuable for the manufacture of food jellies.

The term protopectin is reserved for all *insoluble* pectic substances (9). Because of the instability of protopectin, effective isolation of this compound has not been accomplished. As a result, not much is known about the structure and composition of protopectin, although it is thought to be a much larger molecule than either pectic acid or pectin. It is accumulated in large quantities in some fruits, such as the apple and pear. During the ripening of the fruit, protopectin is converted into the more soluble pectic substances—pectin and pectic acid.

Pentosans. Polymers of five-carbon sugars are also found in plants. Two *pentosans* commonly found are *xylan* and *araban,* which on hydrolysis yield xylose and arabinose, respectively. Xylan is the pentosan most commonly present in plants, being an important constituent of the cell wall matrix. Xylans generally are relatively small unbranched polymers, composed of D-xylose units bound together by $\beta(1 \rightarrow 4)$ links. Also, within the xylan structure other sugar units (e.g., L-arabinose) and sugar acid units (e.g., glucuronic acid) may be found.

Araban is also thought to be a relatively small polymer, composed chiefly of L-arabinose units bound together by $\alpha(1 \rightarrow 5)$ links. Although L-arabinose is the chief sugar present, other sugars such as D-xylose may also be present. Although constituents of the cell wall matrix, the pentosans appear to be reluctantly available as reserve nutrient material. This is especially true under conditions of starvation.

TRANSFORMATION OF CARBOHYDRATES

The state of carbohydrates in plants is a dynamic one. There are numerous examples in the literature describing various transformation reactions between different carbohydrates. Also, since carbohydrates are a potential source of energy, their degradation produces the energy utilized in many of the synthetic reactions of the cell—synthesis of proteins, lipids, etc. In addition, carbon skeletons produced as a result of the transformation and partial degradation of sugars are essential to the construction of proteins, lipids, etc. One of the most common and, in fact, essential features of transformation reactions involving carbohydrates is *phosphorylation.*

Phosphorylation

It is apparent from any study of carbohydrate metabolism that the first step in practically all metabolical reactions involving sugars is phosphorylation. The first inkling of the importance of phosphorylation came from the early studies of Harden and Young in 1908. They discovered that inorganic phosphate was necessary for the fermentation of sugars to occur in cell-free yeast juice. They also noted that *fructose-1,6-diphosphate* accumulated in their reaction mixture if inorganic phosphate was added. Fructose-1,6-diphosphate is sometimes referred to as the *Harden-Young ester.*

One of the most important of the "starting reactions" of carbohydrate metabolism is the phosphorylation of glucose catalyzed by the enzyme *hexokinase*. In this reaction, a phosphate group is transferred to the sixth carbon of glucose from *adenosine triphosphate* (ATP) to form *glucose-6-phosphate*. Glucose-6-phosphate can, in turn, be converted to either *glucose-1-phosphate* or *fructose-6-phosphate*. The former reaction involves the enzyme *phosphoglucomutese* and its cofactor, *glucose-1,6-diphosphate,* and the latter reaction involves the enzyme *phosphoglucoisomerase*. The product of the latter reaction, fructose-6-phosphate, may be further phosphorylated in the presence of ATP and the enzyme phosphofructokinase to form fructose-1,6-diphosphate. We shall see in the following chapter that this last compound occupies a key position in glycolysis.

The interconversion of these phosphate esters can and does occur in the plant. In the case of glucose-6-phosphate and fructose-6-phosphate, the enzyme phosphoglucoisomerase catalyzes the interconversion of these two compounds. So also does the enzyme phosphoglucomutase catalyze the interconversion of glucose-6-phosphate and glucose-1-phosphate. A different enzyme is necessary for the conversion of fructose-1,6-diphosphate back to fructose-6-phosphate. This enzyme is called *fructose-1,6-diphosphatase*. These four phosphate esters may be considered as stepping off points to various metabolic pathways in the metabolizing cell. These conversions are represented in Figure 7-1.

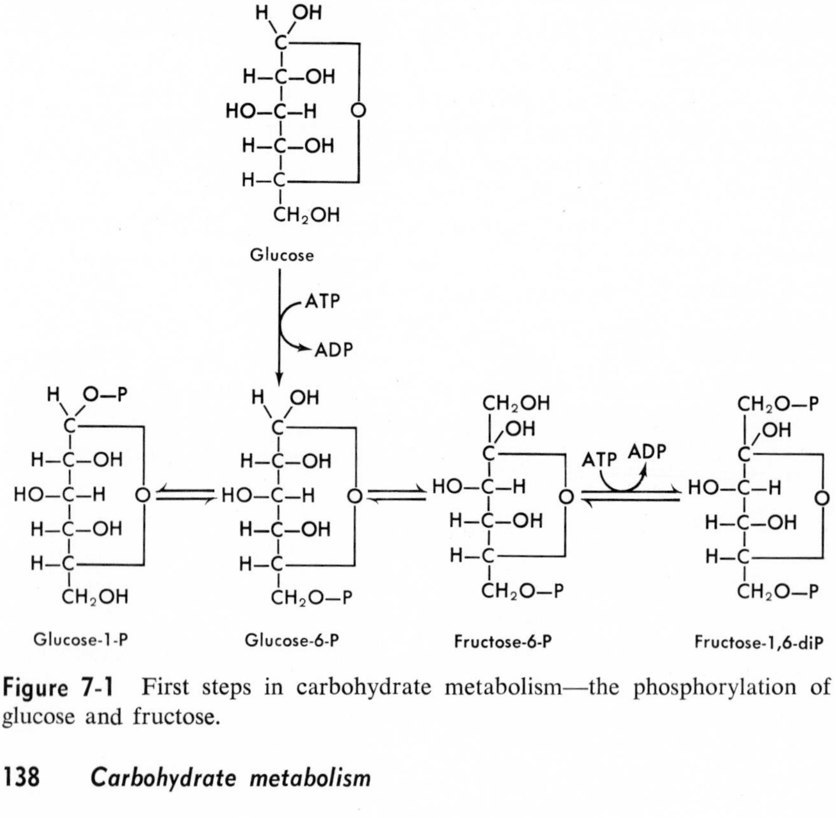

Figure 7-1 First steps in carbohydrate metabolism—the phosphorylation of glucose and fructose.

Synthesis and degradation of sucrose

The biosynthesis of sucrose has been shown to occur in plants by three different pathways. Working with the bacterium *Pseudomonas,* Doudoroff et al. (10) discovered an enzyme capable of catalyzing the formation of sucrose from glucose-1-phosphate and fructose. This enzyme, called *sucrose phosphorylase,* was later isolated from *Pseudomonas* (19, 20).

$$\text{Glucose-1-phosphate} + \text{Fructose} \xrightleftharpoons{\text{Sucrose phosphorylase}} \text{Sucrose} + \text{iP}$$

As a result of carbohydrate transformations, plants are fully capable of obtaining the raw materials for this reaction, making it quite possible that such a reaction may have universal distribution in plants. However, with the exception of one investigation (23), all attempts to demonstrate the activity of this enzyme in higher plants have met with failure.

Sucrose synthesis, at least in higher plants, appears to involve the participation of *uridine diphosphate glucose* (UDPG), a compound first discovered in yeast cells (8). The enzyme *sucrose synthetase* catalyzes the transfer of glucose from UDPG to fructose. In a somewhat similar reaction, the transfer of glucose from UDPG to fructose-6-phosphate is catalyzed by the enzyme *sucrose phosphate synthetase.* Both of these reactions are shown below.

$$\text{UDPG} + \text{Fructose} \xrightleftharpoons{\text{Sucrose synthetase}} \text{UDP} + \text{Sucrose}$$

$$\text{UDPG} + \text{Fructose-6-phosphate} \xrightleftharpoons{\text{Sucrose phosphate synthetase}} \text{UDP} + \text{Sucrose phosphate}$$

The sucrose phosphate formed in the second reaction can be hydrolyzed by a phosphatase enzyme to yield sucrose.

Whether sucrose is synthesized simultaneously in the plant by the above three pathways is not yet clear. However, sucrose synthetase and sucrose phosphate synthetase activity has been observed in many plants (26, 22, 14). On the other hand, sucrose phosphorylase activity has only been observed in a limited number of lower plant forms. The existing evidence suggests that UDPG is an essential feature of the biosynthesis of sucrose in higher plants.

The enzyme *invertase* catalyzes the hydrolysis of sucrose, yielding glucose and fructose.

$$\text{Sucrose} + H_2O \xrightarrow{\text{Invertase}} \text{Glucose} + \text{Fructose}$$

It is thought that this reaction is unidirectional; thus, the hydrolysis goes almost to completion. The fact that invertase has been isolated from a variety of plant tissues suggests that the main route of sucrose degradation in plants may be through the activity of this enzyme. However, this is only speculation, since the role of invertase in the overall picture of carbohydrate metabolism is not, as yet, clear.

Synthesis and degradation of starch

The study of starch metabolism in the plant cell has developed over recent years into a complex and interesting subject. One general conclusion that can be drawn from the numerous studies on this subject is that the synthesis and degradation of starch is under the regulation of a variety of enzymes, some of which have both a synthetic and degradative function, depending upon immediate conditions at the site of action.

Synthesis. In 1940, Hanes (18) detected the presence of *starch phosphorylase* in potato and pea plants and demonstrated its activity in vitro. He found that in the presence of this enzyme and glucose-1-phosphate, a polymer of glucose molecules could be formed. Also required is a primer molecule (acceptor), composed of anywhere from 3 (maltotriose) to an optimal number of 20 glucose residues strung together in $\alpha(1 \rightarrow 4)$ glycosidic linkages.

$$n(\text{Glucose-1-phosphate}) + \text{Acceptor} \xrightleftharpoons{\text{Starch phosphorylase}} \text{Amylose} + n(\text{iP})$$

The glucose of glucose-1-phosphate is added to the nonreducing end of the primer molecule to form an $\alpha(1 \rightarrow 4)$ link at that point. Thus, the enzyme starch phosphorylase catalyzes the addition of glucose units one by one to the nonreducing end of a primer molecule building a straight chain amylose molecule (Figure 7-2).

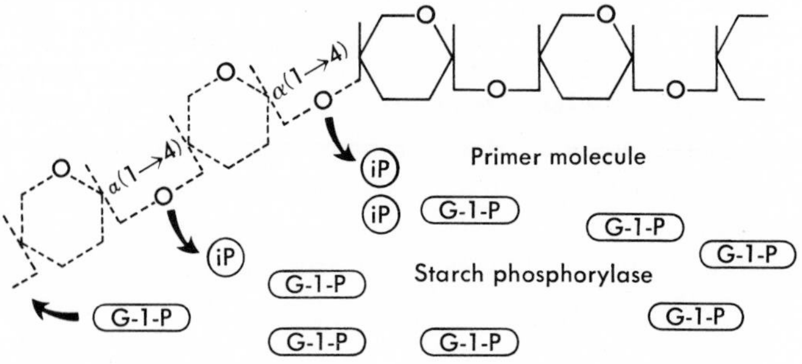

Figure 7-2 Synthesis of an amylose molecule by the addition of glucose units to the nonreducing end of a primer molecule. The reaction is catalyzed by starch phosphorylase.

Starch phosphorylase may also be considered a degradative enzyme. That is, in the presence of inorganic phosphate, starch phosphorylase can catalyze the phosphorolytic cleavage of the $\alpha(1 \rightarrow 4)$ links of amylose to form glucose-1-phosphate molecules, a process known as *phosphorolysis*. Phosphorolysis differs from hydrolysis in that it involves the elements of phosphoric acid instead of water. High concentrations of inorganic phosphate and high pH favor phosphorolysis, while lower pH and lower concentrations of inorganic phosphate favor the synthetic action. Starch phosphorylase has been isolated from a number of plants and appears to have universal distribution (30).

Another enzyme capable of forming $\alpha(1 \rightarrow 4)$ links by the addition of glucose units onto a primer molecule is *UDPG transglycosylase*. This enzyme was first detected in bean, corn, and potato where it was shown to catalyze the transfer of glucose from UDPG to an acceptor or primer molecule. The primer molecule could be maltose, maltotriose (3 glucose units), maltotetrose (4 glucose units), or even a starch molecule (25). When starch is used as the primer molecule, glucose units can be added to either amylose or amylopectin. Thus, UDPG transglycosylase apparently requires the presence of at least one $\alpha(1 \rightarrow 4)$ glycosidic link, such as would be found in maltose, and catalyzes the formation of additional $\alpha(1 \rightarrow 4)$ glycosidic linkages.

$$\text{UDPG} + \text{Acceptor} \xrightleftharpoons[]{\text{UDPG transglycosylase}} \text{UDP} + \alpha(1 \rightarrow 4)\text{-Glucosyl-acceptor}$$

Sucrose may function as a glucose donor in starch synthesis. Akazawa et al. (1) found that the incubation of sucrose-C^{14} with starch granules, sucrose synthetase, and uridine diphosphate (UDP) resulted in a significant amount of the label being transferred to starch. They proposed that the glucose of sucrose is first transferred to UDP to form UDPG, as a result of the reversal of sucrose synthesis. Then the glucose transferred to UDPG is in turn transferred to starch. This scheme explains how a continual supply of UDPG can be maintained for the synthesis of starch (Figure 7-3).

Still another enzyme has been found that will catalyze the formation of $\alpha(1 \rightarrow 4)$ glycosidic links. This enzyme, called *D-enzyme,* was first discovered in potato by Peat et al. (24) and was shown to catalyze the reversible transfer of two or more glucose units from malto-dextrins ($\alpha(1 \rightarrow 4)$-linked glucose chains of more than two units) to a variety of acceptors. If we consider one molecule of maltotriose as a substrate and another as an acceptor, then D-enzyme would catalyze the formation of maltopentaose. The malto-dextrins are added onto the nonreducing end of the acceptor molecule.

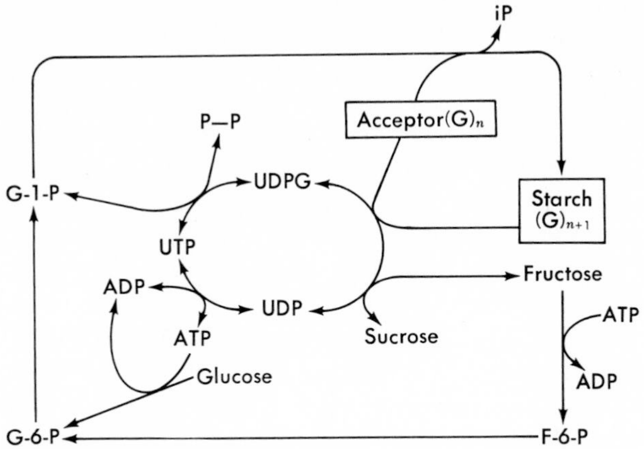

Figure 7-3 A diagram for starch synthesis. F-6-P, G-6-P, and G-1-P represent fructose-6-phosphate, glucose-6-phosphate, and glucose-1-phosphate, respectively. (After Akazawa et al. 1964. Plant Physiol. 39:371.)

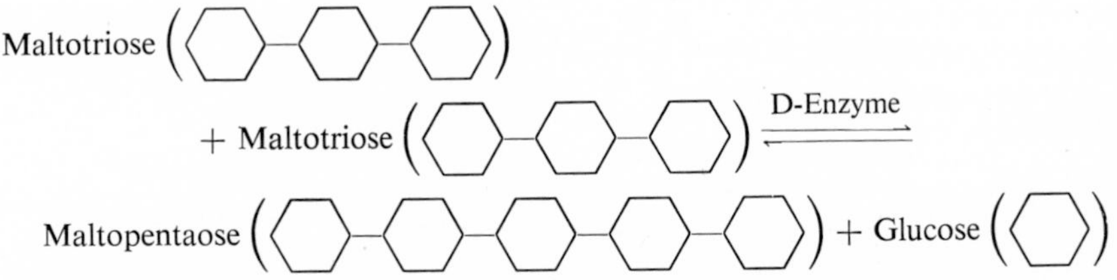

Walker and Whelan (28) have shown that if the glucose that accumulates in the above reaction is removed by some other metabolic reaction, amylose chains of significant length can be built up by D-enzyme. For example, glucose can be phosphorylated if hexokinase and ATP are present.

Starch phosphorylase, UDPG transglycosylase, and D-enzyme all catalyze the formation of $\alpha(1 \rightarrow 4)$ glycosidic links. However, as mentioned before, the starch molecule also contains $\alpha(1 \rightarrow 6)$ glycosidic links at its branching points. Potato extracts contain an enzyme (*Q-enzyme*) capable of forming an amylopectin type molecule, using amylose as a substrate. *Q-enzyme* was first isolated from potato extract by Baum and Gilbert (3). It is thought that Q-enzyme catalyzes the transfer of small chains of glucose units from an amylose type molecule, which we will call the donor molecule, to an acceptor molecule of at least four $\alpha(1 \rightarrow 4)$-linked glucose units. The small chains being transferred are "tacked" onto the sixth carbon of one of the glucose units of the acceptor molecule to form $\alpha(1 \rightarrow 6)$ glycosidic linkages (Figure 7-4).

It is most probable that starch is synthesized as a result of the simul-

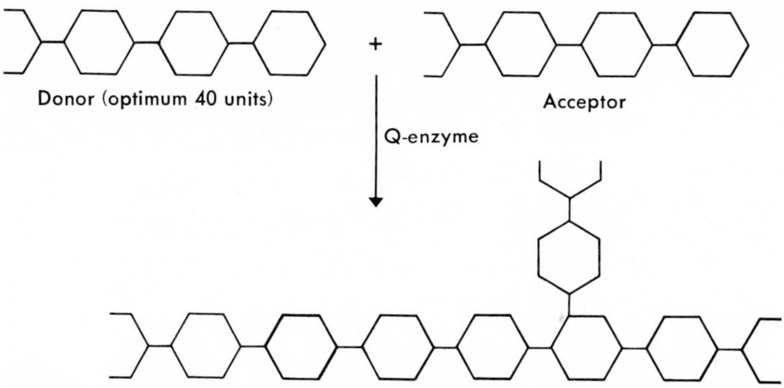

Figure 7-4 Diagrammatic representation of the synthesis of an amylopectin type molecule catalyzed by Q-enzyme.

taneous activity of Q-enzyme and one or more of the enzymes known to catalyze the formation of $\alpha(1 \rightarrow 4)$ linkages. However, this has not been demonstrated, and the question of how amylose and amylopectin can be synthesized together in the same starch granule has not been answered. Indeed, the incubation of Q-enzyme with starch phosphorylase in the same reaction mixture only results in a mixture of branched polysaccharides not in the individual synthesis of amylose and amylopectin (2). Perhaps they are synthesized at different sites on the granule.

Degradation. The α- and β-*amylases* are of primary importance to the degradation of starch. The amylases have been found in a wide variety of plants and represent the best means for the mobilization of carbohydrate reserves in the plant. The amylases are hydrolytic enzymes that catalyze the addition of the elements of water to the $\alpha(1 \rightarrow 4)$ glycosidic linkage.

β-amylase, which is found most abundantly in seeds, has been isolated from several plants. Incubation of this enzyme with amylose will result in the complete degradation of the amylose molecule to maltose. Starting at the nonreducing end of an amylose molecule with an even number of glucose units, β-amylase successively removes maltose units until the molecule is completely degraded to maltose. However, if the amylase molecule happens to be composed of an odd number of glucose units, hydrolysis with β-amylase will result in the formation of maltose and one maltotriose molecule. The maltotriose represents the terminal three glucose units on the reducing end of the amylose molecule. If the molecule happens to be amylopectin, then β-amylase can start at the nonreducing end of each branch and successively remove maltose units to within two glucose units of the $\alpha(1 \rightarrow 6)$ linkages (Figure 7-5).

A study of the activity of the α- and β-amylases will show that their

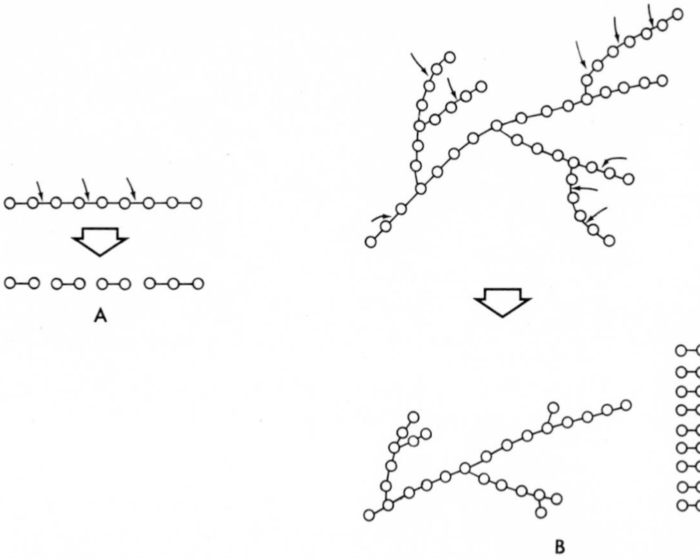

Figure 7-5 Hydrolysis of starch by β-amylase. A. β-amylase hydrolysis of an odd numbered chain. B. β-amylase hydrolysis of an amylopectin molecule.

mode of action is quite different. While β-amylase removes maltose units one-by-one from the nonreducing end of a chain of glucose units, α-amylase attacks at random any $\alpha(1 \rightarrow 4)$ link on the starch molecule. That is, α-amylase may hydrolyze $\alpha(1 \rightarrow 4)$ links at either end or in the middle of the molecule. If a branched chain is attacked, all $\alpha(1 \rightarrow 4)$ links to within three units of the $\alpha(1 \rightarrow 6)$ link can be hydrolyzed. The products of α-amylase activity on starch are a variety of oligosaccharides or dextrins (Figure 7-6).

In addition to the activity of the α- and β-amylases, the enzyme starch phosphorylase can also degrade starch by a phosphorolytic cleavage of $\alpha(1 \rightarrow 4)$ glycosidic linkages. The degradative activity of starch phosphorolase was discussed earlier in the same section of this chapter covering its synthetic activity.

In our discussion of the degradation of starch, we have covered the hydrolysis and phosphorolysis of the $\alpha(1 \rightarrow 4)$ link by the α- and β-amylases and starch phosphorylase. However, total breakdown of the amylopectin molecule is not accomplished by these enzymes because of the presence of the $\alpha(1 \rightarrow 6)$ linkages. In 1951, Hobson et al. (21) isolated an enzyme from broad bean and potato capable of hydrolyzing the $\alpha(1 \rightarrow 6)$ linkage. This enzyme, called *R-enzyme,* is specific for the

○ Glucose unit

↑ Reducing end group

8 1,4′α-Glucosidic linkage

Figure 7-6 Action of α-amylase on amylopectin. A. Amylopectin model. B. Dextrins of medium molecular weight giving, violet, purple, or red iodine color produced by splitting of 4% of the glucosidic linkages of amylopectin. C. Possible structures of limit dextrins from amylopectin breakdown. (After P. Bernfield. 1951. Adv. Enzymol. 12:379.)

$\alpha(1 \rightarrow 6)$ linkages and does not cause the hydrolysis of $\alpha(1 \rightarrow 4)$ linkages. As might be expected, the activity of the α- and β-amylases on the amylopectin molecule is increased considerably in the presence of R-enzyme. With the exception of glucose-1-phosphate, the product of starch phosphorylase activity, the simplest degradative product formed as a consequence of the activity of the above enzymes on starch, is maltose. However, maltose is not a form of sugar that is readily available to the plant. This problem is solved by the almost universal distribution in plants of the enzyme *maltase*. Maltase, which is often found in association with amylases (16), catalyzes the hydrolysis of the glucosidic bond of maltose to yield two molecules of glucose.

We have, therefore, a general overall picture of the synthesis and degradation of starch, starting with glucose and ending with glucose. As noted, several enzymes are involved in the metabolism of starch, and the harmonious activity of a number of them together is required to either build up or break down a starch molecule.

Synthesis and degradation of cellulose

Synthesis. Unlike the metabolism of starch, our knowledge of the metabolism of cellulose is very limited. Most of the information about cellulose synthesis comes from studies on cellulose-producing bacteria of the genus *Acetobacter*. When radioactive C^{14}-labeled carbohydrate intermediates, such as glucose, are fed to cultures of *Acetobacter,* the labeled carbon can eventually be found in cellulose. It has been found that carbon sources other than glucose can also be utilized as intermediates in cellulose synthesis (6), suggesting the cooperation of a complex of enzymes in this process. That is, when carbohydrates other than glucose are fed to *Acetobacter* (e.g., mannitol, glycerol) the enzymes necessary for the conversion of these carbohydrates to glucose have to act before the carbon of these compounds can be incorporated into cellulose.

When *Acetobacter acetigenum* is fed lactic acid labeled in the carboxy

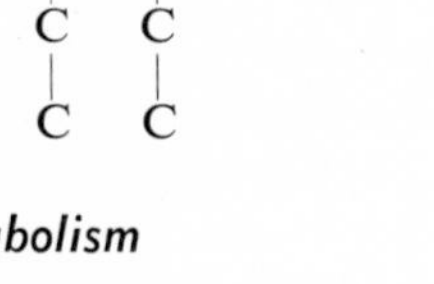

carbon ($—C^{14}OOH$), the label is carried over into cellulose. The symmetrical distribution of the label in the cellulose molecule suggests that the glucose units of cellulose arise by the fusion of two three-carbon compounds (5).

If *A. xylinum* is allowed to use glucose labeled in the first or sixth carbon as substrate for cellulose synthesis, almost all of the label remains intact on the glucose units of the newly synthesized cellulose (17). These findings strongly indicate that when glucose is the sole carbon source, it is incorporated as the intact molecule without any prior reaction or cleavage. Evidence has accumulated suggesting that although glucose does not undergo any prior cleavage, phosphorylation of the glucose molecule might be necessary before conversion to cellulose is possible (27).

Some very interesting work has been done on the possible participation of UDPG in cellulose synthesis, as well as starch synthesis. Glaser (15) found that cell-free enzyme preparations from *A. xylinum* could synthesize cellulose in the presence of glucose-labeled UDPG. However, substitution of C^{14}-labeled glucose for UDPG produces negative results. The synthesis of cellulose in a UDPG system is enhanced considerably by the addition of an acceptor molecule (cellodextrins) to the reaction mixture.

$$\text{UDPG} + \text{Acceptor} \rightarrow \text{UDP} + \beta(1 \rightarrow 4)\text{-Glucosyl-acceptor}$$

Of even greater significance, Brummond and Gibbons (7) demonstrated that a cell-free enzyme preparation from *Lupinus albus* (a higher plant) is able to synthesize cellulose from UDPG. It appears, therefore, that at least in some instances the synthesis of cellulose is analogous to that of starch. More work needs to be done on this aspect of cellulose synthesis, but the UDPG theory does present a promising mechanism for the incorporation of glucose into the cellulose chain.

Degradation. Needless to say, an essential feature of the environment of this world is the degradation of cellulose. If this degradation were not possible, we would literally be "covered" with dead plant material, and there would be an appreciable depletion of atmospheric CO_2. However, nature has provided us with a variety of lower forms of life capable of degrading cellulose, among which certain bacteria and fungi are most important.

According to available evidence, the enzymatic hydrolysis of cellulose can be considered a random attack on the $\beta(1 \rightarrow 4)$ linkage. The cellulose molecule is reduced to cellodextrins and eventually to cellobiose, a disaccharide composed of two glucose units. The enzymes involved in the random hydrolysis of cellulose to cellobiose have not as yet been characterized, but have been grouped under the generic term *cellulase*.

The $\beta(1 \rightarrow 4)$ link of cellobiose can be hydrolyzed by the enzyme cellobiase.

$$\text{Cellulose} \xrightarrow{\text{Cellulases}} \text{Cellodextrins} \longrightarrow \text{Cellobiose} \xrightarrow{\text{Cellobiase}} \text{Glucose}$$

Synthesis and degradation of pectic substances

It is generally felt that the primary pathway for the synthesis of pectic substances is through the mediation of UDPG. This is supported by the fact that both glucose and galactose are good substrates for the synthesis of pectic acid and that UDPG and UDP-galactose are readily interconverted. Figure 7-7 shows a possible pathway by which pectic acid might be syn-

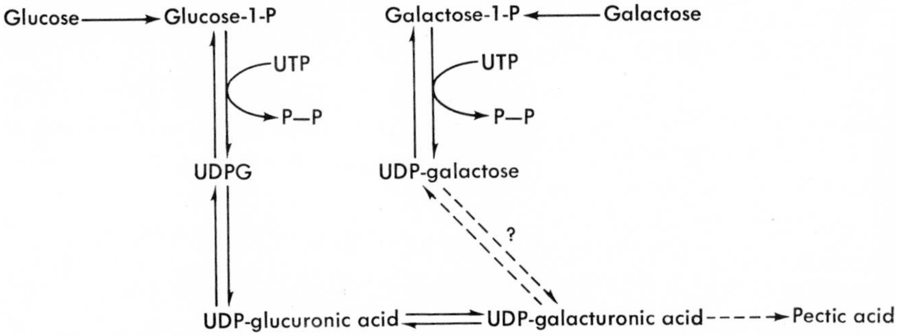

Figure 7-7 Possible pathway of petic acid synthesis.

thesized. From this pathway, we can see where either glucose or galactose can enter into the synthesis of pectic acid. All of the reactions indicated have been demonstrated in plants, except for the incorporation of galacturonic acid from UDP-galacturonic acid into the pectic acid chain. However, this last step seems to be a logical assumption, particularly in view of the participation of UDPG in the synthesis of other polysaccharides, such as starch and cellulose. Methyl groups, which are found in pectic substances esterified to the carboxyl group of the galacturonic acid units, are most likely contributed by *methionine* through *S-adenosylmethionine*. The compound S-adenosylmethionine has been demonstrated to be active in the transfer of methyl groups.

Hydrolysis of the $\alpha(1 \rightarrow 4)$ linkage of pectic substances is catalyzed by the enzyme *pectin polygalacturonase*. Enzymatic hydrolysis of the methyl ester bonds of pectin is catalyzed by *pectin methyl esterase*.

Inulin

Before leaving a discussion of the carbohydrates, mention should be made of the reserve material, *inulin,* predominately found in the compositae plants. Particularly good sources are the tubers of dahlia, chicory, and the Jerusalem artichoke. Inulin is thought to be an unbranched polymer of about 35 fructose units joined by $\beta(2 \rightarrow 1)$ linkages. On hydrolysis, however, inulin yields a small amount of glucose. It is now thought that there are two glucose units in the inulin molecule, one somewhere in the center and the other at the reducing end of the chain to give a sucrose type linkage. Therefore, it should be understood that the molecular structure shown

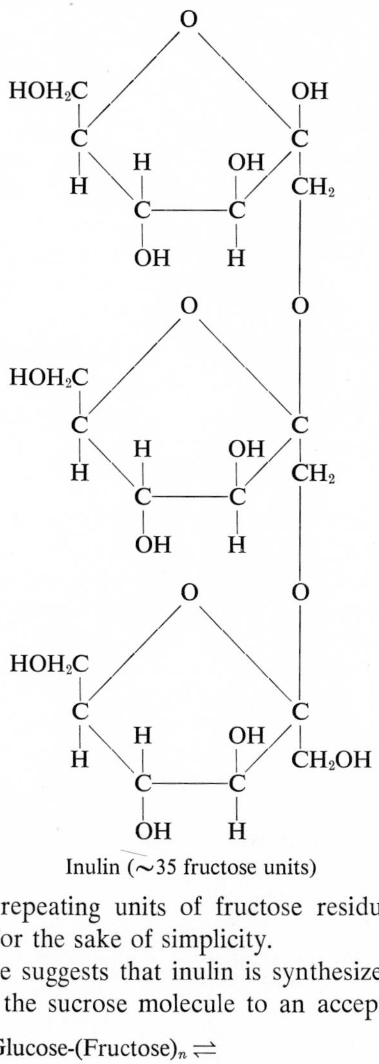

Inulin (~35 fructose units)

above only depicts repeating units of fructose residues, the two glucose units being left out for the sake of simplicity.

Available evidence suggests that inulin is synthesized by the transfer of the fructose part of the sucrose molecule to an acceptor molecule.

$$\text{Glucose-Fructose} + \text{Glucose-(Fructose)}_n \rightleftharpoons \text{Glucose-(Fructose)}_n\text{-Fructose} + \text{Glucose}$$

Enzymes capable of the hydrolysis of the $\beta(2 \rightarrow 1)$ linkages of inulin have been found in the Jerusalem artichoke (11). It has been suggested that these enzymes function in the mobilization of the inulin that is utilized during the sprouting of the artichoke tuber.

SUMMARY

In general, the carbohydrates of plants can be separated into two large groups, one where the primary function is structural support and the other where the primary function is storage. Of all the carbohydrates, starch is the most important storage material and cellulose the most important structural material of plants. Both starch and cellulose are polymeric molecules, composed of repeating glucose units. The glucose units of starch are primarily connected by $\alpha(1 \rightarrow 4)$ glycosidic linkages, and those of cellulose by $\beta(1 \rightarrow 4)$ glycosidic linkages.

Carbohydrates are generally translocated in the plant in the form of sucrose, a disaccharide composed of glucose and fructose in $\beta(1 \rightarrow 2)$ linkage. Sucrose is thought to act as a substrate for the synthesis of inulin, a storage material composed primarily of repeating fructose units.

BIBLIOGRAPHY

1. Akazawa, T., T. Minamikawa, and T. Murata.. 1964. Enzymic mechanism of starch synthesis in ripening rice grains. Plant Physiol. 39: 371.
2. Barker, F., H. Nasr, F. Morrice, and J. Bruce. 1950. Bacterial breakdown of structural starches in the digestive trace of ruminant and non-ruminant mammals. J. Path. 62: 617.
3. Baum, H., and G. A. Gilbert. 1953. A simple method for the preparation of crystalline potato phosphorylase and Q-enzyme. Nature 17: 983.
4. Bernfeld, P. 1951. Enzymes of starch degradation and synthesis. Adv. Enzymol. 12: 379.
5. Bourne, E. J., and H. Weigel. 1954. ^{14}C-cellulose from *Acetobacter acetigenum*. Chem. Ind. 132.
6. Brimacombe, J. S., and M. Stacey. 1962. Cellulose, starch, and glycogen. *In* M. Florkin and H. S. Mason (eds.), Comparative Biochemistry. Academic Press, New York. 4: 27.
7. Brummond, D. O., and A. P. Gibbons. 1964. The enzymatic synthesis of cellulose by the higher plant. Biochem. Biophy. Res. Com. 17: 156.
8. Caputto, R., L. F. Leloir, C. E. Cardini, and A. C. Paladini. 1950. Isolation of the coenzyme of the galactose phosphate-glucose phosphate transformation. J. Biol. Chem. 184: 333.
9. Davies, D. D., J. Giovanelli, and T. A. Rees. 1964. Plant biochemistry. Blackwell Scientific Publications, Oxford.

10. Doudoroff, M., N. Kaplan, and W. Z. Hassid. 1943. Phosphorolysis and synthesis of sucrose with a bacterial preparation. J. Biol. Chem. 148: 67.
11. Edelman, J., and T. G. Jefford. 1964. The metabolism of fructose polymers in plants. Biochem. J. 93: 148.
12. French, D. 1954. The raffinose family of oligosaccharides. Adv. Carbohydrate Chem. 9: 149.
13. Fruton, J. S., and S. Simmonds. 1959. General biochemistry. John Wiley & Sons, New York.
14. Gibbs, M. 1959. Metabolism of carbon compounds. Ann. Rev. Plant Physiol. 10: 329.
15. Glaser, L. 1958. The synthesis of cellulose in cell-free extracts of *Acetobacter xylinum*. J. Biol. Chem. 232: 627.
16. Gottschalk, A. 1958. The enzymes controlling hydrolytic phosphorolytic and transfer reactions of the oligosaccharides. *In* W. Ruhland (ed.), Encyclopedia of plant physiology. 6: 87.
17. Greathouse, G. 1957. Biosynthesis of C^{14} labeled cellulose by *Acetobacter xylinum* IV. From *d*-glucose-1-C^{14}, *d*-glucose-6-C^{14} and glycerol-1,3-C^{14}. J. Am. Chem. Soc. 79: 4505.
18. Hanes, C. S. 1940. The reversible formation of starch from glucose-1-phosphate catalysed by potato phosphorylase. Proc. Roy. Soc. B, 129: 174.
19. Hassid, W. Z., and M. Doudoroff. 1950. Enzymatic synthesis of sucrose and other disaccharides. Adv. Carbohydrate Chem. 5: 29.
20. Hassid, W. Z., and M. Doudoroff. 1950. Synthesis of disaccharides with bacterial enzymes. Adv. Enzymol. 10: 123.
21. Hobson, P. N., W. J. Whelan, and S. Peat. 1951. The enzymatic synthesis and degradation of starch. XIV. R-Enzyme. J. Chem. Soc. 1451.
22. Mendicino, J. 1960. Sucrose phosphate synthesis in wheat germ and green leaves. J. Biol. Chem. 235: 3347.
23. Pandya, K. P., and C. V. Ramakrishnon. 1956. Biosynthesis of sucrose in sugar cane leaves. Naturwiss. 43: 85.
24. Peat, S. W. J. Whelan, and W. R. Rees. 1953. D-Enzyme: A disproportionating enzyme in potato juice. Nature 172: 158.
25. Ranson, S. L., and M. Thomas. 1963. Enzyme action in plant metabolism. *In* W. B. Turrill (ed.), Vistas in botany. The Macmillan Company, New York. 3: 1.
26. Rorem, E. S., H. G. Walker, R. M. McCready. 1960. Biosynthesis of sucrose and sucrose-phosphate in sugar beet leaf extract. Plant Physiol. 35: 269.
27. Schramm, M., Z. Gromet, and S. Hestrin. 1957. Role of hexose phosphate in synthesis of cellulose by *Acetobacter xylinum*. Nature 179: 28.
28. Walker, D. A., and W. J. Whelan. 1959. Synthesis of amylose by potato D-enzyme. Nature 183: 46.
29. Webb, K. L., and J. W. A. Burley. 1964. Stachyose translocation in plants. Plant Physiol. 39: 973.
30. Whelan, W. J. 1958. Starch and similar polysaccharides. *In* W. Ruhland (ed.), The encyclopedia of plant physiology. 6: 154.

31. Wolfrom, M. L., and A. Thompson. 1956. Occurrence of the (1 → 3)-linkage in starches. J. Am. Chem. Soc. 78: 4116.
32. Zimmermann, M. H. 1957. Translocation of organic substances in trees. I. The nature of the sugars in the sieve tube exudate of trees. Plant Physiol. 32: 288.
33. Zimmermann, M. H. 1957. Translocation of organic substances in trees. II. On the translocation mechanism in the phloem of white ash. Plant Physiol. 32: 399.

8

Respiration and fermentation

INTRODUCTION

Primarily this chapter will be concerned with the controlled release and utilization of stored energy by the processes of respiration and fermentation for the support and maintenance of the living system. Important life processes, such as the synthesis of proteins, fats, and carbohydrates, require a certain expenditure of energy. Where does this energy come from, how is it stored, and how is it made available to the living cell? These are some of the questions that will be analyzed in the following pages.

During the process of photosynthesis (to be discussed in a later chapter), light energy is converted to chemical energy and stored in the bonds of complex organic molecules. The major portion of stored energy in plants may be found in the form of carbohydrates, such as starch and glucose. The weakening or breaking of the carbon-carbon bonds of such compounds may release a considerable amount of energy for utilization by the plant.

However, the total amount of energy contained within a compound such as, for example, glucose, is not released all at once, but slowly, in a stepwise series of reactions controlled by enzymes. Generally, a series of reactions in the cell leading to the synthesis or breakdown of organic compounds is referred to as a *metabolic pathway*. In this chapter, then, we will discuss the metabolic pathways of respiration and fermentation and their connection with the controlled release of stored energy.

ADENOSINE TRIPHOSPHATE: AN ENERGY INTERMEDIATE

As mentioned, both energy-yielding and energy-consuming reactions occur within the living cell. The potential or stored energy of one compound (e.g., glucose) is released and utilized, in a most efficient manner, to drive the synthesis of other compounds (e.g., proteins). This energy, now stored in the newly synthesized compound, can, in turn, be made available for other synthetic reactions. What is described here is the coupling of energy-yielding and energy-consuming reactions. However, energy-yielding reactions of the cell occur in many instances in the absence of energy-consuming reactions. The energy released in such a situation would be in the form of heat and lost to the organism. However, nature has provided the cell with a means of temporary energy storage in the form of adenosine triphosphate (ATP). Thus, the energy released in the oxidation of compounds such as

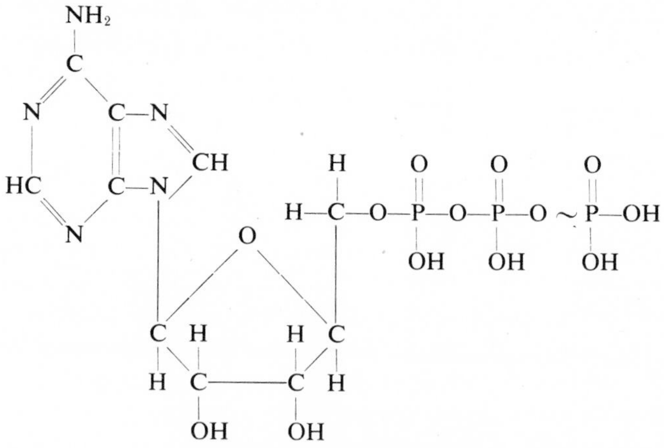

Adenosine triphosphate (ATP)

carbohydrates, lipids, proteins, etc., is immediately utilized in the synthesis of ATP from adenosine diphosphate (ADP) and inorganic phosphate (iP). The chemical energy transferred to ATP can be used to drive synthetic reactions, ADP and iP being released in the process. The bond joining the last phosphate group to ATP is referred to as a *high energy bond* (~). This is actually a misnomer, since many bonds of different organic compounds in the cell contain more energy than that found in the high energy bond of ATP. Perhaps a better term would be one that describes the ability of the last phosphate group of ATP to be readily transferred from one compound to another. In this way, energy is transferred, and this is probably what the term *high energy* was meant to convey originally.

There is, then, an intermediate compound (ATP) capable of receiving energy from one reaction and transferring this energy to drive another reaction. This is of obvious advantage to the living system, since ATP can be formed in the oxidation of a variety of compounds and can be used to drive the synthesis of a variety of compounds. In other words, the oxidation of a compound, such as glucose, can provide the energy, through ATP, for the synthesis of a number of cellular materials. In contrast to fuel burned in man-made engines, where a large amount of released energy is lost in the form of heat, the oxidation of substances in the cell occurs with relatively little energy loss. This is because of the cell's very efficient energy-transfer system mediated by ATP. Here, it is important to understand that the energy locked in a biological compound may be transferred repeatedly. Thus, in a dynamic system, such as the living cell, the stored energy of glucose may be found at one time in ATP and at another time

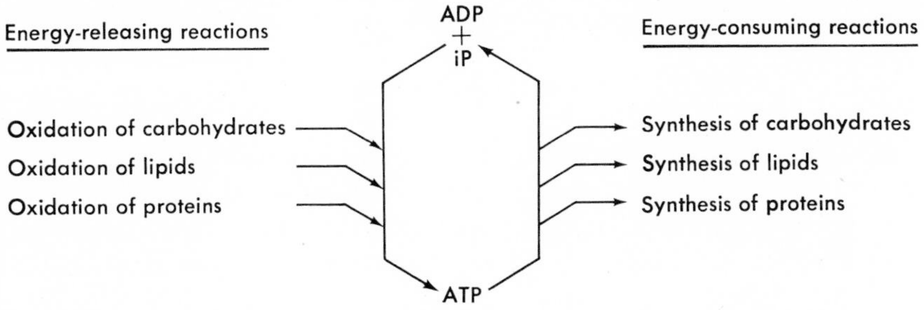

Figure 8-1 An illustration of the role of ATP as an intermediate energy-transfer compound.

locked in the bonds of a protein molecule. A schematic representation of the cyclic manner in which ATP is synthesized and broken down as an intermediate between energy-releasing and energy-consuming reactions is shown in Figure 8-1.

RELEASE OF ENERGY

Within the last 30 years, our knowledge of the metabolic pathways of respiration has improved immensely. Concepts established through the biochemical investigations of a wide variety of organisms leave little doubt that the fundamental aspects of respiration are the same in most forms of life. The glucose molecule that is oxidized in the simple yeast cell travels through the same sequence of reactions as a glucose molecule residing in a leaf of the mighty redwood tree. To be sure, there are some differences to be found, but they are minor and may be excluded from the overall picture of respiration as an essential life process.

The most important feature of respiration is the release of usable energy. The following discussion will analyze to some extent the various metabolic pathways that participate in the release of this energy. In our discussion, we will use the words *oxidation* and *reduction* several times. What is meant by these terms? In its simplest sense, oxidation refers to the removal of electrons from a compound, a process usually accompanied in the cell by the removal of hydrogen. Conversely, the reduction of a compound refers to the addition of electrons to that compound, usually accompanied in the cell by the addition of hydrogen.

Glycolysis

Glycolysis is a term used to describe the sequential series of reactions present in a wide variety of tissues that starts with a hexose sugar (usually glucose) and ends with pyruvic acid. The equation for the overall reaction may be written as:

$$\underset{\text{Hexose}}{C_6H_{12}O_6} \rightarrow \underset{\text{Pyruvate}}{2C_3H_4O_3}$$

It states simply that one molecule of glucose is converted to two molecules of pyruvic acid. However, as mentioned, glycolysis is not a one-step reaction, but a series of closely integrated reactions that lead eventually to pyruvate. Another point to be stressed is that the reactions of glycolysis occur in the absence of oxygen.

Glycolysis may be subdivided into two major steps, the conversion of glucose to fructose-1,6-diphosphate and the splitting of this compound into two three-carbon compounds, which are eventually converted to pyruvic acid.

Three reactions occur in the conversion of glucose to fructose-1,6-diphosphate. First, the sixth carbon of glucose is phosphorylated in the presence of ATP and the enzyme *hexokinase*. The products of this reaction are *glucose-6-phosphate* and ADP. The next reaction involves the conversion of an aldose sugar to a ketose sugar. This reaction is catalyzed by the enzyme *phosphoglucoisomerase* and results in the conversion of glucose-6-phosphate to *fructose-6-phosphate*. The first carbon of fructose-6-phosphate is then phosphorylated in the presence of ATP and the enzyme *phosphofructokinase*. The products of this reaction are *fructose-1,6-diphosphate* and ADP (Figure 8-2).

The second major step in glycolysis involves the splitting of fructose-1,6-

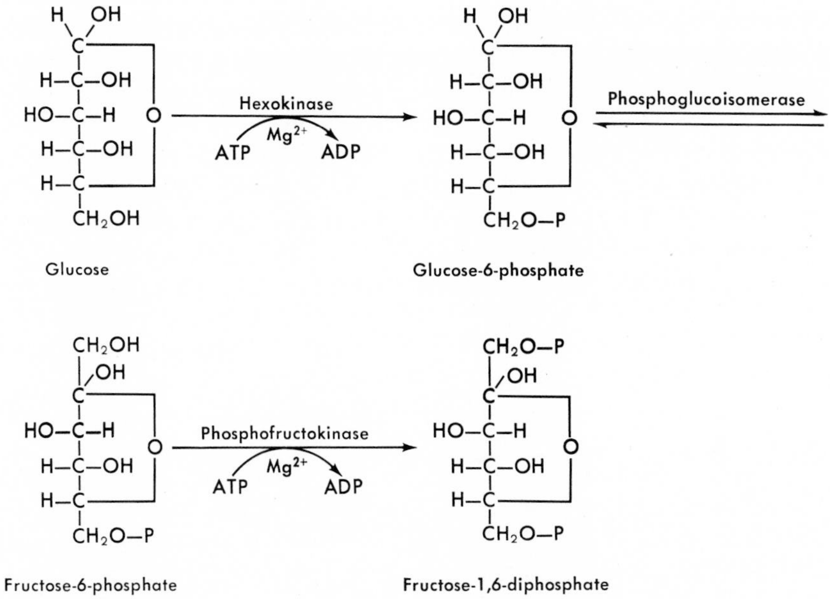

Figure 8-2 Conversion of glucose to fructose-1,6-diphosphate.

diphosphate into two three-carbon compounds, *3-phosphoglyceraldehyde* and *dihydroxyacetonephosphate*. *Aldolase* catalyzes this reaction, and the products formed are interconvertible; that is, an equilibrium exists between the two three-carbon compounds, catalyzed by the enzyme *phosphotriose isomerase*. 3-Phosphoglyceraldehyde is converted to *1,3-diphosphoglyceric acid*. This reaction involves the incorporation or addition of inorganic phosphate to the first carbon of 3-phosphoglyceraldehyde and the reduction of NAD^+. The reaction is catalyzed by the enzyme *phosphoglyceraldehyde dehydrogenase*.

Note that the continual conversion of 3-phosphoglyceraldehyde to other intermediates of the glycolytic pathway causes a shift in the equilibrium between 3-phosphoglyceraldehyde and dihydroxyacetone phosphate. Thus, with continuous conversion to other glycolytic intermediates, more and more dihydroxyacetone phosphate is converted to 3-phosphoglyceraldehyde.

The consumption of inorganic phosphate in the oxidation of 3-phosphoglyceraldehyde is important to the plant, since this phosphate is involved in the synthesis of ATP in the next reaction in the glycolytic sequence. In the presence of ADP and the enzyme *phosphoglyceric kinase,* 1,3-diphosphoglyceric acid is converted to *3-phosphoglyceric acid* and ATP is formed. The 3-phosphoglyceric acid that is formed in the above reaction is transformed to 2-phosphoglyceric acid by the activity of the enzyme *phosphoglyceromutase.* The elimination of the elements of water (dehydration) from 2-phosphoglyceric acid in the presence of *enolase* results in the formation of *phospho-enol-pyruvic acid.* In the presence of ADP and *pyruvic kinase,* phospho-enol-pyruvic acid is converted to *pyruvic acid.* In this reaction, the phosphoric acid residue of phospho-enol-pyruvic acid is transferred to ADP to form ATP. The glycolytic reactions discussed above are shown in Figure 8-3.

Let us now draw up a balance sheet for glycolysis. In the first step, the

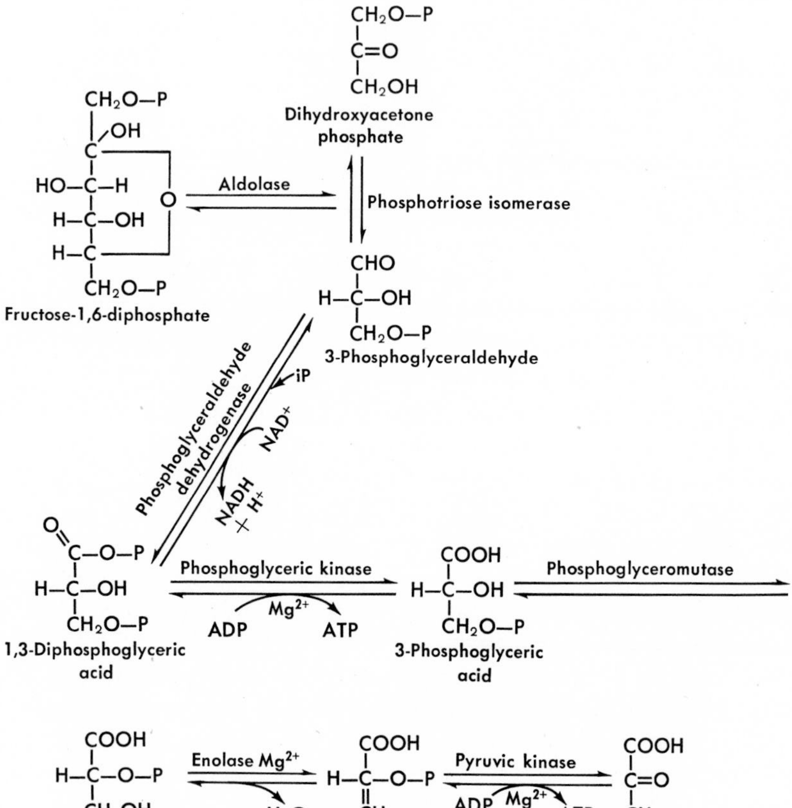

Figure 8-3 Conversion of fructose-1,6-diphosphate to pyruvate.

conversion of glucose to fructose-1,6-diphosphate, there is no energy gain. Indeed, *two* ATP molecules are consumed for every glucose molecule consumed.

$$\text{Glucose} + 2\text{ATP} \rightarrow \text{Fructose-1,6-diphosphate} + 2\text{ADP}$$

However, in the second step, the conversion of fructose-1,6-diphosphate to two molecules of pyruvic acid, *four* ATP molecules are formed—two for each triose split off of fructose-1,6-diphosphate. The following reactions account for the synthesis of ATP.

$$\text{1,3-diphosphoglyceric acid} + \text{ADP} \rightleftharpoons \text{3-phosphoglyceric acid} + \text{ATP}$$
$$\text{phospho-enol-pyruvate} + \text{ADP} \rightleftharpoons \text{pyruvate} + \text{ATP}$$

If we consider the complete glycolytic scheme, the conversion of a molecule of glucose to two molecules of pyruvic acid results in a net gain of *two* ATP molecules.

Fermentation

The overall reaction for fermentation is:

$$\underset{\text{Glucose}}{C_6H_{12}O_6} \rightarrow \underset{\text{Ethanol}}{2CH_3\text{—}CH_2OH} + \underset{\text{Carbon dioxide}}{2CO_2}$$

That is, one molecule of glucose is converted to two molecules of ethanol and two molecules of carbon dioxide. Fermentation, like glycolysis, is a sequential series of reactions that occurs *in the absence of oxygen.* In fact, there is very little difference between the fermentative process and the glycolytic process, most of the intermediate reactions being found in both pathways.

As in glycolysis, glucose is converted to pyruvate during the process of fermentation. However, in fermentation the process goes one step further and converts pyruvate to ethanol and CO_2.

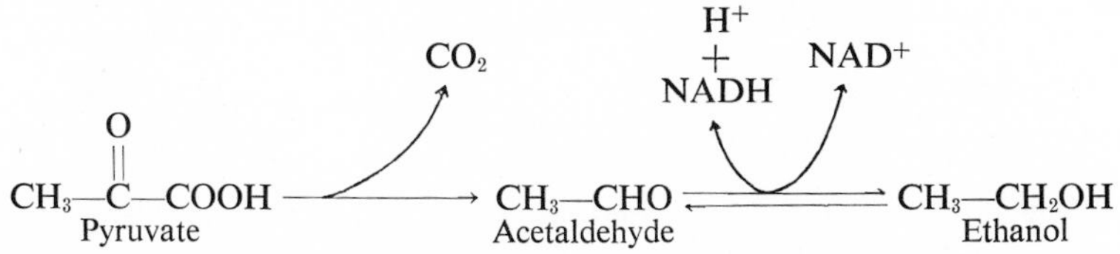

The enzymes catalyzing the two steps of the above reaction are *carboxylase* and *alcohol dehydrogenase.* Since no ATP is produced in the reaction and the rest of the fermentation process is identical to glycolysis, the net gain of ATP per molecule of glucose fermented would be *two.*

Fermentation is the major energy-yielding process of a variety of microorganisms. The microorganisms in such a case are called *anaerobes,* since they are capable of existing and breaking down organic compounds in the absence of oxygen. Indeed, some of these organisms will die if exposed to any appreciable amount of oxygen. In this case they are called *obligate anaerobes.* An example of this type of organism would be *Bacillus botulinus,* which causes the often fatal disease botulism.

Probably the best known of the fermenting organisms are the yeasts. The production of alcohol through fermentation by yeast has been known to man since before the dawn of written history. However, real progress in the biochemical analysis of fermentation was not initiated until the beginning of the twentieth century when Buchner found that cell-free preparations from yeast could ferment glucose (see chapter on enzymes). Yeasts are *facultative anaerobes;* that is, they can exist either in the presence or absence of oxygen.

Although we have only mentioned ethanol and CO_2 as by-products of fermentation, one should be aware that there are other products that may be produced through this process. For example, lactic acid is a by-product of the fermentation of glucose by lactic acid bacteria. This process is best known for its souring effect on milk. In lactic acid fermentation, lactic acid, instead of ethanol, is formed from pyruvate. The enzyme catalyzing this reaction is *lactic acid dehydrogenase.*

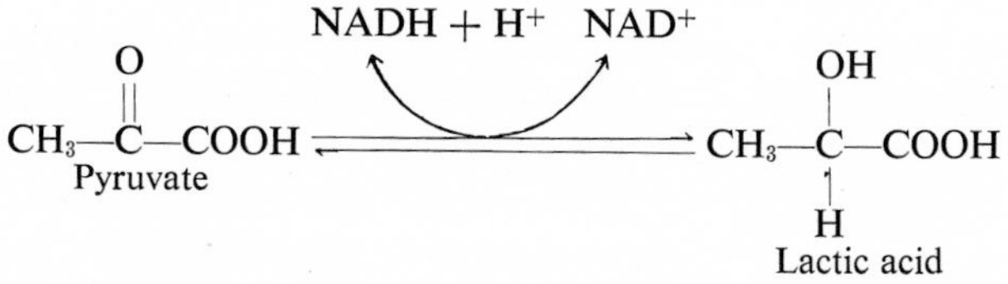

It should be mentioned here that the products of fermentation, ethanol and lactic acid, still contain a considerable amount of energy locked within their structures. The plant does not benefit from this unreleased energy, which indicates that anaerobic respiration, as fermentation is sometimes called, is a relatively inefficient process.

Formation of acetyl coenzyme A

We have shown that the degradation of carbohydrates under anaerobic conditions proceeds via glycolysis to pyruvic acid. Pyruvic acid, then, represents the termination of the glycolytic scheme. However, if sufficient oxygen is present, oxidative decarboxylation of pyruvic acid to form *acetyl coenzyme A* takes place. This reaction is very complex, requiring the presence of at least five essential cofactors and a complex of enzymes

(12, 13, 7). The five cofactors necessary for the successful formation of acetyl coenzyme A are thiamine pyrophosphate (TPP), Mg ions, NAD^+, coenzyme A (CoA), and lipoic acid. Gunsalus (7) has suggested four steps in the formation of acetyl coenzyme A from pyruvic acid.

The first step involves the formation of a complex between TPP and pyruvate, followed by the decarboxylation of pyruvate.

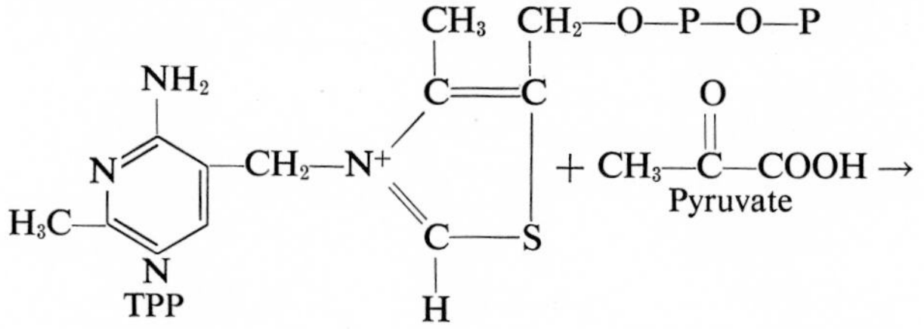

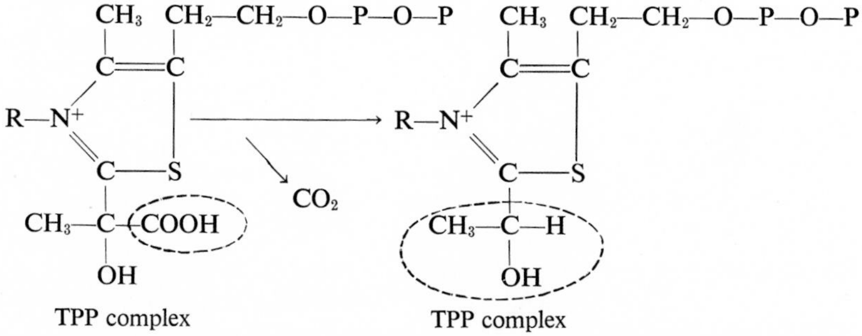

In the second step, the acetaldehyde unit remaining after decarboxylation reacts with the cofactor lipoic acid to form an acetyl-lipoic acid complex. In the reaction, lipoic acid is reduced and the aldehyde is oxidized to an acid. The newly formed acid forms a thioester with lipoic acid.

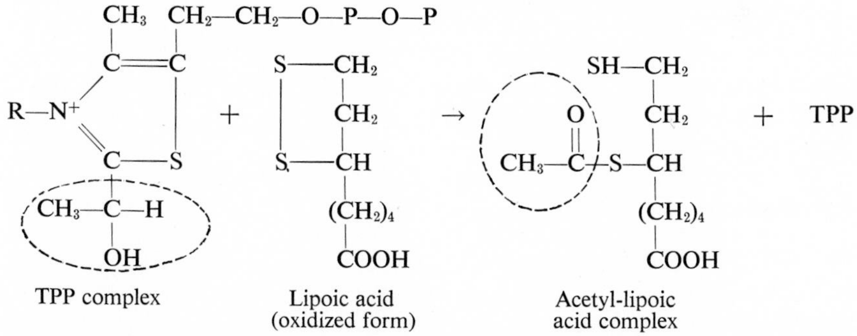

The third step involves the release of the acetyl group from lipoic acid to CoA. The products of this reaction are acetyl CoA and reduced lipoic acid.

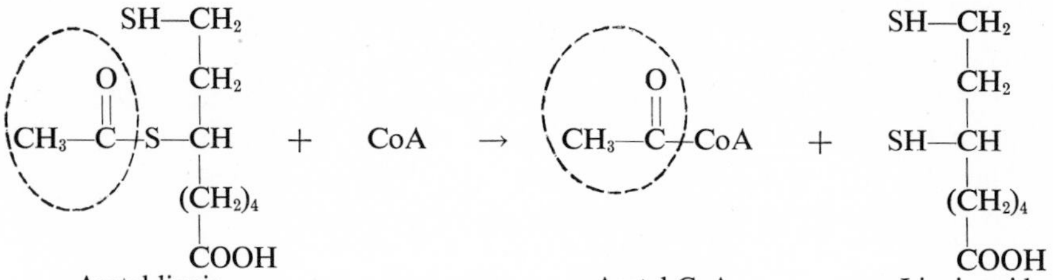

Acetyl-lipoic acid complex; Acetyl CoA; Lipoic acid (reduced form)

The final step involves the regeneration of oxidized lipoic acid by the transfer of electrons from reduced lipoic acid to NAD^+.

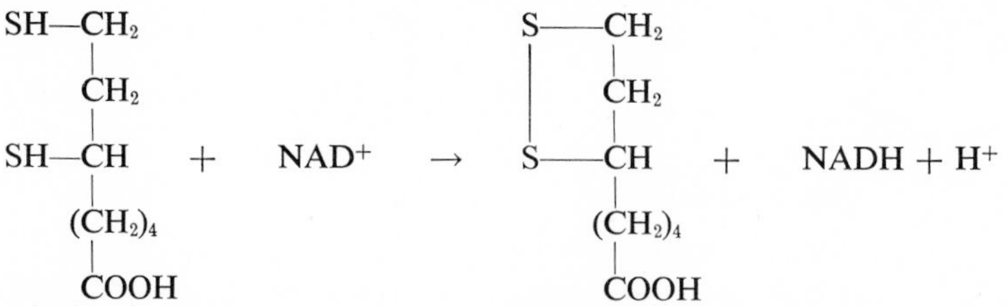

Lipoic acid (reduced form); Lipoic acid (oxidized form)

This last reaction is important because it provides for a continuous supply of oxidized lipoic acid necessary for the formation of acetyl CoA from pyruvic acid. In addition, the two electrons transferred to NAD^+ to form NADH are eventually passed along to the electron transport system (discussed later), resulting in the formation of *three* ATP molecules.

To summarize the above four steps, we have the reaction:

$$\text{Pyruvate} + \text{CoA} + NAD^+ \rightarrow \text{Acetyl CoA} + CO_2 + \text{NADH} + H^+$$

Since TPP and lipoic acid are returned to their original state during the reaction sequence, they have been excluded from this summarizing equation.

Krebs cycle

We have seen where glycolysis and fermentation are relatively inefficient processes so far as the release of energy is concerned. However, under aerobic conditions, pyruvate, the terminal product of glycolysis, can undergo decarboxylation and with CoA form acetyl CoA. Acetyl CoA is the "connecting link" between glycolysis and the *Krebs cycle* (tricarboxylic acid cycle or citric acid cycle), so-named because of the cyclic manner in which the starting compound, *oxaloacetate,* is regenerated. The cycle is named after the English biochemist, H. A. Krebs, who played a major role in its discovery. By means of the Krebs cycle and the *electron transport system,* pyruvate is oxidized to CO_2 and H_2O. Thus, the complete oxidation of glucose to CO_2 and H_2O may occur through the mediation of glycolysis, the Krebs cycle, and the electron transport system. Through its association with the electron transport system, the oxidations of the Krebs cycle can account for the formation of 24 ATP molecules. Thus, the Krebs cycle is far more efficient in the release of energy than either glycolysis or fermentation. The reactions of the Krebs cycle require the presence of oxygen.

Formation of citric acid. The first reaction of the Krebs cycle is the condensation of acetyl CoA with oxaloacetate to form *citric acid* and release CoA.

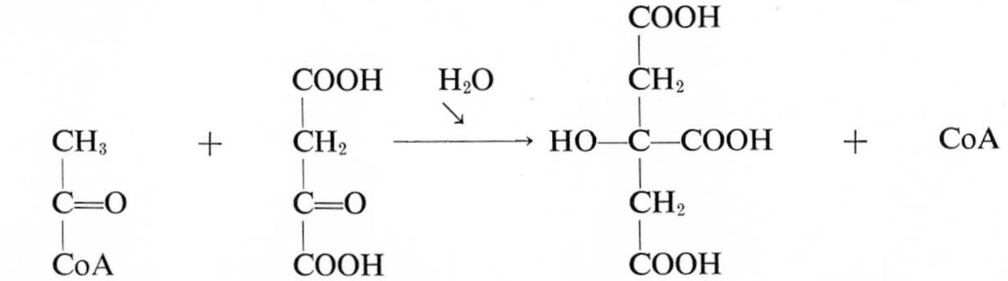

$$
\begin{array}{ccccccc}
 & & & & \text{COOH} & & \\
 & & \text{COOH} & \text{H}_2\text{O} & | & & \\
 & & | & \searrow & \text{CH}_2 & & \\
\text{CH}_3 & + & \text{CH}_2 & \longrightarrow & \text{HO}-\text{C}-\text{COOH} & + & \text{CoA} \\
| & & | & & | & & \\
\text{C}=\text{O} & & \text{C}=\text{O} & & \text{CH}_2 & & \\
| & & | & & | & & \\
\text{CoA} & & \text{COOH} & & \text{COOH} & & \\
\text{Acetyl CoA} & & \text{Oxaloacetic acid} & & \text{Citric acid} & &
\end{array}
$$

The result of this reaction, catalyzed by *condensing enzyme,* is that a four-carbon dicarboxylic acid is converted to a six-carbon tricarboxylic acid.

Regeneration of oxaloacetic acid. Through a series of reactions involving four oxidation steps and three molecules of H_2O (one utilized in the condensation reaction), oxaloacetic acid is regenerated from citric acid. In the process, two molecules of CO_2 and eight H atoms are produced. The reactions leading to the regeneration of oxaloacetic acid from citric acid are given in Figure 8-4.

It is thought that the reversible interconversions of the first three acids of the Krebs cycle—citric acid, *cis-aconitic* acid, and *isocitric acid*—are catalyzed by the same enzyme, *aconitase.* The first reaction involves a hydration of citric acid to form *cis*-aconitic acid. The second reaction calls for the dehydration of *cis*-aconitic acid to yield isocitric acid.

In the presence of *isocitric acid dehydrogenase* and $NADP^+$, *isocitric acid* is converted to *oxalosuccinic acid.* This is the *first* oxidation step of the Krebs cycle, two electrons and two hydrogen ions being removed from isocitric acid and taken up by the coenzyme $NADP^+$ to form NADPH + H^+. The next reaction of the Krebs cycle involves the decarboxylation of oxalosuccinic acid to form *α-ketoglutaric acid.* A *carboxylase* catalyzes this reaction. α-Ketoglutaric acid is a key compound in the metabolism of the plant. Not only is it involved in carbohydrate and lipid metabolism,

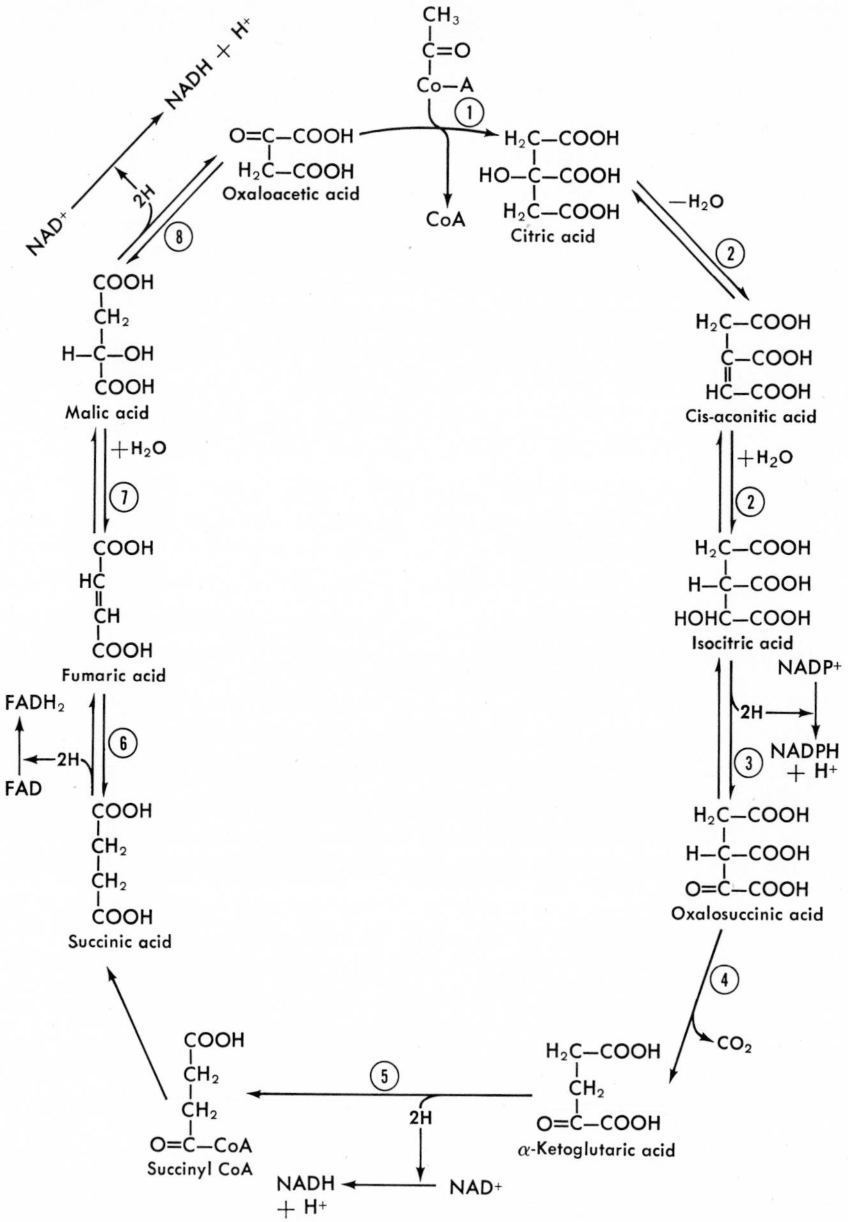

Figure 8-4 Metabolites and reactions of the Krebs cycle. The enzymes as numbered in the reactions are: (1) condensing enzyme, (2) aconitase, (3) isocitric acid dehydrogenase, (4) carboxylase, (5) α-ketoglutaric dehydrogenase, (6) succinic dehydrogenase, (7) fumarase, and (8) malic dehydrogenase.

but it also plays an important role in the synthesis and degradation of amino acids.

The oxidation of α-ketoglutaric acid may be considered analogous to that of pyruvic acid. Thiamine pyrophosphate is required for the initial decarboxylation, and the succinic semialdehyde formed complexes with oxidized lipoic acid. The succinyl moiety of this complex is transferred to CoA, forming succinyl CoA and reduced lipoic acid. Reduced lipoic acid is reoxidized by a NAD-containing enzyme, NAD being reduced in the process. The complex of enzymes catalyzing this series of reactions are collectively called *α-ketoglutaric dehydrogenase.* This last reaction also represents the *second* oxidation step of the cycle. The energy locked within the thioester, succinyl CoA, may be released in the next reaction to form an energy-rich pyrophosphate bond. Thus, in the presence of guanosine diphosphate (GDP) and inorganic phosphate, succinyl CoA is converted to *succinic acid,* and guanosine triphosphate (GTP) is formed.

The oxidation of succinic acid to form *fumaric acid* is interesting, since it is the only Krebs cycle oxidation that does not employ a pyridine nucleotide. Instead, succinic acid is dehydrogenated (oxidized) by the ferriflavoprotein *succinic dehydrogenase.* Nevertheless, two hydrogen ions and two electrons are removed from succinic acid and are used to reduce the flavin prosthetic group, flavin adenine dinucleotide (FAD), of the enzyme succinic dehydrogenase. The oxidation of succinic acid represents the third oxidation step of the Krebs cycle. The product of this reaction, fumaric acid, is hydrated in the presence of *fumarase* to yield *malic acid.*

In the fourth oxidation step of the Krebs cycle, malic acid is converted to *oxaloacetic acid* in the presence of *malic dehydrogenase.* In the process, NAD^+ is reduced, forming $NADH + H^+$. Thus, the regeneration of oxaloacetic acid completes the cycle. In the four oxidation steps four pairs of H ions and four pairs of electrons are removed from intermediates of the cycle. Three of the pairs of H ions and electrons are utilized in the reduction of pyridine nucleotides. The one remaining pair of H ions and electrons is taken up in the reduction of the FAD prosthetic group of succinic dehydrogenase.

Electron transport system

For aerobic organisms, it is essential that the enzymes of the Krebs cycle be associated with those of the *electron transport system.* It is through this association that the pyridine nucleotides (NADP and NAD) and FAD, reduced in the Krebs cycle, are reoxidized. The energy released in these oxidations is utilized in the synthesis of ATP.

The electron transport system consists of a sequential series of cyto-

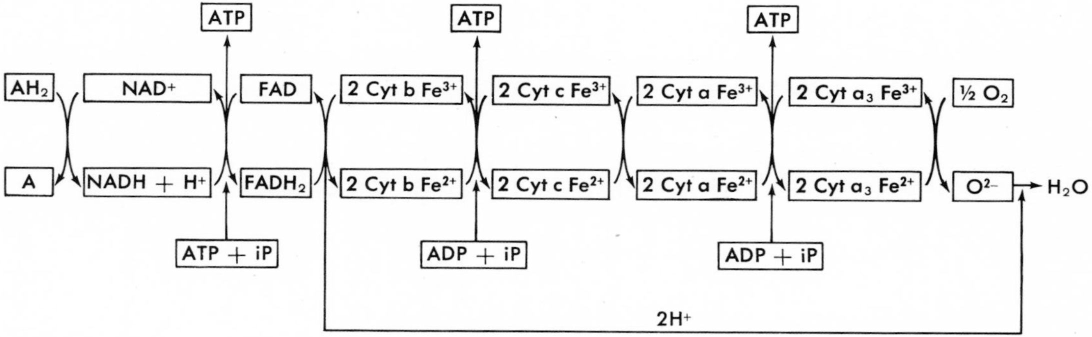

Figure 8-5 The electron transport system. A Krebs cycle intermediate is oxidized releasing two hydrogen atoms in the process. The two electrons possessed by the hydrogen atoms are passed along a sequential series of cytochrome enzymes to oxygen. Three molecules of ATP are produced for every pair of electrons passed along this system. (After A. L. Lehninger. 1965. Bioenergetics. W. A. Benjamin. New York.)

chrome enzymes capable of passing electrons from one to another. Electrons taken up by hydrogen acceptors (NADP, NAD, FAD) in the oxidation steps of respiration are ultimately taken to the electron transport system, where they are passed "down" a chain of cytochrome enzymes. Most important to the living cell is the fact that with each step in this system the energy level of the electron is lowered, the energy difference being transformed into phosphate bond energy by the conversion of ADP to ATP. A schematic representation of the electron transport system is given in Figure 8-5. Note in Figure 8-5 that hydrogen ions are released to the cytoplasm in the reoxidation of $FADH_2$; only the electrons are passed along the cytochromes. A further study of Figure 8-5 will show that for every pair of electrons passed along this system, three ATP are formed. The synthesis of ATP occurs in the oxidation of NADH, in the oxidation of two cytochrome b's, and in the oxidation of two cytochrome a's. At their lowest energy level, the electrons are passed to oxygen from reduced cytochrome a_3, activating the oxygen. In this state, oxygen will accept free hydrogen ions to form water.

A consideration of the complete oxidation of glucose to CO_2 and H_2O will show that there is a net gain of *38 ATP*. Let us explore this in a little more detail. With the exception of the oxidation of succinic acid to form fumaric acid in which two ATP are formed, the following reactions of glycolysis and the Krebs cycle result in the synthesis of three ATP apiece.

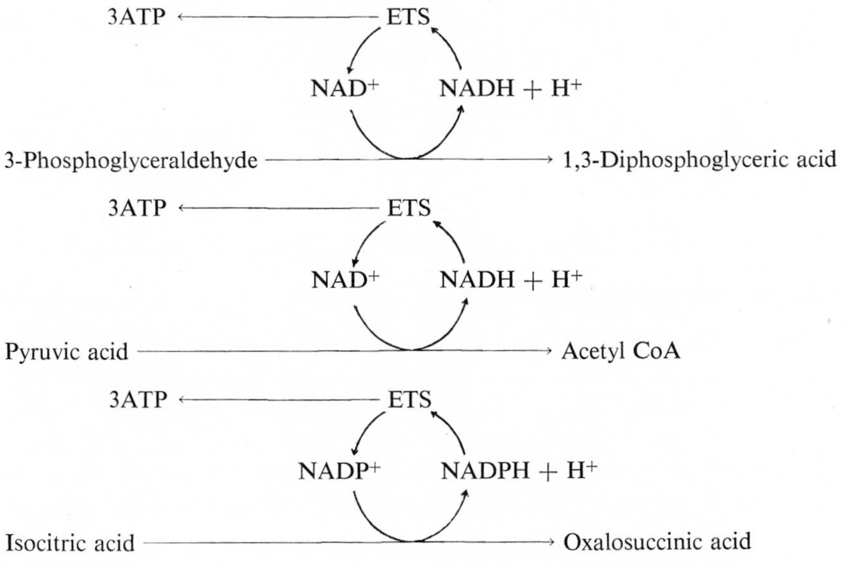

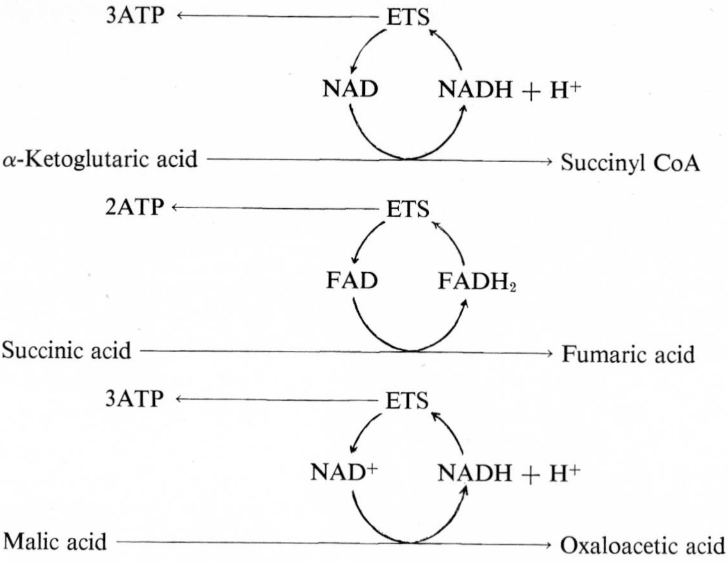

It can be seen from these six reactions that for every three-carbon fragment of glucose oxidized to CO_2 and H_2O, 17 ATP are produced. Since there are two of these fragments, this amounts to 34 ATP. As mentioned previously, there is a net gain of two ATP in glycolysis, bringing the above figure to 36 ATP formed during the oxidation of glucose.

We should also consider the formation of GTP in the conversion of succinyl CoA to succinic acid. Since phosphate transfer can occur from GTP to ADP, one ATP could be gained in this reaction.

$$\text{GTP} + \text{ADP} \rightleftharpoons \text{GDP} + \text{ATP}$$

This would bring the total to 38 ATP for the complete oxidation of glucose.

Hexose monophosphate shunt

Although the major pathway for the aerobic respiration of glucose is through glycolysis and the Krebs cycle, there exists an alternative pathway in many organisms. This pathway, which requires the presence of oxygen, is called the *hexose monophosphate shunt* (sometimes called the direct oxidation pathway or the pentose phosphate shunt). Note in Figure 8-6 that reduced NADP is formed in the reactions forming 6-phosphogluconic acid and ribulose-5-P. If the equivalent of a molecule of glucose is oxidized to CO_2 and H_2O via this cyclic pathway (six turns of the cycle), then 12 molecules of reduced NADP would be formed. In the presence of the enzyme transhydrogenase the hydrogens of NADPH can be transferred to NAD to form NADH. With this in mind we can see where the formation of 12 molecules of reduced NADP via the hexose monophosphate shunt could ultimately lead to the synthesis of 36 molecules of ATP. Thus, capture of energy released in the oxidation of glucose via this pathway is

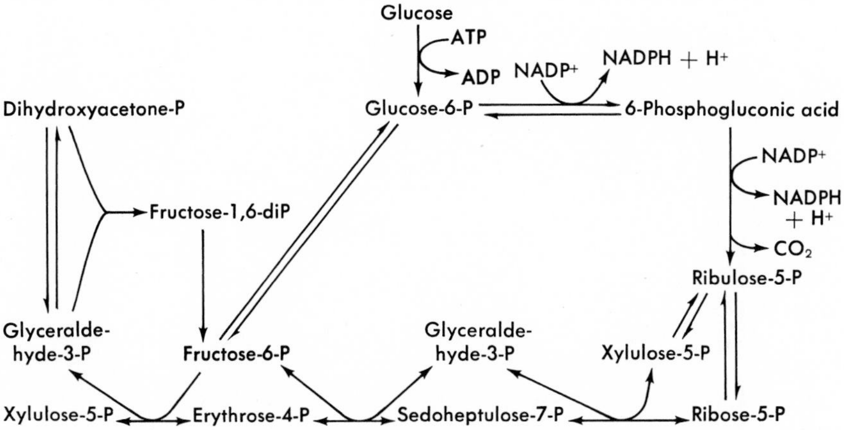

Figure 8-6 The hexose monophosphate shunt.

almost as efficient as that of the glycolytic-Krebs cycle pathway. In addition, the five-carbon intermediates of the hexose monophosphate shunt are important in the synthesis of nucleic acids.

MEASUREMENT OF RESPIRATION

Most methods for measuring the rates of respiration involve quantitative determinations of the CO_2 evolved or the oxygen consumed. One rather simple method involves trapping the CO_2 produced in a barium hydroxide ($Ba(OH_2)$) solution and weighing the barium carbonate ($BaCO_3$) formed. A variation of this method is to have the CO_2 absorbed in NaOH instead of $Ba(OH)_2$ and the amount of CO_2 absorbed determined by titration. However, most determinations of respiration rates are done monometrically by measuring changes in volume of gas in a closed system. Generally, a monometer called a *Warburg apparatus* is used for this type of work. Changes in gas volume due to living material (seeds, tissues, etc.) may be measured by observing a rise or fall of a liquid (Brodie's solution) in the graduated monometer tubes. Since a closed system is utilized in monometric determinations of gas exchange, the rise or fall of Brodie's solution in the tube could only be caused by the living tissue that is being investigated. A diagram of a Warburg monometer is given in Figure 8-7.

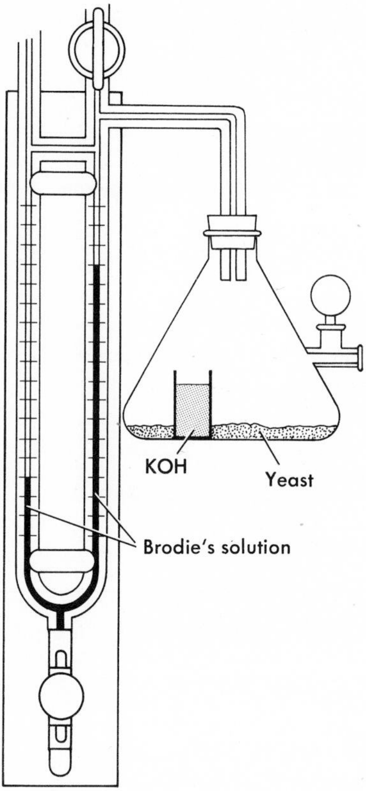

Figure 8-7 Diagram showing the utilization of a Warburg monometer in the measurement of yeast respiration.

The Warburg apparatus has the advantage of being both sensitive and flexible. The respiration of a wide variety of tissues can be measured. External factors that may affect the rate of respiration can be easily controlled and, if the investigator wishes, the effect of these factors on respiration may be measured. In addition, the side arm of a Warburg vessel allows for the convenient introduction of substances active in respiration (stimulants or poisons) at any time during an experiment and their effects can be measured. With the use of the Warburg apparatus, the respiration rates of a great many different plant tissues have been measured under a variety of conditions.

Respiratory quotient

When respiration is being measured, it is usually desirable to determine both the O_2 consumed and the CO_2 evolved. The ratio of CO_2 produced to O_2 consumed is called the *respiratory quotient* (RQ).

$$RQ = \frac{CO_2}{O_2}$$

When a carbohydrate is respired, this ratio is equal to one. However, the RQ of different substrates (proteins, fats, carbohydrates) may vary considerably. For example, substrates that are highly oxidized, such as the acids of the Krebs cycle, will give RQ values greater than one, while substrates that are relatively reduced, such as fats, will yield RQ values less than one.

Generally, when a carbohydrate is respired in the cell, one molecule of oxygen is consumed for every molecule of CO_2 given off. On the other hand, Krebs cycle intermediates are more highly oxidized than carbohydrates and, consequently, need less oxygen for their oxidation to CO_2 and water. For example, the oxidation of malic acid to CO_2 and water gives an RQ value of 1.33. Fats are more reduced than carbohydrates, and thus more oxygen is needed for their respiration. For example, the respiration of a fat may have an RQ value as low as 0.7.

The RQ value of a respiring tissue may provide valuable information to an investigator. From an RQ value, one can obtain a rough indication of the nature of the substrate being oxidized. However, one must realize that a precise identification of the type of substrate being respired by a tissue through RQ values is impossible. For example, if different substrates are being respired simultaneously, then the RQ value obtained is only an average of the RQ values of each individual substrate.

As might be expected, the organs of most mature plants well supplied with carbohydrates show little variation in their RQ values, which range from 0.97 to 1.17 (10). This suggests that the predominate substrate of respiration under normal conditions is carbohydrate. However, plants under starvation conditions will exhibit RQ values consistently below unity. James (10) cites examples such as aging green leaves, leaves in the dark, or detached embryos. The drop in RQ value is a result of more reduced substrates (e.g., fatty acids, proteins) being respired. For example, Yemm (19, 20) has observed RQ values of 0.85 and less for green leaves in the dark.

Germinating seeds offer a good study of the agreement between the RQ value and the substrate being respired. In the seed, fatty oil is usually stored in addition to carbohydrates, and in many cases fatty oils may be the predominate stored reserve. In addition, during germination, proteins are degraded in the storage organs and synthesized in the embryo. In seeds containing large amounts of fat relative to carbohydrate, the RQ values during germination will be considerably lower than one. Seeds with carbohydrate as the principal food reserve will have RQ values near one during germination.

FACTORS AFFECTING THE RATE OF RESPIRATION

Temperature

As with all chemical reactions, the chemical reactions of respiration are sensitive to temperature changes. Since the reactions of respiration are under the control of enzymes, the temperature range in which they may occur is quite narrow. At temperatures approaching 0°C, the rate of respiration becomes very slow. As the temperature rises, so also does the rate of respiration, until temperatures destructive to enzyme activity are reached. A maximum rate may be attained somewhere between 35 and 45°C.

However, when studying the effect of temperature on respiration, one must consider the length of time an organ or plant is exposed to any one temperature level. For example, a four day old pea seedling (*Pisum sativum*) will exhibit an initial increase in respiration rate when the temperature is increased from 25 to 45°C. When left for any length of time at this high temperature, however, the respiration rate will decrease. In other words, a "time factor" has to be considered when studying the effect of temperature on respiration. Apparently, at temperatures above 30°C, factors leading to denaturation of enzymes involved in respiration begin to have an adverse effect. Since denaturation at these temperatures is not immediate, there will be an initial increase in the respiration rate. However, in time this adverse effect will show, and the rate of respiration will drop off. In general, the higher the temperature, the shorter is the time period before the rate of respiration drops off.

Work with pea seedlings by Fernandes (6) illustrates the importance of the time factor in studies of the effect of temperature on respiration (Figure 8-8). Figure 8-8 indicates that 30°C is the optimal temperature for four day old pea seedlings, since there is no dropping off of respiration rate over a long period of time.

Oxygen

In our previous discussion, we mentioned that the presence of oxygen is necessary for Krebs cycle reactions to occur. In addition, we noted that

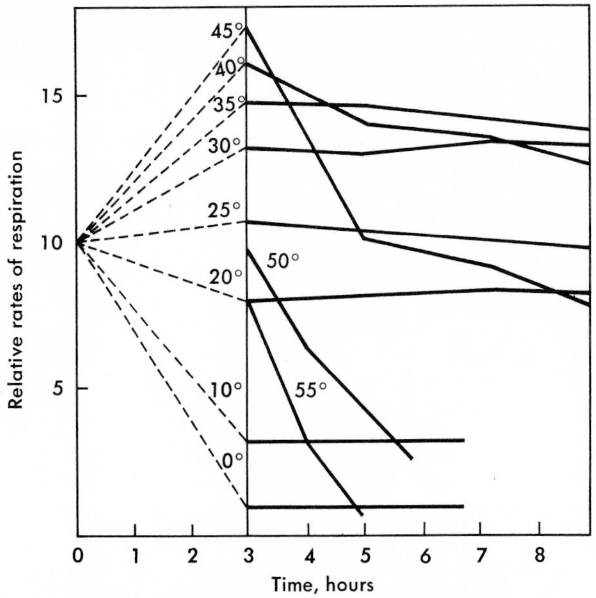

Figure 8-8 The effect of temperature on the rate of respiration of four-day old pea seedlings (*Pisum sativum.*) Note the relationship between temperature, time, and the rate of respiration. The broken lines indicate the time interval between changes of temperature from 25°C to those shown in the figure. (After D. S. Fernandes. 1923. Rec. trav. bot. Néerlandais 20:107.)

oxygen is the terminal acceptor of electrons in the electron transport system. Considering this, we naturally assume that the rate of respiration is sensitive to changes in oxygen concentration. In general, at low oxygen concentrations both aerobic and anaerobic respiration can be expected to occur in the plant. Under these circumstances, RQ values would be greater than one and, in fact, would approach infinity as the concentration of oxygen approached zero. That is, under complete anaerobic conditions, the CO_2 produced would be a product of anaerobic respiration (fermentation) exclusively. As the oxygen concentration is increased, anaerobic production of CO_2 falls off rapidly, aerobic respiration increases, and RQ values approach unity. When an RQ value reaches unity at a certain oxygen concentration, this point is called the *extinction point* (16). At this point, anaerobic respiration ceases. A typical example of these relationships may be seen in Watson's work with Bramley seedling apples (Figure 8-9).

Over a complete range of oxygen concentrations, it is desirable to

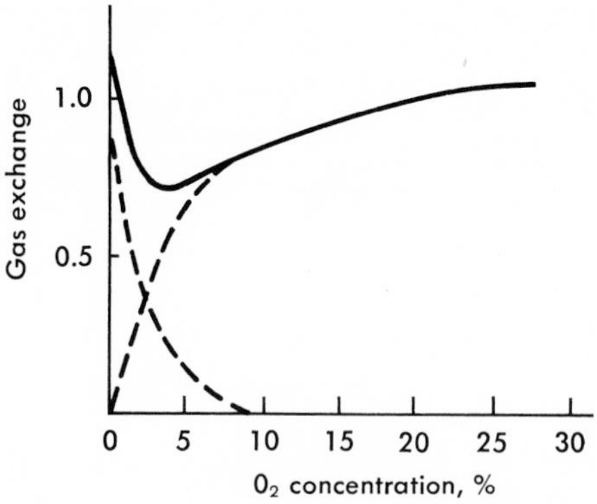

Figure 8-9 Production of CO_2 by Bramley seedling apples at different O_2 concentrations (production rate in air = 1.0). The solid line represents CO_2 emission; the dotted line represents anaerobic CO_2 production, and the broken line represents O_2 consumption at O_2 concentrations less than 10%. (From W. O. James. 1953. Plant respiration. Clarendon Press, Oxford. After Watson. 1932.)

measure both CO_2 production and O_2 consumption. Oxygen consumption gives a measure of aerobic respiration as does CO_2 production after the extinction point has been passed. However, below the extinction point CO_2 production results from both aerobic and anaerobic respiration, while O_2 consumption below this point is still strictly a measure of aerobic respiration. Determining the participation of both gases over a complete range of O_2 concentrations allows one to measure both aerobic and anaerobic respiration.

From numerous studies of the respiration rates of a wide variety of plants, a general statement can be made. As the oxygen concentration increases from zero, the rate of aerobic respiration increases. With most plants this increase is hyperbolic; that is, the rate of increase falls off with increase in oxygen concentration (16). In some plant material, the increase in rate of aerobic respiration is linear over a range of oxygen concentrations. For example, Taylor (18) found this to be true for germinating rice grains. A possible explanation might be that O_2 consumption is limited by an oxygen diffusion barrier, such as might be found in the outer covering of the rice grain. James (10) has indicated that oxygen consumption in this case is proportional to the amount of oxygen diffusing across the barrier, not to oxygen being consumed in respiration.

Carbon dioxide

Increasing the concentration of CO_2 has a definite repressing effect on respiration. This is brought out very nicely in studies by Kidd (11) on the respiration of germinating white mustard seeds (Figure 8-10). Although

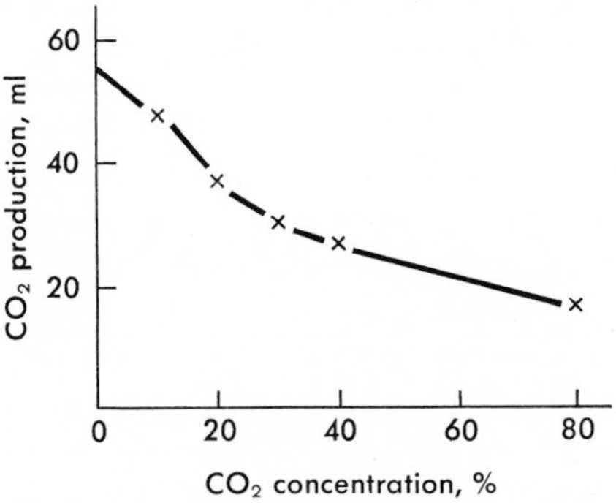

Figure 8-10 Retarding effect of increasing CO_2 concentration on the respiration of germinating white mustard seeds. (Data of F. Kidd. 1915. Proc. Roy. Soc. (London) B, 89:136. (After W. Stiles and W. Leach. 1960. Respiration in plants. Wiley, New York.)

numerous studies of leaf respiration have indicated a depressing effect of CO_2, there is evidence that this effect may be partially indirect. Heath (8) has demonstrated that CO_2 can cause stomatal closure, thus limiting gaseous exchange. This may have the effect of raising the internal concentration of CO_2 considerably and in this way limit respiration.

Inorganic salts

Lundegårdh and Burström (15) observed that the rate of respiration increases when a plant or tissue is transferred from water to a salt solution. The amount by which respiration is increased over normal has been labeled "salt" respiration. This aspect of respiration is discussed in detail in Chapter 14.

Mechanical stimulation

In a series of studies, Audus (1, 2, 3, 4) demonstrated that leaf respiration could be increased by handling, stroking, or bending leaves. In the cherry laurel leaf, this increase caused by handling may reach as high as 18.3%. Response to handling decreases if it is repeated over a period of time. Barker (5) found that the respiration of potato tubers also increases with handling.

Wounding as a respiration stimulator

For over 70 years it has been known that the wounding of plant organs stimulates respiration in that organ. Generally, wounding initiates meristematic activity in the area of the wound, resulting in the development of "wound callus." What connection this might have with the stimulatory effect of wounding on respiration is still in the realm of speculation. An interesting study by Hopkins (9) on potatoes showed a considerable increase in sugar content after a potato had been cut. Perhaps increase in respiration because of wounding is caused by increased availability of respiratory substrate.

SUMMARY

Respiration consists of an ordered series of reactions resulting in a stepwise degradation of glucose (or other organic compounds) to CO_2 and H_2O. The energy released in many of these steps is utilized in the synthesis of ATP from ADP and iP. The ATP molecule represents a means of temporary energy storage, this energy being later used in the various synthetic reactions of the living cell.

Glycolysis and fermentation are relatively inefficient in the production of ATP, while the Krebs cycle associated with the electron transport system comprises the major contribution of ATP to the living cell. Although the degradation of a glucose molecule via glycolysis and the Krebs cycle represents the major pathway of respiration, the hexose monophosphate shunt may be considered an alternate pathway in many organisms.

Finally, respiration rates may be influenced by several environmental factors, including temperature, oxygen concentration, carbon dioxide concentration, concentration of inorganic salts in the culture medium, mechanical handling, and wounding.

BIBLIOGRAPHY

1. Audus, L. J. 1936. Mechanical stimulation and respiration rate in cherry laurel. New Phytologist 34: 557.
2. Audus, L. J. 1939. Mechanical stimulation and respiration in the green leaf. II. Investigation on a number of angiospermic species. New Phytologist 38: 284.
3. Audus, L. J. 1940. Mechanical stimulation and respiration in the green leaf. III. The effect of stimulation on the rate of fermentation. New Phytologist 39: 65.
4. Audus, L. J. 1941. Mechanical stimulation and respiration in the green leaf. Parts IV and V. New Phytologist 40: 86.
5. Barker, J. 1935. Notes on the effect of handling on the respiration of potatoes. New Phytologist 34: 407.
6. Fernandes, D. S. 1923. Aerobe and anaerobe Atmung bei Keimlingen von *Pisum sativum*. Rec. trav. bot. Néerlandais 20: 107.
7. Gunsalus, I. C. 1954. Group transfer and acyl-generating functions of lipoic acid derivatives. pp. 599–604 *In* W. D. McElroy and B. Glass (eds.), Mechanism of enzyme action. John Hopkins Press, Baltimore, Md.
8. Heath, O. V. S. 1950. Studies in stomatal behaviour. V. The role of carbon dioxide in the light response of stomata. J. Exptl. Bot. 1: 29.
9. Hopkins, E. F. 1927. Variation in sugar content in potato tubers caused by wounding and its possible relation to respiration. Botan. Gaz. 84: 75.
10. James, W. O. 1953. Plant respiration. Clarendon Press, Oxford.
11. Kidd, F. 1915. The controlling influence of carbon dioxide. III. The retarding effect of carbon dioxide on respiration. Proc. Roy. Soc. (London) B, 89: 136.
12. Korkes, S., A. Campillo, I. C. Gunsalus, and S. Ochoa. 1951. Enzymatic synthesis of citric acid. III. Pyruvate as acetyl donor. J. Biol. Chem. 193: 721.
13. Korkes, S., A. Campillo, and S. Ochoa. 1952. Pyruvate oxidation system of heart muscle. J. Biol. Chem. 195: 511.
14. Lehninger, A. L. 1965. Bioenergetics. W. A. Benjamin, New York.
15. Lundegårdh, H., and H. Burström. 1933. Untersuchungen über die Salzaufnahme der Pflanzen. III. Quantitative Beziehungen zwischen Atmung und Anionenaufnahme. Biochem. Z. 261: 235.
16. Stiles, W. 1960. The composition of the atmosphere (oxygen content of air, water, soil, intercellular spaces, diffusion, carbon dioxide and oxygen tension). *In* W. Ruhland (ed.), Encyclopedia of plant physiology. 12: 114.
17. Stiles, W., and W. Leach. 1960. Respiration in plants. John Wiley & Sons, New York.

18. Taylor, D. L. 1942. Influence of oxygen tension on respiration, fermentation and growth in wheat and rice. Am. J. Botany 29: 721.
19. Yemm, E. W. 1935. The respiration of barley plants. II. Carbohydrate concentration and carbon dioxide production in starving leaves. Proc. Roy. Soc. (London), B, 117: 504.
20. Yemm, E. W. 1937. The respiration of barley plants. III. Protein catabolism in starving leaves. Proc. Roy Soc. (London), B, 123: 243.

9
Translocation of sugars

INTRODUCTION

Any student of botany can appreciate the fact that the living cells of the plant are dependent upon the photosynthetic cells of the leaves for their nutrient supply. However, some of the distances separating photosynthetic cells from other living cells are relatively large. The need for a rapid and efficient translocation system becomes apparent when one considers the distance separating the living cells of the root from those of the leaves. The solution to the problem of nutrient translocation, in the quantity and with the rapidity necessary to carry on normal cell metabolism, is found in specialized cells of the phloem tissue called *sieve tube elements*. These elements, like those of the xylem tissue, form a network of ducts that extends to every part of the plant, bringing all living cells into close contact with the sugars synthesized in the leaves. This chapter will be primarily concerned with a description of the phloem translocation system and with explanations of possible mechanisms that might be involved.

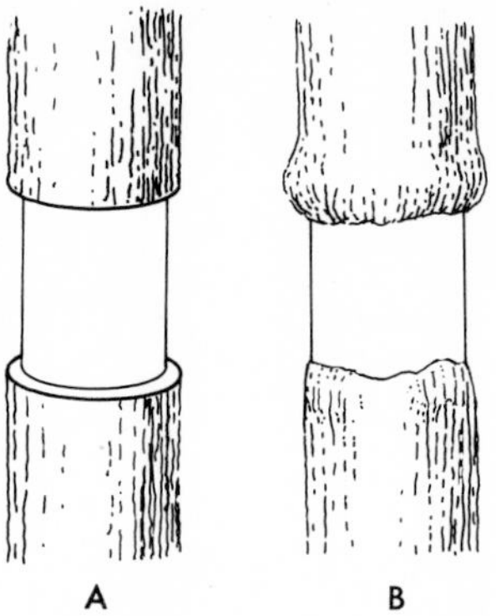

A B

Figure 9-1 A. A trunk of a tree immediately after a circle of bark has been removed. B. The same trunk after a period of time. Note that the materials being translocated from the leaves have accumulated above the girdle, causing this area to bulge.

Although discussions of the translocation of "elaborated sap" were initiated as early as the middle of the seventeenth century, knowledge of the tissues involved was lacking. Indeed, it was thought that preformed substances were absorbed from the soil by the roots and translocated through the wood to the leaves where some changes took place before the now modified substances were retranslocated, also through the wood, in a downward direction. In other words, both upward and downward translocation was considered to occur in the xylem tissue.

The first anatomical and physiological description of the tissues involved in the translocation of organic compounds was given to us by Hartig in 1837. His discovery of sieve tubes in the bark was the first clue to the elaborate system possessed by the plant for nutrient distribution. Hartig demonstrated that nutrients will collect above a stem "girdle," causing the stem tissues to bulge (Figure 9-1). The girdling technique entails the complete removal of a ring of bark from a stem or branch, leaving the wood intact. Substances being translocated from the leaves will accumulate above the girdle, thus proving that the bark and not the wood is concerned with the movement of materials from leaves.

ANATOMY OF PHLOEM TISSUES

Cell types and function

The phloem tissue is primarily composed of *sieve tube elements* and *phloem parenchyma* (15, 9). *Companion cells* usually accompany the sieve tube elements of angiosperms. An analogous type of cell is found accompanying the sieve tube elements of conifers, called an *albuminous cell.* In addition to these cell types, *phloem fibers, sclereids,* and *ray cells* are also found. The position of the phloem tissue in relation to the xylem tissue in a monocotyledon is shown in Figure 9-2.

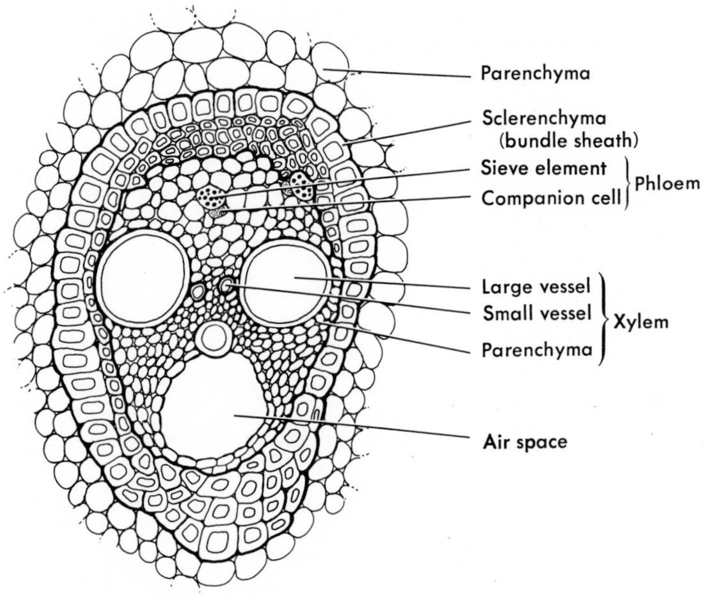

Figure 9-2 Drawing of a vascular bundle of a monocot stem showing the phloem tissue in relation to the xylem tissue.

The large amounts of starch generally found in phloem parenchyma is indicative of the primary function of these cells. However, in addition to storage, phloem parenchyma may also play a minor role in the synthesis and translocation of sugars in the plant. Often the parenchyma of phloem tissues of leaves and green stems contain chloroplasts (9), and have been shown to function in polar symplastic movement of sugars to sieve tube elements (44). Crafts (9) has pointed out that meristematic tissues and storage areas may obtain nutrients from the sieve tube elements via symplastic movement of these *nutrients* through nonpigmented parenchyma cells. In an interesting series of experiments with willow stem segments, Weatherley et al. (57) demonstrated that, depending upon conditions, a nonpolar exchange of sugars may take place between sieve tube elements and adjacent parenchyma.

Much attention has been given to the so-called companion cells because of their close association with sieve tube elements. According to Esau (16), the two cell types are not only ontogenetically related, but also bear a close physiological relationship. One or more companion cells are cut off from phloem mother cells before their differentiation into mature sieve tube elements. Walls separating the two cells are often very thin or abundantly pitted. Death of the companion cell follows loss of function by the sieve tube element. At maturity, sieve elements do not contain nuclei. In contrast, the companion cells do and it has been suggested that companion cells have a nuclear influence over enucleated sieve elements (13). The analogous albuminous cell found in conifers is thought to be similar to the companion cell in its physiological relationship to the sieve tube element.

Phloem ray cells are parenchyma cells that function primarily in storage and lateral transport. Phloem fibers and sclereids have no function other than support.

Sieve tube elements

The sieve tubes or ducts of the bark are admirably suited for the rapid and efficient translocation of large quantities of solutes in the plant. Sieve tubes are composed of sieve tube elements, highly specialized cells of the phloem tissue, which are strung together to form vertical columns. Transverse walls separating the elements develop into specialized areas called *sieve plates,* the sieve areas being traversed by what appears to be cytoplasmic strands. Thus, the cytoplasmic connection is continuous over the entire length of a column of sieve tube elements. Unlike their counterparts in the xylem tissue (vessel elements), the sieve tube elements are living when functional. A longitudinal view of a sieve tube element and adjacent cells is given in Figure 9-3.

The ontogeny of a sieve tube element presents an interesting picture of a cell adapting to a specialized function in the plant. The immature sieve element presents a rather normal cell, consisting of a nucleus and an actively streaming cytoplasm. In addition, the cytoplasm may contain plastids and slime bodies (16). In the young sieve element, cytoplasmic strands may traverse the vacuole, and usually the nucleus is suspended in these strands (9). Cytoplasmic streaming appears to be especially active along the strands.

As the sieve element develops, several changes take place. The nucleus and slime bodies disintegrate. Spheroid bodies found in the cytoplasm of mature elements have been identified as nucleoli released as a result of nuclear disintegration (14). The cytoplasm of a mature element is devoid of an endoplasmic reticulum (1, 17) and appears to be confined to thin layers along the side walls of the cell. Streaming slows and finally stops,

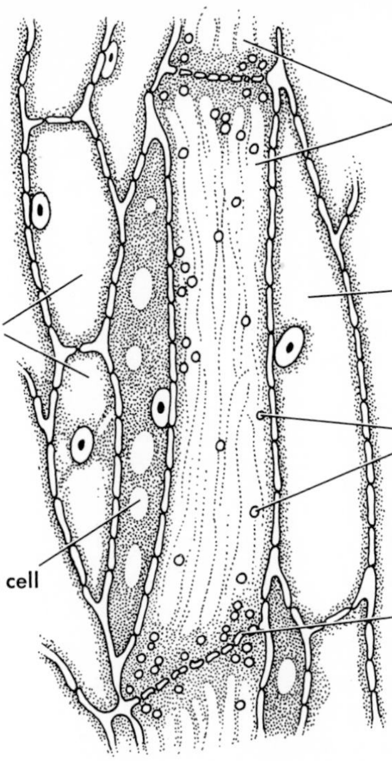

Figure 9-3 Phloem tissue from the stem of *Nicotiana tabacum,* showing a sieve tube element, a companion cell, and phloem parenchyma cells. (After R. Holman and W. Robbins, 1938. Textbook of general botany for colleges and universities. Wiley, New York.)

and mitochondria appear to be missing. In a recent study of the ultrastructure of the secondary phloem of *Tilia americana* (17), mitochondia have been detected, but in relatively low number. These features indicate a slowing down of metabolic activity, and the cytoplasm at this stage is considered to be highly permeable. Connecting strands of cytoplasm are readily observed in mature sieve elements traversing the sieve plates.

SUBSTANCES TRANSLOCATED IN THE PHLOEM

Carbohydrates

Nine-tenths, or even more, of the substances translocated in the phloem are carbohydrates (64). Although this has been shown experimentally, one could assume that this statement is true after considering that the bulk of the plant is composed of carbohydrate materials.

Analyses of the phloem exudates of 16 tree species by Zimmermann (60, 61) have shown that *sucrose* is by far the most dominant carbohydrate translocated. However, in addition to sucrose, some species translocate oligosaccharides, such as *raffinose, stachyose,* and *verbascose*. These sugars are similar to each other in that they consist of sucrose with one or more attached D-galactose units. Also, the sugar alcohol mannitol has been detected in the phloem exudates of some species (60, 62).

Although the hexoses glucose and fructose are commonly present in the phloem tissues of plants, chromatographic analyses of phloem exudates demonstrate the complete absence of these sugars (64, 49). If we consider phloem exudates as true samples of the substances translocated in the phloem, then we must accept the fact that sucrose is the most prominent sugar translocated and that hexoses are not translocated. The glucose and fructose sugars generally found must occur in the nonconducting cells of the phloem tissues as a result of the hydrolysis of sucrose and related sugars (49).

It is significant to note that Swanson and El-Shishiny (51), using a different technique, arrived at the conclusion presented above. Analyses of grape vine sections (*Vitis labruscana* var. Concord) at increasing distances from a leaf supplied with $C^{14}O_2$ produced some very interesting results. First, the largest amount of radioactivity was found in the sucrose fraction of the bark (Table 9-1). Also notice in Table 9-1 that the rela-

Table 9-1 Relative concentrations of C^{14}-labeled sugars in the bark as a function of translocation distance.[a]

Distance of translocation, mm	*Counts/min/mg dry wt of bark*			*Glu/Suc*	*Fru/Suc*
	Suc	*Glu*	*Fru*		
82	8005	661	678	0.083	0.085
202	6268	433	481	0.069	0.077
321	5800	397	402	0.069	0.069
429	4615	220	250	0.048	0.054
652	2942	136	126	0.046	0.043
875	1749	75	69	0.043	0.040
1156	900	34	31	0.037	0.034

[a] After Swanson and El-Shishiny (1958).

tive amounts of labeled glucose and labeled fructose are approximately the same at each section of bark analyzed. Now, if we assume that glucose and fructose are equally labeled as a result of $C^{14}O_2$ assimilation in photosynthesis, then the sucrose synthesized from these hexoses should yield, on hydrolysis, equal amounts of labeled glucose and fructose. A reasonable assumption, therefore, would be that the glucose and fructose detected in the bark sections are products of sucrose hydrolysis and not translocatory sugars.

Assuming that the above conclusion is valid, then we would expect the ratios of labeled hexoses to labeled sucrose to decrease with increasing distances from the leaf assimilating $C^{14}O_2$. This line of reasoning is based on the fact that labeled sucrose at a distance from the experimental leaf has had less time to be hydrolyzed than sucrose in the immediate area of the leaf. An examination of Table 9-1 will show the above expectation to be fully correct, the ratios decreasing from a high of about 0.084 to a low of 0.036. The above evidence strongly supports the concept that sucrose is the principal sugar translocated in the phloem and that hexoses are not translocated. The hexoses generally found on analyses of phloem tissues are thought to be products of the hydrolysis of sucrose and related sugars.

In the above study, it was concluded that hexoses appearing in the sieve tube elements were the result of the hydrolysis of sucrose. Essentially, the same conclusion was arrived at by Burley (6) in a study of sucrose translocation in soybean and raspberry. However, it should be noted that in at least two studies of phloem translocation in sugar cane, the data collected indicate that sucrose remains intact while moving in the phloem ducts (21, 22).

Nitrogenous compounds

It is common knowledge that amino acids and amides are translocated out of senescent leaves and flowers and relocated in younger areas of the plant. Furthermore, the movement of these nitrogenous compounds takes place primarily in the phloem. Exudate analyses by Mittler (36, 37) for nitrogenous compounds translocated in the sieve tube elements of willow stems have detected the presence of glutamic acid, aspartic acid, threonine, alanine, serine, leucine, valine, phenylalanine, asparagine, glutamine, and γ-aminobutyric acid. Actually, very little work on the detection of these compounds in the phloem has been done, but undoubtedly future workers will find most, if not all, of the natural amino acids and amides in sieve tube exudates. Mittler's work is a giant stride in that direction.

Apparently, the concentration of nitrogenous compounds in phloem exudates is affected by the different developmental stages of the plant. For example, in *Salix* these compounds are present in highest concentration and variety during rapid leaf growth and at the end of the growing season, when leaf senescence is prevalent (49). During the greater portion of the growing season, however, nitrogenous compounds are present in the phloem in very low concentration. For example, Zimmermann (60) has found that the concentration of amino acids and amides in the sieve tube exudates of white ash is usually less than 0.001*M*.

GENERAL ASPECTS OF PHLOEM TRANSLOCATION

We have discussed so far the anatomy of the phloem tissue and the organic materials translocated in the phloem ducts. We will now consider the direction and rate of movement of these substances.

Direction of movement

Bidirectional movement. It is obvious from the previous discussion of phloem transport that the movement of organic materials in the plant is *bidirectional.* That is, substances are translocated in opposite directions in the stem simultaneously. Photosynthate moving out of the leaves may be translocated in the direction of the root or it may move toward growing points, where flowers or fruits may be in the process of development. The mobiiization of organic materials in storage organs, such as tap roots, tubers, bulbs, etc., for the nourishment of seedling growth is generally in an upward direction. The retranslocation of materials out of aging leaves and into young actively growing leaves is obviously an upward movement. In a very elegant study of phloem transport in bean plants, Biddulph and Cory (4), using $C^{14}O_2$-feeding and fluorescence techniques, have shown that leaves nearest the root transport metabolites primarily to the root. Leaves nearest the top of the plant transport to the stem apex, while leaves in an intermediate position translocate metabolites in both directions. Figure 9-4 shows the distribution of labeled metabolites after the primary leaf of a squash plant has been fed $C^{14}O_2$ (58). Note in Figure 9-4 that metabolites moved to both the upper and lower parts of the plant.

That organic materials move in both directions in the stem simultaneously has been unequivocally shown with the use of radioactive tagging techniques. What has not been shown is whether materials move in different directions in different phloem ducts or in the same duct simultaneously. This problem is still, as yet, unsolved and can only be solved by the actual demonstration of either unidirectional or bidirectional movement in one sieve duct, a rather difficult job indeed. However, Biddulph and Cory (4) demonstrated that bidirectional movement in bean plants took place in separate phloem bundles.

Lateral movement in a tangential direction. Several studies of translo-

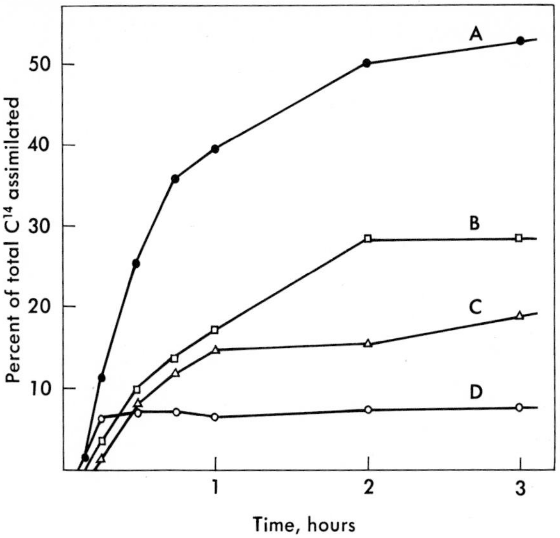

Figure 9-4 Distribution of labeled metabolites after the primary leaf of a squash plant had been fed $C^{14}O_2$. Note that radioactivity is found in both the upper and lower sections of the plant. A. Total export. B. Upper plant. C. Lower plant. D. Petiole. (After J. A. Webb and P. R. Gorham. 1964. Plant Physiol. 39:663.

cation patterns show that materials moving in the phloem ducts generally move in a linear fashion. That is, sugars moving out of a leaf into the main translocation stream will move both up and down the stem in line with the supplying leaf. Very little *tangential* movement takes place. It is commonly observed, for example, that annual rings of trees directly under large branches or on the side of a tree receiving less competition from surrounding neighbors are considerably wider than the opposite side. Defoliation of one side of a plant frequently will cause asymmetrical growth, growth on the defoliated side being considerably reduced.

A study of translocation patterns in the sugar beet by Joy (25) produced some very interesting results. When $C^{14}O_2$ was fed to a leaf, labeled metabolites were found only in leaves directly above or below the supplying leaf. This is in agreement with our previous discussion emphasizing the absence of tangential movement. However, Joy found that if he removed all fully expanded leaves from one side of the plant (leaving only young immature leaves) and then fed $C^{14}O_2$ to a mature leaf on the intact side of the plant, he could induce tangential movement. Radioactive metabolites were found not only above and below the supplying leaf, but also in the young leaves left intact on the otherwise defoliated side (Figure 9-5). Apparently, young leaves deprived of photosynthate (by defoliation

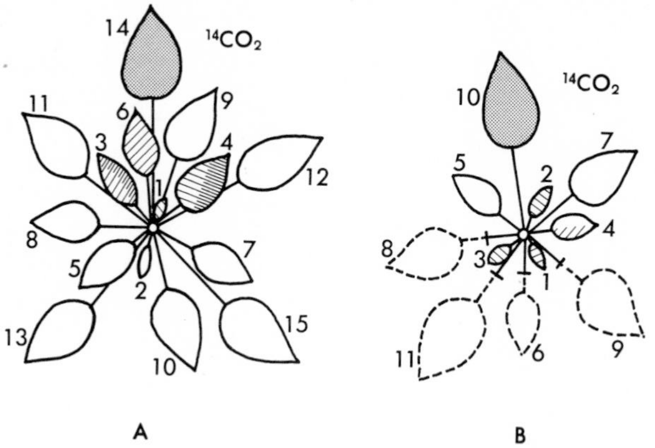

Figure 9-5 A. Distribution of C^{14} in leaves of a sugar beet plant one week after a single mature leaf was fed $C^{14}O_2$ for four hours. The shading is roughly equivalent to intensity of activity. Note that C^{14} was translocated to young leaves on one side of the plant only. B. Fully expanded leaves were removed from one side of the plant leaving only young immature leaves. $C^{14}O_2$ was then fed to a mature leaf on the intact side of the plant. Radioactivity is found on both sides of the plant. The leaves are numbered in accordance with age; that is, the higher numbered leaves are the more mature leaves and the low numbered leaves are the youngest leaves. (After K. W. Joy. 1964. J. Exptl. Botan. 15:485.)

of the mature leaves) can place a high enough demand on leaves on the opposite side of the plant to cause some tangential movement. Joy points out, however, that the complicated vascular anastomosis found in beet may aid in this type of transport and that distribution patterns in other plants may be much more rigidly defined. It should be noted, however, that tangential movement has been shown in other plant species, for example, by Biddulph (2) in bean and by Peel (42) in willow.

Distribution patterns at different developmental stages in the tobacco plant show both bidirectional and tangential movement (46). The seventh leaf (counting from the bottom) of four different tobacco plants—ages 68, 81, 107, 135 days—was allowed to photosynthesize in $C^{14}O_2$ for 30 minutes followed by a 5.5 hour period of photosynthesis under normal

Figure 9-6 Distribution patterns at different developmental stages in the tobacco plant showing both bidirectional and tangential movement. Counting from the bottom, the seventh leaf of four tobacco plants—ages 68, 81, 107 and 135 days—was fed $C^{14}O_2$ for 30 minutes followed by a 5.5 hour period of photosynthesis under normal conditions. Blackened areas indicate leaves containing C^{14}. See Table 9-2 for the intensity of radioactivity in μc found in the treated leaf, other leaves, stem and root of each plant (After Shiroya et al. 1961. Can. J. Botany 39:855.)

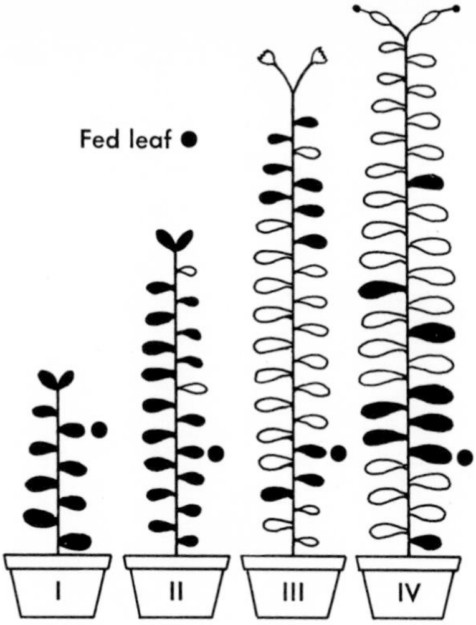

Table 9-2 The intensity of radioactivity in μc found in the treated leaf, other leaves, stem, and root of the four tobacco plants shown in Figure 9-6.[a]

	Plant			
Part	*I*	*II*	*III*	*IV*
treated leaf	131.2	155.9	93.3	136.7
other leaves	1.3	6.2	trace	trace
stem	34.4	10.1	10.8	12.7
root	1.7	0.9	1.8	5.9

[a] After Shiroya et al. (1961).

conditions. The additional 5.5 hour period allowed for complete distribution of the label without any appreciable redistribution taking place. On completion of the experiment, the leaves, stems, and roots were analyzed for C^{14} (Figure 9-6 and Table 9-2).

Radioactive carbon was found in the roots of all four plants. However, the bulk of radioactivity was found in the stems. The pattern of distribution of radioactive carbon shown in Figure 9-6 demonstrates that areas of high metabolic activity, such as the actively growing stem and young leaves, are particularly good "sinks" for the deposition of translocated carbohydrates. Note that the radioactive carbon moved both up and down the stem.

Let us consider, now, the lack of C^{14} in leaves 11 and 19 of plant II. A consideration of Figure 9-7 will show that the phyllotaxis[1] of plant II

[1] The system or order of arrangement of leaves on a plant axis.

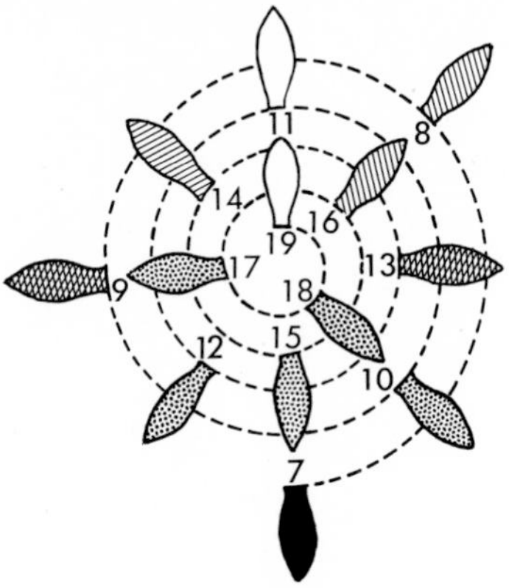

Figure 9-7 Phyllotaxis showing the distribution of C^{14} in plant II of Figure 9-6. The degree of shading indicates relative activity. The leaves are numbered from the seventh leaf (treated leaf) upward to the nineteenth leaf. (After Shiroya et al. 1961. Can. J. Botany 39:855.)

was such that leaves 11 and 19 were situated exactly opposite leaf 7 ($C^{14}O_2$-fed leaf). Note also that as the tangential distance from the fed leaf increases, there is a progressive decrease in radioactivity. That is, leaves 10, 12, 15, 17, and 18 have more C^{14} than leaves 9 and 13. Leaves 9 and 13, in turn, have more C^{14} than leaves 8, 14, and 16. Leaves 11 and 19, being directly opposite leaf 7, have no C^{14}. The above experiment demonstrates that in the tobacco plant some tangential movement takes place, but it is definitely inferior to vertical movement.

Lateral movement in a radial direction. Radial transfer from the phloem to the xylem tissues has been observed in a wide variety of plants. In fact, loss of labeled metabolites from the phloem to the xylem through radial transport has been shown in the bean plant to reach values of 25% or more, as compared to their concentration in the phloem (3). Because of their position as continuous connections between the phloem and xylem, vascular rays are thought to facilitate, considerably, radial movement.

Translocation rates and velocities

When one estimates the amount of material needed to maintain the rapid growth of storage organs, he becomes aware of the importance of translocation rates for the movement of substances in the phloem tissues. Early workers obtained these rates by noting the increase in dry weight of fruits, tubers, storage roots, and other organs that import large amounts of materials from the phloem ducts. However, there are many difficulties inherent in this method, and several other measures have to be taken before actual rates can be calculated. For example, corrections have to be made for local synthesis of metabolites if photosynthetic tissues are used. Also, one has to calculate losses due to respiration, condensation, and relocation of metabolites. In many cases, these losses cannot be directly measured, causing certain assumptions to be made, which suggest that translocation rates obtained in this manner are only indicative of the actual rates occurring.

With the advent of tracing techniques, however, fairly accurate translocation rates have been obtained. Usually, these methods entail the feeding of a leaf or leaves $C^{14}O_2$, which in turn is assimilated in the photosynthetic process. The progress of the radioactive metabolites so formed is followed by detection of radioactivity at different distances along the stem. Some of the translocation rates that have been obtained by utilizing the technique of tracing a radioactive isotope are given in Table 9-3.

If we consider the relatively small amount of area in the complex of sieve tubes available for translocation, it is remarkable that the high rates shown in Table 9-2 can be obtained. This situation is further complicated

Table 9-3 Translocation rates in different plant species obtained through the use of radioactive tracers.

Plants	*Rate, cm/hr*	*Source*
red kidney bean	107	Biddulph and Cory, 1957
sugar beet	85–100	Kursanov et al., 1953
concord grape	60	Swanson and El-Shishiny, 1958
willow	100	Weatherley et al., 1959
sugarcane	270	Hatch and Glasziou, 1964
sugarcane	84	Hartt et al., 1963
straight-necked squash	290	Webb and Gorham, 1964
soybean	100	Vernon and Aronoff, 1952
pumpkin	40–60	Pristupa and Kursanov, 1957

by the fact that several thousands of sieve plates have to be traversed before a metabolite from the leaf can reach the root of a plant. For example, Weatherley et al. (57) found that for every 16 cm traveled in a willow stem, 1600 to 2000 sieve plates had to be traversed. Later in this chapter, we will discuss certain mechanisms that may explain how translocation rates can be so high while meeting so much resistance in the phloem ducts.

Different metabolites with different translocation rates. Several investigators have noted that different metabolites are translocated at different rates in the phloem ducts. When a solution containing tritiated water[2] (THO), P^{32}, and C^{14}-sucrose is fed to the leaves of a 12 day old bean plant, different translocation rates are obtained for the individual radioactive substances (3). The C^{14}-sucrose moves considerably faster (107

[2] In tritiated water (THO), one or both of the stable hydrogen atoms of H_2O are replaced by the radioactive isotope tritium (H^3).

cm/hr) than either THO or P^{32}, both of which move at the rate of 87 cm/hr. Similar results were obtained by Gage and Aronoff (18) when they introduced a solution of C^{14}-fructose and THO to a cut petiole of a 3 week old soybean plant. In this situation, the radioactive sugar moves much faster than THO. According to the authors of the above studies, sugars and water may be, to a great extent, independent of each other when translocated in the phloem. In addition, studies by Nelson and Gorham (41) have indicated that different amino acids move at different speeds in the phloem.

Factors affecting translocation

Several factors are known to affect translocation rates in plants. The most important of these are temperature, light, metabolic inhibitors, concentration gradients, mineral deficiencies, and hormones. This list of factors is by no means complete, but represents those factors that have been studied most frequently.

Temperature. An analysis of the effect of temperature on translocation rates is complicated by the influence of temperature on other plant processes that may directly or indirectly affect the movement of solutes. Thus, the influence of temperature on photosynthesis, respiration, auxin synthesis, etc., in all probability has a profound influence on translocation rates. Nevertheless, a definite relationship between temperature and rate of translocation has been demonstrated.

By varying the temperature of a plant and measuring the increase or decrease in the dry weights of different organs, indirect measures of translocation rates may be obtained. The assumption is that the dry weight of an organ reflects the rate of movement of solutes into that organ. Using the above method, Hewitt and Curtis (23) demonstrated that the optimum temperature for translocation in bean plants is between 20 and 30°C (curve 2 in Figure 9-8).

When a plant is subjected to a range of temperatures, its entire metabolism is influenced, making it difficult to obtain a true picture of the effect of temperature on translocation per se. In an attempt to circumvent this problem, Swanson and Böhning (50) tried localized temperature treatments. In their experiments, bean plants were grown at a temperature of 20 ± 1°C. The petiole of one leaf of each plant was fitted with a "temperature jacket" and the blade of that leaf immersed in a sucrose solution. The plants were then placed in dark cabinets where the temperature was kept constant at 20 ± 1°C. Thus, with the exception of the treated petiole, the entire plant was subjected to the same constant temperature. After 135 hours of treatment, the increase in length of the stem during this time

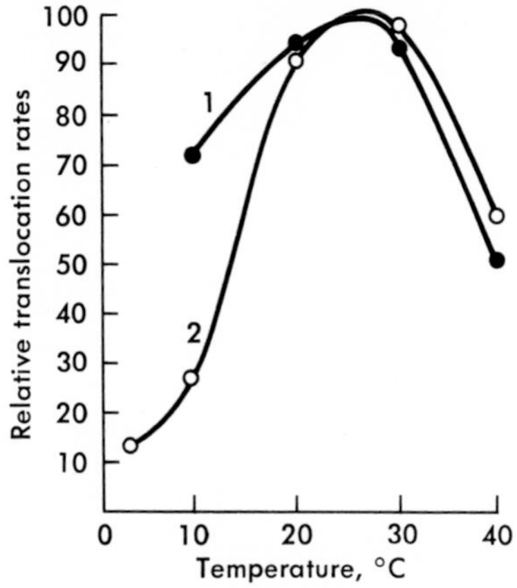

Figure 9-8 The translocation of carbohydrates in bean as affected by temperature. Curve 1 describes the effect of temperature when applied only to the petiole of one leaf (blade immersed in a solution of sucrose). (After C. A. Swanson and R. H. Böhning. 1951. Plant Physiol. 26:557.) Curve 2 describes the effect of temperature when applied to the whole plant. (After S. P. Hewitt and O. F. Curtis. 1948. Am. J. Botany 35:746.)

was taken as a measure of the rate of movement of sucrose through the treated petiole to the stem. Curve 1 in Figure 9-8 illustrates the data collected in this experiment. The results agree remarkably well with those of Hewitt and Curtis (curve 2) where the whole plant was subjected to fluctuations in temperature. A study of Figure 9-8 does establish one very important point, that the translocation of solutes is influenced by temperature in much the same manner as other physiological processes. That is, the rate of translocation increases with temperature to a maximum and then decreases due to the detrimental effects of high temperature.

Only recently have we been able to obtain data on the translocation of radioactive sugars as influenced by different temperatures. Sugarcane plants fed $C^{14}O_2$ have been shown to have translocation rates that increase with increase in temperature. Thus, sugarcane plants subjected to air temperatures of 20, 24.5, and 33°C have translocation rates of 84.0, 93.6, and 120 cm/hr, respectively (20). The distribution of radioactivity 90 minutes after $C^{14}O_2$ treatment at the above temperatures is shown in Figure 9-9.

It appears that the temperature of the root as compared to the shoot may have an influence on which direction (up or down from a $C^{14}O_2$-supplied leaf) sugars will move in a plant. Thus, Hartt (20) found that when root temperature is kept higher than shoot temperature, translocation to the root increases and translocation to the top decreases. When the situation is reversed—shoot temperature higher than root temperature—translocation to the top is increased and translocation to the roots decreased (Figure 9-10). One can assume from Figure 9-10 that the root and top of the sugarcane provide "sinks" for the utilization of C^{14}-sugars translocated from the treated leaf. The respiratory activities of these plant parts are enhanced by an increase in temperature. Therefore, an increase in root temperature over shoot temperature will increase downward translocation.

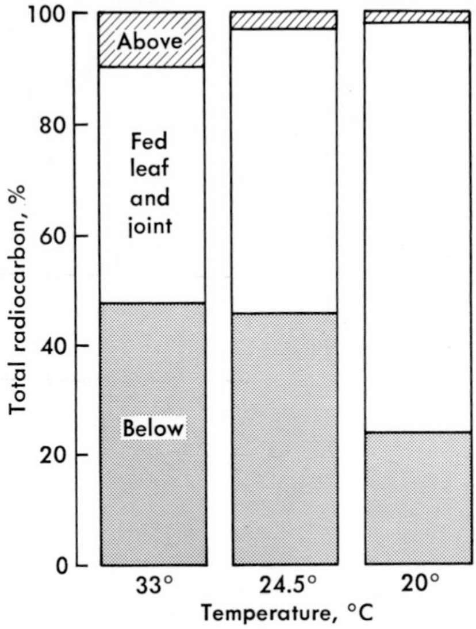

Figure 9-9 Distribution of C^{14} in sugar cane as affected by air temperature. Data were obtained 90 minutes after $C^{14}O_2$ was fed to one leaf. (After C. E. Hartt. 1965. Plant Physiol. 40:74.)

Upward translocation will be increased if shoot temperature is higher than root temperature.

Light. As we shall see in a later chapter, the assimilation of CO_2 increases with increase in light intensity. The root/shoot dry weight ratio of wheat increases with increasing light intensities, indicating that translocation to the root compared to the shoot increases with light intensity (Table 9-4).

Table 9-4 The root/shoot dry weight ratio of wheat showing an increase with increase in light intensities. This indicates that translocation to the root compared to the shoot increases with light intensity.[a]

Light intensity, ft-c	*Root/shoot ratio*
200	0.14
500	0.17
1000	0.27
1750	0.32
2500	0.32
5000	0.43

[a] Data of D. J. C. Friend, V. A. Helson, and J. E. Fisher, as reported by C. D. Nelson 1963. *In* Environmental control of plant growth. Academic Press, New York.

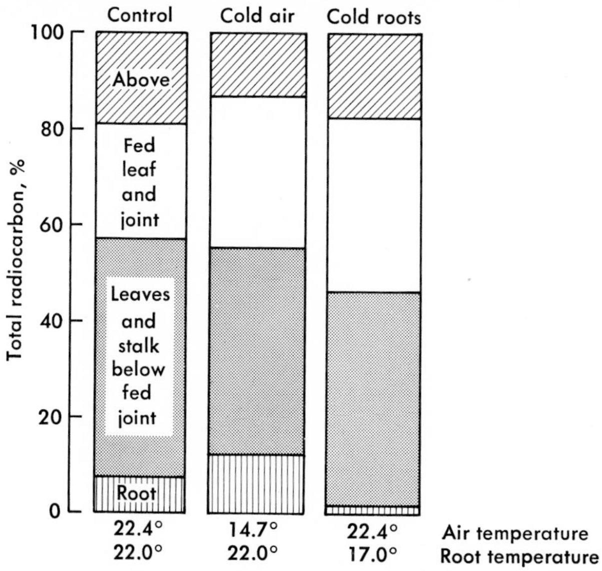

Figure 9-10 Distribution of C^{14} after translocation for six days as affected by air and root temperature regulated separately. Note that when root temperature is kept higher than shoot temperature, translocation increases to the root and decreases to the top. When root temperature is kept lower than shoot temperature, translocation decreases to the root and increases to the top. (After C. E. Hartt. 1965. Plant Physiol. 40:74.)

A study of the translocation of radioactive metabolites in the light and in the dark with soybean plants by Nelson and Gorham (40) has produced some interesting results. They first allowed two 30-day old soybean plants to photosynthesize in $C^{14}O_2$ for 15 minutes after which one plant was allowed to remain in the light an additional 3 hours. The other plant was placed in the dark, also for a 3 hour period. When the plant parts were analyzed, it was found that the light plants translocated in 3 hours about 2% of their total radioactivity to the stem tip and 4.4% to the roots. The dark plants, on the other hand, translocated in 3 hours only 0.5% of their total radioactivity to the stem tip, while the roots received 16.5%. One can postulate from such data that root translocation is favored over shoot translocation in the dark.

Nelson and Gorham also studied the translocation of radioactive sucrose deposited in solution on the leaf blades of soybean plants. Translocation of the C^{14}-sucrose was allowed to occur for 14 hours in the light for one plant and for 14 hours in the dark for another. The results of this experiment are shown in Figure 9-11.

It is of considerable interest that only 1% of the radioactivity left the

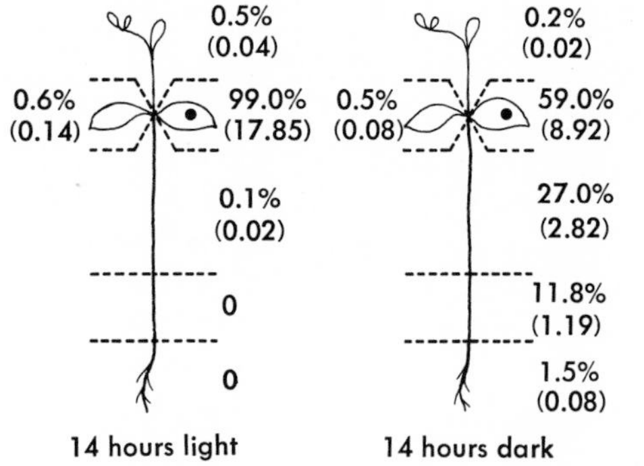

Figure 9-11 Translocation of C^{14} metabolites under the influence of both light and dark conditions. The results are expressed as percent of C^{14} recovered. (After C. D. Nelson and P. R. Gorham. 1957. Can. J. Botany 35:339.)

leaf after 14 hours of illumination, whereas in the dark about 40% of the radioactivity moved in the direction of the roots. It appears that externally applied sugars are translocated only reluctantly in the light. It again appears that in the dark, root translocation is definitely favored.

Metabolic inhibitors. Metabolic inhibitors have been shown to inhibit phloem translocation (26, 59, 55). Some of the inhibitors used include 2,4-dinitrophenol (DNP), arsenite, azide, iodoacetic acid, fluoride, and hydrogen cyanide. It is rather difficult to assess, however, whether the inhibitor has its effect on the metabolism of the conducting elements per se or on the metabolism of the supplying and receiving cells. It is conceivable that the inhibitor could be carried to the photosynthesizing mesophyll cells of the leaf, where it would inhibit cell-to-cell transport of photosynthate to the phloem conducting elements. It is just as possible for a metabolic inhibitor to be carried to the receiving cells or "sinks," where it might impede the deposition of translocated metabolites. In both cases, the rate of translocation would be inhibited. Indeed, Swanson (49), in a review of the subject, has claimed that work with inhibitors indicates that translocation rates are more a function of the metabolism of the supplying and receiving tissues than of the metabolism of the conducting cells themselves.

We must keep in mind, however, that the sieve tube elements are living when functional. Therefore, one cannot dismiss the possibility that energy-producing processes might be involved in translocation. In a recent review, Kursanov (30) has emphasized the role of metabolism in phloem transport. With this in mind, it is not difficult to assume at least a partial effect of metabolic inhibitors on translocation through a direct retarding influence on the metabolism of the conducting elements.

Concentration gradients. It is generally believed that the direction of sugar flow in the sieve tubes is along a gradient of decreasing total sugar concentrations. Early work by Mason and Maskell (32, 33) on the translocation of sugars in the cotton plant demonstrated that the movement of sugars follows a "diffusion pattern"—that is, a correlation between rate of transport and sugar gradient in the bark exists. They found that the direction of translocation is always from a region of high concentration to a region of low concentration. These authors also found that defoliation causes the sugar gradient to disappear (see review by Mason and Phillis (34)).

In more recent work, Zimmermann (60, 62, 63) found concentration gradients in white ash to be about 0.01 mole/m and positive in the downward direction of the trunk. Defoliation experiments by Zimmermann produced some interesting results. As with the work of Mason and Maskell, removal of carbohydrate supply caused the sugar gradient in the sieve tube system to disappear. However, some of the concentration gradients of individual sugars became negative (Figure 9-12).

The significance of sugar concentration gradients in phloem translocation will be further discussed in the succeeding section dealing with translocation mechanisms.

Mineral deficiencies. Perhaps the most significant work concerning the role of minerals in phloem transport has been done with boron. Gauch and Dugger (19) found that boron greatly facilitated the absorption and translocation of C^{14}-sucrose in tomato plants (Figure 9-13). According to these authors, an ionizable complex is formed between boron and sucrose, which moves through cell membranes much more readily than non-borated sucrose.

Sucrose is not the only compound aided in its translocation by boron. The growth regulators, 2,4-dichlorophenoxyacetic acid, indole acetic acid, 2,4,5-trichlorophenoxyacetic acid, and α-naphthalene acetic acid, when applied with sucrose to the leaves of a bean plant are translocated much more efficiently in the presence of boron (35). Supporting evidence for the above work was obtained from boron-sufficient and boron-deficient tomato plants exposed to $C^{14}O_2$ for 20 minutes (47). More fixed C^{14} was translocated in the boron-sufficient plants.

Aside from the very noticeable effects of boron, very little is known about

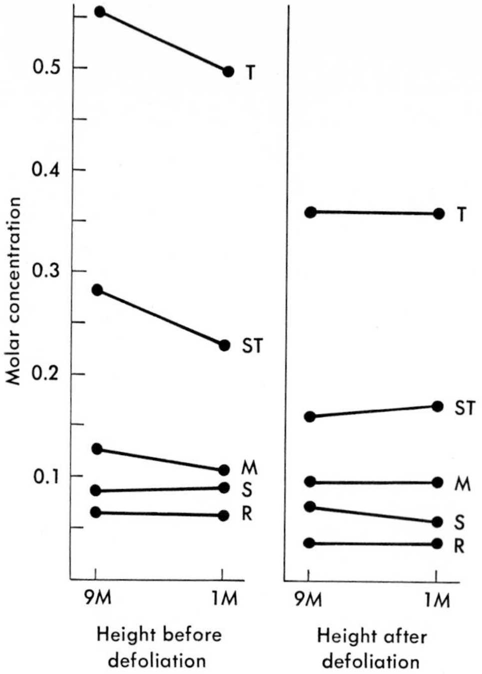

Figure 9-12 Concentration gradients along a tree trunk of white ash (*Fraxinus americana*) before and after defoliation. Note the disappearance of gradients as a result of defoliation, some of the gradients becoming slightly negative. T = total concentration, ST = stachyose, M = sucrose, and R = raffinose. (After M. H. Zimmermann. 1958. Plant Physiol. 33:213.)

the influence of mineral deficiency on phloem translocation. Phosphorus deficiency has been implicated as influencing adversely the translocation of 2,4-dichlorophenoxyacetic acid (45) and phosphorus (27). It is hard to assess whether phosphorus deficiency affects phloem translocation per se or has its influence through modifying the metabolism of supplying and receiving tissues. Indeed, it has been suggested by at least one investigator (48) that even the influence of boron on sugar translocation may be indirect, rather than direct as proposed by Gauch and Dugger. According to Skok (48), the effect of boron on sugar translocation is related to its being necessary for cellular activity in apical meristems, rather than to a direct enhancement of diffusion through membranes via the formation of a sugar-borate complex.

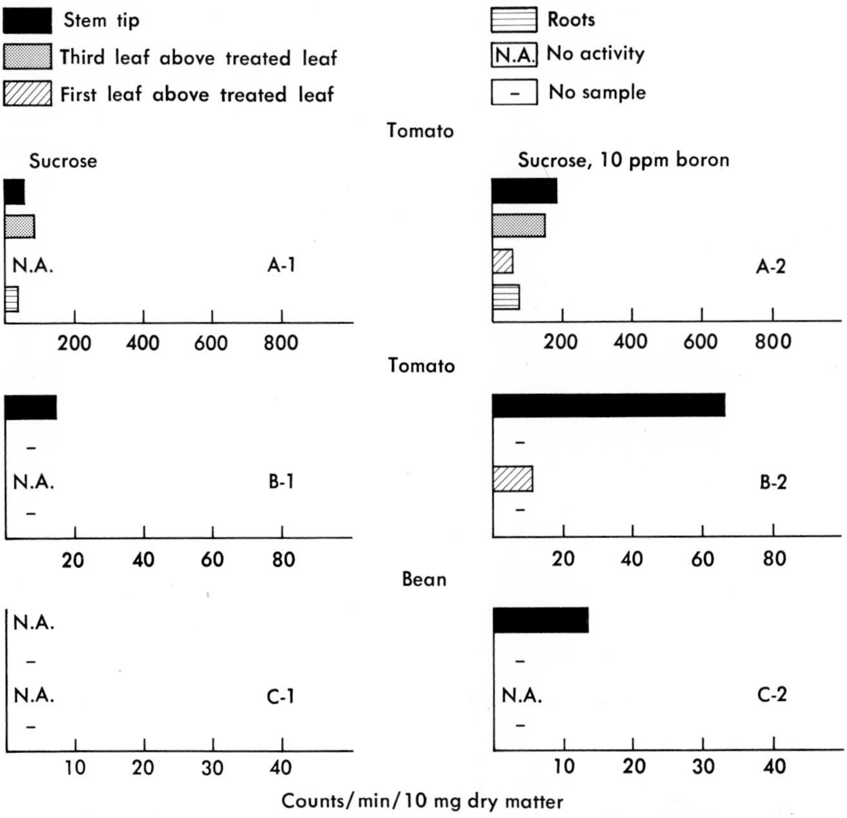

Figure 9-13 The intensity of radioactivity (C^{14}) in various plant parts as a result of the movement of labeled sucrose (or its hydrolytic products) from a lower leaf immersed for 24 hours in a solution of labeled sucrose or labeled sucrose plus boron. A. Tomatoes cultured in sand, receiving no boron in the substrate, and subjected to a 48-hour dark period prior to and during treatment. B. Soil-grown tomatoes receiving complete nutrition and kept in the light. C. Soil-grown snap bean plants receiving complete nutrition and subjected to a 48-hour dark period prior to and during treatment. (After H. G. Gauch and W. M. Dugger, Jr. 1953. Plant Physiol. 28:457.)

Hormones. Plant hormones are closely associated with the actively growing centers of the plant and, therefore, would at the very least have a strong indirect effect on phloem translocation. Cellular and tissue growth stimulated by growth hormones puts a heavy demand on translocated metabolites for building materials and energy. Many investigators believe that the metabolism of these growth centers (sinks) has a strong influence on translocation.

Very little information has been obtained on direct effects of plant hormones on translocation. However, experiments by DeStigter (12) with *Cucumis melo* and *Cucurbita ficifolia* suggest a direct hormonal influence on phloem translocation. A graft of *C. melo* on *C. ficifolia* will only take if the seedling stock retains its leaves (Figure 9-14A). Why this happens is clearly demonstrated with $C^{14}O_2$. As shown in Figure 9-14B, photosynthate assimilated in the leaves of *C. melo* is not translocated to the stock. However, one has only to graft one leaf of the stock (*C. ficifolia*) to the scion (*C. melo*) for uninhibited translocation to occur. If photosynthate from the grafted leaf and the scion is translocated uninhibited to the root, the graft will take (Figure 9-14C). The above described experiment by DeStigter suggests that some hormone present in leaves may be necessary for proper phloem translocation.

The plant hormone kinetin appears to affect the translocation of soluble nitrogen compounds (38). If a leaf of *Nicotiana rustica* is removed from the plant, there is a migration of soluble nitrogen compounds from the

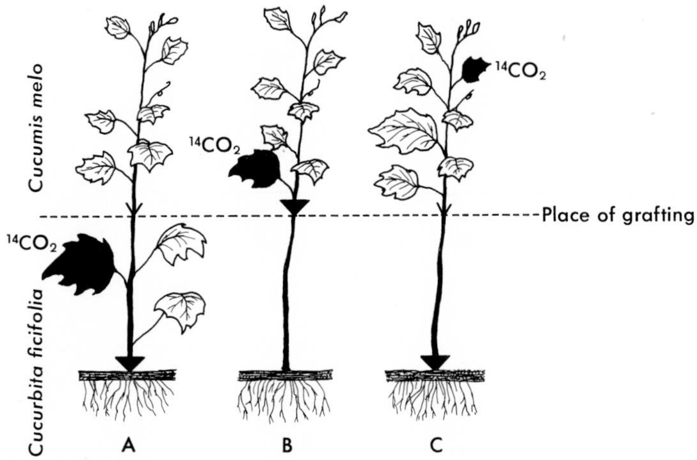

Figure 9-14 Possible direct effect of plant hormones on translocation. A. Graft of *C. melo* on *C. ficifolia* with leaves. The graft takes and translocation takes place normally. B. Graft of *C. melo* on *C. ficifolia* without leaves. Graft does not take because translocation of photosynthate from *C. melo* to *C. ficifolia* is blocked. C. Graft of *C. melo* on *C. ficifolia* without leaves, but with one *C. ficifolia* leaf grafted to *C. melo*. Graft takes and translocation of photosynthate takes place normally. Redrawn from A. L. Kursanov. 1963. *In* R. D. Preston (ed.) Advances in botanical research. Academic Press, New York. After H. C. M. DeStigter. 1961. Acta Botan. Neerlandica 10:466.)

blade into the petiole. Because of this, a regeneration of protein cannot occur in the blade, and it rapidly turns yellow. However, if the blade is sprayed with kinetin, the blade will remain green; that is, the migration of soluble nitrogen compounds out of the blade into the petiole is retarded. Moreover, if only one-half of the blade is sprayed with kinetin, a migration of soluble nitrogen from the unsprayed half to the sprayed half will occur. In other words, kinetin promotes the accumulation of soluble nitrogen.

MECHANISMS OF PHLOEM TRANSLOCATION

No one theory on the mechanism of phloem translocation has gained general acceptance. Perhaps the reason for this is that no mechanism has been presented that can account for all the different aspects of phloem translocation. However, several different mechanisms have been described and defended in various ways by their proponents. We will discuss two of these, the mass or pressure flow hypothesis and the protoplasmic streaming hypothesis.

Mass or pressure flow hypothesis

The physiological basis of the mass or pressure flow hypothesis, described first by Münch in 1930, rests on the assumption that a *turgor pressure gradient* exists between the supplying and receiving tissues. Metabolites are thought to be carried passively in the positive direction of the gradient. In other words, in the pressure flow system we have a unidirectional flow of solutes and water through the sieve ducts driven by a turgor pressure gradient. For example, let us examine the physical system shown in Figure 9-15.

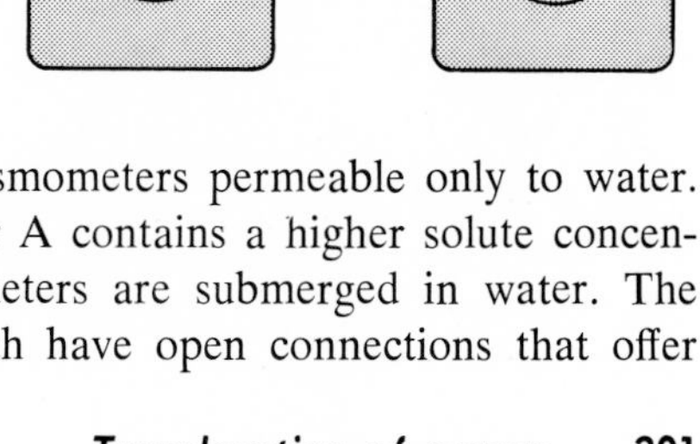

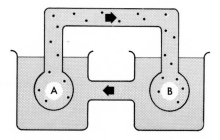

Figure 9-15 A simple physical system demonstrating the mass or pressure flow hypothesis. Further explanation in text.

Let us assume that A and B are osmometers permeable only to water. Let us further assume that osmometer A contains a higher solute concentration than B and that both osmometers are submerged in water. The osmometers and water containers both have open connections that offer little resistance to the flow of solutes and water. Since this is a closed system and the wall of the osmometers are differentially permeable, water will enter A and B, causing a turgor pressure to develop. However, osmometer A will develop a higher turgor pressure, since it contains a higher concentration of solute, and this greater pressure will be transmitted throughout the system by virtue of the open connection between the two osmometers. If the walls of A and B are uniformly elastic, a negative diffusion pressure deficit should develop in B as a result of the above conditions. Thus, a circulating system is created. Water is induced to flow from A to B, solutes being carried along passively. Water is "pushed" out of B by virtue of the *negative* diffusion pressure that has developed and is recirculated via the open connection between the water containers. A, then, is the supplying osmometer, and B is the receiving osmometer.

If we apply the above system to the plant, A would represent the supplying cells of the leaf and B the receiving cells of some plant organ (e.g., the root). The connecting links between the osmometers and water containers would represent the sieve and xylem ducts, respectively.

With this picture in mind, we can see how sugars would be carried from supplying to receiving organs without any expenditure of energy on the part of the plant. However, it is hard to reconcile the pressure flow theory with several facts that have been established concerning the phloem transport system.

First of all, a prerequisite to phloem translocation is that the sieve tube elements have to be living to translocate. In addition, the translocation of solutes is influenced by temperature and metabolic inhibitors in much the same manner as other physiological processes (see Figure 9-8). These facts suggest that the translocation of metabolites is not a passive process, but requires an expenditure of energy on the part of the sieve tube elements. Proponents of the pressure flow mechanism, however, have pointed out that temperature and metabolic inhibitor treatments affect the basal metabolism of the sieve tube elements and not translocation per se. In addition, they point out that metabolic activity is at a very low point in the actively translocating sieve tube element and that no nucleus is present indicating that metabolic energy is not a participating factor in phloem transport.

As Swanson (49) has pointed out, it is generally recognized that the movement of sugars out of the leaf chlorenchyma into the sieve tube elements may occur against a concentration gradient. Thus, cell-to-cell movement of solutes in the leaf tissues and the final dumping of the solutes into the sieve tube elements could be considered an active process requiring energy. Recent investigations have suggested that sugar phosphates and an active carrier system may be involved. The finding that sugar beet leaves contain significant quantities of sucrose phosphate (5) together with the finding that ATP accelerates the movement of photosynthate from the mesophyll cells to the phloem (29) definitely suggests that the phosphorylation of sugars may be an important factor in their movement across cell membranes. Thus, phosphorylation may facilitate the transport of sucrose across membranes, or it may activate the sucrose molecule enabling it to unite with a carrier to form a complex, which can easily cross cell membranes (30). The possible path that sucrose may take from the chloroplast to the sieve tube elements is shown in Figure 9-16. The up-

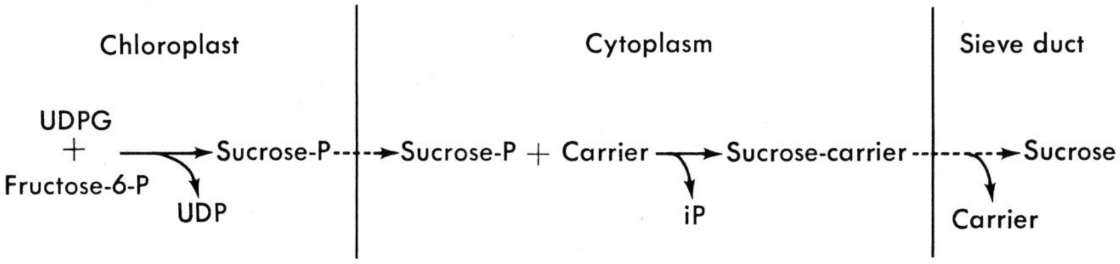

Figure 9-16 A possible mechanism for the transport of sucrose from the chloroplast to the sieve tubes.

take of sugars by the receiving cells from the phloem ducts is also thought to proceed through some active process—perhaps somewhat similar to the transport of sugars into the phloem ducts.

Thus, we see there are strong arguments against phloem translocation being a purely passive process as Münch had originally described it. At the very least, energy is necessary for the absorption of sugars by the sieve tube elements and for their uptake from the sieve tube elements by the receiving cells.

The pressure flow hypothesis accounts only for a unidirectional flow of metabolites. However, it is generally accepted that bidirectional movement takes place in plants. Bidirectional movement cannot occur in the same phloem duct within the physical limits of the pressure flow hypothesis. Crafts (8) has suggested, however, that the leaf may serve two "sinks," one toward the apex and one toward the root. That is, metabolites would leave the leaf in separate phloem ducts. Thus, we would have bidirectional movement, but in separate phloem ducts. This could be possible under the pressure flow system.

Studies of phloem translocation have also produced considerable evidence in support of the pressure flow theory. As mentioned before, positive concentration gradients have been found in the stems of a number of plants (32, 33, 60, 62, 63). The disappearance of these gradients on defoliation of the plant supports the concept of pressure flow. The common observance of phloem exudate moving out of an incision in the stem, rapidly at first and then at a steadier rate, demonstrates that the sieve tube elements are, in fact, under pressure. Also, the fact that the volume of exuding substance greatly exceeds the volume of any cut sieve tube elements in the immediate area of the incision shows that the exuding substance has been translocated over a considerable distance.

On consideration of the evidence for and against the pressure flow concept, we are left in doubt as to its workability as it was originally conceived by Münch. The modern trend is to confine the pressure flow concept to the sieve tubes only, accepting the fact that energy is required for the absorption of sugars by the sieve tube elements and for the uptake of sugars from these elements by the receiving cells.

Protoplasmic streaming hypothesis

To anyone who has microscopically examined a living root or epidermal hair, the movement of the living protoplasm is a sight not easily forgotten. We do not understand the mechanism of this movement, although we do know that those factors affecting physiological processes in general affect the movement of protoplasm in the cell. Also commonly observed in living cells are relatively large granular materials, which appear to be carried along with the actively moving protoplasm. This suggests, at the very least, that the protoplasm is capable of moving relatively large amounts of solid materials from one end of a cell to the other.

Protoplasmic streaming was first described by deVries in 1885 as a means for solute translocation in the plant. In essence, the theory assumes that solute particles are caught up in the circulating cytoplasm of the sieve tube element and carried from one end of the cell to the other. Presumably, these particles pass across sieve plate areas by diffusing through cytoplasmic strands connecting one element to another.

The protoplasmic streaming hypothesis has had many proponents since its origin with deVries. Perhaps its most eloquent defender is the American plant physiologist Otis Curtis. He has pointed out (10, 11) that streaming could account for the rapid movement of large amounts of metabolites and for the simultaneous bidirectional flow of these metabolites.

However, in recent years the protoplasmic streaming hypothesis has received little support. The strongest objection to this concept is that movement of solutes in this manner would require a metabolically active cytoplasm. As mentioned before, the cytoplasm of a mature functional sieve tube element is metabolically inactive and devoid of a nucleus. On the other hand, protoplasmic streaming has recently been observed in sieve tube elements (52, 53, 54, 7). Up until the investigations of Thaine (52, 53, 54) and Canny (7), cytoplasmic streaming had never been observed in mature sieve elements and this fact stood as one of the strongest criticisms of the protoplasmic streaming hypothesis. These two men observed, in carefully prepared petiolar tissue, that the phloem ducts are traversed by cytoplasmic strands (transcellular strands). In these strands, both Thaine and Canny observed the movement of particles from one element to the next. Furthermore, particles could be seen moving in opposite direction in adjacent strands. This would constitute bidirectional movement in only one phloem duct (Figure 9-17).

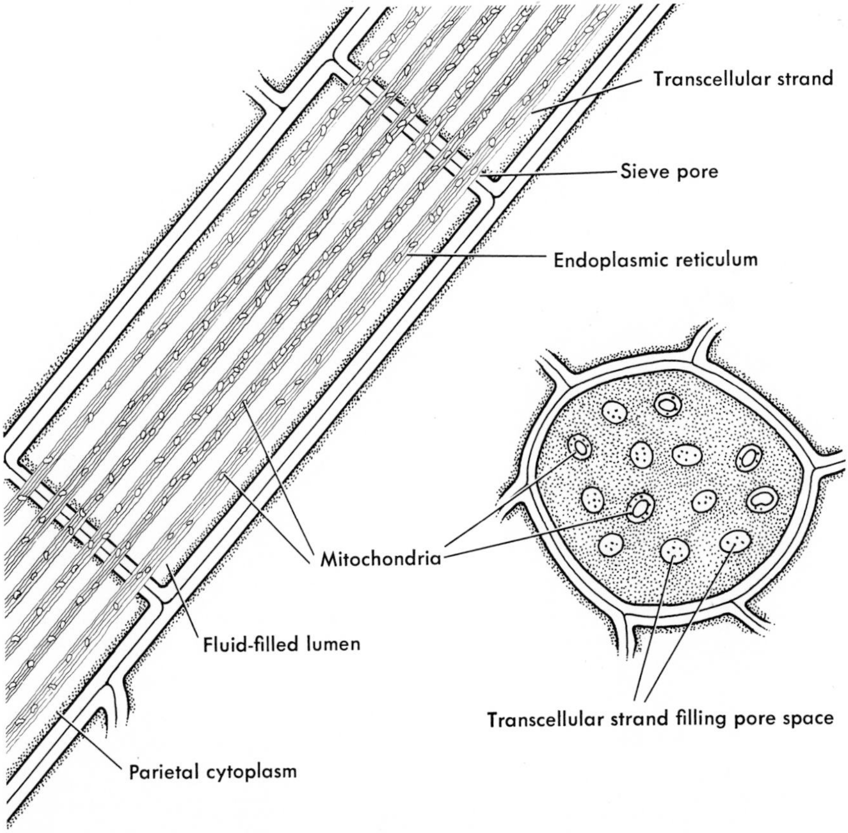

Figure 9-17 The movement of solute particles from one sieve tube element to the next via transcellular strands—an argument for the protoplasmic streaming theory. (After R. Thaine. 1964. J. Exptl. Botan. 15:470)

The presence of actively streaming transcellular strands of cytoplasm forming a connecting link between linearly arranged mature sieve tube element presents a strong argument in defense of the protoplasmic streaming hypothesis. Rapid and efficient movement of solutes over relatively long distances can adequately be explained on the basis of transcellular strands. In addition, simultaneous bidirectional movement can occur within the confines of one sieve duct. Also consistent with this hypothesis are the findings that factors, such as temperature and metabolic inhibitors, which affect rates of translocation, also affect cytoplasmic streaming.

While very good evidence exists for the protoplasmic streaming hypothesis, this is also true for the mass flow hypothesis. In addition, weaknesses in both theories have been found. Perhaps in the future we will find that translocation in plants can be explained through the acceptance of certain aspects of both theories. As it stands now, neither theory can completely answer the criticisms that have been leveled at them.

SUMMARY

The translocation of solutes takes place primarily in the phloem ducts, which, through a complex branching system, reach virtually all areas of the plant. These ducts are composed of linearly arranged sieve tube elements whose separating transverse walls develop into specialized areas called sieve plates. In contrast to its counterpart in the xylem, the vessel element, the sieve tube element is living when functional.

Of the various compounds found in the translocation stream, sucrose is by far the most abundant. However, other substances, such as a few oligosaccharides, amino acids, amides, different mineral elements, etc., are also found. The common hexoses (glucose, fructose, mannose, galactose) are generally considered to be absent from the translocation stream.

In addition to movement up and down the plant, the radial and tangential movement of solutes in the phloem tissues has been demonstrated. Rates of translocation have been calculated for a variety of plants, and have been found to vary considerably. In fact, different solutes moving in the translocation stream have been found by some investigators to move at different rates. Factors affecting translocation are temperature, light, metabolic inhibitors, concentration gradients, mineral deficiencies, and growth hormones.

Various theories have been presented to explain the physical possibility of phloem translocation as it occurs in plants. Of these, only two, the mass flow and the protoplasmic streaming theories, have gained large followings.

BIBLIOGRAPHY

1. Beer, M. 1959. Fine structure of phloem of Cucurbit as revealed by the electron microscope. Proc. Intern. Botan. Congr., 9th congr., Montreal, Canada 2: 26.

2. Biddulph, S. F. 1956. Visual indications of S^{35} and P^{32} translocation in the pholem. Am. J. Botany 43:143.
3. Biddulph, O., and R. Cory. 1957. An analysis of translocation in the phloem of the bean plant using THO, P^{32}, and C^{14}. Plant Physiol. 32: 608.
4. Biddulph, O., and R. Cory. 1965. Translocation of C^{14} metabolites in the phloem of the bean plant. Plant Physiol. 40: 119.
5. Buchanan, J. 1953. The path of carbon in photosynthesis. XIX. The identification of sucrose phosphate in sugar beet leaves. Arch. Biochem. Biophys. 44: 140.
6. Burley, J. 1961. Carbohydrate translocation in raspberry and soybean. Plant Physiol. 36: 820.
7. Canny, M. J. 1962. The mechanism of translocation. Ann. Botan. 26: 603.
8. Crafts, A. S. 1951. Movement of assimilates, viruses, growth regulators, and chemical indicators in plants. Botan. Rev. 17: 203.
9. Crafts, A. S. 1961. Translocation in plants. Holt, Rinehart & Winston, New York.
10. Curtis, O. F. 1935. The translocation of solutes in plants. McGraw-Hill Book Company, New York.
11. Curtis, O. F., and D. G. Clark. 1950. An introduction to plant physiology. McGraw-Hill Book Company, New York.
12. DeStigter, H. C. M. 1961. Translocation of C^{14} photosynthates in the graft muskmelon/*Cucurbita ficifolia.* Acta Botan. Neerlandica 10: 466.
13. Esau, K. 1939. Development and structure of the phloem tissue. Botan. Rev. 5: 373.
14. Esau, K. 1947. A study of some sieve-tube inclusions. Am. J. Botany 34: 224.
15. Esau, K. 1950. Development and structure of the phloem tissue. II. Botan. Rev. 16: 67.
16. Esau, K. 1960. Anatomy of seed plants. John Wiley & Sons, New York.
17. Evert, R. F., and L. Murmanis. 1965. Ultrastructure of the secondary phloem of *Tilia americana.* Am. J. Botany 52: 95.
18. Gage, R., and S. Aronoff. 1960. Radioautography of tritiated photosynthate arising from HTO. Plant Physiol. 35: 65.
19. Gauch, H. G., and W. M. Dugger, Jr. 1953. The role of boron in the translocation of sucrose. Plant Physiol. 28: 457.
20. Hartt, C. E. 1965. The effect of temperature upon translocation of C^{14} in sugarcane. Plant Physiol. 40: 74.
21. Hartt, C. E., H. P. Kortschak, A. J. Forbes, and G. O. Burr. 1963. Translocation of C^{14} in sugarcane. Plant Physiol. 38: 305.
22. Hatch, M. D., and K. T. Glasziou. 1964. Direct evidence for translocation of sucrose in sugarcane leaves and stems. Plant Physiol. 39: 180.
23. Hewitt, S. P., and O. F. Curtis. 1948. The effect of temperature on loss of dry matter and carbohydrate from leaves by respiration and translocation. Am. J. Botany 35: 746.

24. Holman, R., and W. Robbins. 1938. Textbook of general botany for colleges and universities. John Wiley & Sons, New York.
25. Joy, K. W. 1964. Translocation in sugar beet. I. Assimilation of $C^{14}O_2$ and distribution of materials from leaves. J. Exptl. Botan. 15: 485.
26. Kendall, W. A. 1955. Effect of certain metabolic inhibitors on translocation of P^{32} in bean plants. Plant Physiol. 30: 347.
27. Koontz, H., and O. Biddulph. 1957. Factors affecting absorption and translocation of foliar applied phosphorus. Plant Physiol. 32: 463.
28. Kursanov, A. L., M. V. Turkina, and I. M. Dubinina. 1953. Die Anwendung der Isotopenmethode bei der Erforschung des Zuckertransportes in der Pflanze. C. R. Acad. Sci. U.R.S.S. 68: 1113.
29. Kursanov, A. L., and M. I. Brovchenko. Fiziol. Rastenü. 8: 270.
30. Kursanov, A. L. 1963. Metabolism and the transport of organic substances in the phloem. *In* R. D. Preston (ed.), Advances in botanical research. Academic Press, New York. 1: 209.
31. Lopuskinsky, W. 1964. Effect of water movement on ion movement into the xylem of tomato roots. Plant Physiol. 39: 494.
32. Mason, T. G., and E. J. Maskell. 1928. Studies on the transport of carbohydrates in the cotton plant. I. A study of diurnal variation in the carbohydates of leaf, bark, and wood, and the effects of ringing. Ann. Botan. 42: 189.
33. Mason, T. G., and E. J. Maskell. 1928. Studies on the transport of carbohydrates in the cotton plant. II. The factors determining the rate and the direction of movement of sugars. Ann. Botan. 42: 571.
34. Mason, T. G., and E. Phillis. 1937. The migration of solutes. Botan. Rev. 3: 47.
35. Mitchell, J. W., W. M. Dugger, Jr., and H. G. Gauch. 1953. Increased translocation of plant growth modifying substances due to application of boron. Science 118: 354.
36. Mittler, T. E. 1953. Amino acids in phloem sap and their excretion by aphids. Nature 172: 207.
37. Mittler, T. E. 1958. Studies of the feeding and nutrition of *Tuberolachnus salignus* (Gmelin) (Homoptera, Aphididae.) II. The nitrogen and sugar composition of ingested phloem sap and excreted honeydew. 35: 74.
38. Mothes, K., and L. Engelbrecht. 1961. Kinetin and its role in nitrogen metabolism. *In* International botanical congress, 9th Montreal. University of Toronto Press, Toronto, Canada 2: 996.
39. Nelson, C. D. 1963. Effect of climate on the distribution and translocation of assimilates. *In* Environmental control of plant growth. Academic Press, New York. 149–174.
40. Nelson, C. D., and P. R. Gorham. 1957. Uptake and translocation of C^{14}-labeled sugars applied to primary leaves of soybean seedlings. Can. J. Botany 35: 339.
41. Nelson, C., and P. Gorham. 1959. Translocation of C^{14}-labeled amino acids and amides in the stems of young soybean plants. Can. J. Botany 37: 431.

42. Peel, A. J. 1964. Tangential movement of C^{14}-labeled assimilates in stems of willow. J. Exptl. Botan. 15: 104.
43. Pristupa, N. A., and A. L. Kursanov. 1957. Descending flow of assimilates and its relation to the absorbing activity of roots. Plant Physiol. (USSR) (Fiziol. Rast.) 4: 395.
44. Roeckl, B. 1949. Nachweis eines Konzentrationshubs zwischen Palisadenzellen und Siebröhren. Planta 36: 530.
45. Rohrbaugh, L. M., and E. L. Rice. 1956. Relation of phosphorus nutrition to the translocation of 2,4-dichlorophenoxyacetic acid in tomato plants. Plant Physiol. 31: 196.
46. Shiroya, M., C. D. Nelson, and G. Krotkov. 1961. Translocation of C^{14} in tobacco at different stages of development following assimilation of $C^{14}O_2$ by a single leaf. Can. J. Botany 39: 855.
47. Sisler, R. M., W. M. Dugger, Jr., and H. G. Gauch. 1956. The role of boron in the translocation of organic compounds in plants. Plant Physiol. 31: 11.
48. Skok, J. 1957. Relationship of boron nutrition to radiosensitivity of sunflower plants. Plant Physiol. 32: 648.
49. Swanson, C. A. 1959. Translocation of organic solutes. F. C. Steward (ed.), *In* Plant physiology. Academic Press, New York. 2: 481.
50. Swanson, C. A., and R. H. Böhning. 1951. The effect of petiole temperature on the translocation of carbohydrates from bean leaves. Plant Physiol. 26: 557.
51. Swanson, C. A., and E. D. H. El-Shishiny. 1958. Translocation of sugars in grapes. Plant Physiol. 33: 33.
52. Thaine, R. 1961. Transcellular strands and particle movement in mature sieve tubes. Nature 192: 772.
53. Thaine, R. 1962. A translocation hypothesis based on the structure of plant cytoplasm. J. Exptl. Botan. 13: 152.
54. Thaine, R. 1964. The protoplasmic-streaming theory of phloem transport. J. Exptl. Botan. 15: 470.
55. Ullrich, W. 1961. Zur Sauerstoffabhängigkeit des Transportes in den Siebröhren. Planta 57: 402.
56. Vernon, L. P., and S. Aronoff. 1952. Metabolism of soybean leaves. IV. Translocation from soybean leaves. Arch. Biochem. Biophys. 36: 383.
57. Weatherley, P. E., A. J. Peel, and G. P. Hill. 1959. The physiology of the sieve tube. Preliminary experiments using aphid mouth parts. J. Exptl. Botan. 10: 1.
58. Webb, J. A., and P. R. Gorham. 1964. Translocation of photosynthetically assimilated C^{14} in straight-necked squash. Plant Physiol. 39: 663.
59. Willenbrink, J. 1957. Über die Hemmung des Stofftransports in den Siebröhren durch lokale Inaktivierung verschiedener Atmungenzyme. Planta 48: 269.
60. Zimmermann, M. H. 1957. Translocation of organic substances in trees. I. The nature of the sugars in the sieve tube exudate of trees. Plant Physiol. 32: 288.

61. Zimmermann, M. H. 1957. Translocation of organic substances in trees. II. On the translocation mechanism in the phloem of white ash. Plant Physiol. 32: 399.
62. Zimmermann, M. H. 1958. Translocation of organic substances in the phloem of trees. *In* K. V. Thimann (ed.), The physiology of forest trees. Ronald Press, New York.
63. Zimmermann, M. H. 1958. Translocation of organic substances in trees. III. The removal of sugars from the sieve tubes in the white ash. (*Fraxinus americana* L.). Plant Physiol. 33: 213.
64. Zimmermann, M. H. 1960. Transport in the phloem. Ann. Rev. Plant Physiol. 11: 167.

Part FOUR

Photosynthesis

10

The pigments and structure of the photosynthetic apparatus

INTRODUCTION

Without doubt, one of the most interesting and complex problems facing man today is the unraveling of the mysteries of photosynthesis. The living mechanism has learned to capture a photon of light and utilize the energy therein to raise one electron from an electron pair to a higher level. The duration of this excited state generally is very brief, the electron returning to the ground state in 10^{-8} to 10^{-7} seconds. On the return trip the excess energy is released in a number of ways. Life has learned to delay the return to the ground state, bringing the electron back through its biological mechanism and utilizing the excess energy to drive the life processes. This capture of the photon and the conversion of its light energy to chemical energy is the unique property of plants, a process called *photosynthesis*.

HISTORY

When one considers the importance, indeed the absolute necessity of photosynthesis to life, it is surprising what little attention the process attracted before the eighteenth century. By this time agriculture had existed for more than 10,000 years, and practical discussions of crop production had been written at least 2000 years before (16). The early Greeks taught that the plant obtained its food directly from the earth, which had converted plant and animal debris to a form readily absorbed by roots. The obvious increase in crop production as a result of the addition of plant and animal matter to the soil gave credence to this theory, leaving it practically uncontested until the eighteenth century.

In the early 1600's a simple but nevertheless important experiment was performed by Van Helmont. He planted a willow seedling weighing 2 kg in a tub of carefully weighed soil and followed its growth for five years. All that was provided to the willow was rain water. At the end of the five year period the willow weighed 75 kg, and the soil had only lost a few grams in dry weight. Thus, Van Helmont concluded that it was water and not soil that contributed to the growth of the plant. We know today that those few grams of material taken up from the soil were of vital importance and, in fact, essential to growth. We also know today that water did not contribute appreciably to the mass of the willow tree. It is unfortunate that Van Helmont and his colleagues did not look a little beyond the obvious in their interpretation of this experiment. Certainly, progress toward the elucidation of the process of photosynthesis would have been considerably furthered.

It was left to Woodward in 1699 to state that more than water was required by plants. After growing sprigs of mint in various samples of water, which included rain water, river water, Hyde Park drainage water, etc., he concluded that:

> Vegetables are not formed of water but of a certain peculiar terrestrial matter. It has been shown that there is a considerable quantity of this matter contained in rain, spring and river water; that the greatest part of the fluid mass that ascends up into plants does not settle there but passes through their pores and exhales up into the atmosphere; that a great part of the terrestrial matter, mixed with water, passes up into the plant along with it and that the plant is more or less augmented in proportion as the water contains a greater or less quantity of that matter; from all of which we may reasonably infer, that earth, and not water, is the matter that constitutes vegetables.*

* This and the following two quotations are from W. Loomis, 1960. Historical introduction. *In* Encyclopedia of plant physiology. Springer, Berlin. 5: Part I, 85–114.

Since the chemistry of carbon dioxide was, as yet, unknown, ignorance of its role in the growth of plants is excusable. However, it is surprising what little attention was paid to the role of light in plant growth. Hales, often referred to as the "father of plant physiology," may have had some insight into this role when he wrote in 1727:

> Plants very probably draw through their leaves some part of their nourishment from the air . . . may not light, also by freely entering surfaces of leaves and flowers, contribute much to ennobling the principles of vegetables.

Studies by Priestley in 1772 were concerned only with the gas exchange that accompanies the process of photosynthesis. Priestly wrote that air "contaminated" by the burning of a candle could not support life in a mouse. He noted, however, that if a sprig of mint were grown in this same air, the air could be rendered "pure," enabling it to support a living mouse again. He also observed that the sprigs of mint flourished in the so-called "contaminated" air.

Although Priestley did recognize the difference in gas exchange between animals and plants when he concluded:

> . . . plants, instead of affecting the air in the same manner with animal respiration, reverse the effects of breathing and tend to keep the atmosphere sweet and wholesome when it has become noxious in consequence of animals either living and breathing or dying and putrefying in it,

he did not recognize the role of either carbon dioxide or light in photosynthesis.

However, Ingenhousz, a contemporary of Priestley, in 1779 reported that plants purified the air only in the presence of light. He also wrote that only the green parts of the plant produced the purifying agent (oxygen), while nongreen tissues contaminated the air. Thus, Ingenhousz recognized the participation of chlorophyll and light in the photosynthetic process.

Although Priestley had flirted with the idea of CO_2 absorption and utilization when he noted that plants "thrived in a most surprising manner" in the "putrid air" in which a mouse had died and partially decayed, he did not establish that fixed air (CO_2) was responsible for this effect.

It was left to Senebier in the years 1782 through 1788 to prove the importance of fixed air, recognizing also that the production of oxygen by plants is dependent upon the presence of carbon dioxide. Actually, it was not until Lavoisier's study of the composition of carbon dioxide in 1796 that Ingenhousz suggested that this compound is an important source of carbon for plants.

In 1804 de Saussure published his *Recherches Chimiques sur la Végéta-*

tion (21) to which the history of so many of the physiological functions of plants may be traced. He agreed with Ingenhousz that two types of gas exchange occur, one in the light and another in darkness, and that green tissues alone carry on the process of carbon dioxide absorption and oxygen evolution in light. He also recognized, to a limited extent, the participation of water in photosynthesis.

The establishment of the law of the conservation of energy by Robert Mayer in 1842 was a giant step toward the elucidation of the problem of energy transfer in photosynthesis. It was Mayer who stated that the ultimate source of the energy utilized in both plants and animals is the sun and that this light energy when absorbed by plants is converted to chemical energy in the process of photosynthesis.

Despite the great efforts of these brilliant men, the mechanism of photosynthesis still remained a mystery until 1905 when an English plant physiologist by the name of Blackman (2) startled the scientific world by demonstrating that photosynthesis is not only a photochemical reaction but also a biochemical reaction. As we know today, the photochemical reaction, or light reaction, is exceedingly rapid and requires light energy. On the other hand, the biochemical reaction, or dark reaction, is independent of light energy and proceeds at a relatively slow rate. Therefore, according to Blackman, the rate of photosynthesis is conditioned by the rate of the dark reaction. The light and dark reactions of photosynthesis will be discussed in more detail in this and the following two chapters.

Although Blackman's contribution was remarkable for that time, there was still very little known as to the nature of the light and dark reactions of photosynthesis. It was not until 32 years after Blackman's discovery that some solid information on the nature of the light reaction was provided.

An English biochemist by the name of Hill (14) demonstrated that isolated chloroplasts in the presence of light, water, and a suitable hydrogen acceptor evolve oxygen in the absence of carbon dioxide. His experiments provided evidence that the evolution of oxygen is involved in the light reaction and that the O_2 of photosynthesis comes from water and not from carbon dioxide.

THE NATURE OF LIGHT

Toward the middle of the seventeenth century it was generally believed that light consisted of a stream of minute particles (corpuscles), which were emitted by light sources, such as the sun or the flickering flame of a candle. These minute particles penetrated transparent material and were reflected from the surfaces of opaque material. This explanation of the nature of light was spoken of as the "corpuscular theory."

Although the corpuscular theory was widely accepted at this time, Christian Huygens noted in 1670 that the laws of reflection and refraction could better be explained on the basis of a wave theory rather than a corpuscular theory. However, the wave theory was not immediately accepted, and it was not until experiments by Fresnel and Young in 1827 that the corpuscular theory was found to be inadequate. In addition, Maxwell showed that an oscillating electrical circuit could radiate electromagnetic waves. The velocity of the propagation of these waves was found to be 3×10^{10} cm/sec. This was remarkably close, if not identical, to the measured velocity of propagation of light, developing a very strong case for the existence of light as electromagnetic waves of very short wavelength. The problem at this point appeared to be solved. However, one very puzzling observation seemed to contradict the wave theory of light, the phenomenon of photoelectric emission (ejection of electrons from a conductor by light incident on its surface). Any change in wavelength of the incident radiation covering a limited spectral region produces changes in the distribution of photoelectron kinetic energies. But, if the wavelength remains fixed, the distribution of electron energies also remains fixed. This is true even if the intensity of the incident radiation is increased or decreased. Also there is a direct proportional relationship between the number of electrons and the radiation intensity. With this evidence, Einstein (6) postulated that the energy in a light beam, instead of being distributed through space in the electric and magnetic fields of an electromagnetic wave, is concentrated in small particles called *photons*. Thus, because of the quantization of electromagnetic radiation by Einstein, people were led to consider the photon as a type of particle giving some validity to the corpuscular theory. However, since the photon was considered to have a frequency, and the energy of a photon was believed proportional to its frequency, some of the wave theory was retained. The essential fact of this discussion is that in order to understand the nature of light one must appreciate its dual wave-particle characteristics.

The wavelengths of light capable of affecting plant growth lie between 0.00003 and 0.00008 cm. It is obvious that the use of such large units of measure to describe the length of a wave of light would be an awkward nuisance. Therefore, wavelengths are expressed in much smaller units, such as the micron (μ), the millimicron (mμ), and the angstrom (Å). One micron is a millionth of a meter, one millimicron is one one-thousandth of a micron, and one angstrom is one ten-thousandth of a micron.

$$1\ \mu = 10^{-6}\ \text{m} = 10^{-4}\ \text{cm}$$

$$1\ \text{m}\mu = 10^{-9}\ \text{m} = 10^{-7}\ \text{cm}$$

$$1\ \text{Å} = 10^{-10}\ \text{m} = 10^{-8}\ \text{cm}$$

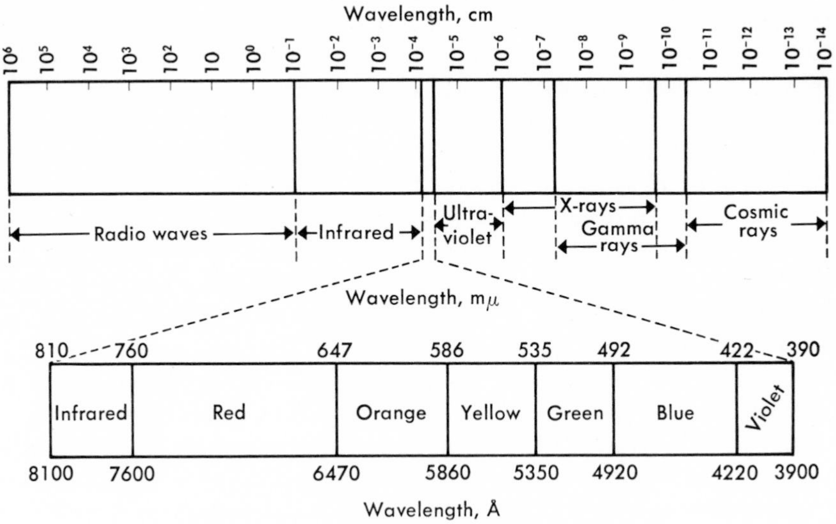

Figure 10-1 The electromagnetic spectrum.

Most studies of light effects on plants employ millimicrons or angstroms. The electromagnetic spectrum is shown in Figure 10-1.

PIGMENTS INVOLVED IN PHOTOSYNTHESIS

It is hard to conceive of life originating or existing without the ability to absorb radiant energy and convert it to chemical energy. As Bentley Glass (10) has so aptly stated, "life is a photochemical phenomenon." The chemical compounds most important in this conversion of light energy to chemical energy are the pigments that exist within the chloroplasts or chromatophores of plants. It is through these agencies that light initiates the process of photosynthesis.

Chlorophyll pigments

The chlorophylls, the green pigments of the chloroplast, are the most important photosynthetic plant pigments, and today at least seven types may be distinguished: chlorophylls a, b, c, d, and e, bacteriochlorophyll, and bacterioviridin. Chlorophylls a and b are the best known and most abundant and are found in all autotrophic organisms except pigment-containing bacteria. Chlorophyll b is also absent from the blue-green, brown, and red algae. Chlorophyll a is usually thought of as being blue-green, while chlorophyll b is yellow-green. The other chlorophylls (c, d, e) are found only in algae and in combination with chlorophyll a. Bacteriochlorophyll and bacterioviridin are the pigments found in photosynthetic bacteria.

The chlorophyll molecule has a cyclic tetrapyrrolic structure (porphyrin) with an isocyclic ring containing a magnesium atom at its center. Extending from one of the pyrrole rings is a long chain alcohol, the phytol part of the chlorophyll molecule. The empirical formula of the chlorophyll molecule is $C_{55}H_{72}O_5N_4Mg$. The molecular structure is shown in Figure 10-2.

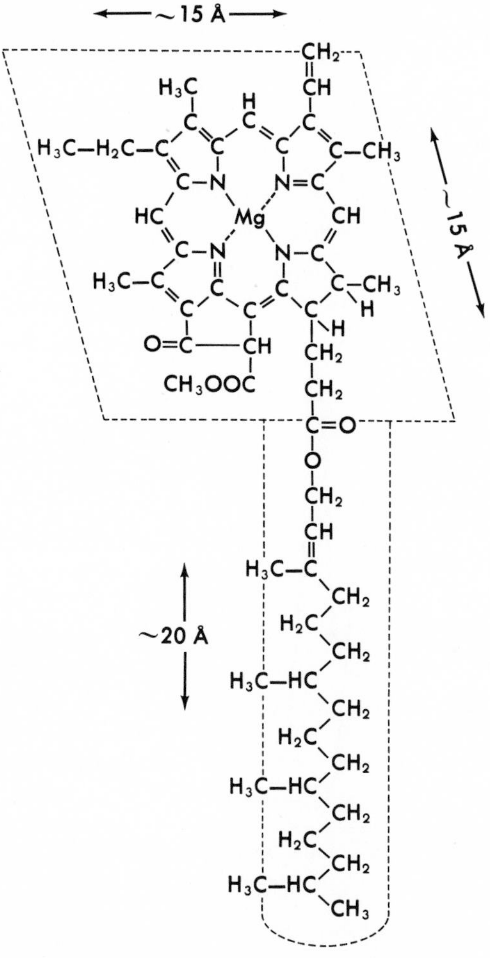

Figure 10-2 The chlorophyll a molecule. The approximate dimensions of the porphyrin ring and phytol chain are given. (Redrawn from J. Wolken. 1961. Euglena: an experimental organism for biochemical and biophysical studies. Rutgers University Press, New Brunswick, N.J., Copyright 1961 by The Institute of Microbiology.)

One could say the structure of the molecule roughly resembles a "tennis racket" having a large flat head (the porphyrin part) and a long handle or tail (the phytol part). The phytol, which is esterified with the carboxyl group on the C_7 atom of the chlorophyll molecule, is a long chain alcohol containing one double bond. It is thought that the phytol chain is related to carotenoids and can be regarded as derivable from vitamin A. The difference between chlorophyll a and b may be found at the C_3 atom. With chlorophyll a, there is a methyl group attached and with chlorophyll b, an aldehyde group.

Chlorophyll a   Chlorophyll b

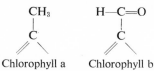

In addition to their minor difference in molecular structure, these chlorophylls also differ in absorption spectra (Figure 10-3) and solubilities.

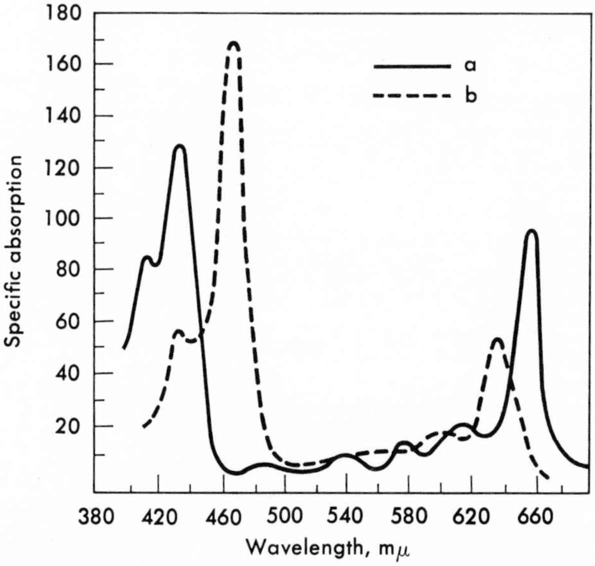

Figure 10-3 Absorption spectra of ether extracts of chlorophylls a and b. (After F. Zscheile and C. Comar. 1941. Botan. Gaz. 102: 463.)

For example, petroleum ether is a good solvent for chlorophyll a, while methyl alcohol is considered best for chlorophyll b.

Both chlorophylls a and b show an absorption maximum in the blue-violet region with peaks of about 429 mμ and 453 mμ, respectively, and with minor peaks at 410 mμ and 430 mμ. In addition to absorbing in the blue-violet region, chlorophylls a and b have a secondary absorption maximum in the red region with peaks of about 660 mμ and 642 mμ, respectively. The absorption maximum of these most important photosynthetic pigments should give a hint as to the quality of light most effective in the process of photosynthesis.

It must be understood that the absorption spectra just discussed are of extracts of chlorophyll, that is, chlorophyll in an organic solvent. The absorption spectra of chlorophyll in vivo may be quite different. Indeed, the absorption spectra of the chlorophylls differ slightly when in different solvents. Often the wavelength positions of the peaks may vary by a few millimicrons with chlorophyll extracted from different species. Whether these differences are because of chemical differences in the chlorophyll of different plants or to different methods applied in the laboratory is not clearly understood.

Chlorophyll synthesis. How the chlorophylls and iron porphyrins are synthesized within the living cell has not, as yet, been conclusively shown. However, relatively recent studies by Granick (12) on the metabolism of heme and chlorophyll and by Shemin (23) on the biosynthesis of porphyrins have demonstrated some of the steps involved. The condensation of glycine and succinyl CoA leads to the formation of the unstable α-amino-β-ketoadipic acid, which, on decarboxylation, yields δ-aminolevulinic acid.

$$
\begin{array}{ccc}
\text{COOH} & \text{COOH} & \\
| & | & \\
\text{CH}_2 & + \quad \text{CH}_2 & \longrightarrow \\
| & | & \\
\text{NH}_2 & \text{CH}_2 & \\
& | & \\
& \text{O=C-S-CoA} & \\
\text{Glycine} & \text{Succinyl CoA} &
\end{array}
$$

$$
\overset{\displaystyle \text{NH}_2}{\underset{\displaystyle }{\text{HOOC-CH}}}\!-\!\underset{\displaystyle O}{\overset{\displaystyle ||}{C}}\!-\!\text{CH}_2\!-\!\text{CH}_2\!-\!\text{COOH} \xrightarrow{-\text{CO}_2}
$$

α-Amino-B-ketoadipic acid

$$
\overset{\displaystyle \text{NH}_2}{\underset{\displaystyle O}{\text{H}_2\text{-C-}\overset{\displaystyle }{C}}}\!-\!\text{CH}_2\!-\!\text{CH}_2\!-\!\text{COOH}
$$

δ-Aminolevulinic acid

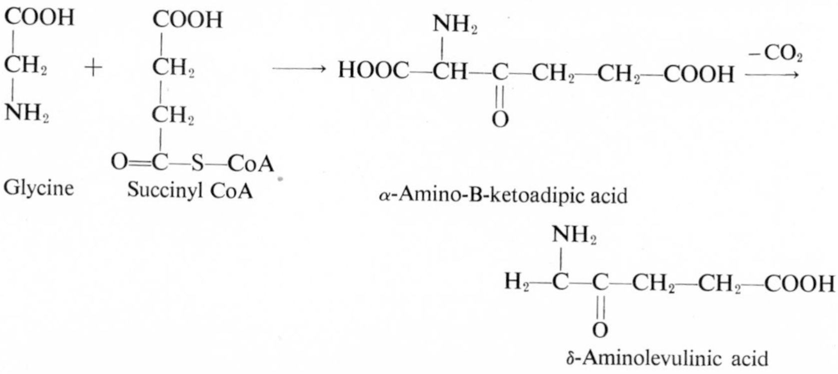

Two molecules of δ-aminolevulinic acid could then condense to form porphobilinogen. Four molecules of this last compound could then contribute to the synthesis of porphyrin. The synthesis of chlorophyll proceeds in a series of reactions as follows:

The last step, the reduction of protochlorophyll to form chlorophyll in the presence of light, is strongly supported. The seedlings of higher plants grown in the dark (etiolated) are yellow-green in color. The very light green color indicates the presence of traces of protochlorophyll, a

2 molecules of δ-aminolevulinic acid $\xrightarrow{-2H_2O}$

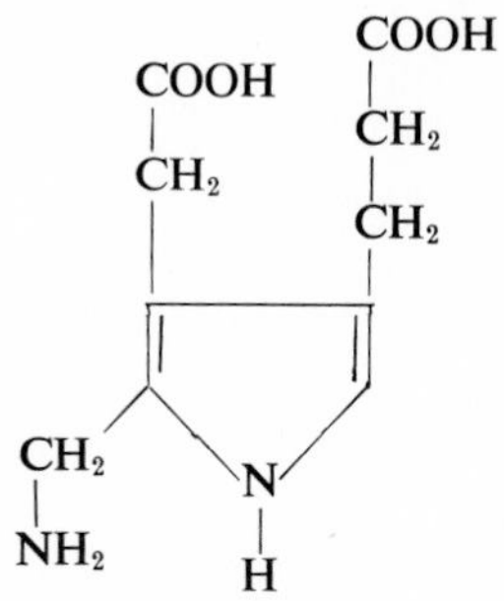

Porphobilinogen

$\xrightarrow{\text{4 molecules}}$

Some hypothetical porphyrin → Uroporphyrinogen III (colorless tetrapyrrole) → Coproporphyrinogen III (colorless) →

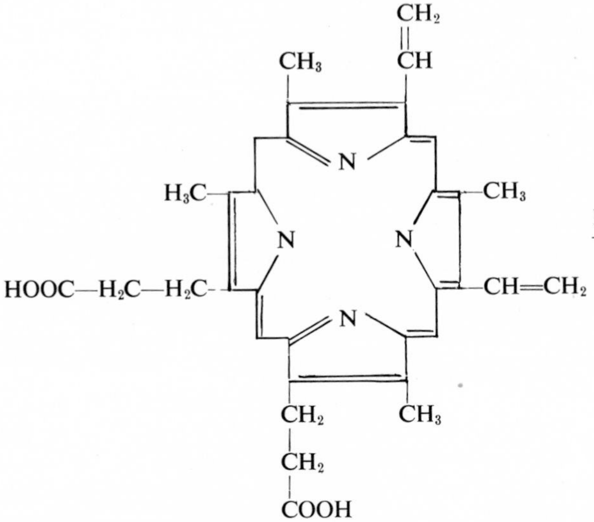

Protoporphyrin-9 (pink)

$\xrightarrow{Mg^{2+}}$

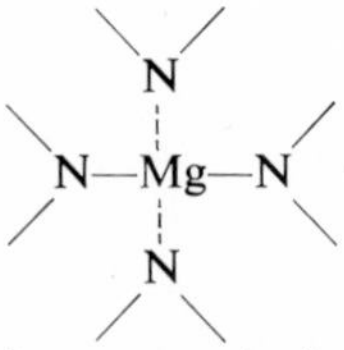

Mg-protoporphyrin-9

$\xrightarrow{\text{Several steps}}$ ⟶

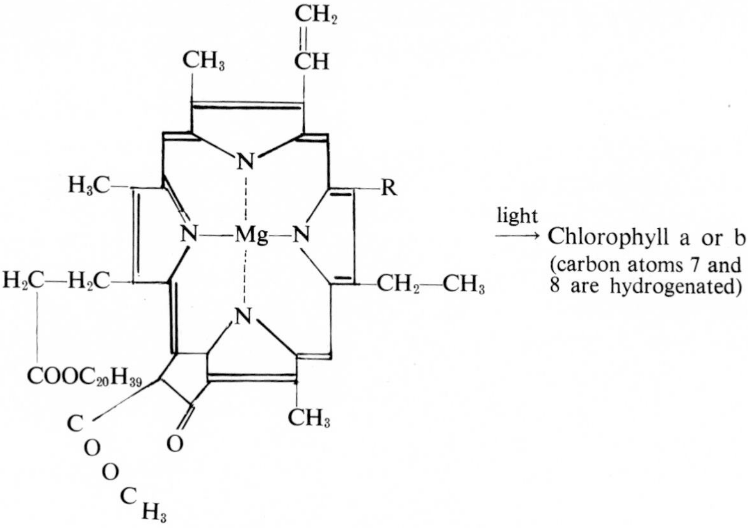

Protochlorophyll

compound closely related to chlorophyll, but lacking two hydrogens on carbon atoms 7 and 8. If these seedlings are treated with light of relatively low intensities, the formation of chlorophyll immediately takes place. Although the light requirement appears to be absolute in angiosperms, in some plants, such as conifers, chlorophyll can be synthesized in complete darkness by the enzymatic reduction of protochlorophyll to chlorophyll.

There is a close relationship between the chlorophylls and the metalporphyrins of the living cell, the blood pigment heme, and the cytochromes. The major difference between the chlorophylls and these other compounds is that chlorophyll has magnesium and a phytol tail, while the cytochromes and hemes have iron and lack a phytol tail. It is rather interesting, however, that all of these compounds appear to originate along the same biochemical pathways.

Carotenoid pigments

Carotenoids are lipid compounds that are distributed widely in both animals and plants and range in colors from yellow to purple. Carotenoids are present in variable concentrations in nearly all higher plants and in many microorganisms (e.g., red and green algae, photosynthetic bacteria, and fungi) (11). *Carotene,* the first carotenoid to be named, was isolated from carrot root tissue by Mackenroder in 1831. However, it was not until after 1925 that the structures of some of the carotenoids were definitely established by several investigators, notably Karrer, Jucker, Lederer, Kuhn, and Zechmeister.

One can consider the natural carotenoids as derivatives of *lycopene,* a red pigment found in tomatoes as well as many other plants. Lycopene is a highly unsaturated, straight chain hydrocarbon composed of two identical units joined by a double bond between carbon atoms 15 and 15′. The empirical formula is $C_{40}H_{51}$. It is likely that each half of the molecule is derived from four isoprene units, isoprene having the formula $CH_2 = C(CH_3) - CH = CH_2$. Thus, carotenoids are composed of eight isoprene-like residues. Molecular structures of three carotenoids are shown on p. 225.

The major carotenoid found in plant tissues is the orange-yellow pigment β-carotene, which is generally accompanied by varying amounts of α-carotene (0–35%) (17).

Hydrogen carotenoids (i.e., carotenoids that consist exclusively of carbon and hydrogen) are termed carotenes, and those carotenoids containing oxygen are called *xanthophylls.* The xanthophylls are more abundant in nature than the carotenes and in growing leaves may exceed the concentration of carotenes by about 2:1 (11). The major xanthophylls generally found in green leaves are shown in Table 10-1.

Table 10-1 The major xanthophylls found in green leaves.[a]

Pigment	*Structure*	*Relative amounts, % of total*
cryptoxanthin	3-hydroxy-β-carotene	4
lutein	3,3-dihydroxy-α-carotene	40
zeaxanthin	3,3-dihydroxy-β-carotene	2
veolaxanthin	5,6,5′,6′-diepoxyzeaxanthin	34
neoxanthin	$C_{40}H_{56}O_4$ (exact structure unknown)	19

[a] Data from Goodwin (1960).

Carotenoids, like chlorophyll, are located in the chloroplast and in the chromatophore (27, 29, 3), occurring there as water-soluble protein complexes. As Goodwin (11) suggests, the chlorophylls and carotenoids may be attached to the same protein, forming a complex known as *photosynthin.* It is thought by many investigators that the specific orientation of the carotenoids in relation to the chlorophylls within the lamellar system of the chloroplast is an important aspect of the photosynthetic process.

As might be expected, most of the studies of the physiological role of the

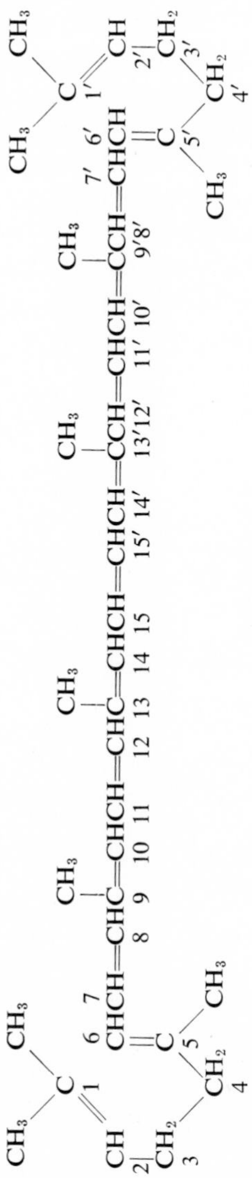

Lycopene

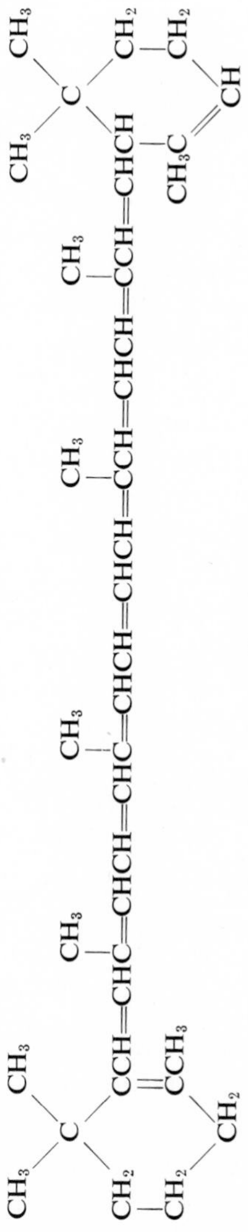

α-Carotene

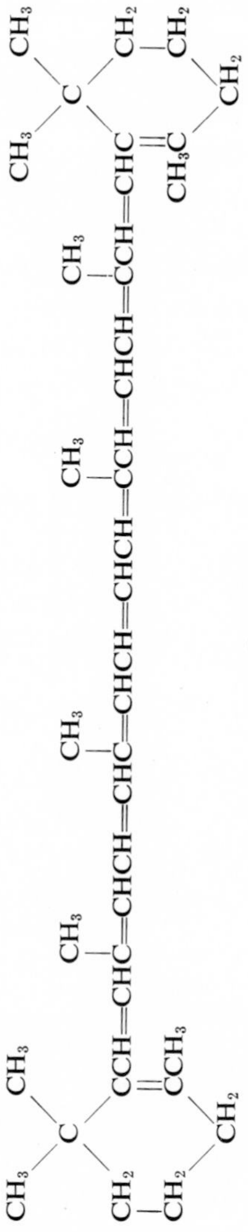

β-Carotene

carotenoids have centered around its relationship with vitamin A and animal nutrition. However, in recent years more attention has been given to the role of carotenoids in plants. Carotenoids function in *photosynthesis* (26), *phototropisms* (25), and protection against physiological damage due to excessive light (24).

In photosynthesis. Because of the presence of carotenoids in all photosynthetic tissue, one might anticipate its role in photosynthesis. However, this role must be secondary since tissues rich in carotenoids and devoid of chlorophyll do not photosynthesize. Many investigators (5) believe that light energy absorbed by carotenoids is transferred to chlorophyll a and there utilized in the photosynthetic process. Strong evidence that this is so has been shown by Wassink and Kersten (26). They found that light absorbed by carotenoids resulted in the fluorescence of chlorophyll. The absorption spectrum of β-carotene is shown in Figure 10-4.

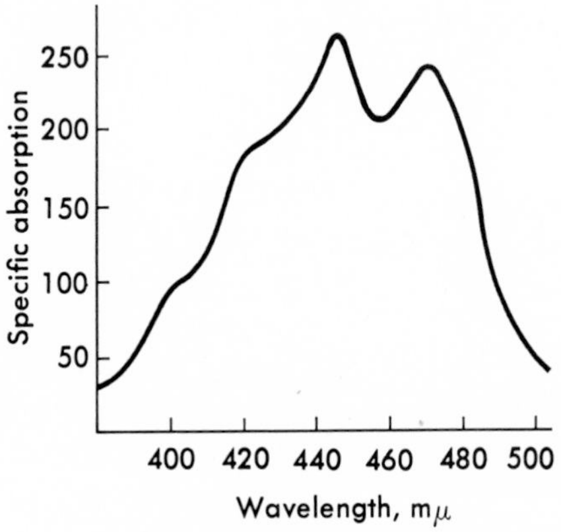

Figure 10-4 Absorption spectrum of β-carotene in hexane. (After F. Zscheile et al. 1942. Plant Physiol. 17: 331.)

In phototropisms. Strong evidence for the participation of carotenoids in the bending of the *Avena coleoptile* toward a unilateral source of light is found by comparing the action spectrum for this bending with the absorption spectrum of the carotenoids present. The action spectrum for phototropic bending in the *Avena* seedling has two bands in the blue region (about 440 and 470 mμ), and it is in this region that carotenoids absorb the most light (see Figure 10-4). Since it is the *photoinactivation* of auxin on the illuminated side that causes the phototropic response, carotenoids may be active in the destruction of auxin. Galston (9) disagrees with this conclusion, pointing out that accuracy achieved in action spectrum measurements is not sufficient to distinguish between β-carotene and the pigment riboflavin, which has an absorption spectrum very similar to β-carotene. In fact, Galston believes that riboflavin, not β-carotene, is active in auxin inactivation.

In protection against excessive light. That carotenoids protect against *photooxidations* has been demonstrated by Stanier (24) with photosynthetic bacteria and by Sager (20) with algae. The blue-green mutant of *Rhodopseudomonas spheroides* is practically devoid of carotenoids and is vulnerable to chlorophyll-catalyzed photooxidations in the presence of oxygen. However, the cell will grow and photosynthesize under anaerobic conditions. This protective role of the carotenoid pigments against photooxidation has been demonstrated in much the same manner for diphenylamine-treated cells of *Rhodospirillum rubrum,* also devoid of carotenoid pigments (4).

A pale green mutant of *Chlamydomonas* has been found to be almost devoid of carotenoid pigments. As might be expected, this mutant must be grown exclusively in the dark. It dies when grown in the light (20).

Phycobilins

It appears that the red and blue *biliproteins,* called *phycoerythrins* and *phycocyanins,* respectively, are found only in algae. At least, they have only been isolated from algae (19). The chromophore moiety of the biliprotein, called a *phycobilin,* is strongly attached to the associated protein, making the study of phycobilins in the pure state very difficult. Consequently, most of our information on these pigments comes from studies of the pigment-protein complex.

The absorption spectra of the phycobilins are most interesting when one considers that they are active in the transfer of light energy to chlorophyll for utilization in the process of photosynthesis. The absorption spectrum of R-phycoerythrin has peaks at 495, 540, and 565 mμ with quite a bit of absorption as a whole over the range from 495 to 565 mμ (7). The absorption spectrum of R-phycocyanin has peaks at 550 and 615 mμ with absorption relatively high over this range (550–615 mμ) (15).

We have mentioned that, in addition to the chlorophylls, carotenoids and phycobilins are active in absorbing light energy, which is utilized in photosynthesis. The role of carotenoids and phycobilins is indirect in that the energy they absorb is transferred to chlorophyll before it becomes "active" in photosynthesis. Experimental evidence of the participation of pigments other than chlorophyll (sometimes called accessory pigments) in photosynthesis may be obtained in a comparison of the absorption spectrum of a living cell with its action spectrum. An action spectrum is obtained by measuring the rate of photosynthesis induced by light of different wavelengths and of the same intensity. An example of an action spectrum is given in Figure 10-5.

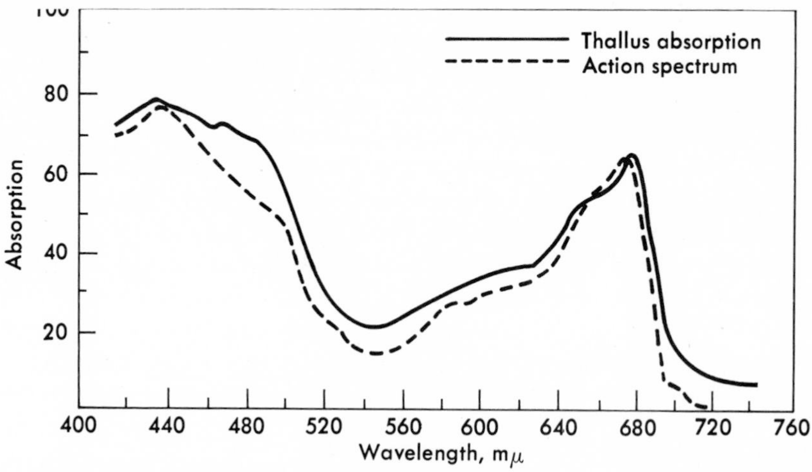

Figure 10-5 Action spectrum and absorption spectrum for the thallus of the green alga *Ulva taeniata*. Note that photosynthesis is active in the 480–500 mμ wavelengths, indicating some transfer of energy from the carotenoids to chlorophyll. (Reprinted by permission of The Rockefeller University Press from J. Gen. Physiol. 1950. 33: 389.) (After Haxo and Blinks.)

THE CHLOROPLAST

The whole wonderful process of photosynthesis takes place from start to completion in the *chloroplast,* a cytoplasmic particle of surprisingly complex architecture. The absorption of light energy and carbon dioxide and the ultimate conversion of the carbon dioxide to starch with the evolution of oxygen all take place within the illuminated chloroplast. It is through this cytoplasmic particle and its counterpart in photosynthetic bacteria, the *chromatophore,* that literally the whole system of living organisms now in existence is sustained.

Structure of the chloroplast

The contents of the chloroplast are enclosed in an "envelope" consisting of two membranes with an enclosed space. These membranes are smooth and continuous with no perforations or regularly attached particles (20).

Evidence has been obtained that the envelope is differentially permeable. For example, Mudrack (18) observed that chloroplasts in *Agapanthus umbellatus* were plasmolyzed and deplasmolyzed in the same sense as that of the cell when exposed to solutions of different osmotic pressures.

A cross section of the chloroplast reveals several membranes stacked on top of each other. These membranes are paired, forming stacks of *discs*. The *matrix* (sometimes called stroma) of the chloroplast may be found both within the discs and surrounding them. On or within this lamellar system the chlorophylls and presumably the other pigments are found. Depending upon the type of chloroplast, the pigments are found evenly distributed on the lamellar discs or concentrated in certain specific areas on the disc. If these concentrated areas are layered one on top of the other, the complete stack is known as a *granum*. In each case, however, the matrix surrounds not only the granum as a whole, but each individual disc as well.

In addition to the lamellar system, granules, lipid droplets, starch grains, and vesicles may be found in the matrix. Eye spots and pyrenoid bodies, often found in algal cells, are also found in the matrix. Figure 10-6 illustrates a schematic drawing of a typical chloroplast.

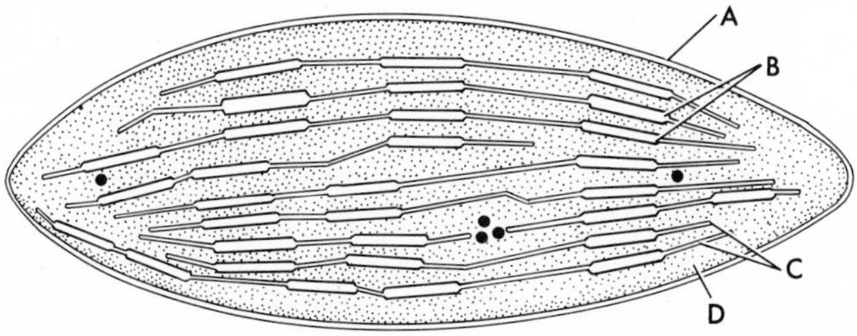

Figure 10-6 Schematic representation of a mature chloroplast. A = double membrane chloroplast envelope. B = granum, C = lamellae, and D = matrix. (After D. von Wettstein. 1959. *In* The photochemical apparatus—its structure and function. Brookhaven Symp. Biol. 11: 138)

Sager (20) examined altered chloroplasts from mutant strains of *Chlamydomonas,* in which one or more of the normal components of the chloroplast was missing, in an attempt to determine what effect, if any, the missing component had on the structural organization of the chloroplast. She found that the presence of chlorophyll was necessary for lamellar formation and that the presence or absence of carotenoids, unlike chlorophyll, had no noticeable effect on the structural organization of the chloroplast.

The chloroplast lamellae. As mentioned before, the photosynthetically active pigments are confined to the lamellar system of the chloroplasts. In the lower forms of plant life, the pigments are evenly distributed over the entire surface of the lamellae, while in the higher forms of plant life, they are restricted to certain areas of the lamellae. These areas are usually found layered on top of each other, the stacks being called *grana*.

Wolken (29) and Calvin (3) have proposed that the chloroplast is a lamellar structure composed of lipid and aqueous protein layers. Monomolecular films of chlorophyll molecules oriented in a specific manner separate these layers. The chlorophyll molecule is "polar," having a hydrophilic porphyrin "head" and a lipophilic phytol "tail." Thus, when it is located between aqueous protein and lipid layers, the porphyrin part extends into the aqueous protein and the phytol part into the lipid layer (8, 29). So, instead of a haphazard arrangement, the chlorophyll molecules are uniformly oriented between alternating aqueous protein and lipid layers. On the basis of these considerations, Wolken has presented a schematic molecular model of the chloroplast illustrating a possible arrangement of the pigment molecules in the lamellar discs (Figure 10-7A).

In this model, tetrads of chlorophyll molecules are arranged in such a way that the reactive isocyclic rings of the porphyrin "heads" are all turned toward each other. The phytol "tails" are separated as far as possible from each other, thus diminishing any interaction. More than enough room is left for the arrangement of carotenoid molecules within this network of chlorophyll molecules.

Calvin (3) has given us a molecular model of the chloroplast (Figure 10-7B) that is similar to that of Wolken's. He also has layers of lipid alternating with layers of aqueous proteins, the different layers being separated each time by a monomolecular layer of chlorophyll and carotenoid molecules.

As mentioned before, enough evidence on the fine structure of the chloroplast and chlorophyll analysis has accumulated for us to postulate that chlorophyll is arranged in a monomolecular layer at the interfaces between lipid and protein layers. The next problem would be to determine in what way the chlorophyll molecule is oriented in the lamellae. If the porphyrin heads of the chlorophyll molecules were to lie flat with the surface of the lamellae, their greatest cross-sectional area would be available for the interception of light quanta. Increasing the angle of inclination with the surface of the lamellae up to 90° would, of course, decrease the available cross-sectional area. The dominant thought today is that the porphyrin head lies at an angle of 45° with the surface of the lamellae, as pictured in Dr. Calvin's molecular model of the chloroplast.

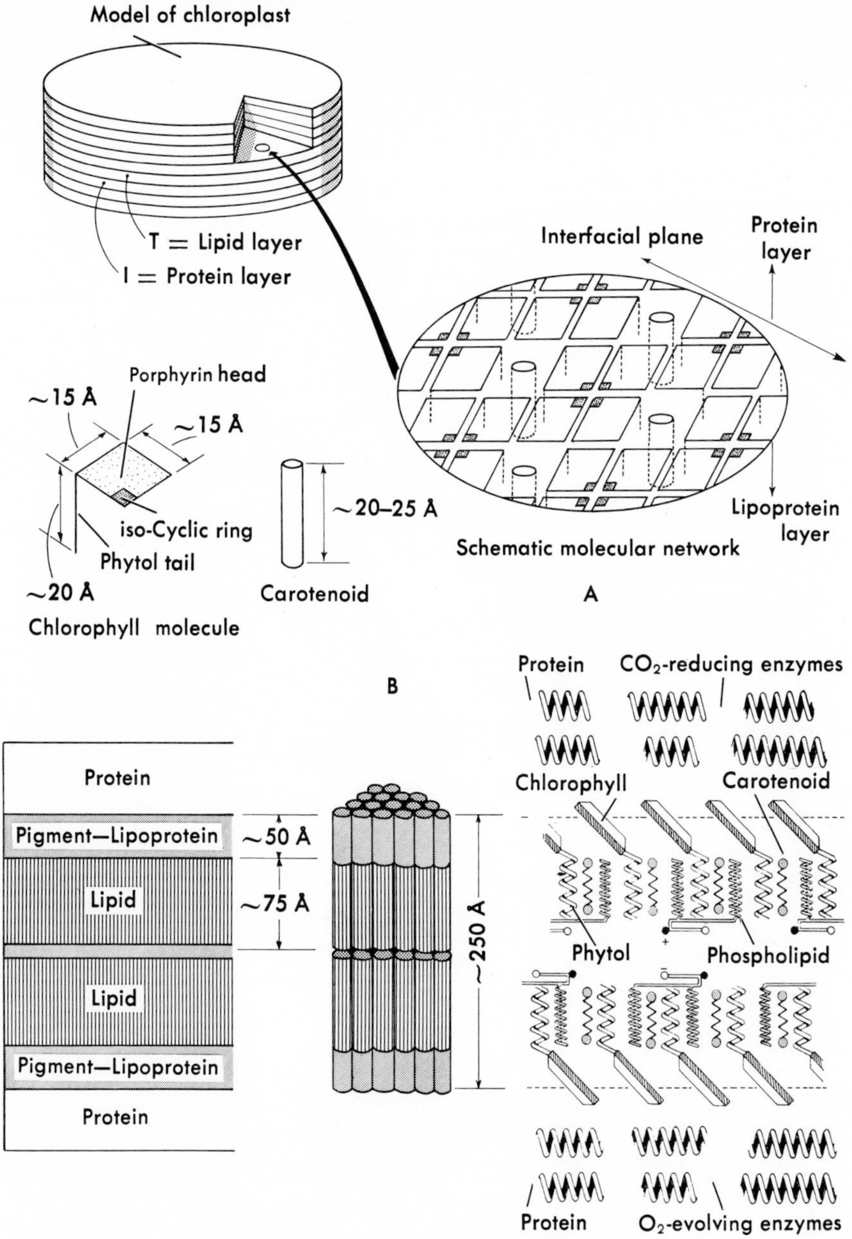

Figure 10-7 Molecular models of the chloroplast. A. As proposed by Wolken and Schwertz. B. As proposed by Calvin. (Part A reprinted by permission of The Rockefeller University Press from J. Gen. Physiol. 1953. 37: 111. Part B from M. Calvin. 1959. *In* The photochemical apparatus—its structure and function. Brookhaven Symp. Biol. 11: 160.)

The formation of the chloroplast

As with mitochondria, the problem of change in the number of chloroplasts in a cell has never been solved satisfactorily. Some believe that they arise *de novo,* while others believe some sort of replication is involved. A form of replication has been suggested indirectly by observations of plastids, which for some reason or another have lost their capacity to produce chlorophyll. These plastids apparently give rise to plastids also devoid of chlorophyll. However, in defense of plastids being produced *de novo* in the cell, Calvin (3) has demonstrated, in a most eloquent way, how the cell could construct a lamellar system.

The similarities between the two cytoplasmic particles, chloroplasts and mitochondria, are surprising. Both are basically lipo-protein complexes, in both respiratory enzymes and pigments are found, in both ATP is produced, both increase in number in the cell, both are enclosed by a double membrane, and both contain an internal lamellar system.

Von Wettstein (28), with the aid of the electron microscope, has followed the development of the chloroplast from the early proplastid stage to the fully mature chloroplast. The stages, as outlined in Figure 10-8,

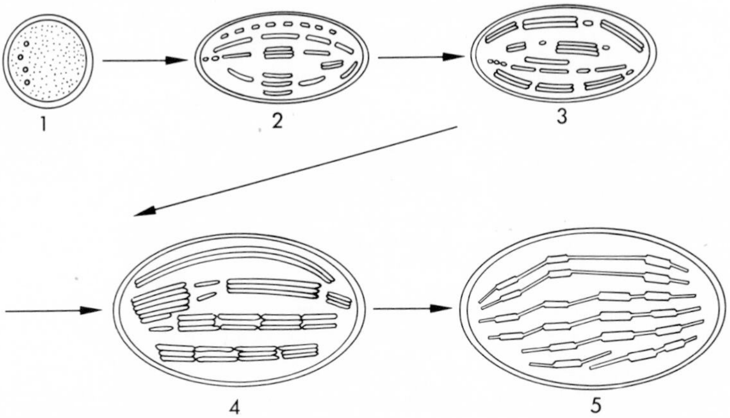

Figure 10-8 Chloroplast development. See text for discussion. (After D. von Wettstein. 1959. *In* The photochemical apparatus—its structure and function. Brookhaven Symp. Biol. 11: 138.)

are as follows: (1) early proplastids give rise to vesicles, which appear to bleb off the inner membrane of the proplastid, (2) the vesicles attach to each other and arrange themselves in layers, (3) further fusion and growth in surface area of the newly formed lamellar discs takes place (double membrane characteristic of the lamellae is easily distinguished at this point), (4) multiplication of the lamellae to form a more or less continuous lamellar system, and (5) differentiation of grana.

THE BACTERIAL CHROMATOPHORE

One still finds in some texts that the pigments of photosynthetic bacteria are soluble rather than confined to organized structures. However, since the pioneer work of Schachman et al. (22), it has been accepted generally that the pigments of photosynthetic bacteria are localized in structures called *chromatophores*. The composition of chromatophores isolated from the purple sulfur bacterium *Chromatium* is shown in Table 10-2.

Table 10-2 The Composition of Lyophilized Chromatophores. The percent composition on a dry weight basis has been converted to grams per "mole" Ch. by employing the "molecular weight" of 13 million. By assigning an average molecular weight to each substance, it is possible to obtain an estimate of the number of molecules of each substance in a chromatophore. The mole ratio represents a "minimal unit" of composition. This unit represents a molecular weight of about 40,000.[a]

Substance	*%*	*g/"mole" Ch.*	*Molecular weight*	*Molecules/Ch.*	*Mole ratio*
Carotenoid	1.5	2.0×10^5	700	300	1
Bacteriochlorophyll	4.2	5.5×10^5	900	600	2
Phospholipid	22.3	30×10^5	900[b]	3,000	10
Protein	61.0	80×10^5	120[c]/A.A.	67,000 A.A.	220 A.A.
Other	11.0	12.5×10^5			

[a] After J. A. Bergeron (1959).
[b] Cephalin with C_{16} fatty acids.
[c] Round value for average amino acid.

The chromatophore is a hydrophilic structure, which is highly stable toward nondenaturing solvents, indicating the existence of a protein shell at its surface (1). If treated with warm denaturing solvents, the pigments are easily extracted. Bordering the protein layer on the inside is a layer of lipid, the two layers (protein and lipid) being separated by a monomolecular layer of pigment molecules. Note the similarities with the chloroplast models previously discussed. Also, as in the chloroplast, the chlorophyll molecules are oriented so that the porphyrin head is in contact with the protein layer and the phytol tail projected into the lipid layer. Figure 10-9 shows a model of the chromatophore proposed by Bergeron (1).

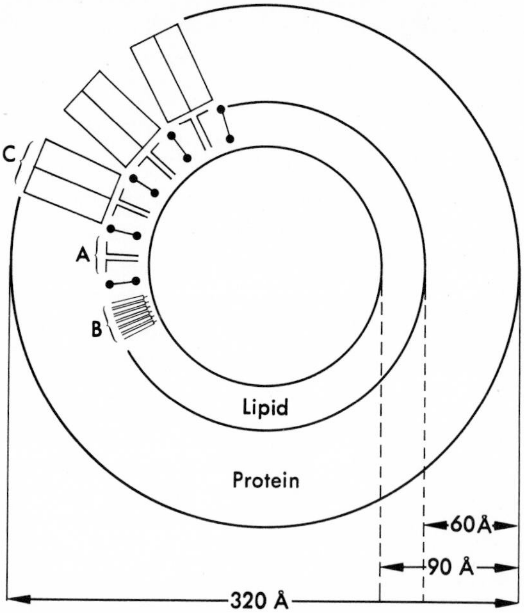

Figure 10-9 Molecular representation of the chromatophore. The pigment molecules (A) aligned in a monolayer are bounded internally by a phospholipid (B) monolayer and externally by a 60-Å-thick protein (C) layer. (After J. Bergeron. 1959. *In* The photochemical apparatus—its structure and function. Brookhaven Symp. Biol. 11: 118.)

BIBLIOGRAPHY

1. Bergeron, J. 1959. The bacterial chromatophore. *In* The photochemical apparatus—its structure and function. Brookhaven Symp. Biol. 11: 118.
2. Blackman, F. 1905. Optima and limiting factors. Ann. Botany 19: 281.
3. Calvin, M. 1959. From microstructure to macrostructure and function in the photochemical apparatus. *In* The photochemical apparatus—its structure and function. Brookhaven Symp. Biol. 11: 160.
4. Cohen-Bazire, G., and R. Stanier. 1958. Inhibition of carotenoid synthesis in photosynthetic bacteria. Nature 181: 250.
5. Duysens, L. 1956. Energy transformations in photosynthesis. Ann. Rev. Plant Physiol. 7: 25.
6. Einstein, A. 1905. Über einen die Erzeugung und Verwandlung des Lichtes betreffenden heuristischen Gesichtspunkt. Ann. Physik 17: 132.
7. French, C., and V. Young. 1956. The absorption, action and fluorescence

spectra of photosynthetic pigments in living cells and in solutions. *In* Radiation biology. McGraw-Hill Book Co., New York. 3: 343.
8. Frey-Wyssling, A. 1957. Macromolecules in cell structure. Harvard University Press, Cambridge, Mass.
9. Galston, A. 1950. Phototropism II. Botan. Rev. 16: 361.
10. Glass, B. 1961. Summary. *In* W. McElroy and B. Glass (eds.), Light and life. Johns Hopkins Press, Baltimore, Md.
11. Goodwin, T. 1960. Chemistry, biogenesis and physiology of the carotenoids. *In* W. Ruhland (ed.), Encyclopedia of plant physiology. Springer, Berlin. 5: Part 1, 394.
12. Granick, S. 1954. Metabolism of heme and chlorophyll. *In* D. Greenberg (ed.), Chemical pathways of metabolism. Academic Press, New York. 2: 287.
13. Haxo, F., and L. Blinks. 1950. Photosynthetic action spectra of marine algae. J. Gen. Physiol. 33: 389.
14. Hill, R. 1937. Oxygen evolved by isolated chloroplasts. Nature 139: 881.
15. Lemberg, R. 1928. Die Chromoproteide der Rotalgen. I. Justus Liebigs. Ann. Chem. 461: 46.
16. Loomis, W. 1960. Historical introduction. *In* W. Ruhland (ed.), Encyclopedia of plant physiology. Springer, Berlin. 5: Part 1, 85.
17. Mackinney, G. 1935. Leaf carotenes. J. Biol. Chem. 111: 75.
18. Mudrack, K. 1956. Über Grössen und Strukturänderungen der Chloroplasten in Rohrzucker und Elektrolytlosungen. Protoplasma (Wien) 47: 461.
19. O'hEocha, C. 1962. Phycobilins. *In* R. Lewin (ed.), Physiology and biochemistry of algae. Academic Press, New York.
20. Sager, R. 1959. The architecture of the chloroplast in relation to its photosynthetic activities. *In* The photochemical apparatus—its structure and function. Brookhaven Symp. Biol. 11: 101.
21. Saussure, Theód de. 1804. Recherches chimiques sur la végétation. V. Nyon, Paris.
22. Schachman, H., A. Pardee, and R. Stanier. 1952. Studies on the macromolecular organization of microbial cells. Arch. Biochem. 38: 245.
23. Shemin, D. 1956. The biosynthesis of porphyrins; the succinate-glycine cycle. *In* D. Green (ed.), Currents in biochemical research. Interscience Publishers, New York.
24. Stanier, R. 1959. Formation and function of the photosynthetic pigment system in purple bacteria. *In* The photochemical apparatus—its structure and function. Brookhaven Symp. Biol. 11: 43.
25. Thimann, K., and G. Curry. 1961. Phototropism. *In* W. McElroy and B. Glass (eds.), Light and life. Johns Hopkins Press, Baltimore, Md.
26. Wassink, E., and J. Kersten. 1946. Observations sur le spectre d' absorption et sur le role des carotinoides dans la photosynthese des diatomées. Enzymologia 12: 3.
27. Weir, T., and C. Stocking. 1952. The chloroplast: structure, inheritance and enzymology. Botan. Rev. 18: 14.

28. von Wettstein, D. 1959. The formation of plastid structures. *In* The photochemical apparatus—its structure and function. Brookhaven Symp. Biol. 11: 138.
29. Wolken, J. 1961. Euglena: an experimental organism for biochemical and biophysical studies. Rutgers University Press, New Brunswick, N.J.
30. Wolken, J., and F. Schwertz. 1953. Chlorophyll monolayers in chloroplasts. J. Gen. Physiol. 37: 111.
31. Zscheile, F., and C. Comar. 1941. Influence of preparative procedure on the purity of chlorophyll components as shown by absorption spectra. Botan. Gaz. 102: 463.
32. Zscheile, F., J. White, B. Beadle, and J. Roach. 1942. The preparation and absorption spectra of five pure carotenoid pigments. Plant Physiol. 17: 331.

11

The light and dark reactions of photosynthesis

INTRODUCTION

The pigment system of the chloroplast first absorbs light energy and then passes it on via intermediates to the products of photosynthesis. How is this light energy absorbed? How is it transported? What intermediates are involved? These are just some of the questions that may be asked about the light reaction of photosynthesis.

RADIENT ENERGY

When a chlorophyll molecule absorbs a light quantum, the molecule is excited; that is, it is brought from its normal ground state to an excited state (higher energy level). Not all quanta are able to lift chlorophyll to a higher state of energy. First the light has to be absorbed, and, secondly, the quantum absorbed has to have a sufficient amount of energy to do the job. The energy in a quantum may be determined from the wavelength of radiation, the energy being greater the shorter the wavelength. This is shown in Planck's law:

$$q\,(\text{quantum}) = hv = \frac{hc}{\lambda}$$

where h is Planck's constant (6.624×10^{-27} erg sec); v is the frequency of light in waves per second; c is the velocity of light (2.998×10^{10} cm/sec); and λ is the wavelength expressed in centimeters. According to Einstein's law of photochemical equivalence, only one molecule or atom can be excited or activated by one quantum; that is, one quantum of light, regardless of its energy level, will only activate one molecule. Usually, the amount of energy absorbed by a mole of a substance is considered rather than the energy absorbed by one molecule. Therefore, one would need N quanta (N = Avogadro number = 6.02×10^{23}) to excite 1 mole (N molecules) of substance. We can say that N quanta is 1 mole of quanta (1 einstein). A mole of quanta is known as a photochemical equivalent, and the energy (E) contained in a photochemical equivalent may be calculated from the following equation.

$$E = Nhv$$

Now, if we substitute c/λ for v we get:

$$E = \frac{Nhc}{\lambda}$$

$$E = \frac{(6.02 \times 10^{23})(6.624 \times 10^{-27})(2.998 \times 10^{10})}{\lambda}\ \text{erg/mole}$$

$$E = \frac{1.197 \times 10^{8}}{\lambda}\ \text{erg/mole}$$

and if we convert erg to calories (1 erg = 0.239×10^{-7} cal),

$$E = \frac{2.86}{\lambda}\ \text{cal/mole}$$

At this point, we have the wavelength in centimeters, which should be converted to angstroms to get:

$$E = \frac{2.86 \times 10^{8}}{\lambda}\ \text{cal/mole}$$

With the above equation one can obtain the photochemical equivalent in calories per mole for any wavelength, for example:

4000 Å ... 71500 cal/mole

5000 Å ... 57200 cal/mole

6000 Å ... 47667 cal/mole

In this manner we can determine the amount of energy that is being absorbed at any one wavelength.

FREE RADICALS

There are many instances in the literature where free radicals are mentioned in connection with the photosynthetic process. Free radicals are atoms or molecules containing an unpaired electron and are produced when bonds are broken symmetrically in homolytic reactions. In such reactions electron pairs are divided, one electron going to each nucleus. If a free radical contains only one unpaired electron, it is called a monoradical, and if two unpaired electrons, a biradical. An example of a biradical can be demonstrated by the irradiation of ethylene.

$$H_2C{=}CH_2 \xrightarrow{\text{Light}} H_2\dot{C}{-}\dot{C}H_2$$

In fact, a free biradical is almost always produced when a double bond between two carbon atoms is changed to a single bond.

Electrons pair because only two electrons can occupy the same energy state, and these two electrons must have spins, or angular momentum, about their axis in *opposite* directions. This is known as the *Pauli exclusion principle*. The electron has been observed to have an intrinsic magnetic moment and can be pictured as a spinning, charged body which sets up its own magnetic field. All electrons possess the same intrinsic spin, which is characterized by a spin quantum number *s*, the magnitude of which is always $\frac{1}{2}$. If we define this spin in relation to a magnetic field direction, we can assign a spin of $+\frac{1}{2}$ or $-\frac{1}{2}$ to an electron. According to Pauli's principle, two electrons in the same orbit would have opposite spins, thus neutralizing their magnetic momenta. The resulting spin would be zero $(+\frac{1}{2} - \frac{1}{2} = 0)$. For example, in a helium atom the spins of its two electrons in the ground state are in opposite directions, and the total spin of the atom is zero. This type of state is known as the singlet state because the total spin can only have the single value zero in a given direction.

In free radicals the spin of an unpaired electron is not compensated for by a partner electron spinning in the opposite direction and so has a resulting spin of $+\frac{1}{2}$ or $-\frac{1}{2}$. In a biradical the resulting spin would be $+1$ or -1. Because of a resulting spin other than zero, free radicals act as paramagnetic substances; that is, when attracted by a magnet, they assume a position parallel to that of a magnetic force.

These properties of free radicals make them very useful in the detection of photobiological processes. In 1945, Zavoisky discovered *electron spin resonance* (ESR) absorption, which initiated the development of spectrophotometers capable of detecting the presence of unpaired electrons. An illustration of the principle of magnetic resonance absorption measurements is given in Figure 11-1.

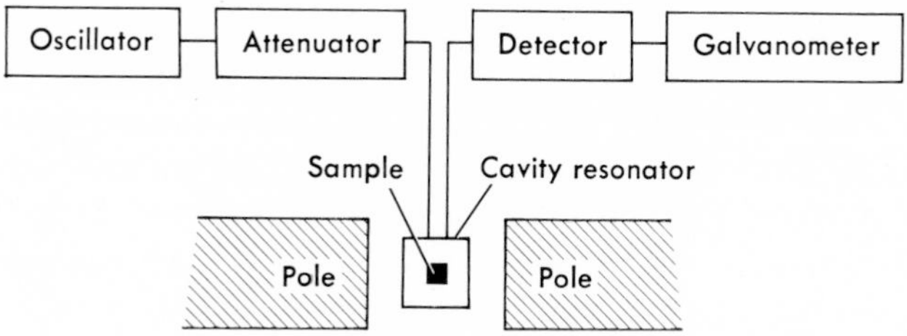

Figure 11-1 Schematic representation of the principle of magnetic resonance absorption measurements (After P. W. Selwood. 1956. Magnetochemistry. Interscience Publishers, New York.)

The ESR phenomenon is related to the intrinsic magnetic moment arising from the spin of the electron. When an unpaired electron is placed between the poles of a magnet, the electron, generating its own magnetic field, will orient itself with or against the external field. There is a significant difference in energy between these two fields. The separation between these two energy levels is a function of the external magnetic field. Thus, one may create an energy difference of his own choosing by merely adjusting the strength of the external magnetic field. The energy involved may be calculated from the equation:

$$\Delta E = h\nu = gBH$$

where ΔE is the energy difference; h is Planck's constant; ν is the frequency; B is a constant, the Bohr magneton (0.927×10^{-20} erg/gauss); and H is the magnetic field strength in gauss. The interaction between the magnetic moment of the electron and the external magnetic field is given by g, which has a value of 2.0023. Interaction between the electron spin and the electron's orbital angular momentum may cause the g value to deviate slightly from the 2.0023 value.

ESR measurements have been made on a variety of biological materials, such as illuminated chloroplasts, heme proteins, bacterial cells, and oxidation-reduction systems. An example of ESR measurements of illuminated whole spinach chloroplasts is shown in Figure 11-2. Note that temperature

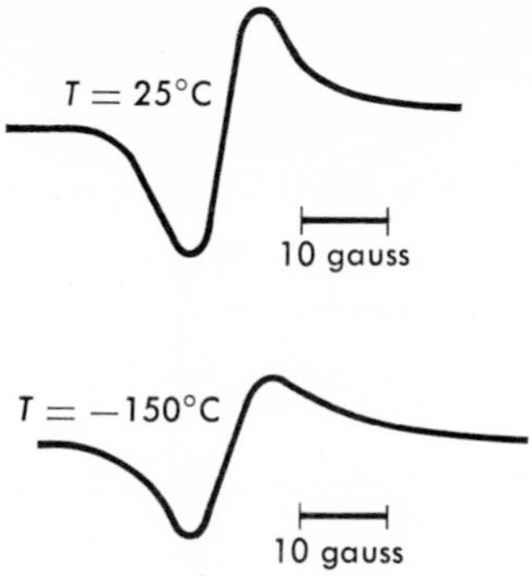

Figure 11-2 Electron spin resonance of whole spinach chloroplasts at 25°C and at −150°C. (After M. Calvin. 1959. *In* The photochemical apparatus—its structure and function. Brookhaven Symp. Biol. 11: 160.)

does not have a significant effect on the photo-induced signals, suggesting the lack of enzyme participation.

TRANSFER OF ENERGY

Not all of the pigment molecules absorb light or are activated at once. Light energy absorbed by one pigment molecule is thought to be transferred through many other pigment molecules before reaching its site of action. This transfer of light energy may be from one chlorophyll a molecule to another, from chlorophyll b to chlorophyll a, from carotenoids to chlorophyll a, or from phycobilins to chlorophyll a (20).

To understand how energy can be transferred from molecule to molecule, we must first have a working knowledge of the excited states of molecules, including the *ground* or *singlet state,* the *excited singlet state,* and the *triplet state.* In the ground state, the spins of paired electrons are in opposite direction (Pauli's exclusion principle), the total spin being zero. If one electron of a pair absorbs a quantum of light, it will then exist for a very short period of time in a higher energy level (excited singlet state), returning to its former level in about 10^{-8} sec. When light energy is absorbed by a system, it does not just disappear, but has to appear as radiation energy or some other form. Thus, with the return of the electron from the excited singlet state to the ground state, the energy previously absorbed is given off as radiation energy. This is known as *fluorescence* and is temperature-independent (Figure 11-3).

There is always the possibility that the electron brought to a higher energy level (excited singlet state) by the absorption of a quantum of light may also have its spin reversed. Since two electrons cannot exist at the same energy level with parallel spins, this excited electron cannot return to its companion. The electron is said to be "trapped" at a high energy level, and the electron is in what is called the *triplet state* which,

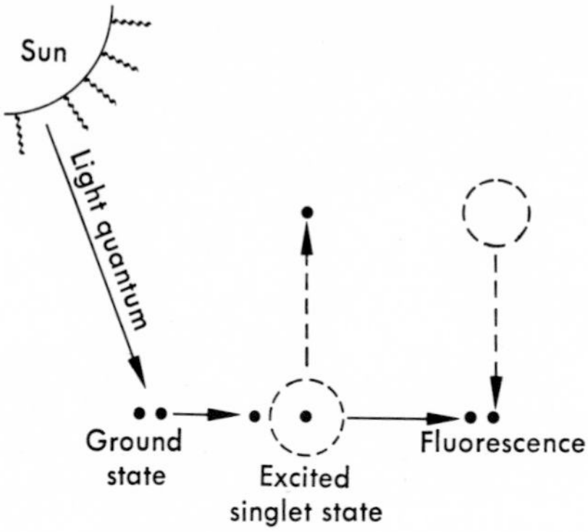

Figure 11-3 Diagram depicting the absorption of a light quantum by an electron, causing the electron to jump to a higher energy level. When the electron returns to the ground state, the excess energy is given off as radiation energy (fluorescence).

due to a slight loss of energy, is at a lower energy level than the excited singlet state. However, the electron can have its spin changed again and return from the triplet state to the ground state, giving off its excess energy in the form of radiation. This process is termed *phosphorescence* and is also temperature-independent.

However, transitions from the excited singlet state or triplet state to the ground state that involve the release of "excess" energy in the form of radiation are of no particular significance to the biological system. It is the migration and conversion of this "excess" energy to chemical energy that is important.

The transport of electrons in the reversible oxidation-reduction of organic compounds proceeds in two successive univalent steps (25). Thus, in the oxidation-reduction reactions involving NAD^+ or $NADP^+$, a free radical should be produced, and its detection should be possible through ESR measurements. Experimental proof of the existence of free radicals in the transfer of electrons in biological reactions has been demonstrated by Commoner et al. (19, 18, 17), who studied various systems, including the alcohol dehydrogenase system:

$$\text{Alcohol} + \text{NAD}^+ \xrightarrow[\text{Dehydrogenase}]{\text{Alcohol}} \text{Acetaldehyde} + \text{NADH} + \text{H}^+$$

They found that free radicals could be detected in the reaction mixture of alcohol, NAD^+, and alcohol dehydrogenase. They also detected free radicals in the reverse reaction, which includes the reaction mixture acetaldehyde, NADH, and alcohol dehydrogenase. No paramagnetism was demonstrated by any of the compounds of the dehydrogenase system when measured alone. Since oxidation-reduction reactions involving organic compounds do occur within the photosynthetic mechanism, free radicals should be detected as, indeed, they are (see Figure 11-2). Also, the fact that free radicals are present suggests that electron transport is taking place.

Another possibility that has been suggested for energy transfer in photosynthesis is that the chloroplast may be operating on semiconductor principles (25, 13). Semiconductors are composed of materials possessing electrical properties intermediate between conductors, in which electrons are moved very rapidly, and insulators where very little, if any, electron transport takes place. Actually, the idea that giant macromolecules may have properties similar to the semiconductors studied in crystal physics belongs to Szent-Gyorgyi (36). He proposed that proteins may be able to conduct electrons within their electronic structure. It was this pioneer work on proteins that led to the description of the chloroplast as a semiconductor-like unit. The mobile electrons in a semiconductor system are unpaired and can be detected by ESR measurements (16). In fact, Calvin (14) has claimed that the light-induced ESR signal observed in chloroplasts kept at temperatures low enough to rule out enzyme activity must be due to semiconductors.

Free-electronic energy transfer between chlorophyll molecules may also take place by resonance. According to this hypothesis, energy may be transferred from one molecule to another or between atom groups of the same molecule. Before resonance transfer can take place certain conditions must be fulfilled. For example, the energy donor has to be fluorescent at frequencies that the energy acceptor is able to absorb; that is, the fluorescence spectrum of the energy donor must overlap the absorption spectrum of the energy acceptor. In addition, molecules must be packed relatively close (1000 Å and less) for good resonance energy transfer to take place. In the molecular models of the chloroplast shown in Figure 10-7, one can easily see that the pigment molecules are packed sufficiently close for this phenomenon to take place.

PRODUCTION OF ASSIMILATORY POWER

Having discussed some of the aspects of photochemical reactions, we are now ready to construct a scheme for photosynthesis. The question arises, should this scheme be confined to the chloroplast or should the complete cell be considered also? For over 100 years photosynthesis was known to be connected to the chloroplast, but it was not known whether or not photosynthesis was completely confined to this cytoplasmic particle. In fact, for a good many years it was thought that only the light reaction occurred in the chloroplast and that CO_2 reduction occurred in the cytoplasm of the cell. However, in 1954 it was found that isolated chloroplasts, under suitable experimental conditions, could assimilate carbon dioxide (6).

Therefore, the enzymes involved in the reduction of carbon dioxide and the *assimilatory power* (*reducing power*) needed to accomplish this assimilation must be present and perhaps produced within the confines of the chloroplast. Several questions had to be answered. What is the assimilatory power involved and how is it produced? What systems are involved in the synthesis of assimilatory power? At what point is light energy actually converted to chemical energy? What role does water play in this overall scheme?

Arnon and his group, working with isolated chloroplasts, have produced a general scheme for photosynthesis. We will use this scheme for discussing the initial reactions of photosynthesis, not for its uniqueness, but for its general agreement with theories offered by numerous other investigators.

Carbon dioxide assimilation

Fixation of CO_2 by isolated chloroplasts both in the presence of light and in the dark is shown in Figure 11-4. The reduction of CO_2 is accompanied by the evolution of O_2, which is in close agreement with the well-known photosynthetic quotient $O_2/CO_2 = 1$. As one can see from Figure 11-4, the

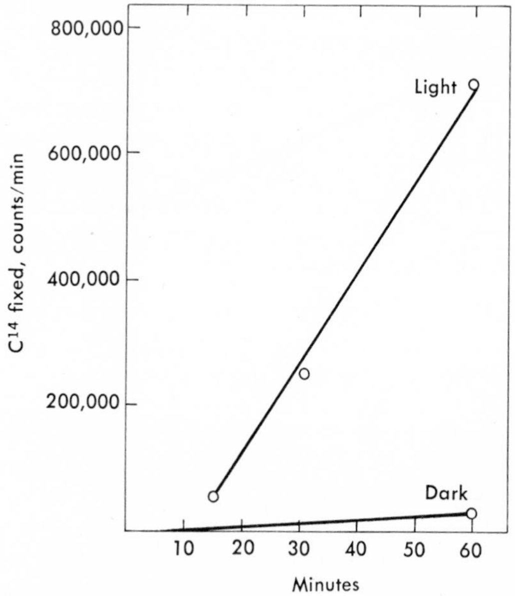

Figure 11-4 $C^{14}O_2$ fixation by isolated spinach chloroplasts in light and dark. (After Allen et al. 1955. J. Am. Chem. Soc. 77: 4149.

reduction of CO_2 is completely light-dependent and proceeds at a constant rate for at least 1 hour.

With the use of radioactive carbon dioxide and chromatographic techniques, Arnon's group was able to identify several soluble and insoluble products, including phosphate esters of glucose; fructose; ribulose; sedoheptulose; dihydroxy-acetone and glyceric acid; glycolic, malic and aspartic acids; alanine; glycine; dihydroxyacetone; and glucose. By treating the insoluble products with salivary amylase, they obtained maltose and glucose. The formation of maltose on treatment with salivary amylase is considered to be a specific test for starch formation by isolated chloroplasts in the presence of CO_2, H_2O, and light and without the aid of cytoplasmic enzyme systems or sources of energy.

Photosynthetic phosphorylation

With the discovery that CO_2 can be assimilated in isolated chloroplasts came the realization that the chloroplast must contain the enzymes necessary for this assimilation and must be able to produce the ATP essential for the formation of the main photosynthetic products. Arnon et al. (7) in 1954 demonstrated that the isolated chloroplast can, in the presence of light, produce ATP. They termed the process *photosynthetic phosphorylation.* This brought forth a hitherto unknown fact, that mitochondria are not the only cytoplasmic particles capable of ATP formation. Also, ATP formation in chloroplasts differs from that in mitochondria in that it is independent of respiratory oxidations. The independence of photosynthetic phosphorylation from molecular oxygen is demonstrated in Figure 11-5. What is truly significant here is that light energy is being converted to ATP; that is, there is a *conversion of light energy to chemical energy.*

But, ATP is only one of the necessary requirements for the reduction of CO_2 to the carbohydrate level. A reductant must be formed in photosynthesis that will provide the "hydrogens" or electrons for this reduction. As far back as 1951, Arnon (2) demonstrated that isolated chloroplasts are capable of reducing pyridine nucleotides when exposed to light. The photochemical reaction had to be coupled with an enzyme system capable of utilizing the reduced pyridine nucleotide as quickly as it is formed. It was found that $NADPH_2$ is the reduced pyridine nucleotide active in photosynthesis (8). In the presence of H_2O, ADP, and orthophosphate (P), substrate amounts of NADP were reduced, accompanied by the evolution of oxygen in accordance with the equation:

$$2ADP + 2P + 2NADP + 4H_2O \rightarrow 2ATP + O_2 + 2NADPH_2 + 2H_2O$$

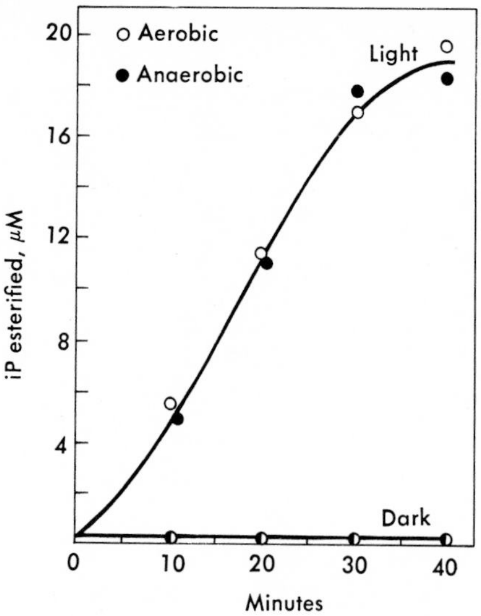

Figure 11-5 Incorporation of inorganic phosphate to form ATP by broken chloroplasts. Note the light-dependence and oxygen-independence of photosynthetic phosphorylation. After D. Arnon. 1959. *In* The photochemical apparatus—its structure and function. Brookhaven Symp. Biol. 11: 181.)

As shown by this equation and Figure 11-6, the evolution of 1 mole of O_2 is accompanied by the reduction of 2 moles of NADP and esterification of 2 moles of orthophosphate. Together, ATP and $NADPH_2$ provide the energy requirements for CO_2 assimilation. Arnon called this power *assimilatory power* (ATP + $NADPH_2$).

With the discovery of flavin mononucleotide (FMN) and vitamin K as cofactors in photosynthetic phosphorylation (39) and the coupling of NADP reduction with ATP formation, three separate pathways for photosynthetic phosphorlyation began to unfold. It was found that the formation of ATP in the presence of NADP is independent of the presence of oxygen when either cofactor, FMN or vitamin K, is added in optimal amounts (Figure 11-7). In addition, FMN and vitamin K were found to catalyze separate pathways of photosynthetic phosphorylation (40, 41), since maximal rates of phosphorylation will take place with either FMN or vitamin K as a catalyst. Also, the FMN system and vitamin K system exhibit different sensitivities to dinitrophenol and *o*-phenanthroline. The

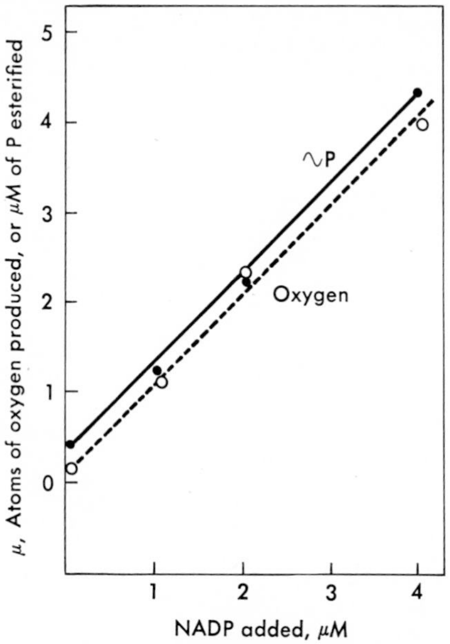

Figure 11-6 Incorporation of inorganic phosphate by isolated chloroplasts to form ATP in the presence of different concentrations of NADP. Note the linear agreement between the amount of NADP supplied and the amount of inorganic phosphate taken up. Also note that the evolution of oxygen parallels phosphate uptake. (After D. Arnon. 1959. *In* The photochemical apparatus—its structure and function. Brookhaven Symp. Biol. 11: 181.)

vitamin K system is less sensitive than the FMN system to both of these compounds (3).

Both the FMN and vitamin K pathways for photophosphorylation are referred to as cyclic in nature; that is, upon the absorption of a quantum of light a high energy electron is released from a chlorophyll molecule and then returned to it via the FMN and/or vitamin K pathway. Thus, chlorophyll acts as both an *electron donor* and an *electron acceptor* within a closed circuit. The phosphorylation that takes place in both these pathways is referred to by Arnon as *cyclic photophosphorylation*. In *noncyclic photophosphorylation* the electron is not returned to the chlorophyll molecule,

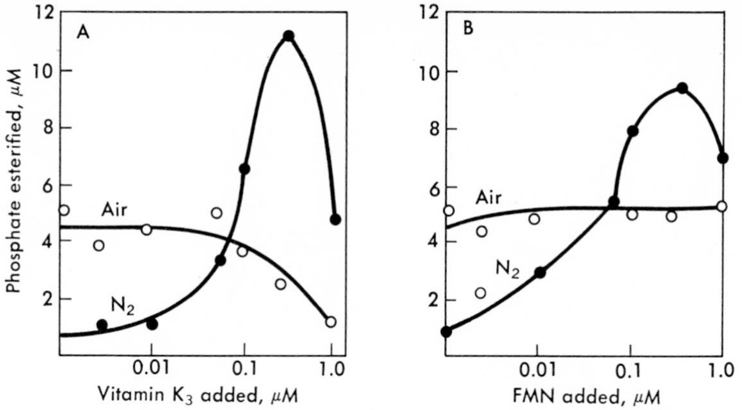

Figure 11-7 Effect of vitamin K_3 and FMN concentration on cyclic photophosphorylation by spinach chloroplasts in nitrogen and air at a high light intensity. (After D. Arnon. 1961. *In* W. D. McElroy and B. Glass (eds.), Light and life. Johns Hopkins Press, Baltimore, Md.

but is taken up in the reduction of NADP. These pathways are summarized in Figure 11-8.

The excitation of a chlorophyll molecule by a quantum of light and the subsequent release of an electron may be represented as follows:

$$\text{Chl} + h\nu \rightarrow \text{Chl}^*$$

$$\text{Chl}^* \rightarrow [\text{Chl}]^+ + e$$

where Chl* represents an excited chlorophyll molecule; $[\text{Chl}]^+$ is the oxidized form of the chlorophyll molecule (minus an electron); and *e* represents the released electron. In the vitamin K pathway two electrons from two excited chlorophyll molecules are returned to chlorophyll via vitamin K and a cytochrome in a cyclic manner. The "excess" energy of the electron is utilized in the formation of ATP. Phosphorylation most likely takes place with the oxidation of the terminal cytochrome (4). It is quite possible that phosphorylation may also take place with the oxidation of vitamin K.

$$2(\text{Chl} + h\nu) \longrightarrow 2[\text{Chl}]^+ + 2e^-$$

$$\text{Vit. K}_{\text{ox}} + 2e^- \longrightarrow \text{Vit. K}_{\text{red.}}$$

$$\text{Vit. K}_{\text{red.}} + 2\text{Fe}^{3+}\,\text{cyt}_\text{I} \longrightarrow \text{Vit. K}_{\text{ox.}} + 2\text{Fe}^{2+}\,\text{cyt}_\text{I}$$

$$2\text{Fe}^{2+}\,\text{cyt}_\text{I} + 2[\text{Chl}]^+ + \text{ADP} + \text{H}_3\text{PO}_4 \longrightarrow 2\text{Fe}^{3+}\,\text{cyt}_\text{I} + 2\text{Chl} + \text{ATP}$$

Sum: $\text{ADP} + \text{H}_3\text{PO}_4 + 2h\nu \longrightarrow \text{ATP}$ (after Arnon, 1960)

Cyclic passage of the electron also takes place in the FMN pathway via

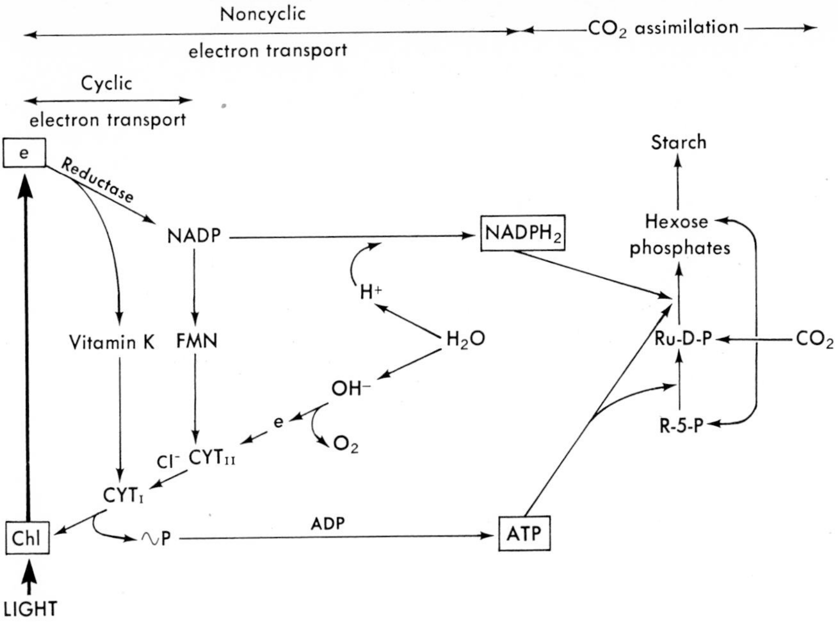

Figure 11-8 Schematic representation of the path of electrons in photosynthesis and the formation of assimilatory power (ATP + $NADPH_2$). On absorption of light quanta by chlorophyll, electrons are raised to a higher level of energy and then expelled. The electron may then return in a cyclic manner to the chlorophyll molecule via the vitamin K or FMN pathways with its excess energy being utilized for phosphate bond energy to form ATP. In the noncyclic electron transport the electrons accepted by NADP are replaced by OH^- ions provided by the photolysis of H_2O. Hydrogen ions (H^+) are also provided to NADP as a result of the photolysis of H_2O, thus forming $NADPH_2$. With the formation of assimilatory power, CO_2 may then be reduced to the carbohydrate level. (After D. Arnon, 1960. *In* W. Ruhland (ed.), Encyclopedia of plant physiology. Springer, Berlin. 5: Part 1, 773.

reductase, FMN, cytochrome II, and cytochrome I (catalyzed by chloride ion), with final acceptance by the chlorophyll molecule.

$$2(\mathrm{Chl} + h\nu) \longrightarrow 2[\mathrm{Chl}]^+ + 2e^-$$

$$\mathrm{NADP}^+ + 2e^- \xrightarrow{\text{Reductase}} \mathrm{NADPH} + \mathrm{H}^+$$

$$\mathrm{NADPH} + \mathrm{H}^+ + \mathrm{FMN} \longrightarrow \mathrm{NADP}^+ + \mathrm{FMNH_2}$$

$$\mathrm{FMNH_2} + 2\mathrm{Fe}^{3+}\,\mathrm{cyt_{II}} \longrightarrow \mathrm{FMN} + 2\mathrm{Fe}^{2+}\,\mathrm{cyt_{II}}$$

$$2\mathrm{Fe}^{2+}\,\mathrm{cyt_{II}} + 2\mathrm{Fe}^{3+}\,\mathrm{cyt_{I}} \longrightarrow 2\mathrm{Fe}^{3+}\,\mathrm{cyt_{II}} + 2\mathrm{Fe}^{2+}\,\mathrm{cyt_{I}}$$

$$2\mathrm{Fe}^{2+}\,\mathrm{cyt_{I}} + 2[\mathrm{Chl}]^+ + \mathrm{ADP} + \mathrm{H_3PO_4} \longrightarrow 2\mathrm{Fe}^{3+}\,\mathrm{cyt_{I}} + 2\mathrm{Chl} + \mathrm{ATP}$$

Sum: $$\mathrm{ADP} + \mathrm{H_3PO_4} + 2h\nu \longrightarrow \mathrm{ATP}$$ (after Arnon, 1960)

Finally, in the noncyclic pathway the electron is not returned to the chlorophyll molecule, but is taken up by $NADP^+$. The electron taken over by $NADP^+$ is stabilized by binding protons (H^+) resulting from the decomposition of H_2O. The chlorophyll molecule then regains its lost electron via cytochromes from the OH ions that were left unbalanced after H^+ was linked to $NADP^+$. The remaining [OH] radicals are dismutated to form H_2O and O_2.

$$2(\text{Chl} + h\nu) \longrightarrow 2[\text{Chl}]^+ + 2e^-$$

$$2H_2O \longrightarrow 2H^+ + 2OH^-$$

$$NADP^+ + 2H^+ + 2e^- \xrightarrow{\text{Reductase}} NADPH + H^+$$

$$2OH^- + 2Fe^{3+}\,\text{cyt}_{II} \longrightarrow \tfrac{1}{2}O_2 + H_2O + 2Fe^{2+}\,\text{cyt}_{II}$$

$$2Fe^{2+}\,\text{cyt}_{II} + 2Fe^{3+}\,\text{cyt}_{I} \longrightarrow 2Fe^{3+}\,\text{cyt}_{II} + 2Fe^{2+}\,\text{cyt}_{I}$$

$$2Fe^{2+}\,\text{cyt}_{I} + 2[\text{Chl}]^+ + ADP + H_3PO_4 \longrightarrow 2Fe^{3+}\,\text{cyt}_{I} + 2\text{Chl} + ATP$$

Sum: $$NADP^+ + 2H_2O + ADP + H_3PO_4 + 2h\nu \longrightarrow NADPH + H^+ + \tfrac{1}{2}O_2 + ATP + H_2O$$

(after Arnon, 1960)

With the production of ATP and reduced NADP, the plant is now ready to reduce CO_2 to the carbohydrate level. We must now leave Dr. Arnon's work and turn to Dr. Calvin's study of the "path of carbon in photosynthesis" for which he received the Nobel Prize in 1961.

THE CARBON COMPOUNDS OF PHOTOSYNTHESIS

To Liebig belongs the credit for the first theory on carbon reduction in photosynthesis; he suggested that plant acids are intermediates between CO_2 and sugars. However, no experimental evidence was given in support of this theory, which was developed primarily because the plant acids represent compounds intermediate in reduction between CO_2 and sugars and because ripening fruit is at first sour and later becomes sweet.

The first really strong opposition to Liebig's theory was offered by Baeyer (9) when he proposed that CO_2 is first reduced to formaldehyde followed by condensation of the formaldehyde molecules to form sugars. As is often the case, the relative simplicity of the formaldehyde theory rallied a strong following behind it although very little experimental evidence was given in support of it. Indeed, formaldehyde, even at very low concentrations, is toxic to many plants. Paechnatz (31) found that *Elodea, Chlorella,* and *Tropaeolum* were not capable of the utilization of formaldehyde for the formation of sugar. In fact, she found that concentrations of formaldehyde as low as 0.003% were toxic to both respiration and photosynthesis.

Radioactive tracing

Obviously, the "path of carbon in photosynthesis" was not to be found solely in theory, but in careful laboratory experimentation where each step is carefully analyzed and unequivocally proven a participant in the overall sequence leading to the reduction of CO_2 to sugar. This presented immense problems because of the dual role of many of the enzyme systems involved in respiration and photosynthesis. With this constant mixing of the intermediates of photosynthesis and respiration, it was just about impossible to pinpoint just what compound belonged to what system. The existing methods and instrumentation at that time presented no solution to this most complex problem. What was needed was a method of "tagging" compounds in timed experiments with living, photosynthesizing organisms and placing these compounds in their correct sequence.

With the use of radioactive carbon dioxide, the first steps toward solving this dilemma were taken (32, 33). It was found that fixation of radioactive carbon dioxide ($C^{11}O_2$) by barley leaves and *Chlorella* took place not only in the light but also in the dark. However, the dark fixation of CO_2 occurred only when the leaves were exposed to short periods of darkness. After 3 hours of darkness no fixation of CO_2 occurred in the barley leaves. Early workers were unsuccessful in their attempts to identify the initial products of photosynthesis, but did establish that in these products a carboxyl group is present and that this group contains most of the radioactivity. Because of the short half-life of C^{11} (22 minutes), the pioneer work of these investigators was limited to very brief analytical procedures. This obstacle was overcome with the identification of another radioactive isotope of carbon, C^{14}, with a half-life of 5000 years (33).

Work with the radioactive tracings of the assimilation of CO_2 in photosynthesis practically came to a standstill during World War II. After the war, however, work with $C^{14}O_2$ picked up, gathered momentum, and finally, Calvin and his laboratory produced their remarkable work, the mapping and identification of the intermediates involved in the assimilation of CO_2 in photosynthesis.

The radioautograph

In addition to the use of the radioisotope C^{14}, a combination of paper chromatography and radioautography has been employed. Paper chromatography provides a means for good separation of small quantities of intermediates from very complex mixtures. Radioautography enables investigators to identify on a chromatogram those compounds that are radioactive and therefore involved in the photosynthetic assimilation of $C^{14}O_2$. The complete chromatogram is exposed to sensitized photographic film, which will develop spots on areas in contact with radioactive spots on the chromatogram. Quantitative evaluation of the concentrations of each metabolite present may be obtained by simultaneously exposing a compound with a known amount of C^{14} and then comparing the relative densities. A radioautograph from an experiment on photosynthesis is shown in Figure 11-9.

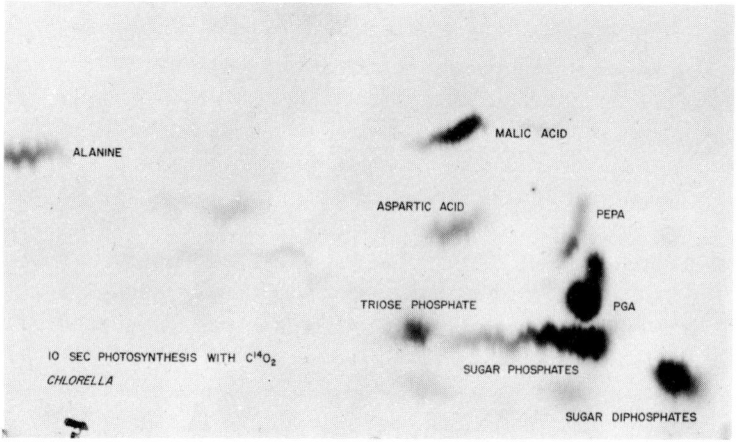

Figure 11-9 A radioautograph showing some of the metabolites of photosynthesis after a 10-second exposure of *Chorella* to $C^{14}O_2$. (Courtesy of Dr. Bassham, Lawrence Radiation Laboratory, Berkeley, California.)

Type of plants used

Calvin and co-workers selected *Chlorella* and *Scenedesmus* for study. These green algae are particularly adapted to studies dealing with the assimilation of carbon dioxide. They are small, unicellular, and can easily be maintained under laboratory conditions. In addition, they can readily be grown in clonal cultures, thus permitting work with large populations and, consequently, minimizing individual variation. Most important, however, is the fact that a great deal of work has been published about the physiology of these two organisms. Application of this knowledge to the culturing of these organisms makes possible the use of uniform and reproducible biological material, which is essential to any detailed metabolic study.

Problem of limited exposure to tagged CO_2

One more problem remained to be solved. A method had to be found that allowed for very short times of exposure to $C^{14}O_2$ in order to limit the labeling of compounds to the first few steps of the carbon assimilation pathway. This problem has been solved in a most simple and ingenious way. A suspension of algae (*Chlorella* or *Scenedesmus*) is allowed to photosynthesize under conditions of constant temperature and illumination in a clear transparent reservoir. Carbon dioxide is bubbled into the reservoir at a concentration saturating for photosynthesis. Under these circumstances steady-state conditions presumably are reached. The algal cells are then forced through a narrow transparent tube into a beaker of boiling methanol, instantly terminating all metabolic activity. Photosynthesis continues in the tube as in the reservoir. The length of the tube is known and the time needed for an algal suspension to traverse the tube is also known. Therefore, when $C^{14}O_2$ in water is injected into the tube at certain specific points, the time of algae exposure to radioactive carbon can be calculated. This time of exposure may vary from 1 to 15 sec. The alcohol is then evaporated, and the algal cells subjected to the analytical procedures described above. The incorporation of radiocarbon was found to be linear with time of exposure, suggesting steady-state conditions. A schematic representation of the apparatus used by Calvin and his co-workers is shown in Figure 11-10.

After an exposure of only 5 sec to $C^{14}O_2$, most of the radioactive carbon is found in 3-phosphoglyceric acid (3-PGA), a three-carbon compound

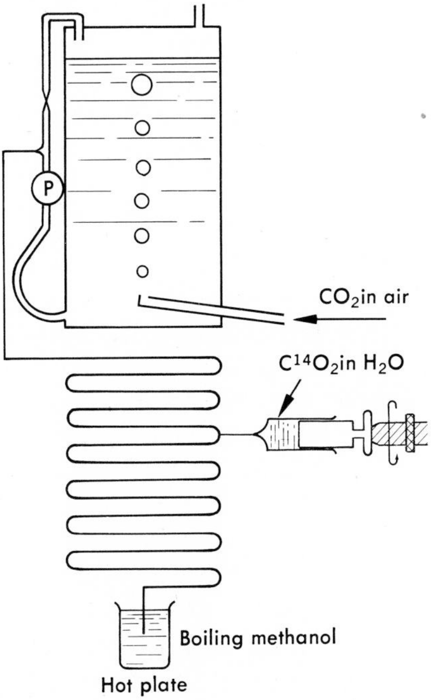

Figure 11-10 Flow-through system for short-time exposure to $C^{14}O_2$. (After J. Bassham et al. 1954. J. Am. Chem. Soc. 76: 1760.)

normally considered a constituent of glycolysis. Moreover, most of the radiocarbon is located in the carboxyl group of this compound. Increase in the time of exposure to $C^{14}O_2$ to 30–90 sec found most of the isotopic carbon in hexose phosphates as well as 3-PGA. Since the 3 and 4 carbons of the hexose phosphates contained most of the radioactivity, it is reasonable to assume they arose from 3-PGA by a reversal of the glycolytic pathway via 3-phosphoglyceraldehyde, fructose-1,6-diphosphate, glucose-6-phosphate, and glucose-1-phosphate. From glucose-1-phosphate both starch and sucrose can be synthesized directly. It may also be of importance to mention that NADPH is the reagent that reduces 3-PGA to 3-phosphoglyceraldehyde in photosynthesis, although in glycolysis NADH is involved.

Initial acceptor of CO_2

The question arises as to what compound or compounds give rise to 3-PGA; that is, what compound is the initial acceptor of the carbon dioxide molecule? Is a two-carbon compound carboxylated to form 3-PGA or is a five-carbon compound carboxylated and then cleaved enzymatically to form two 3-PGA molecules? Calvin obtained evidence that a five-carbon compound, ribulose-1,5-diphosphate (RuDP), is the initial acceptor of the CO_2 molecule.

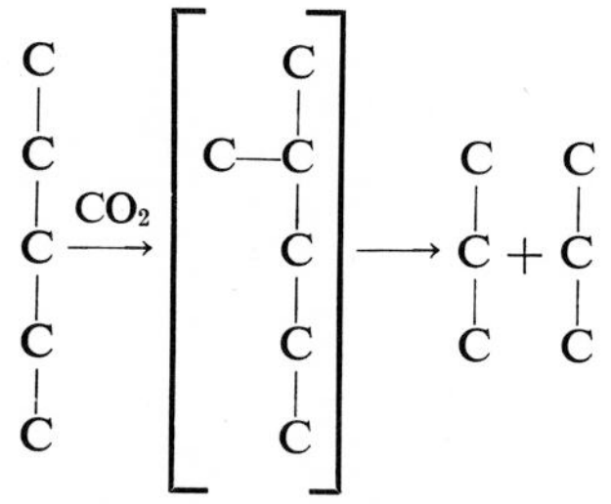

RuDP is formed from ribulose-5-phosphate, an important metabolite of the hexose monophosphate shunt, indicating that members of this metabolic pathway are needed for the regeneration of RuDP. This theory is supported by the demonstration of radioactive carbon in sedoheptulose phosphate, a member of the hexose monophosphate shunt, after only brief exposure to $C^{14}O_2$ (11). Stronger evidence for RuDP being the initial CO_2 acceptor was found when the distribution of radioactive carbon was studied under light and dark conditions. A change from light to dark produced significant changes in the concentrations of 3-PGA and RuDP. There was a marked increase in 3-PGA and a decrease in RuDP. This relationship is shown in Figure 11-11.

Presumably, a steady-state condition exists when the cells are illuminated, 3-PGA and RuDP continually being formed and broken down. However,

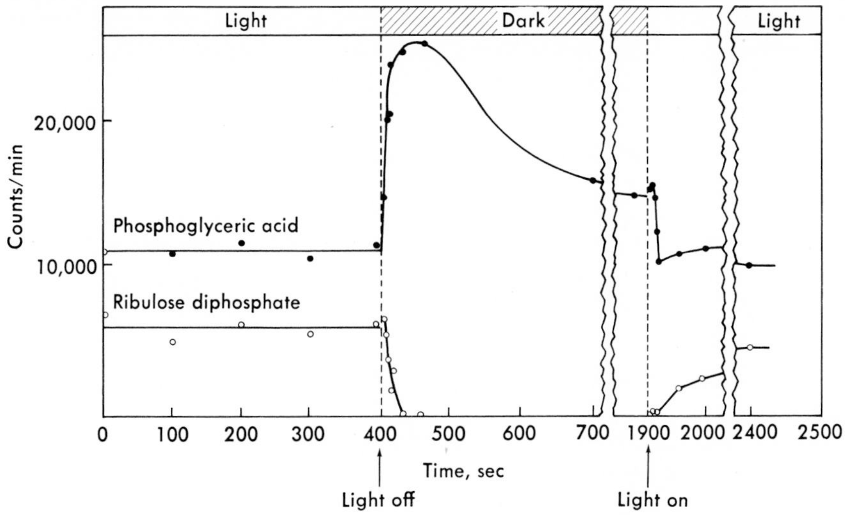

Figure 11-11 Effect of the presence and absence of light on the concentration of 3-PGA and RuDP. (After J. A. Bassham and M. Calvin. *The Path of Carbon* in Photosynthesis, © 1957. Reprinted by permission of Prentice-Hall, Inc., Englewood Cliffs, New Jersey.)

when the light is turned off, there is a sharp increase in 3-PGA, suggesting that the carboxylation by which 3-PGA is formed is a dark reaction, that is, not requiring any of the cofactors produced in the light reactions of photosynthesis. But, the reactions by which 3-PGA is reduced to 3-phosphoglyceraldehyde shows a definite dependence on these cofactors. ATP and NADPH (or NADH) are known to be necessary for this reduction and, as Arnon has pointed out, these cofactors (assimilatory power) are produced in the light reactions of photosynthesis. Since these cofactors are found in the cell in only very small amounts, it was presumed that they are used up very quickly when the light is turned off. Therefore, 3-PGA would continue to be formed until the supply of CO_2 acceptor (RuDP) is used up. However, because of the very small quantity of necessary cofactors present, the reaction by which 3-PGA is used up would cease very soon after the lights are turned off. With the increase in 3-PGA, there is a rapid decrease in RuDP, suggesting that compound as the initial acceptor of the CO_2 molecule (11).

The Calvin cycle

Through the determination of the relative concentrations of radioactive carbon in the different hexoses, pentoses, heptuloses, etc., under different conditions of illumination, Calvin and co-workers were able to map out a metabolic path of carbon assimilation hitherto unknown. This path is shown in Figure 11-12.

PHOTOSYNTHESIS VERSUS RESPIRATION

The question that has puzzled many investigators in the past and still remains a problem today is, can photosynthesis be called the reverse of respiration? In many texts even today photosynthesis and respiration are expressed as an inverse relationship.

$$CO_2 + 2H_2O \underset{\text{Respiration}}{\overset{\text{Photosynthesis}}{\rightleftharpoons}} (CH_2O) + O_2 + H_2O$$

This is a highly simplified version of what really goes on, showing only the by-products of each system.

In respiration, the main pathway for the oxidation of a glucose molecule is through glycolysis, the Krebs cycle, and biological oxidation. Some evidence has been presented that during photosynthesis the Krebs cycle may proceed in the opposite direction, that is, in a reductive direction (28). For example, the reductive carboxylation of α-ketoglutaric acid to isocitric acid, which is assumed to occur in photosynthesis, is the reverse of the oxidative decarboxylation of isocitric to α-ketoglutaric acid, which does occur in respiration. In addition, Ochoa et al. (29) have demonstrated the oxidative decarboxylation of malic acid to give pyruvic acid and CO_2, which also may be considered a reverse of respiration. Indeed, with the exception of the reaction glucose to glucose-6-phosphate, all the reactions of respiration are considered to be reversible. The in vivo reduction of 3-PGA to fructose-1,6-diphosphate upon illumination of isolated chloroplasts has been demonstrated by Ochoa and Vishniac (30), who suspended the chloroplasts in a reaction mixture containing 3-PGA, ATP, NAD^+, Mg ions, and the necessary enzymes. The steps in this reaction sequence are as follows:

$$2NAD^+ + 2H_2O \xrightarrow{\text{Light}} 2NADH + 2H^+ + O_2$$

$$2(\text{3-PGA}) + 2ATP \overset{Mg^{2+}}{\rightleftharpoons} 2(\text{1,3-PGA}) + 2ADP$$

$$2(\text{1,3-PGA}) + 2NADH + 2H^+ \rightleftharpoons 2(\text{3-Phosphoglyceraldehyde} + 2NAD^+ + 2pH)$$

$$2(\text{3-Phosphoglyceraldehyde}) \rightleftharpoons \text{Fructose-1,6-diphosphate}$$

No fructose-1,6-diphosphate is formed in the absence of illumination, and the first step in the above reaction sequence is the only one requiring light. As one can readily see, the direction of this reaction sequence is exactly

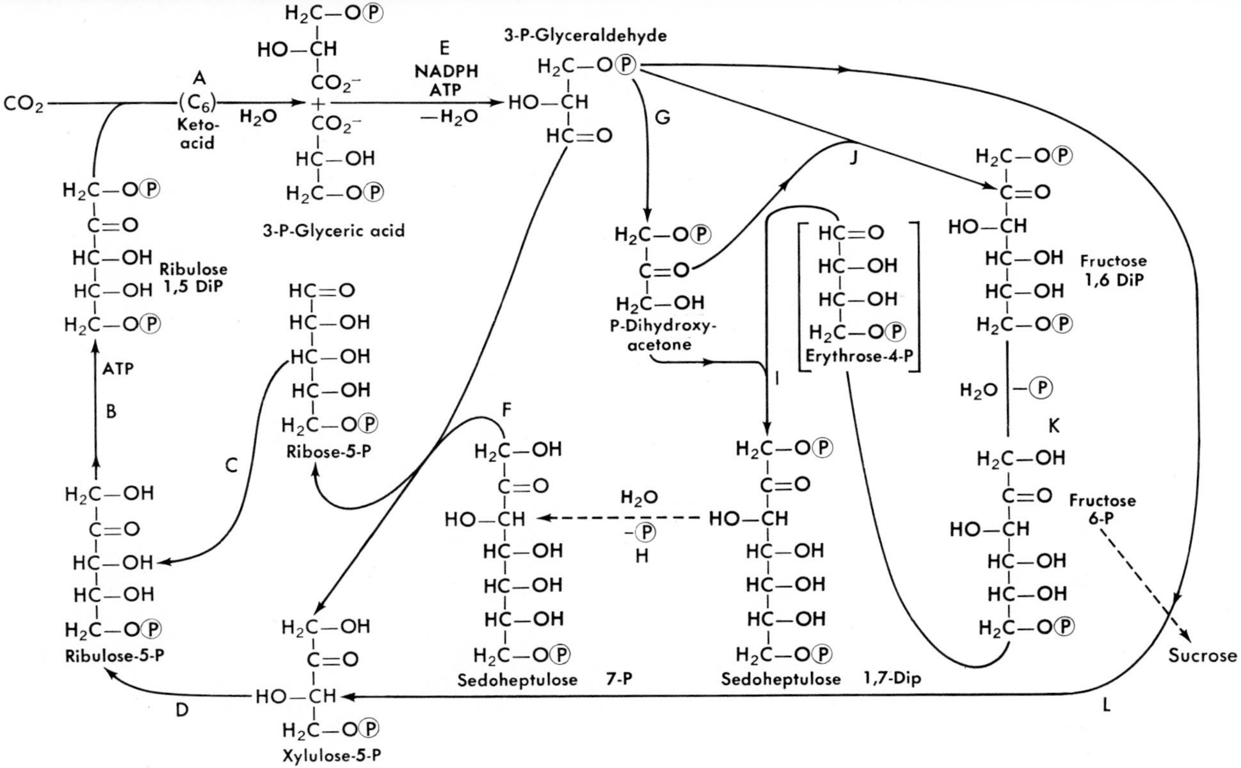

Figure 11-12 The Calvin cycle. Enzymes are as follows: A, carboxydismutase; B, phosphopentokinase; C, phosphopentoisomerase; D, phosphoketopentose epimerase; E, triose phosphate dehydrogenase; F, tranksketolase; G, phosphotriose isomerase; H, phosphatase; I, aldolase; J, aldolase; K, phosphatase; L, transketolase. (After M. Calvin. 1956. J. Am. Chem. Soc. 78: 1895)

the reverse of what one finds in respiration. Moreover, the participation of chloroplasts and the necessity of light suggest a reverse of respiration by photosynthesis.

The incorporation of C^{14} by malic acid and fumaric acid during steady-state photosynthesis with $C^{14}O_2$ has been reported by Calvin and Bassham (15). They suggested that these acids may be formed by reduction of oxaloacetic acid, a product of the carboxylation of phosphoenolpyruvic acid.

Although the above evidence suggests that photosynthesis is a simple reversal of respiration, much evidence has accumulated disagreeing with this hypothesis. For example, several investigators have shown that metabolites of the Krebs cycle could not be considered among the primary products of CO_2 fixation (37, 38, 23). Experiments with the leaves of some higher plants have shown that the Krebs cycle proceeds in the light as in the dark (26, 27, 22). Thus, despite the vast amount of data that have been collected on photosynthesis and respiration, it cannot be said with any assurance that photosynthesis is the simple reversal of respiration.

MEASUREMENT OF PHOTOSYNTHESIS

Study of a natural process necessitates the finding of a quantitative system of measurement that will enable the scientist to compare the process under natural and unnatural conditions. With a system for measuring the rate of photosynthesis, the effect of one factor involved in the process may be measured. For example, light intensity may be varied, while all other factors are kept constant, allowing the investigator to measure the influence of light on the rate of photosynthesis.

In most cases the rate of photosynthesis may be followed by measuring the gas exchange. Either the amount of oxygen evolved or the amount of carbon dioxide taken up is measured. A few of the more popular means of measuring photosynthesis are given below.

Bubble counting

Probably the simplest and best method for classroom and laboratory demonstrations of photosynthesis is the counting of bubbles of oxygen given off by a submerged plant. A plant or part of a plant is placed in a glass vessel, usually a test tube, containing a dilute sodium or potassium bicarbonate solution and the test tube submerged in a constant temperature bath. Counting the number of bubbles evolved by the plant in a period of time gives a rough estimate of the rate of photosynthesis.

With this method one can measure the effect of temperature and light (quality and quantity) on photosynthesis. For example, the temperature of the bath may be fluctuated and the light kept constant to measure the influence of temperature on the photosynthetic rate. If the temperature of the bath and the light intensity are kept constant and the wavelength of light varied, the influence of the quality of light can be observed. Lastly, influence of the quantity of light may be measured by varying the intensity of light while keeping temperature constant.

Usually a sprig of *Elodea* (*Anacharis canadensis*), an aquatic species, is employed for this technique. A detailed description of the above procedure may be found in most plant physiology laboratory manuals.

Manometric method

The manometric technique is by far the most popular for fundamental research of photosynthesis. Although the initial expense for equipment is high, the overall technique is relatively simple, and very accurate measurements may be obtained. A manometer called the *Warburg apparatus* is the one most widely used of the many different manometers that have been developed.

A manometer measures changes in volume of gas in a closed system. If the gas volume in the manometer is kept constant at a constant temperature, any changes in the gas volume due to living material may be measured by observing a rise or fall of a liquid (Brodie's solution) in the graduated manometer tubes. The rise or fall of the liquid indicates changes in gas volume because of gas exchange by the tissue or organism under investigation. A schematic representation of a Warburg manometer is given in Figure 8-7 on page 170.

Measure of the photosynthesis of plant material in a Warburg flask (i.e., the gas exchange that occurs over a period of time) is termed *apparent photosynthesis*. To obtain a measure of *true photosynthesis* under these circumstances, one must make adjustments for the gas exchanges in respiration. Some of the oxygen given off in photosynthesis is used up in respiration and some of the CO_2 given off in respiration is taken up in photosynthesis. Generally, an investigator will measure the respiration of an identical sample in the dark. It is easily seen that the apparent photosynthetic rate is less than the true photosynthetic rate by the amount of CO_2 given off in respiration.

Uptake of CO_2 measured

Previously, plant physiologists measured CO_2 uptake by passing a stream of air over a plant in a closed container and then bubbling a sample of the now "used" air through an alkaline solution. Titration of the alkaline solution would reveal how much CO_2 was dissolved in the solution. This could be compared with a control and the amount of CO_2 taken up by the plant calculated.

However, the above procedure is rapidly becoming obsolete due to a relatively new method known as *infrared absorption by* CO_2. This method takes advantage of the ability of CO_2 to absorb certain wavelengths of infrared. The intensity of the absorption bands will decrease as the concentration of CO_2 in air decreases. This method has the advantage of giving instantaneous recording of the CO_2 concentration in a stream of air passing over a plant in a closed vessel.

Uptake of $C^{14}O_2$ measured

Although radioactive carbon dioxide has been used primarily to identify the compounds involved in photosynthesis, it can also be used to measure the rate of photosynthesis. Decrease in the radioactivity of the introduced sample of $C^{14}O_2$ over a period of time would give a very accurate description of the photosynthetic rate. Also, the amount of $C^{14}O_2$ taken up can be measured directly for radioactivity by an analysis of the plant material involved.

BIBLIOGRAPHY

1. Allen, M., D. Arnon, J. Capindale, E. Whatley, and L. Durham. 1955. Photosynthesis by isolated chloroplasts. III. Evidence for complete photosynthesis. J. Am. Chem. Soc. 77: 4149.
2. Arnon, D. 1951. Extracellular photosynthetic reactions. Nature (London) 167: 1008.
3. Arnon, D. 1959. Chloroplasts and photosynthesis. *In* The photochemical apparatus—its structure and function. 11: 181.
4. Arnon, D. 1960. The chloroplast as a functional unit in photosynthesis. *In* W. Ruhland (ed.), Encyclopedia of Plant Physiology. Springer, Berlin. 5: Part 1, 773.
5. Arnon, D. 1961. Cell-free photosynthesis and the energy conversion process. p. 489–569 *In* W. D. McElroy and B. Glass (eds.), Light and life. Johns Hopkins Press, Baltimore, Md.
6. Arnon, D., M. Allen, and F. Whatley. 1954. Photosynthesis by isolated chloroplasts. Nature (London) 174: 394.
7. Arnon, D., F. Whatley, and M. Allen. 1954. Photosynthesis by isolated chloroplasts. II. Photosynthetic phosphorylation, the conversion of light into phosphate bond energy. J. Am. Chem. Soc. 76: 6324.
8. Arnon, D., F. Whatley, and M. Allen. 1957. Triphosphopyridine nucleotide

as a catalyst of photosynthetic phosphorylation. Nature (London) 180: 182.
9. Baeyer, A. 1870. Über die Wasserentziehung und ihre Bedeutung für das Pflanzenleben und die Gährung. Ber. dtsch. chem. Ges. 3: 63.
10. Bassham, J., A. Benson, L. Kay, A. Harris, A. Wilson, and M. Calvin. 1954. The path of carbon in photosynthesis. XXI. The cyclic regeneration of carbon dioxide acceptor. J. Am. Chem. Soc. 76: 1760.
11. Bassham, J., and M. Calvin. 1957. The path of carbon in photosynthesis. Prentice-Hall, Inc., Englewood Cliffs, N.J.
12. Bradley, D., and M. Calvin. 1955. The effect of thioctic acid on the quantum efficiency of the Hill reaction in intermittent light. Proc. Natl. Acad. Sci. (U.S.) 41: 563.
13. Calvin, M. 1956. The photosynthetic carbon cycle. J. Am. Chem. Soc. 78: 1895.
14. Calvin, M. 1959. From microstructure to macrostructure and function in the photochemical apparatus. *In* The photochemical apparatus—its structure and function. Brookhaven Symp. Biol. 11: 160.
15. Calvin, M., and J. Bassham. 1962. The photosynthesis of carbon compounds. W. A. Benjamin, Inc., New York.
16. Commoner, B. 1961. Electron spin resonance studies of photosynthetic systems. *In* W. D. McElroy and B. Glass (eds.), Light and life. Johns Hopkins Press, Baltimore, Md.
17. Commoner, B., J. Heise, B. Lippincott, R. Norberg, J. Passoneau, and J. Townsend. 1957. Biological activity of free radicals. Science 126: 57.
18. Commoner, B., J. Heise, and J. Townsend. 1956. Light-induced paramagnetism in chloroplasts. Proc. Natl. Acad. Sci. 42: 710.
19. Commoner, B., J. Townsend, and G. Pake. 1954. Free radicals in biological materials. Nature 174: 689.
20. French, C. S. 1960. The chlorophylls *in vivo* and *in vitro*. *In* W. Ruhland (ed.), Encyclopedia of plant physiology. Springer, Berlin. 5: Part 1, 252.
21. Hassid, W., R. McCready, and R. Rosenfels. 1940. Determination of starch in plants. Ind. Eng. Chem. 12: 142.
22. Jolchine, G. 1956. Les acides organiques des feuilles de *Bryophyllum Daigremontianum* Berger. Bull. Soc. Chim. Biol. (Paris) 38: 481.
23. Kandler, O., and M. Gibbs. 1956. A symmetric distribution of C^{14} in the glucose phosphates formed during photosynthesis. Plant Physiol. 31: 411.
24. Katz, E. 1949. Chlorophyll fluorescence as an energy flowmeter for photosynthesis. *In* J. Franck and W. Loomis (eds.), Photosynthesis in plants. Iowa State College Press, Ames, Iowa.
25. Michaelis, L. 1946. Fundamentals of oxidation and reduction. *In* D. Green (ed.), Currents in biochemical research. Interscience Publishers, New York.
26. Moyse, A., and G. Jolchine. 1955. L'action de la lumiere sur la β-carboxylation et les oxydations dans les feuilles de Bryophyllum. Bull. Soc. Chim. Biol. (Paris) 39: 725.
27. Moyse, A., and G. Jolchine. 1956. Les variations quantitatives des acides organiques des feuilles de Bryophyllum à l'obscurité et à la lumière en

fonction de la tension partielle de l'oxygène. Bull. Soc. Chim. Biol. (Paris) 38: 761.
28. Ochoa, S. 1946. Enzymatic mechanisms of carbon dioxide assimilation. *In* D. Green (ed.), Currents in biochemical research. Interscience Publishers, New York.
29. Ochoa, S., A. Mehler, and A. Kornberg. 1948. Biosynthesis of dicarboxylic acids by carbon dioxide fixation. I. Isolation and properties of an enzyme from pigeon liver catalyzing the reversible oxidative decarboxylation of *l*-malic acid. J. Biol. Chem. 174: 979.
30. Ochoa, S., and W. Vishniac. 1952. Carboxylation reactions and photosynthesis. Science 115: 297.
31. Paechnatz, G. 1938. Zur Frage der Assimilation von Formaldehyd durch die grüne Pflanze. Z. Botan. 32: 161.
32. Ruben, S., W. Hassid, and M. Kamen. 1939. Radioactive carbon in the study of photosynthesis. J. Am. Chem. Soc. 61: 661.
33. Ruben, S., and M. Kamen. 1940. Photosynthesis with radioactive carbon. IV. Molecular weight of the intermediate products and a tentative theory of photosynthesis. J. Am. Chem. Soc. 62: 3451.
34. Ruben, S., and M. D. Kamen. 1940. Radioactive carbon in the study of respiration in heterotrophic systems. Proc. Natl. Acad. Sci. (U.S.) 26: 418.
35. Selwood, P. W. (1956). Magnetochemistry. Interscience Publishers, New York.
36. Szent-Gyorgyi, A. 1941. The study of energy-levels in biochemistry. Nature 148: 157.
37. Warburg, O. 1958. Photosynthesis. Science 128: 68.
38. Warburg, O., H. Klotzech, and G. Krippahl. 1957. Über das Verhalten einiger Aminosäuren in Chlorella bei Zusatz von markierter Kohlensäure. Z. Naturf. 126: 481.
39. Whatley, F., M. Allen, and D. Arnon. 1955. Photosynthetic phosphorylation as an anaerobic process. Biochim. Biophys. Acta 16: 605.
40. Whatley, F., M. Allen, and D. Arnon. 1957. Cofactors of photosynthetic phosphorylation. Plant Physiol. 32 (Suppl.) iii.
41. Whatley, F., M. Allen, and D. Arnon. 1959. Photosynthesis by isolated chloroplasts. VII. Vitamin K and riboflavin phosphate as cofactors of cyclic photophosporylation. Biochim. Biophys. Acta 32: 32.

12

Factors affecting the rate of photosynthesis

INTRODUCTION

Photosynthesis, like any other physical-chemical process, is affected by the conditions of the environment in which it occurs. The chemical portion of photosynthesis proceeds within the very narrow limits allowed by the enzymes that drive it. The physical portion, while not quite as exacting as the chemical portion when considered as an entity in itself, must operate within the limits set by the chemical portion if the whole process is to go to completion (the reduction of CO_2 to the carbohydrate level). In the succeeding pages we will discuss to some extent the effects of different external factors on the rate of photosynthesis.

LIMITING FACTORS

Probably, the first serious attempts to discuss the dependence of photosynthesis on external factors were by students of the concept of the *three cardinal points,* a theory first expounded by Sachs in 1860. According to this concept, there is a *minimum, optimum,* and *maximum* for each factor in relation to photosynthesis. For example, with any given species there may be a minimum temperature below which no photosynthesis takes place, an optimum temperature at which the highest rate takes place, and a maximum temperature above which no photosynthesis will take place. These relationships are shown graphically in Figure 12-1.

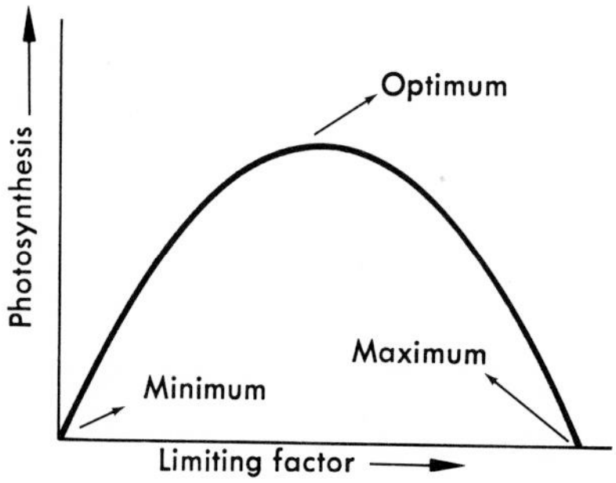

Figure 12-1 Graphic representation of the concept of the three cardinal points.

However, on application of this theory, most investigators have been confronted with fluctuating optimums. A scientist may find that the optimum concentration for CO_2 found in one experiment changes in another experiment without realizing that the second experiment may have been carried out under different conditions of light and temperature. Obviously, the external factors affecting photosynthesis cannot be treated individually, but have to be treated in relation to one another.

Matters remained as such until early in the twentieth century when Blackman proposed his *principle of limiting factors.* The origin of this theory goes back 20 years before the concept of the three cardinal points. Blackman's *principle of limiting factors* is actually a modification of Liebig's *law of the minimum,* which states that the rate of a process controlled by several factors is only as rapid as the slowest factor permits.

Blackman claimed that, if all other factors are kept constant, the factor under consideration will affect the rate of photosynthesis, starting at a minimum below which no photosynthesis takes place and ending with an optimum at which a plateau would be established; that is, the rate would remain constant despite further increases in that factor. At this point some other factor becomes limiting. It was realized by Blackman that, when dealing with biological material, extremes of any controlling factor usually have a detrimental effect (e.g., freezing, denaturation of protein). Therefore, on continual increase of the factor under observation the plateau mentioned will dip, the rate of photosynthesis diminishing until no longer measurable. These relationships are illustrated in Figure 12-2. Now, if any one

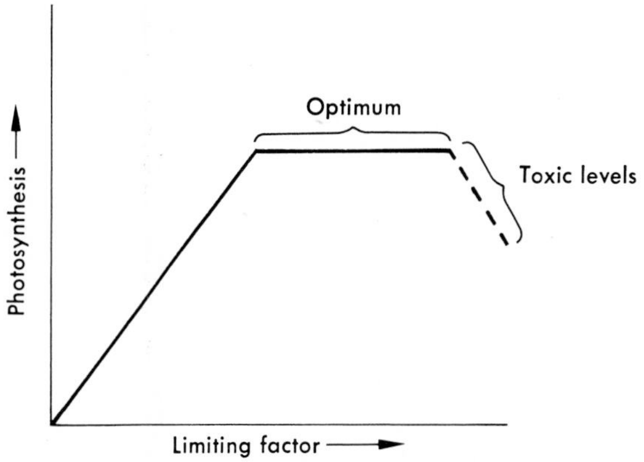

Figure 12-2 Graphic representation of Blackman's "principle of limiting factors," considering only one factor while all others are held constant.

of the other factors being held at a constant level is allowed to increase, a new optimum for the first factor will be reached. This changing of the optimum will continue until a third factor becomes limiting, etc. Therefore, several plateaus may be reached when studying the rate of photosynthesis under the changing conditions of several external factors. These relationships, considering only two factors, are given graphically in Figure 12-3.

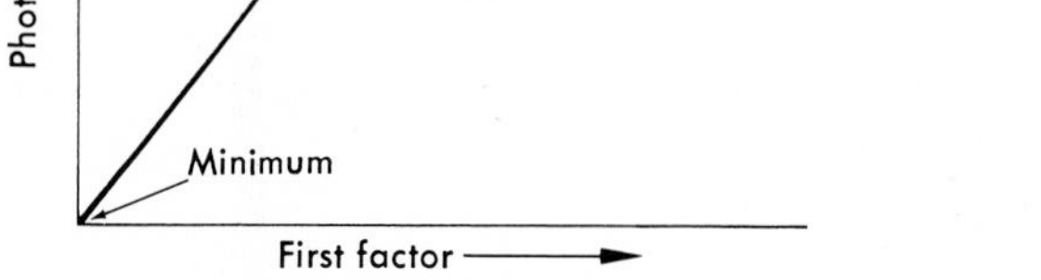

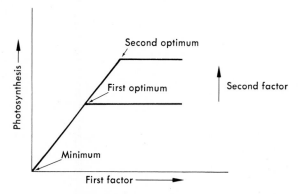

Figure 12-3 Graphic representation of Blackman's "principle of limiting factors," considering changes in two factors, all others being held constant.

Blackman insisted on attributing to biological materials the precise characteristics of a physical system. In other words, the rate of photosynthesis should increase proportionally with an increase in the limiting factor, and there should be a sharp break in the curve and a plateau formed at exactly the point where another factor becomes limiting. However, in practice most investigators found a "curving" approach to a plateau rather than a sharp break. In many cases, at lower concentrations of the limiting factor, there did appear to be a proportional relationship between rate and the quantity of the limiting factor present, but at higher concentrations this was not so (Figure 12-4).

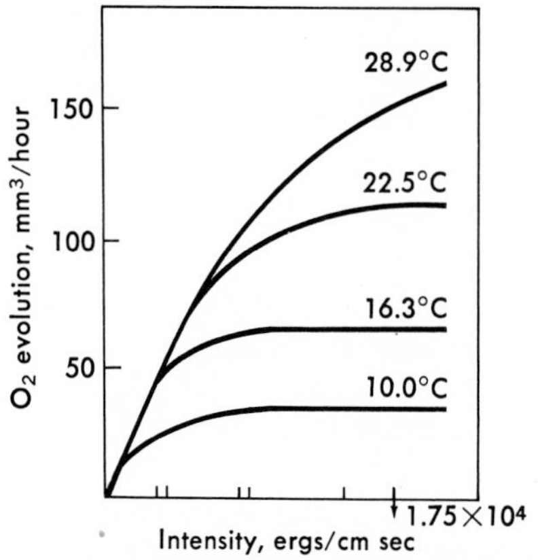

Figure 12-4 Effect of increasing light intensity on rate of photosynthesis by *Chlorella* at different temperatures. (After E. Wassink et al. 1938. Enzymologia 5: 100.)

Soon after the establishment of Blackman's principle of limiting factors criticism began to mount against its exact quantitative approach. Reinterpretation of earlier observations and even of Blackman's own observations showed that the data collected did not agree entirely with the curves as shown in Figure 12-3. There were some investigators whose data did appear to fit very closely the curves as Blackman drew them, giving rise to the suggestion that Blackman's "principle" is strictly valid under ideal conditions (27). However, after one studies a living system on a molecular or submolecular level, it is hard to conceive that anything so complex as photosynthesis could act in the precise manner that Blackman and his followers would have us believe. Blackman's real contribution was in the discovery that the effect of external factors on the rate of photosynthesis can be measured individually within *certain limits;* that is, an approximation of their effects can be obtained.

Light

A study of the effect of light on the rate and quantity of photosynthesis would have to include the following factors: light reflected, absorbed, and transmitted; intensity, quality, and duration of available light; and destructive effects of light. The first consideration should be, what "useful" light (absorbed light) is available to the plant? That is, what portion of the available light is the pigment complex of any given species able to absorb? Something should also be known about the plant organ most responsible for the reception of light. This organ is, of course, the leaf. As anyone who has grown plants knows, the leaves of a plant arrange themselves in such a way as to intercept the greatest amount of light possible. In addition, the anatomy of the leaf, the primary photosynthetic organ, is particularly adapted for the efficient absorption of light and performance of photosynthesis.

As mentioned before, the plant is capable of using only a very small portion of the incident electromagnetic radiation that falls on a leaf. We are speaking now of that radiation absorbed by the pigment complex of the leaf. Each pigment has its own absorption spectrum, usually represented by a curve showing the amount of light absorbed at each wavelength. If one examines the absorption spectra for the major pigments of a leaf (chlorophylls a and b and β-carotene), he can readily see why most leaves are green in color. The chlorophylls absorb heavily in the blue and red regions of the spectrum (see Figure 10-3) and β-carotene mostly in the blue region (see Figure 10-4). Most of the light reflected, then, is in the green region, giving the leaf a green color (Figure 12-5).

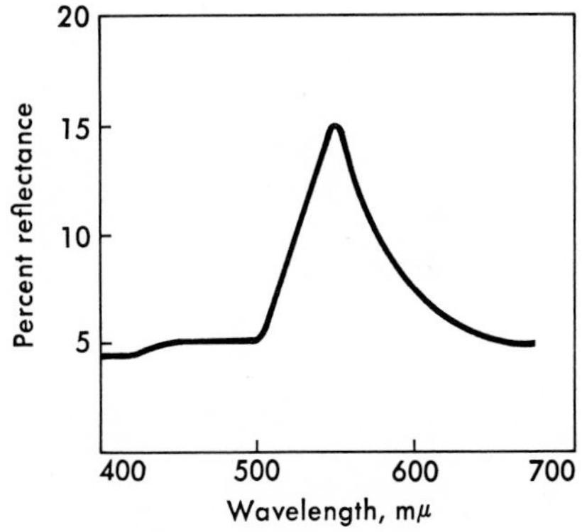

Figure 12-5 Percentage of reflectance from leaves of *Syringa vulgaris* (lilac). (After W. Billings and R. Morris. 1951. Am. J. Botan. 38: 327.)

Studies by Billings and Morris (3) on the amount of light reflected by a geranium leaf have shown that peak reflectance is found at about 550 mμ and, at this wavelength, about 15% of the incident light is reflected. A sharp rise in percentage of reflectance was also observed, starting at 675 mμ and reaching a plateau at 725 mμ. About 50% of the incident light is reflected at this plateau. In general, it was found that the reflectance properties of most green leaves are about the same. However, the amount of reflectance is influenced by the environment of the leaf and its surface characteristics. For example, greater leaf reflectance (up to 26.6% at 550 $m\mu$) is found in environments where there is greater exposure to light (such as desert localities). In addition, hairs growing on the surface of the leaf will increase the reflectance significantly (3). Dull and glossy surfaces can also influence the reflectance of light by a leaf.

As one might expect, the greatest absorption is found in the thicker leaves with, of course, a lower percentage of transmitted light (light that passes completely through the leaf) as compared to thinner leaves. The average green leaf will transmit only about 10% of the incident infrared-free white light (25, 31). Leaves, in general, are almost transparent to infrared and far red radiation (27). Consequently, workers have found that the average leaf transmits anywhere from 25 to 35% of the incident sunlight, which includes infrared radiation.

Light intensity. A direct relationship can be demonstrated between the rate of photosynthesis and the intensity of light, provided that no other factor is limiting. If the rate of photosynthesis is plotted against light intensity, this direct relationship is shown at the lower light intensities. As the intensity of light is increased, however, there is a falling off of the photosynthetic rate because of some other limiting factor or the destructive effects of high light intensity. Also, the point of saturation may be reached, at which time the rate of photosynthesis will remain stationary. The relationship between photosynthetic rate and light intensity at different temperature levels can be seen in Figure 12-4.

Most measurements of the rate of photosynthesis at different light intensities are taken under controlled laboratory conditions. When this relationship is studied in the field under natural conditions, many variables must be taken into consideration. For example, on bright sunny days the CO_2 concentration of the atmosphere is usually the limiting factor, not light intensity. However, on cloudy days light may be the limiting factor (Figure 12-6).

Another variable to be considered is the shading effect of one species on another or even the shading effect of outer leaves on the inner leaves of a tree. As pointed out before, leaves are almost transparent to infrared radiation, therefore allowing the understory of a forest, for example, to receive light a great deal richer in the longer wavelengths. And, of course, the intensity of light reaching the forest floor is greatly diminished, making light a limiting factor under these conditions. Heinicke and Childers (11) have studied the rate of photosynthesis by an apple tree under natural conditions. They found that the rate steadily increased with light intensity up to about full sunlight even though saturation intensity for a single exposed leaf would be a good deal lower. For example, about one-fourth

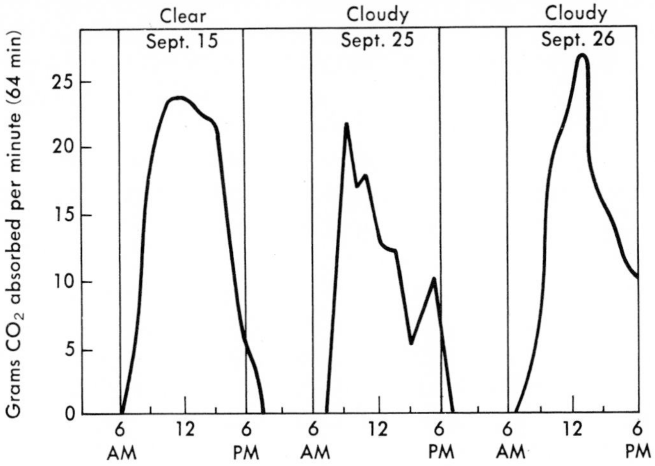

Figure 12-6 Diurnal assimilation of CO_2 by alfalfa on three different days. September 15 was cloudless, while September 25 and 26 were cloudy days. (Adapted by permission from *Photosynthesis in Plants* edited by James Franck and W. E. Loomis, © 1949 by the Iowa State University Press. (After Thomas and Hill.)

of full summer sunlight (2500–3000 ft-c) is all that is needed for maximum photosynthesis in a single, normally exposed leaf of corn (39). Undoubtedly, the need for higher light intensities for maximum photosynthesis of an entire tree is due to partial illumination of the inner leaves.

Optimum or saturation intensities may vary considerably for different species. Some plants grow very well in shaded habitats, while others need to be exposed directly to sunlight. An interesting situation has been described by Bormann (5) concerning shade adaptation by *Pinus taeda* seedlings. It appears that young seedlings of this species can become shade-adapted when growing underneath the canopy of older trees, while older seedlings and young trees are unable to survive. It would be nice if Bormann's observations were followed up by a study of the physiological reasons (more chloroplasts, greater efficiency, etc.), for this adaptation.

Photooxidation. When the intensity of light incident on a photosynthesizing organ is increased beyond a certain point, the cells of that organ become vulnerable to chlorophyll-catalyzed *photooxidations*. As a result, many more chlorophyll molecules become excited than can possibly be utilized, causing noticeable damaging side effects. Photooxidation is especially acute in the presence of oxygen (33, 13, 42), resulting in the bleaching of chlorophyll and inactivation of important enzymes. Apparently, some of the first enzymes affected are those involved in protein synthesis since Thomas (36) has observed a decrease in protein synthesis and an increase in carbohydrate synthesis at high light intensities.

In addition to oxygen, the presence or absence of carotenoids and the concentration of carbon dioxide influence the amount of photooxidation that will take place. As pointed out earlier, carotenoids have a protective role in photooxidation. The idea that carotenoids act as antioxidants (react preferentially with activated oxygen) has been suggested (9). With high concentrations of carbon dioxide, the photooxidative consumption of oxygen occurs at much higher light intensities. Much less protection is afforded when the concentration of carbon dioxide is lowered (12).

Duration of light period. It is logical to assume that a greater quantity of photosynthesis will take place in a plant exposed to longer periods of light. Experiments by Gessner (10) with *Elodea* have shown uninterrupted and continuous photosynthesis for up to at least six days with rate variations of 25%. Studies on the effect of prolonged periods of light on photosynthesis in higher plants have been made by Mitchell (21) and Böhning (4) with the similar conclusion that photosynthesis may be sustained for relatively long periods of time without any noticeable damaging effect on the plant.

Carbon dioxide

The concentration of carbon dioxide in the air is relatively small, about 3 parts in 10,000 or 0.03% by volume. This amount, although small, is relatively constant, providing a steady and adequate supply of carbon dioxide to the plant world. Since the plant population, which utilizes a good deal more carbon dioxide than it gives off, far exceeds the animal population of the world, one would think that the CO_2 concentration of the atmosphere would not remain constant. Obviously, carbon dioxide is supplied to the atmosphere from other sources in addition to animal respiration. What then are these sources?

Carbon dioxide supply. The fact that the greatest single source of carbon dioxide may be found in plant not animal respiration comes as a surprise to most people. Probably the largest single contribution is made by the bacteria found in the soil, fresh water, and the ocean. The oxidation or decay of organic matter in just about every location is brought about by these organisms, a process by which most of the carbon trapped in the organic material is released as carbon dioxide. There is little doubt that this source of CO_2 alone exceeds that of all animal respiration.

Another source of lesser importance, but still significant, is the combustion of fuels, which results in the liberation into the atmosphere of hundreds of thousands of tons of carbon dioxide annually. Under these circumstances it would not be surprising if the air over industrial centers and cities is significantly higher in carbon dioxide concentration. In a fanciful way of thinking, the combustion of fuels may be thought of as drawing on a saving account banked by nature. During the Carboniferous Age, about 300,000,000 years ago, conditions for plant growth were the best they ever were in the earth's history. The world resembled a large greenhouse of high humidity and high CO_2 concentration. It has been suggested that the CO_2 concentration of the atmosphere at that time was a good 200 to 300 times the concentration found today. Because of the vast amount of photosynthesis that took place during this period, millions of tons of carbon were trapped and stored within plant tissues. Large quantities of this plant material accumulated under the mud and water of swamps where conditions prevented decay and eventually they formed the giant coal beds and oil pools of today.

By far the most important factor in the stabilization of the atmospheric CO_2 concentration is the ocean water, which represents immense stores of CO_2 in many different forms. Much of the oceanic CO_2 is available for photosynthesis by plants. The respiration of marine plants and animals releases CO_2 into the water. Part of the CO_2 trapped by marine plants in photosynthesis is released either by the respiration of the organism that consumes it or when the organism dies and decays. Also, the lime for shells of many different marine animals is obtained from the conversion of calcium bicarbonate ($Ca[HCO_3]_2$) to calcium carbonate ($CaCO_3$). Half of the CO_2 tied up in calcium bicarbonate is released in this reaction. Certain marine animals whose shells are made of calcium phosphate carry the above reaction still further, releasing all of the CO_2 held by the calcium. Today, nearly three-fourths of the earth's surface is covered with ocean water, and it is estimated that this vast body of water contains 80 times as much carbon as the atmosphere in forms available to plants. Indeed, it has been suggested, at least on theoretical grounds that carbon dioxide concentrations of the atmosphere and the oceans are maintained in a dynamic equilibrium, a drop in the CO_2 concentration of the atmosphere being compensated for by a release of CO_2 from the ocean (20). Of course, an increase in atmospheric CO_2 concentration results in dissolution of CO_2 in the oceans. This equilibrium probably is the primary factor in the stabilization of the CO_2 concentration of the atmosphere. Volcanoes and mineral springs also release CO_2 into the atmosphere, but their contribution is almost insignificant.

The reduction of the CO_2 concentration of the atmosphere can be achieved by forces other than photosynthesis. For example, in the weathering or decomposition of feldspars, CO_2 is utilized and eventually tied up in an unusable chemical form. The chemical decomposition of orthoclase, one mineral of the feldspar class, is as follows:

$$\underset{\text{Orthoclase}}{KAlSi_3O_8} + H_2O + CO_2 \rightarrow \text{Clay} + \underset{\text{Silica}}{SiO_2} + \underset{\text{Potassium carbonate}}{K_2CO_3}$$

The overall cycle of carbon dioxide in nature thus involves a very complex maze of reactions. Figure 12-7 gives a schematic representation of this cycle.

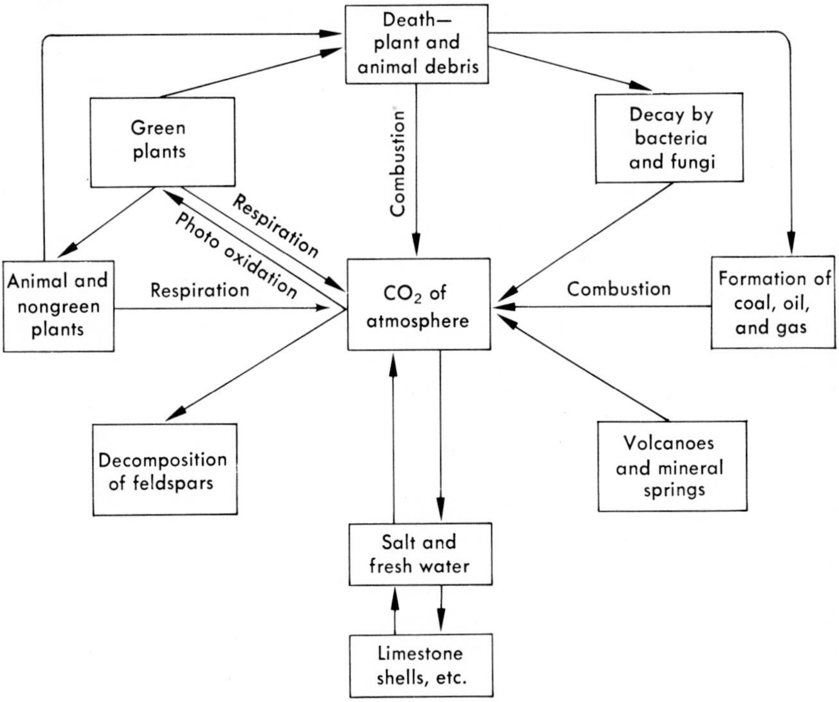

Figure 12-7 Carbon cycle in nature.

Absorption of carbon dioxide. The rate of diffusion of carbon dioxide through the stomatal pores of a leaf and the interfering factors involved have been studied by scientists for more than 60 years. The first extensive investigations into this problem were performed by Brown and Escombe (6) when they studied the rate of diffusion of CO_2 through circular pores. They found proportional agreement between the diameter of isolated circular pores (2–6 mm in diameter) and the rate of diffusion of CO_2. They also determined, with the use of multiperforate septa, that maximum diffusion occurred through pores 380 μ in diameter, spaced 10 diam apart.

In other words, when the pores were placed this far apart, they did not interfere with each other. In most cases the stomates in living material are spaced more than 10 diam apart, suggesting to Brown and Escombe that maximum diffusion of CO_2 occurs at the surface of most leaves.

In agreement with Brown and Escombe, Ting and Loomis (38) found that the rate of diffusion of water vapor (they assume also CO_2 diffusion) through isolated circular pores is proportional to the diameter of that pore (Figure 12-8).

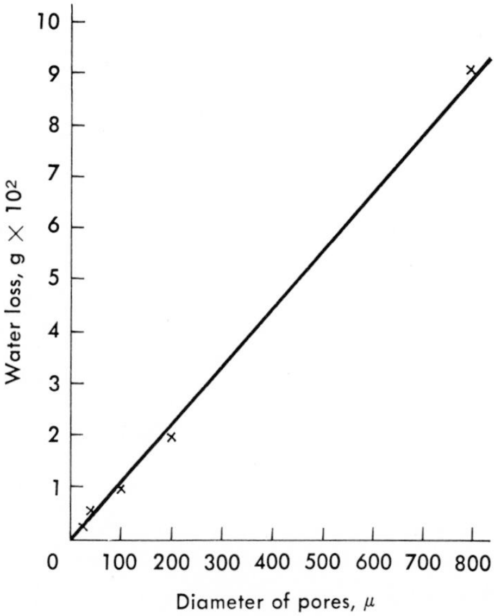

Figure 12-8 Diffusion of water vapor through single-pore membranes as a function of pore diameter. (After I. Ting and W. Loomis. 1963. Am. J. Botan. 50: 866.)

However, they found fault with the assumption that stomates spaced 10 diam apart would not interfere with each other so far as the diffusion of CO_2 or water vapor is concerned. There was considerable interference when pores of a multiperforate septa were spaced 10 diam apart. Figure 12-9 gives their data comparing diffusion per pore in multiperforate membranes with diffusion through single pores of the same diameter.

Ting and Loomis also studied the effect of stomatal closing and reached the conclusion "that diffusion from or into a leaf with the stomates almost completely closed may not be significantly different from diffusion with the stomates fully open." This supported work by Mitchell (21) who

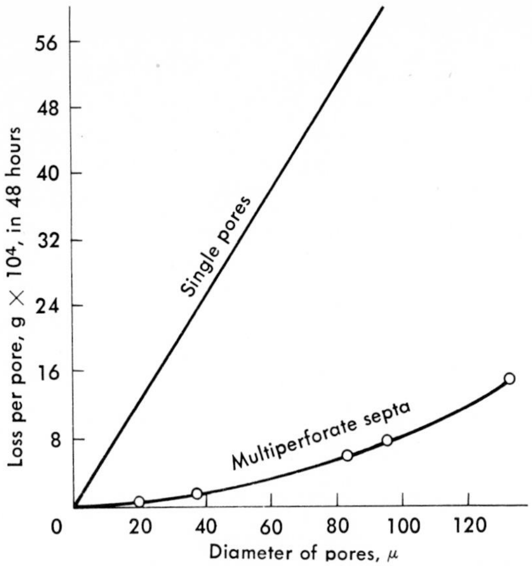

Figure 12-9 Comparison of diffusion through single-pore membranes with diffusion through multiperforate membranes. Note the considerable amount of interference in multiperforate membranes. (After I. Ting and W. Loomis. 1963. Am. J. Botan. 50: 866.)

demonstrated that stomates closing as a result of a water deficit do not affect the rate of photosynthesis, which remains continuous and unchanged until the leaf is wilted. Mitchell had this to say: "The amount of CO_2 absorbed by leaves in which the stomates appeared closed was approximately equal to the amount absorbed by the same leaves when the stomates were open." Verduin and Loomis (39) obtained similar results with corn leaves, finding near normal CO_2 absorption in visibly wilted leaves.

Carbon dioxide concentration. A correlation between carbon dioxide concentration and rate of photosynthesis was first recognized in the quantitative studies of Kreusler (14, 15), Brown and Escombe (7), and Pantanelli (24). These investigators observed that there is an increase in the rate of photosynthesis with an increase in the concentration of CO_2 at the lower levels of CO_2 concentrations. A decline in rate was noted at higher concentrations. Later Blackman and his co-workers disputed the observation that relatively high concentrations of CO_2 are inhibitory to photosynthesis. Instead, they claimed that after an optimum concentration is reached, the rate of photosynthesis remains constant over a wide range of CO_2 concentrations. In general, this is true except that the rate curves for photosynthesis are not strictly of the Blackman type. A good representation of the effect CO_2 concentration has on the rate of photosynthesis may be seen in Figure 12-10.

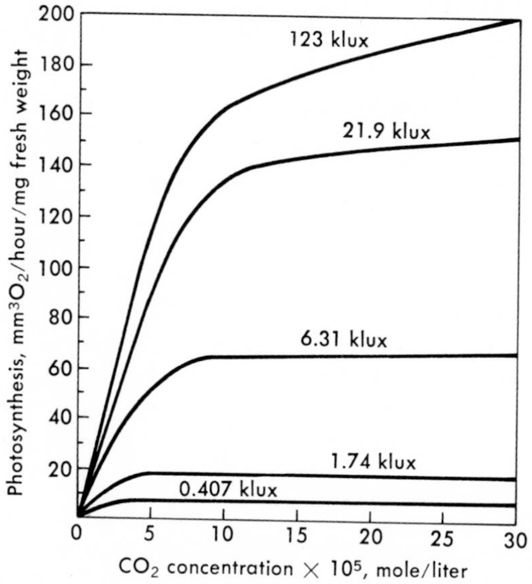

Figure 12-10 Effect of carbon dioxide concentration on rate of photosynthesis at different intensities of light. Klux = 1000 meter candles. (Reprinted by permission of The Rockefeller University Press from J. Gen. Physiol. 1938. 22: 21.

The question arises, could the concentration of CO_2 be increased indefinitely without injury to the plant? It is very difficult, if not impossible, to state in a general way what concentrations of CO_2 are saturating. One can see quite easily that because of the many biochemical and structural differences found in different plants, there would be a wide range of saturating concentrations for any number of plants. Some plants have the structural capacity to allow for the entrance of CO_2 in a more efficient manner, while others may have a greater or lesser quantity of enzymes for fixation of carbon. Still other plants may reach their maximum photosynthetic rate at a lower light intensity and, in so doing, affect the amount of CO_2 utilized. Also making it very difficult to establish the saturation point is the fact that CO_2 becomes toxic or inhibitory when the physiological range is surpassed. For example, the inhibitory effect may be present at stimulatory concentrations of CO_2; that is, the inhibitory effects may be masked by the general overall growth of the plant in a CO_2-enriched atmosphere. Plants differ in their ability to tolerate high concentrations of CO_2. There is some experimental evidence indicating that laboratory organisms, such as *Chlorella* and *Scenedesmus,* are more tolerant to high concentrations of CO_2 than the leaves of higher plants (23, 34, 1, 16). In one study, treatment of tomatoes with high concentrations of CO_2 resulted in the formation of necrotic areas on the leaves. When normal conditions were restored, new leaves developed, and the tomato plants took on a normal healthy appearance again. When the CO_2-enrichment treatments were repeated, necrotic areas again appeared, strongly indicating that the CO_2 treatments caused the leaf injury (36).

Although we have discussed the consistency of the normal CO_2 concentration of the atmosphere, there are examples where deviation from the average 0.03% is considerable. Undoubtedly, in areas of concentrated photosynthesis, such as over a forest canopy or immediately over dense corn or wheat fields, the CO_2 concentration is significantly diminished during the daylight hours. In a study by Verduin and Loomis (39), the CO_2 concentration at a height of 100 cm over a maize field was found to drop from an average high of 0.0675% at night to a low of 0.045% in the morning. This study not only demonstrates how rapidly the CO_2 concentrations can drop over dense vegetation as a result of photosynthesis, but also clearly points out how rapidly the concentration rises when photosynthesis ceases and respiration plays an unchallenged role.

One more important consideration when speaking of the percent concentration of CO_2 surrounding a plant is the altitude at which the plant is growing. Although the concentration of atmospheric CO_2 is 300 ppm at sea level and at 15,000 feet, the partial pressure of CO_2 is a good deal less at the higher altitude, dropping proportionally with increase in height. At 15,000 feet the partial pressure of CO_2 is a little less than half the partial pressure of CO_2 at sea level. The actual significance of this drop in the partial pressure of CO_2 at high altitudes so far as photosynthesis is concerned is confusing since there have been reports of unusually high rates of photosynthesis for some alpine plants (35).

Temperature

As in all life processes, photosynthesis is restricted to a temperature range that roughly corresponds to that tolerated by protein compounds, which are generally active at temperatures above 0°C and below 60°C. Although the photochemical part of photosynthesis is independent of temperature, the biochemical part, which is controlled by enzyme activity, is strictly temperature-dependent. However, there appears to be wide variance and adaptability among plants in their ability to tolerate temperature extremes.

Injury at temperature extremes. The rate of photosynthesis is retarded both directly and indirectly by cold temperatures. In a direct manner low temperatures inhibit the rate of photosynthesis by lowering the activity of enzymes involved in the dark reactions of photosynthesis. Indirectly, the process of photosynthesis is affected in an adverse manner by the formation of ice outside and inside the cell. The formation of ice within the outer walls of a plant creates drought conditions by draining water from the living cells. Ice forming inside a cell not only drains the cell of free water, but also causes mechanical injury, upsetting the architecture of the cell and of chloroplasts in the cell. Also, such mechanical injury may destroy the permeability properties of the membranes (including the chloroplast membranes) of the cell. In addition, Rabinowitch (28) has pointed out that the colloidal structure of the cytoplasm and the chloroplasts may be modified by mechanical forces.

As is well known, all the vital functions of the cell can be terminated by exposure to high temperatures. Of course, at very high temperatures "thermal death" is almost immediate. At temperatures slightly above the temperature range of the organism, death is not immediate, but is a slow steady process, which can be observed by noting the diminishing rate of some vital process (e.g., photosynthesis). The adverse effects of high temperatures may at first be reversible, but soon, upon lengthening of exposure time, become irreversible. Although "thermal death" usually occurs in most leaves and algae at 55–60°C (28), thermal inhibition of photosynthesis occurs at significantly lower temperatures, suggesting that the effect is on the photosynthetic apparatus itself rather than on the surrounding cytoplasm. With short-time exposure, the stimulation of photosynthesis above the optimum can occur, indicating that thermal injury must be a slow destructive process as might be found in the thermal deactivation of enzymes (28). This is illustrated very nicely in a study by Noddack and Kopp (22) investigating temperature effects on the photosynthesis of *Chlorella* (Figure 12-11). With short-time exposures, a 30°C optimum can be reached. But, when the same organism is exposed three times as long to the same temperature range, an optimum of only about 22°C is reached.

Temperature effects on the rate of photosynthesis. In general, increase in temperature results in an acceleration of photosynthesis when other factors are not limiting. This increase is linear at the lower temperatures, starts to drop off as higher temperatures are reached, and finally reaches an optimum above which photosynthesis is inhibited. The optimum response depends upon the species tested and the length of time it is exposed (Figure 12-12).

The effect of temperature on the rate of photosynthesis is roughly comparable to temperature effects on enzyme reactions, a fact supporting the theory that the deactivation of enzymes is the major cause of the inhibition

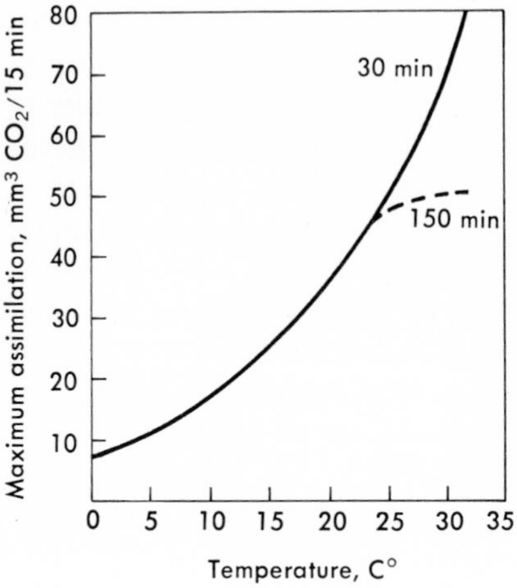

Figure 12-11 Effect of temperature on photosynthesis. Note that an optimum is reached with short-time exposure. When the time of exposure to high temperature is increased, there is a drop in the optimum. (After W. Noddack and C. Kopp. 1940. Z. Physik. Chem. 187A: 79.)

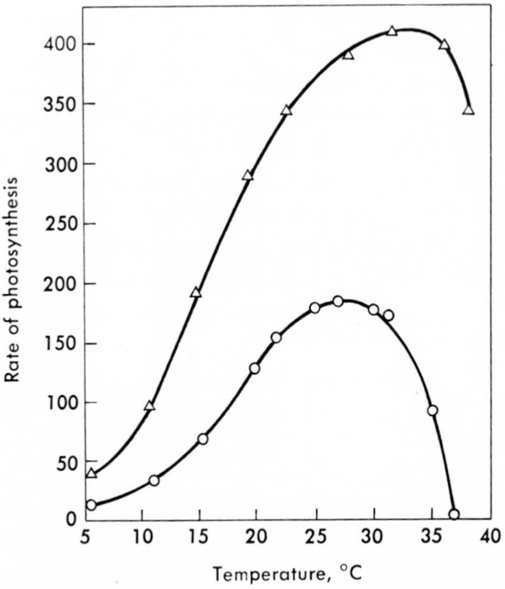

Figure 12-12 Effect of temperature on rate of photosynthesis at high light intensities. Note variations in tolerance for temperature of the two organisms, *Nitzschia closterium* (○) and *N. Palea* (△). (After H. Barker. 1935. Arch. Mikrobiol 6: 141.)

of photosynthesis at high temperatures. Most likely this theory is true. However, one must remember that there are other factors involved that may be undetectable. For example, the rate of CO_2 absorption may be limiting at very high rates of photosynthesis even though the optimum concentration of CO_2 is present. Accumulation of end products may also affect the photosynthetic rate in an adverse manner.

Under natural conditions the optimum photosynthetic response is very seldom reached. In most cases light or CO_2 concentration or both are limiting. This is clearly illustrated by the findings of Thomas and Hill (37) that the influence of temperature on the rate of photosynthesis under field conditions is practically nonexistent in a range from 16 to 29°C.

Oxygen

As surprising as it may seem, the concentration of oxygen in the atmosphere (21%) has been found by some investigators to be inhibitory to photosynthesis. This is illustrated very nicely by the work of McAlister and Myers (19) showing the effect of high and low concentrations of oxygen on the photosynthetic rate of wheat plants (Figure 12-13).

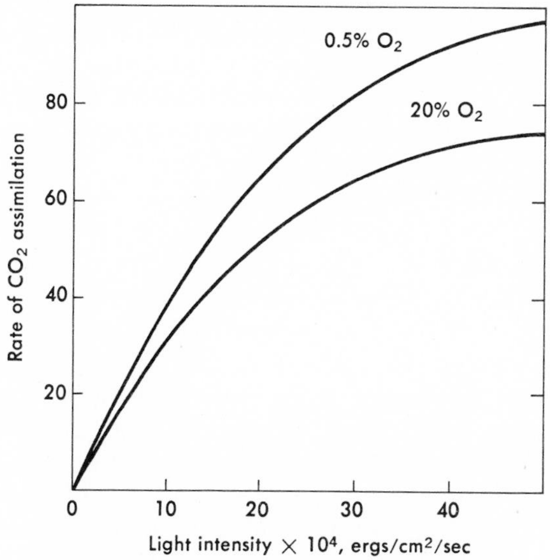

Figure 12-13 Effect of oxygen concentration on rates of photosynthesis of wheat plants at different light intensities. (After E. McAlister and J. Myers. 1940. Smithsonian Inst. Misc. Collections 99, No. 6.)

However, conflicting results have been obtained with *Chlorella* as a test organism. The photosynthetic rate of this organism remains unchanged in pure nitrogen and in air (21% O_2), but is retarded in pure oxygen (41). In this case, then, the atmospheric concentration of oxygen is not inhibitory.

Let us examine some of the reasons why oxygen may be inhibitory to photosynthesis. First of all, oxygen is a necessary component of respiration, a process that competes with photosynthesis for certain important intermediates. Since these intermediates are common to both processes, we can expect a certain intermingling and a mutual influence. The presence of oxygen would favor a more rapid respiratory rate, allowing the process of respiration to compete favorably for the common intermediates. Photosynthesis would, of course, be retarded if the supply of any one of these intermediates should be depleted below a certain level.

Secondly, oxygen may compete with carbon dioxide for hydrogen and become reduced in place of carbon dioxide (9). Coenzymes, reduced photochemically, may contribute their hydrogen to oxygen rather than carbon dioxide, thus retarding photosynthesis.

Thirdly, there is strong evidence that the triplet state of the chlorophyll molecule is an important intermediate in photosynthesis. Oxygen has been shown to be an effective quencher of the triplet state of chlorophyll, thus inhibiting photosynthesis (17).

The inhibiting effect of oxygen on photosynthesis appears to be experimentally established. However, the relationship between this inhibition and the photosynthetic process is in no manner definitely defined.

Water

It is hard to establish whether or not a deficiency in water supply has a direct inhibitory effect on photosynthesis. The amount of water actually needed for the photosynthetic process is very small in comparison to the amount needed to maintain the living plant. Thus, it is thought that long before a deficiency in the supply of water becomes inhibitory to photosynthesis in a direct manner, the indirect effects of a shortage of water will have had their toll on the entire living system. This, of course, would retard photosynthesis along with the other vital processes of the biological mechanism.

Many investigators have noticed reduced rates of photosynthesis in water-deficient soils. For example, Schneider and Childers (29) noted a 50% reduction in the photosynthesis of apple trees grown in soil allowed to dry gradually. This reduction was observed before evidence of wilting of the leaves could be seen. Similar results were obtained by Loustalot

(18) with pecan trees, the greatest reduction in photosynthesis coming when conditions favored high transpiration rates.

Undoubtedly, these inhibitory effects are primarily because of decreased hydration of the protoplasm and stomatal closure. Removal of water from the protoplasm will affect its colloidal structure and in so doing affect metabolic processes such as respiration, photosynthesis, etc. Enzymatic efficiency is impaired by dehydration of the protoplasm, which, of course, inhibits the rate of vital processes. According to Rabinowitch (26), photosynthesis is more sensitive to dehydration than other metabolic processes (e.g., respiration). One reason for this might be the physical damage that dehydration may cause to the micromolecular structure of the photosynthetic system. The importance of the arrangement of molecules in the chloroplast has been previously discussed.

It has been thought by many investigators that the primary factor in the retarding of photosynthesis by dehydration is stomatal closure. When a water deficit occurs in a plant, it causes the stomates of the leaves to close, causing a decrease in the absorption of CO_2. Since carbon dioxide concentration of the atmosphere is usually low enough to be the limiting factor in photosynthesis under natural conditions, a decrease in its absorption should slow the rate of photosynthesis. However, this theory has been seriously challenged by several workers in the field. For example, Mitchell (21) found that the rate of photosynthesis remains unchanged until the leaf is wilted. Verduin and Loomis (39) found that CO_2 absorption remains practically unimpaired in visibly wilted *Zea* leaves. Finally, Ting and Loomis (38) have concluded that "diffusion remains high and approximately uniform until the stomates are closed."

The point made above is that stomates appearing closed to microscopic observance are, in fact, opened enough for almost normal CO_2 absorption. It appears, then, since there is a gradual slowing of the rate of photosynthesis under dehydrating conditions, that more than stomatal closure is involved. Most likely many factors are involved of which stomatal closure is only one and by no means the only factor.

BIBLIOGRAPHY

1. Ballard, L. 1941. The depressant effect of carbon dioxide upon photosynthesis. New Phytologist 40: 276.
2. Barker, H. 1935. Photosynthesis in diatoms. Arch. Mikrobiol 6: 141.
3. Billings, W., and R. Morris. 1951. Reflection of visible and infrared radiation from leaves of different ecological groups. Am. J. Botan. 38: 327.
4. Böhning, R. 1949. Time course of photosynthesis in apple leaves exposed to continuous illumination. Plant Physiol. 24: 222.

5. Bormann, F. 1956. Ecological implications of changes in photosynthetic response of *Pinus taeda* seedlings during ontogeny. Ecology 37: 70.
6. Brown, H., and F. Escombe. 1900. Static diffusion of gases and liquids in relation to the assimilation of carbon and translocation in plants. Phil. Trans. Roy. Soc. London 193B: 223.
7. Brown, H., and F. Escombe. 1902. The influence of varying amounts of carbon dioxide in the air on the photosynthetic process of leaves and on the mode of growth of plants. Proc. Roy. Soc. 70B: 397.
8. Freeland, R. 1944. Apparent photosynthesis in some conifers during winter. Plant Physiol. 19: 179.
9. Gaffron, H. 1960. Energy storage. *In* F. C. Steward (ed.), Plant physiology. Academic Press, New York. 1b: 3.
10. Gessner, F. 1937. Untersuchungen über Assimilation und Atmung submerser Wasserpflanzen. Jb. wiss. Botan. 85: 267.
11. Heinicke, A., and N. Childers. 1937. The daily rate of photosynthesis during the growing season of 1935, of a young apple tree of bearing age. Cornell Univ. Agr. Expt. Sta. Mem. 201: 3.
12. Hill, R., and C. Whittingham. 1953. The induction phase of photosynthesis in *Chlorella* determined by a spectroscopic method. New Phytologist 52: 133.
13. Kandler, O., and F. Schötz. 1956. Untersuchungen über die photoxydative Farbstoffzerstörung und Stoffwechselhemmung bei *Chlorella* mutanten und panaschierten Oenotheren. Z. Naturforsch 11b: 708.
14. Kreusler, U. 1885. Über eine Methode zur Beobachtung der Assimilation und Athmung der Pflanzen und über einige diese Vorgänge beeinflussenden Momente. Lau. Jahrb. 14: 913.
15. Kreusler, U. 1887. Beobachtungen über die Kohlensäure-Aufnahme und-Ausgabe (Assimilation und Athmung) der Pflanzen. II. Mittheilung. Abhängigkeit von Entwicklungszustand-Einfluss der Temperatur. Lau. Jahrb. 16: 711.
16. Livingston, R., and J. Franck. 1940. Assimilation and respiration of excised leaves at high concentrations of CO_2. Am. J. Botan. 27: 449.
17. Livingston, R., and E. Fujimore. 1957. Interactions of chlorophyll in its triplet state with oxygen, carotene, etc. Nature 180: 1036.
18. Loustalot, A. 1945. Influence of soil moisture conditions on apparent photosynthesis and transpiration of pecan leaves. J. Agr. Research 71: 519.
19. McAlister, E., and J. Myers. 1940. The time course of photosynthesis and fluorescence observed simultaneously. Smithsonian Inst. Misc. Collections 99, No. 6.
20. Meyer, B., and D. Anderson. 1952. Plant physiology. D. Van Nostrand Company, Inc., Princeton, N.J.
21. Mitchell, J. W. 1936. Effect of atmospheric humidity on rate of carbon fixation of plants. Botan. Gaz. 98: 87.
22. Noddack, W., and C. Kopp. 1940. Z. physik. Chem. 187A: 79.
23. Österlind, S. 1948. The retarding effect of high concentrations of carbon

dioxide and carbonate ions on the growth of a green alga. Physiol. Plant 1: 170.

24. Pantanelli, E. 1903. Abhängigkeit der Sauerstoffausscheidung belichteter Pflanzen von äusseren Bedingungen. Jahrb. Wiss. Botan. 39: 167.
25. Pokrowski, G. 1925. Über die Lichtabsorption von Blättern einiger Bäume. Biochem. Z. 165: 420.
26. Rabinowitch, E. 1945. Photosynthesis and related processes. Vol. I. Interscience Publishers, New York.
27. Rabinowitch, E. 1951. Photosynthesis and related processes. Vol. II, Part I. Interscience Publishers, New York.
28. Rabinowitch, E. 1956. Photosynthesis and related processes. Vol. II, Part 2. Interscience Publishers, New York.
29. Schneider, G., and N. Childers. 1941. Influence of soil moisture on photosynthesis, respiration, and transpiration of apple leaves. Plant Physiol. 16: 565.
30. Seybold, A. 1932. Über die optischen Eigenschaften der Laubblätter. Planta 16: 195.
31. Seybold, A. 1932. Über die optischen Eigenschaften der Laubblätter. II. Planta 18: 479.
32. Smith, E. 1938. Limiting factors in photosynthesis: light and carbon dioxide. J. Gen. Physiol. 22: 21.
33. Stainer, R. 1959. Formation and function of the photosynthetic pigment system in purple bacteria. *In* The photochemical apparatus—its structure and function. Brookhaven Symp. Biol. 11: 43.
34. Steemann-Nielsen, E. 1955. Carbon dioxide as carbon source and narcotic in photosynthesis and growth of *Chlorella pyrenoidosa.* Physiol. Plant 8: 317.
35. Talling, J. 1961. Photosynthesis under natural conditions. Ann. Rev. Plànt Physiol. 12: 133.
36. Thomas, M. 1955. Effect of ecological factors on photosynthesis. Ann. Rev. Plant Physiol. 6: 135.
37. Thomas, M. D., and G. R. Hill. 1949. Photosynthesis under field conditions. pp. 19–52 *In* J. Franck and W. E. Loomis (eds.), Photosynthesis in plants. Iowa State College Press, Ames, Iowa.
38. Ting, I. and W. Loomis. 1963. Diffusion through stomates. Am. J. Botan. 50: 866.
39. Verduin, J., and W. E. Loomis. 1944. Absorption of carbon dioxide by maize. Plant Physiol. 19: 278.
40. Wassink, E. C., and J. A. H. Kersten. 1946. Observations sur le spectre d'absorption et sur le role des carotinoides dans la photosynthese des diatomées. Enzymologia 12: 3–32.
41. Wassink, E., D. Vermeulen, G. Reman, and E. Katz. 1938. On the relation between fluorescence and assimilation in photosynthesizing cells. Enzymologia 5: 100.
42. Wolken, J., and A. Mellon. 1957. Light and heat in the bleaching of chloroplasts in *Euglena.* Biochim. Biophys. Acta 25: 267.

Part FIVE

Mineral nutrition

13

Detection, occurrence, and availability of the essential elements

INTRODUCTION

In the following three chapters, we will discuss the fundamental principles of mineral nutrition, a subject recognized very early in the history of agriculture, but not very clearly understood. In primitive agricultural societies, it was, undoubtedly, observed that additions of plant and animal debris to the soil increased crop yield. We have already mentioned Woodward's observation in 1699 that plants can survive and grow better in muddy water than in rain water, a very strange observation at the time, but an easily explainable one today. However, the ease with which we explain this phenomenon today is based on the accumulative work of the many pioneer scientists, like Woodward, that came before us.

For the actual recognition of the dependence of plants on elements contained in the soil, credit must be given to de Saussure. In his book *Recherches chimiques sur la Végétation,* published in 1804, de Saussure clearly demonstrates that the inorganic mineral elements contained in the ash of plants are obtained from the soil via the root system. He maintained that mineral elements, including nitrogen, supplied by the soil were essential to the growth and development of the plant. Despite the strong experimental evidence presented by de Saussure's work, the contribution of the inorganic constituents of plant ash to the general welfare of the plant was not recognized until supported by Liebig in 1840. The prestige that Liebig enjoyed and his brilliance as a scientist was all that was needed for general acceptance of the evidence of the essential role played by the inorganic components of the plant. One can say that Liebig's address to the British Association for the Advancement of Science in 1840 provided the "springboard" to today's vast knowledge of mineral nutrition.

VARIOUS ELEMENTS FOUND IN PLANTS

Major elements

Serious attempts to determine experimentally the mineral content of plants were made by Sachs and Knop as far back as 1860. Using liquid cultures, they were able to show that ten elements are essential to the plant. These they listed as carbon (C), hydrogen (H), oxygen (O), nitrogen (N), phosphorus (P), potassium (K), calcium (Ca), sulfur (S), magnesium (Mg), and iron (Fe). These ten elements were generally accepted as all that a plant needed for normal growth and development. However, we know today that there are at least five other elements, although required in minute amounts, that are essential to the growth of most plants and several additional elements specifically required by certain plants.

Trace elements

Because the analytical methods in the time of Sachs and Knop were crude by today's standards, minute amounts of certain elements in plants (called *trace elements*) could not be detected. In addition, contamination of the water cultures could not be avoided to the extent needed to eliminate trace amounts of minerals. Therefore, elements required in trace amounts remained undetected and their necessary function in the plant unknown. In the early part of the twentieth century with the use of better measuring devices and greater care with sterile techniques, the requirement of some of these trace elements began to be observed. The first on record is the observation of Bertrand (8) that the element manganese (Mn) is needed for normal plant growth. By 1939 the necessity of the trace elements Mn, zinc (Zn), boron (B), copper (Cu), and molybdenum (Mo) had been detected in various plants. Our list, then, of the elements necessary for the normal growth and development of the majority of plants numbers 15. These are C, H, O, N, P, K, Ca, S, Mg, Fe, and the trace elements Mn, Zn, B, Cu, and Mo.

In addition to these, other elements have been shown to be essential for the normal growth of certain plants. However, evidence of their essential requirement for growth in the majority of plants is lacking. These elements include sodium (Na), aluminum (Al), silicon (Si), chlorine (Cl), gallium (Ga), and cobalt (Co).

METHODS OF DETECTION

Several of the methods used in the early study of plant nutrition are still in use today. The analysis of plant ash and the use of liquid and sand cultures are techniques used for the study of plant nutrition in laboratories throughout the world. However, these methods have been refined and improved upon.

Ash analysis

A reasonably reliable means of detecting the mineral element content of a plant is to subject the plant to high temperatures (about 600°C) and then analyze its ash content. Only the mineral elements are present, all of the organic compounds having been decomposed and passed off in the form of gases. The primary elements (carbon, hydrogen, and oxygen) are therefore given off as CO_2, water vapor, and oxygen. In addition to carbon, hydrogen, and oxygen, the element nitrogen cannot be detected accurately with this method, since some of it is given off in the form of ammonium or nitrogen gas. All of the other mineral elements that were absorbed from the soil are present in the plant ash. An example of the ash analysis of the mineral content of *Zea mays* is given in Table 13-1.

Although the analysis of plant ash may be thought of as a method of determining the relative quantities of mineral elements in a plant, it is, at best, a crude technique. Too many variables are present to give accurate, reliable results. For example, vaporization or sublimation of some of the elements may be caused by the high temperatures. Generally, the elements are not present in pure state in the ash, but are in the form of oxides. Finally, the qualitative and quantitative analyses of the ash for the different elements present is dependent on different chemical treatments. The

Table 13-1 An ash analysis of Pride of Saline corn plants grown at Manhattan, Kansas.[a]

Element	*Weight, grams*	*Total dry weight, %*
nitrogen	12.2	1.459
phosphorus	1.7	0.203
potassium	7.7	0.921
calcium	1.9	0.227
magnesium	1.5	0.179
sulfur	1.4	0.167
iron	0.7	0.083
silicon	9.8	1.172
aluminum	0.9	0.107
chlorine	1.2	0.143
manganese	0.3	0.035
undetermined elements	7.8	0.933

[a] After *Plant Physiology* by E. C. Miller. Copyright 1938. McGraw-Hill Book Company. Used by permission.

accumulative error resulting from these facts is too large to allow heavy reliance on any quantitative data obtained from the ash analysis of plant tissue.

Solution cultures

It did not take scientists long to realize the impracticality of using soil as a medium for growth in any serious study of plant mineral requirements. To render a soil free of the mineral elements used by plants and then control the amounts of nutrients made available to the roots imbedded in the soil is impossible. On the other hand, solution cultures provide an excellent means for controlling the quantity and relative proportions of mineral salts given to a plant in any one experiment. Two other good reasons for using solution cultures in mineral nutrition studies are the excellent solvent characteristics of water and the relative ease with which water can be freed of most contaminating influences.

Good quantitative studies may be made of the nutritional needs of plants using water as a medium. However, careful attention to small details is necessary to achieve good results. Due to the fact that satisfactory growth may be achieved with extremely small amounts of trace elements, contamination problems are always present. Some of the sources of contamination are the rooting medium, reagents used, containers, the water, cutting implements, seed, and the dust in the surrounding atmosphere. Obviously, total elimination of these contaminating influences is imposisble, but they can be kept to a minimum.

Several studies have shown that the best containers for solution cultures are made of borosilicate glass or natural polyethylene (20). However, even with the use of these materials, some contamination may be expected, such as the presence of boron in borosilicate glass and, perhaps, molybdenum and cobalt in polyethylene. Water distilled in metal stills usually is contaminated with trace amounts of copper, zinc, and molybdenum. Redistillation of water in stills made entirely of borosilicate glass is necessary to remove these elements (43, 55). Another satisfactory method of ridding water of contaminating trace elements is to pass it over cation and anion exchange resins (21).

In early studies of plant nutrition, the nutrient reagents used presented a major source of contamination. These reagents had to be purified by various means before trace element deficiencies could be demonstrated. Reagents may be purchased today that are pure enough for most studies, but even these contain trace amounts of contaminants.

From the discussion above, one can see that most of the difficulties encountered in mineral nutrition studies are associated with trace element contamination. A study of deficiencies caused by major nutrients can be easily accomplished because of the relatively large amounts needed for normal growth. Here, a small amount of contamination is not a serious problem.

With proper attention given to the problems discussed above, the next step is to prepare stock solutions from inorganic salts containing the necessary elements for normal plant growth. Once stock solutions are prepared and the proper containers obtained and filled with deionized water, nutrient solutions may be prepared by simply adding, in the correct proportion, the necessary inorganic salts from the stock solutions. Several satisfactory formulas for nutrient solutions have been prepared. Two of these are shown in Table 13-2.

A simple manipulation of the complete formula so that one of the necessary elements is left out provides a solution in which the deficiency symptoms caused by the lack of that element may be studied. The roots of the plant to be studied are submerged in the nutrient solution, the stem projecting through an opening cut in the container cover. To give a more rigid system, the stem is generally held stationary in this opening by some inert padding material such as cotton. The container needs to be covered in order to eliminate as much as possible contamination due to atmospheric dust. For good root growth and mineral salt absorption, it is often necessary to provide some means of aeration. A diagrammatic representation of a solution culture is given in Figure 13-1.

Table 13-2 Two nutrient solution formulas.[a]

(1) Salt	gram/liter	Salt	mg/liter
KNO_3	1.02	H_3BO_3	2.86
$Ca(NO_3)_2$	0.492	$MnCl_2 \cdot 4H_2O$	1.81
$NH_4H_2PO_4$	0.23	$CuSO_4 \cdot 5H_2O$	0.08
$MgSO_4 \cdot 7H_2O$	0.49	$ZnSO_4 \cdot 7H_2O$	0.22
		$H_2MoO_4 \cdot H_2O$	0.09
		$FeSO_4 \cdot 7H_2O$ 0.5%	0.6 ml/liter
		Tartaric acid 0.4%	(3x weekly)

(2) Salt	gram/liter	ppm	mM/liter
KNO_3	0.505	K, 195; N, 70	5.0
$Ca(NO_3)_3$	0.820	Ca, 200; N, 140	5.0
$NaH_2PO_4 \cdot 2H_2O$	0.208	P, 41	1.33
$MgSO_4 \cdot 7H_2O$	0.369	Mg, 24	3.0
Ferric citrate	0.0245	Fe, 5.6	0.1
$MnSO_4$	0.002230	Mn, 0.550	0.01
$CuSO_4 \cdot 5H_2O$	0.000240	Cu, 0.064	0.001
$ZnSO_4 \cdot 7H_2O$	0.000296	Zn, 0.065	0.001
H_3BO_3	0.001860	B, 0.370	0.033
$(NH_4)_6Mo_7O_{24} \cdot 4H_2O$	0.000035	Mo, 0.019	0.0002
$CoSO_4 \cdot 7H_2O$	0.000028	Co, 0.006	0.0001
NaCl	0.005850	Cl, 3.550	0.1

[a] Part (1) from D. I. Arnon and D. R. Hoagland. 1940. Soil Sci. 50: 463. Part (2) from E. J. Hewitt. 1963. *In* F. C. Steward (ed.), Plant Physiology. Academic Press, New York.

Sand cultures

Solid media, such as sand or crushed quartz, is generally easier to work with than a liquid medium. On the other hand, purification problems are more difficult to cope with. However, today it is possible to purchase highly purified silica sand or crushed quartz that is very low in available trace elements. The added attraction of a solid culture is that the roots are growing in a natural medium and no means of support needs to be provided. Nutrient solutions are added to the solid culture by three different ways; pouring over the surface (*slop culture*), dripping on the surface (*drip culture*), and forcing solution up from the bottom of the container (*subirrigation*). In all three systems, the nutrient solutions added drain out through an opening in the bottom of the container. In subirrigation, the solution is collected in a reservoir and used repeatedly. The pumping ap-

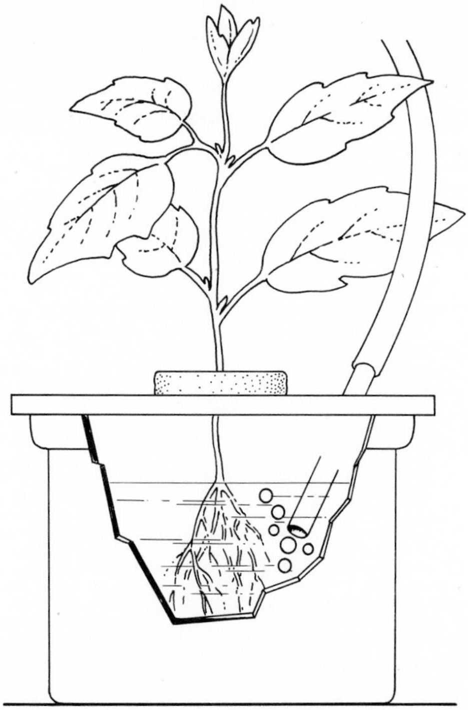

Figure 13-1 Cutaway view of a solution culture. Note method of aeration.

paratus used in this system may be attached to a timing mechanism, which may be set to give periodic irrigation to the sand.

Of the three methods, the slop culture is the easiest to manipulate, but offers the least control. The drip culture may be set up so that the amount of solution being added is equal to the amount of solution draining off. This method allows for continuous nutrient supply and partial control of the amount of nutrients reaching the root system. The last system, subirrigation, may be set up to work automatically and also gives partial control of the amount of nutrients reaching the plant roots. The subirrigation system is the most desirable of the three systems, but the hardest and most expensive to set up initially.

OCCURRENCE OF THE VARIOUS ELEMENTS

Because of their relative importance and abundance in the plant, carbon, hydrogen, oxygen, and nitrogen will not be covered in this chapter, but will receive more extensive attention in separate chapters.

Phosphorus

Phosphorus is present in the soil in two general forms, inorganic and organic. In the organic form, phosphorus may be found in nucleic acid, phospholipids, and inosital phosphates, compounds common to the organic fraction of the soil. To the author's knowledge, there have been no reports of plants absorbing organic phosphorus, either from the solid or solution phase of the soil. Therefore, organic phosphorus represents an unusable form of the element with respect to the plant. However, organic compounds are eventually decomposed and phosphorus is released in an inorganic form, which is readily taken up by the plant.

Much of the phosphorus of the soil solution is present in the inorganic form, mainly as the phosphate ions $H_2PO_4^-$ and HPO_4^{2-} (57). The quantity of either ion present is dependent upon the pH of the soil solution, the lower pH favoring the $H_2PO_4^-$ ion and the higher pH, HPO_4^{2-}.

Phosphate ions are adsorbed very strongly to the solid phase of the soil, resulting in a very low concentration of phosphate in the soil solution. Work with radioactive phosphorus has revealed that continuous exchange reactions occur between the free inorganic phosphate ions of the soil solution and phosphate ions adsorbed to the solid phase (34, 39, 40). Data from a study of phosphorus exchange reactions between the solid and liquid phases of the soil are given in Figure 13-2.

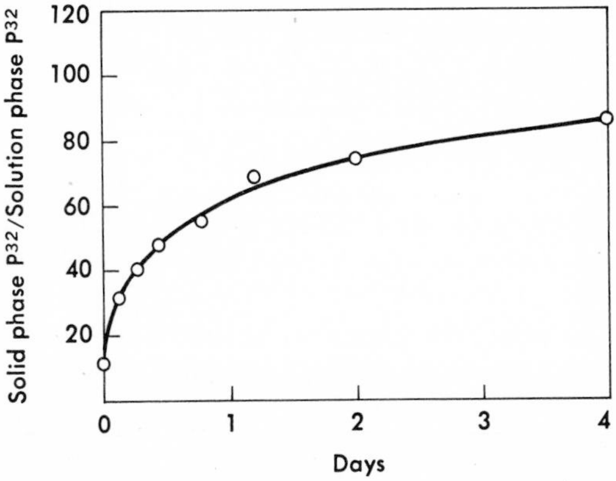

Figure 13-2 The ratio of solid phase P^{32} to solution phase P^{32} is plotted against time following the addition of a trace amount of P^{32} inorganic orthophosphate to a suspension of Caribou soil. (After C. D. McAuliffe et al. 1948. Soil Sci. Soc. Am. Proc. 12: 119.)

The data given in Figure 13-2 were obtained by McAuliffe et al. (34). A soil sample was first allowed to stand in water for four days to provide sufficient time for any phosphate originally present in the solid and liquid phase to come to equilibrium. A small amount of radioactive P^{32}-inorganic phosphate in solution was then added to the system. Since, as shown in Figure 13-2, most of the P^{32} was soon adsorbed to the solid phase, we can infer that an equilibrium exists between the phosphorus of the solid and liquid phases of the soil and that most of the phosphorus is adsorbed to the solid phase.

Availability of phosphorus. Several factors control the availability of phosphorus. Of these the most important are (1) pH of the soil solution, (2) dissolved aluminum and iron, (3) available calcium, (4) anion exchange, and (5) presence of microorganisms.

(1) *pH of the soil solution.* Three different forms of the phosphate ion may be encountered over the pH range found in soil solutions. Under very acid conditions, the monovalent form ($H_2PO_4^-$) is prevalent; the divalent form (HPO_4^{2-}) is present in the intermediate pH range, and the trivalent form (PO_4^{3-}) exists under alkaline conditions. At a pH reading intermediate between two of the ionic levels, two ionic forms of the phosphate ion may be found. Thus, it is possible at a pH of 6 to have both the monovalent and divalent phosphate ion present in the soil solution.

Phosphorus is readily absorbed by the plant in the ionic form. However, as stated above, phosphate is adsorbed very firmly, thus limiting the supply of phosphate ion to the plant.

(2) *Dissolved aluminum and iron.* Under very acid conditions, enough soluble aluminum and iron is present to precipitate phosphate as iron and aluminum phosphates, a form of phosphorus that is unavailable to the plant. Strong evidence for precipitation reactions involving aluminum and iron has been presented (14, 24). The phosphate ion reacts with $Al(OH)_3$ and $Fe(OH)_3$ in the following manner.

$$Al(OH)_3 + H_2PO_4^- \rightarrow Al(OH)_2H_2PO_4$$

$$Fe(OH)_3 + H_2PO_4^- \rightarrow Fe(OH)_2H_2PO_4$$

(3) *Available calcium.* Calcium may react with all three forms of the phosphate ion to give the salts monocalcium phoshate ($Ca(H_2PO_4)_2$), dicalcium phosphate (Ca_2HPO_4), and tricalcium phosphate ($Ca_3(PO_4)_2$). Because of its solubility in water, monocalcium phosphate represents a form of phosphorus that is available to the plant. The dicalcium phosphate is only slightly soluble in water, but will release phosphorus to the plant. However, tricalcium phosphate, which is formed under alkaline conditions, precipitates phosphate in an almost insoluble form, making it unavailable

to the plant. Magnesium acts in much the same manner as calcium, forming mono-, di-, and trimagnesium phosphates.

The presence of excessive amounts of calcite ($CaCO_3$) in the dry alkaline soils of some of our western states creates a serious problem in phosphorus nutrition. Phosphorus is usually applied to phosphorus-deficient soils as superphosphate. Superphosphate contains available phosphates, such as $Ca(H_2PO_4)_2$, which react with $CaCO_3$ to form the insoluble $Ca_3(PO_4)_2$. Thus, phosphorus added in this manner to an alkaline soil containing $CaCO_3$ is never made available to the plant.

The importance of pH to the availability of phosphorus is brought out strikingly in the above discussion. In acid soils, phosphorus availability is limited by the presence of soluble aluminum and iron, and in alkaline soils, its availability is hampered by the formation of insoluble calcium phosphate salts. Thus, it appears that for the best results in phosphorus nutrition, soil pH conditions between 6 and 7 are necessary.

(4) *Anion exchange.* Anion exchange may take place between the minerals contained in the clay micelles of soil and the phosphate ion, a reaction somewhat similar to that involving aluminum and iron hydroxides. Presumably, the anion $H_2PO_4^-$ replaces a hydroxyl anion on the surface of the clay micelle under mild acid conditions.

$$\text{Clay micelle}\!-\!OH + H_2PO_4^- \rightleftharpoons \text{Clay micelle}\!-\!PO_4H_2 + OH^-$$

The addition of hydroxy ions to the soil, such as occurs in liming operations, will shift the reaction to the left, releasing the phosphate anion. Lime applied to an acid soil will also release phosphate, and, in addition, lime applied to an acid soil will raise the pH, thus releasing phosphate from aluminum and iron complexes. However, overliming, which may cause a pH rise to over 7, could again tie up phosphate in the form of insoluble calcium phosphates.

(5) *Presence of microorganisms.* In soils high in organic matter, there is generally a high population of microorganisms. A significant proportion of inorganic phosphate may be "biologically fixed" under these circumstances. The phosphorus temporarily fixed in the organic structures of these organisms is eventually returned to the soil in a bound form. After mineralization, it may be utilized again by the plant.

Calcium

Generally, calcium is the major exchange cation of fertile soils (33). However, the major portion of calcium in the soil is found in a nonexchangeable form, chemically bound in primary minerals such as anorthite

($CaAl_2Si_2O_8$). Through weathering, this calcium can be made available. We have already mentioned the presence of calcite ($CaCO_3$) of soils in semiarid and arid regions and the general occurrence of insoluble calcium phosphate salts in alkaline soils. Some of this calcium is available to the plant, depending upon the solubility of the salt and the degree of alkalinity.

Much of the exchangeable calcium of the soil is adsorbed onto the surface of clay micelles. These micelles are commonly thought of as being disc-shaped bodies with a surface-enveloping layer of negative charges. The micelle, as a whole, may be said to be negatively charged. The negative charges of the micelle attract cations such as H^+ and Ca^{2+} rather strongly, these cations being readily adsorbed to the surface of the micelle (Figure 13-3).

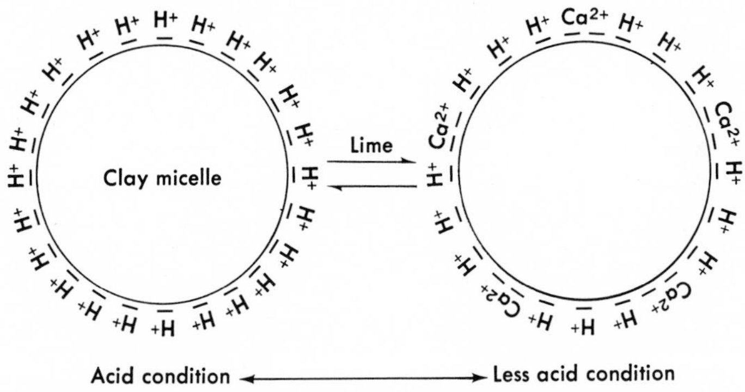

Figure 13-3 Effect of liming on clay micelles in an acid soil. Cation exchange takes place with some Ca^{2+} being absorbed to the surface of the micelle.

The reaction shown in Figure 13-3 is reversible. That is, if the hydrogen ion concentration is raised, Ca ions will be released and the H ions will take their place. This phenomenon is known as *cation exchange*.

Other cations, such as Mg^{2+}, Na^+, and K^+, may also become adsorbed to the surface of clay micelles. However, Ca^{2+} appears to be the most active in this respect.

Liming. We have already discussed some of the undesirable characteristics of an acid soil. Specifically, we mentioned the activity of soluble aluminum and iron compounds, which tend to tie up free phosphate ions. What may be done to remedy undesirable acid conditions in a soil?

It is thought that one of the main reasons for an acid condition is the lack of exchangeable metallic cations and a predominance of exchangeable hydrogen ions. Addition of cations, such as calcium or magnesium, can alleviate acid conditions and, at the same time, supply essential elements to the soil. The most effective and economical method of controlling soil pH is the application of lime. Lime to the chemist is calcium oxide (CaO), but to the farmer, it is any compound containing calcium or magnesium capable of counteracting the harmful effects of an acid soil (37).

In an acid soil we have clay micelles with a predominance of exchangeable hydrogen ions adsorbed to their surfaces. With the addition of lime compounds, such as calcium carbonate ($CaCO_3$) or calcium oxide (CaO), many of the hydrogen ions are replaced by calcium ions. In addition, the released hydrogen ions are tied up in the form of water. The final result is a raise in pH and an increase in the supply of exchangeable calcium ions (Figure 13-4).

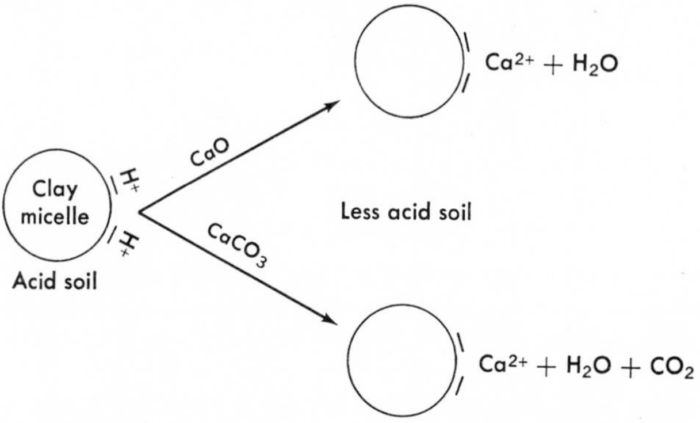

Figure 13-4 Occurrence of cation exchange between calcium and hydrogen ions resulting from the application of lime compounds to an acid soil.

One should be cognizant of the harmful effects of liming, as well as the beneficial effects. Overliming a soil may cause the pH of the soil to rise above 7. In sandy soils, for example, where the protective buffering effect of organic matter is absent, many harmful conditions may result from overliming. We have already discussed the tendency of calcium and phosphate to form insoluble calcium phosphate salts under alkaline conditions, making both calcium and phosphate unavailable to the plant. In addition, with a rise in pH to above 7, important elements, such as manganese, iron, zinc, and copper, are definitely less available to the plant (31, 30). Boron availability may also be hindered by overliming.

Magnesium

Magnesium is present in the soil in water-soluble, exchangeable, and fixed form and is present in primary minerals (10). Like calcium it is an exchangeable cation. However, magnesium is much less abundant than calcium. Therefore, much less of this cation is adsorbed to clay micelles and hence less is available to the plant through cation exchange. By far, the greatest amount of soil magnesium is found in magnesium silicates, a form unavailable to plants until weathering processes cause release of the magnesium in a soluble or available form (7). The availability of fixed magnesium from some minerals has been studied by Longstaff and Graham (28). Their data are given in Table 13-3.

Table 13-3 Uptake of magnesium by soybean plants from some minerals of the soil.[a]

Mineral	*Mg in plant tissue, %*	*Uptake of Mg, mg/pot*	*Condition of plant*
check	0.16	16.0	Mg deficiency
hornblende	0.15	17.5	Mg deficiency
talc	0.19	21.2	Mg deficiency
magnesite	0.20	41.8	Normal
olivine	0.24	47.1	Normal
dolomite	0.29	51.8	Normal

[a] After W. H. Longstaff and E. R. Graham. 1951. Soil Sci. 71: 167.

As shown in Table 13-3, fixed magnesium in minerals such as magnesite ($MgCO_3$), olivine ($(MgFe)_2SiO_4$), and dolomite ($MgCO_3 \cdot CaCO_3$) is available to plants in satisfactory amounts for growth. In fact, dolomite and its products are the most popular and economic sources of magnesium fertilizer (17).

Magnesium-deficient areas in the U.S. are chiefly confined to the sandy soils of the eastern seabord where agricultural soils have to be furnished periodically with a magnesium supplement such as dolomite. It appears that soils developed on sandstones, granites, and coastal sands are relatively low in magnesium, while soils developed on basic rock and dolomitic limestones have an abundance of magnesium (7).

Potassium

Potassium is present in the soil in a nonexchangeable or fixed form, an exchangeable form, and a soluble form. Although there is a relatively high content of this element in the soil, most of it is nonexchangeable and, therefore, unavailable to the plant. When we speak of an element being unavailable, especially with respect to potassium, we mean that utilization of the element in its present form by the plant is not possible. However, availability of potassium in potassium-bearing minerals, such as biotite, muscovite, and illite, is made possible through normal weathering processes. In fact, there have been some reports concluding that the major portion of potassium removed by crops from the soil comes from non-exchangeable sources. An illustration of the various forms of potassium in the soil in the presence of the clay mineral illite is given in Figure 13-5.

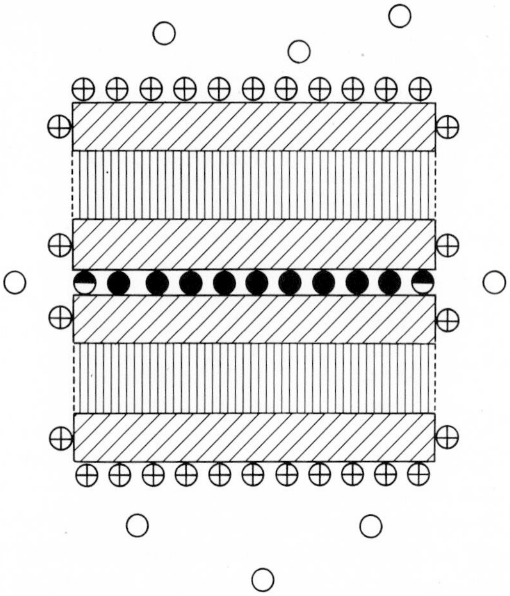

Figure 13-5 Schematic representation of dissolved, exchangeable, fixed, and lattice-bound potassium on illite. = Si—O layer; = Al—O—OH layer; ○ = K^+ in soil solution; ⊕ = exchangeable K^+; ◒ = fixed K^+; ● = lattice-bound K^+. (After L. Wiklander. 1958. *In* W. Ruhland (ed.), Encyclopedia of plant physiology. Springer, Berlin. 4: 118.

The nature and mechanism of potassium fixation and its release in an available form has been reviewed by Wiklander (57). Through leaching and weathering processes, some of the lattice potassium ions are released. The empty "holes" left by the migrating potassium ions may be filled by calcium, magnesium, or hydronium ions (H_3O), resulting in partial expansion of the mineral and a depletion in its supply of potassium. On application of potassium salts to the soil, the "alien ions" are released from the lattice and replaced by the newly added potassium ions. However, the newly fixed K ions are not held as securely as the original K ions and are therefore more available to the plant.

An equilibrium exists between the soluble, exchangeable, and fixed forms of potassium.

$$\text{Soluble K} \rightleftharpoons \text{Exchangeable K} \rightleftharpoons \text{Fixed K}$$

Like all equilibriums, a change in the concentration of any one of the constituents will cause a shift toward stabilization. For example, depletion of the soluble K in the soil by the plant and soil microorganisms will cause a release of exchangeable K, which, in turn, will cause the slow release of fixed K. This sort of a situation is desirable because adsorbed and fixed K, which are not readily leached from the soil, can be made available to the plant.

Sulfur

Soil sulfur is found primarily in the organic fraction (44), but may also be found in minerals such as pyrite, cobaltite, gypsum, and epsomite and in the soil solution as the sulfate ion (SO_4^{2-}). Sulfur is taken up by the plant as the sulfate ion. Like the phosphate ion, the sulfate ion is weakly adsorbed, the adsorption increasing with a decrease in soil pH. Adsorption is favored by the presence of hydrated oxides of iron and aluminum (57). The sulfate ion is generally thought of as replacing hydroxyl ions in clay minerals, a process known as *anion exchange*. Operations such as liming, which tend to bring the soil pH up by adding hydroxyl ions, cause the release of sulfate ions from the soil particles and their replacement by the hydroxyl ions.

Organic sulfur is made available to the plant through *biological oxidation*. Through the activity of certain microorganisms, sulfur is transformed from the organic form to the sulfate ion, the form of sulfur that higher plants absorb. Not only do soil microorganisms oxidize organic sulfur, but also sulfide minerals, such as ferrous sulfide (FeS). Where there is good aeration, moisture, and suitable temperature, FeS can be chemically oxidized to elemental sulfur. The elemental sulfur is then oxidized to sulfate by sulfur bacteria. The two-step oxidation of ferrous sulfide in soil was first demonstrated by Wiklander et al. (58) and may be written as follows:

$$FeS + H_2O + \tfrac{1}{2}O_2 \xrightarrow[\text{oxidation}]{\text{Chemical}} Fe(OH)_2 + S$$

$$2S + 2H_2O + 3O_2 \xrightarrow[\text{oxidation}]{\text{Biological}} 2H_2SO_4$$

Biological oxidation in the soil of pyrite (FeS_2) has also been demonstrated, sulfuric acid being the final product (57).

Another source of soil sulfur is the atmosphere, the sulfur being brought to the soil by rain and snow (59). Near industrial centers, this source may reach significant proportions. The direct absorption of sulfur dioxide by the soil (and perhaps by plants) can also be considered a source of soil sulfur (3).

Iron

Soils generally are not deficient in iron, but may be deficient in exchangeable and soluble forms of iron. Appreciable quantities of iron are present in minerals, in hydrated oxides such as limonite ($Fe_2O_3 \cdot 3H_2O$), and in the sulfide form (10). Iron is most available to the plant in the ferrous form, but significant quantities of the ferric ion may also be absorbed.

The availability of iron to the plant is controlled rather sharply by the soil pH. In acid soils, appreciable amounts of iron are dissolved in the soil solution and available to the plant. However, in neutral or alkaline soils, iron is much more insoluble. In fact, one of the dangers of overliming is that the resulting increase in pH will cause symptoms of iron deficiency to appear in plants. However, even in soils poor in soluble iron, this element may be available by the direct contact of plant roots with iron-containing soil particles (13).

Manganese

According to Leeper (25), the manganese of the soil may exist in the bivalent, trivalent, and/or tetravalent forms. The bivalent ion may be found dissolved in the soil solution or as an exchangeable ion adsorbed to the soil colloids, both of which are available to the plant. The exchangeable bivalent ion is significant in manganese nutrition, since very little of the soil manganese is likely to be found dissolved in the soil water (54). Much of the manganese of the soil is tied up in insoluble compounds in the tri- and tetravalent forms and to a lesser extent in the bivalent form and thus is nonchangeable or unavailable to the plant. Also, manganese combined in the organic form is unavailable. The major portion of the insoluble compounds are tetravalent and trivalent oxides of manganese.

Since it is the reduced form of manganese (bivalent ion) that is absorbed by the plant, poorly aerated, acid soils should favor the availability of manganese. Under these conditions, the tri- and tetravalent forms may be reduced to the bivalent form. Conversely, well-aerated alkaline soils will favor the oxidation of manganese, thus making it unavailable to the plant.

Manganese oxides, such as Mn_2O_3 and MnO_2, are formed under these conditions. Obviously, this is another situation where liming the soil, thus raising the pH, may cause the unavailability of an essential element.

The conversion of bivalent manganese to the tri- and tetravalent forms may also occur through biological oxidation (32). The activity of microorganisms in this respect is most prevalent in neutral or slightly alkaline soils (44). In addition, Quastel reports that the higher valency forms of manganese may also be biologically reduced to the bivalent form and thus made available to the plant. A schematic representation of manganese conversion in the soil is shown in Figure 13-6.

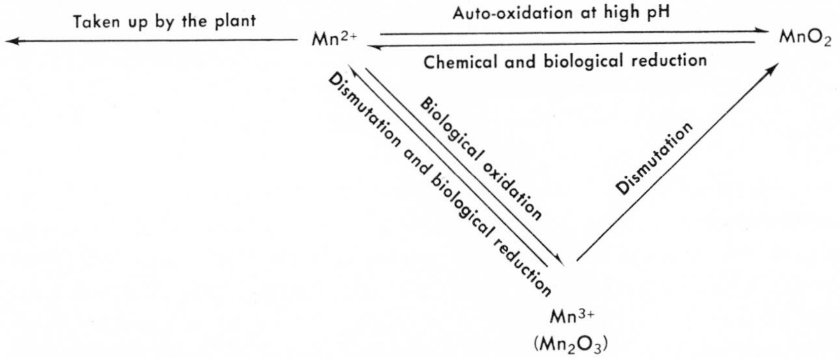

Figure 13-6 A schematic representation of manganese conversion in the soil under aerobic condition. (After Mann and Quastel, 1951).

The amount of phosphate in the soil may indirectly affect the availability of manganese. Thus, the addition of calcium hydrogen phosphate to soil has been shown to increase the uptake of manganese (9). An increase in soluble manganese because of the formation of soluble manganese phosphates has been suggested as the reason for this increased absorption.

Copper

The major portion of the copper of primary rock is present as chalcopyrite ($CuFeS_2$), which is the probable source of natural deposits of copper sulfide in the soil (10). Very little copper is found dissolved in the soil solution. Wiklander (57) estimates that the soil solution of ordinary soils contains 0.01 ppm copper, and the actual water-soluble amount does not exceed 1% of the soil.

The divalent copper cation is adsorbed very strongly to the soil colloids and organic materials of the soil (19), a form in which it is relatively exchangeable. Adsorption of copper as a complex monovalent ion ($CuOH^+$,

$CuCl^+$) has been demonstrated in organic soils (29) and on clay minerals (36).

Soil copper also may form very stable complexes with the organic matter of the soil and in this form is nonexchangeable. In addition, copper may be found in nonexchangeable form as a constituent of the organic debris or as a component of primary and secondary minerals (57). The unavailability of copper tied up in organic matter has been emphasized by Steenbjerg (48) who pointed out that this may be one of the major causes of copper deficiency in organic soils.

The addition of calcium hydrogen phosphate to the soil appears to cause a decrease in the uptake of copper by sour orange (9). It has been suggested that the formation of insoluble copper phosphate may be the reason for this phenomenon.

Zinc

According to Bould (10), zinc occurs in the ferromagnesian minerals, magnetite, biotite, and hornblende. Weathering of these minerals releases zinc in the divalent form, which is readily adsorbed onto soil and organic matter in exchangeable form. Although little is known about the concentration of zinc in the soil solution, it is generally thought to be quite low.

As with many other essential elements, one of the factors controlling the availability of zinc is the soil pH. The availability of zinc decreases with increase in pH, making it very likely that symptoms of zinc deficiency may occur in plants growing in alkaline soils. Camp (12) has noted that zinc deficiency may occur in *Citrus* growing in a soil with a pH above 6. It is thought that the increasing availability of zinc with a decrease in pH is a consequence of the action of acids on the solubility of ZnS and $ZnCO_3$ and on the rate of weathering of zinc-bearing minerals (57).

As with copper, the addition of calcium hydrogen phosphate to the soil results in a decrease in zinc uptake by plants (46, 9). One reason given for the decreased uptake is the formation of relatively insoluble zinc phosphate in the soil.

Boron

Boron appears in exchangeable, soluble, and nonexchangeable forms in the soil, that is, as boric acid (H_3BO_3), calcium or magnesium borates, and as a constituent of silicates (57, 10). Like zinc, the dissolved boron content in the soil solution is very low. Analyses of different soils have indicated that the amounts of boron in organic soils may be higher than that found in acid soils of humid regions where boron deficiency is likely to occur.

As with manganese and zinc, raising the pH of the soil causes boron to become less available to the plant. The probable reason for this is the formation of insoluble boron compounds. However, this view has been challenged by Drake et al. (16), who claim that over a wide range of pH the solubility of boron is unaffected. Perhaps the solution to this controversy may be found in the well-known observation that liming a soil may cause the unavailability of boron. In a liming operation, the pH of a soil is usually raised, which would appear to support the suggestion that raising the pH of a soil makes boron less available. However, liming a soil also increases its calcium content, and Reeve and Shive (45) have found that increasing amounts of calcium in sand cultures causes decreasing uptake of boron in tomato plants. Since liming is a common method of raising soil pH, perhaps the explanation for the observation that increasing the pH decreases the availability of boron is not found in the influence of pH, but in the influence of calcium.

The addition of calcium hydrogen phosphate to the soil decreases the uptake of boron just as it decreases zinc and copper uptake (9). It is not clear whether this is because of the calcium added or because of the phosphate added as it was with copper and zinc.

Molybdenum

According to Wiklander (57), molybdenum is present in soils in three forms: dissolved in the soil solution as molybdate ions (MoO_4^{2-} or $HMoO_4^-$), adsorbed to soil particles in an exchangeable form, and in a nonexchangeable form as a constituent of soil minerals and organic matter. Although there are few, if any, studies on the amount of molybdenum dissolved in the soil solution, it generally is thought to be extremely low. Barshad (6), in an analysis of California soils, found that the water-soluble molybdenum content ranged from 0.3 to 3.9 ppm of dry soil. Even this very small amount is considered to be unusually high (54). In contrast to all of the other trace elements, molybdenum becomes more available with increase in soil pH (6).

Part of the molybdenum content of the soil exists in the forms of three oxides, molybdenum trioxide (MoO_3), molybdenum dioxide (MoO_2), and molybdenum pentoxide (Mo_2O_5) (4). Molybdenum in these forms is unavailable to the plant. This is especially true of the more reduced oxides (MoO_2 and Mo_2O_5)—but the trioxide may readily be made available by reaction with the cations of the soil. Here we have oxidation making an element more available, a situation in contrast to manganese where the reduced state was more available.

The adsorption of molybdenum ions to clay minerals and hydrated oxides resembles that of the sulfate and phosphate anions (57). Thus, molybdenum anions will exchange with hydroxyl ions (OH^-) on these substances.

Other elements

Several studies, first initiated by Osterhout (41, 42), have demonstrated that *sodium* may be essential to the growth of some marine algae. More recently, it has been definitely shown that sodium is required for the growth and development of several blue-green algae (2). It has also been pointed out that sodium may partially substitute for potassium. This has been discovered in both higher (18) and lower plants (1).

It appears that *silicon* may also be required by some plants. For example, Sommer (47) has demonstrated that the growth of rice and millet improves when silicon is added to the culture medium. Lipman (27) has concluded that silicon improves the growth of barley and sunflower plants. Since it is well known that several algae classes contain silicified structures, silicon is considered essential for these plants.

In several early studies *aluminum* was found to improve growth in a variety of plants (see review by Stiles (53). However, aluminum is better known for its toxic rather than its beneficial effects when present in excessive amounts. Thus, McLean and Gilbert (35) have reported that lettuce, beetroot, timothy, and barley all are sensitive to aluminum toxicity.

In several early studies of mineral nutrition it was concluded that *chlorine* is an essential element to some plants. Lipman (27) showed that chlorine could improve the growth of buckwheat and garden peas. Recently, Broyer et al. (11) demonstrated the necessity of chlorine for the normal growth of tomato plants. They suggested that *bromine* may substitute for chlorine. This was later confirmed by Ulrich and Ohki (56), who demonstrated that chlorine or bromine is essential for the growth of sugar beet. We have already discussed the requirement of chlorine in cyclic and noncyclic photophosphorylation.

It is doubtful that any plant requires *gallium*. However, Steinberg (49, 50) has demonstrated the need for this element in the fungus *Aspergillus niger* and in a higher plant, *Lemna minor* (duckweed). However, in later studies (51, 52) he achieved only limited success in demonstrating a gallium requirement in these organisms.

Although *cobalt*, as a component of vitamin B_{12}, is required by some animals, its requirement in plants has only been described for a few blue-green algae (22). Many instances, however, of cobalt toxicity in plants have been described (see review by Stiles (53)).

BIBLIOGRAPHY

1. Allen, M. B. 1952. The cultivation of Myxophyceae. Archif. Mikrobiol. 17: 34.
2. Allen, M. B., and D. I. Arnon. 1955. Studies on nitrogen-fixing blue-green algae. I. Growth and nitrogen fixation by *Anabaena cylindrica* Lemm. Plant Physiol. 30: 366.
3. Alway, F. J., A. W. Marsh, and W. J. Methley. 1937. Sufficiency of atmospheric sulfur for maximum crop yields. Proc. Soil Sci. Soc. Am. 2: 229.
4. Amin, J. V., and H. E. Joham. 1958. A molybdenum cycle in the soil. Soil Sci. 85: 156.
5. Arnon, D. I., and D. R. Hoagland. 1940. Crop production in artificial solutions and in soils with special reference to factors influencing yields and absorption of inorganic nutrients. Soil Sci. 50: 463.
6. Barshad, I. 1951. Factors affecting the molybdenum content of pasture plants. I. Nature of soil molybdenum, growth of plants and soil pH. Soil Sci. 71: 297.
7. Beeson, K. C. 1959. Magnesium in soils—sources, availability and zonal distribution. *In* D. J. Horvath (ed.), Magnesium and agriculture. Proc. West Virginia Univ. Symp. 1–11.
8. Bertrand, G. 1905. Sur l'emploi favorable du manganèse comme engrais. C. R. Acad. Sci. Paris 141: 1255.
9. Bingham, F. T., J. P. Martin, and J. A. Chastain. 1958. Effects of phosphorus fertilization of California soils on minor element nutrition of *Citrus*. Soil Sci. 86: 24.
10. Bould, C. 1963. Mineral nutrition of plants in soils. *In* F. C. Steward (ed.), Plant physiology. Academic Press, New York. 3: 15.
11. Broyer, T. C., A. B. Carlton, C. M. Johnson, and P. R. Stout. 1954. Chlorine—a micronutrient element for higher plants. Plant Physiol. 29: 526.
12. Camp, A. F. 1945. Zinc as a nutrient in plant growth. Soil Sci. 60: 156.
13. Chapman, H. D. 1939. Absorption of iron from finely ground magnetite by citrus seedlings. Soil Sci. 49: 309.
14. Cole, C. V., and M. L. Jackson. 1950. Colloidal dihydroxy dihydrogen phosphates of aluminum and iron with crystalline character established by electron and x-ray diffraction. Physic. Colloid. Chem. 54: 128.
15. de Saussure, N. T. 1804. Recherches Chimiques sur la Végétation. Paris.
16. Drake, M., D. H. Sieling, and G. D. Scarseth. 1941. Calcium-boron ratio as an important factor in controlling boron starvation. J. Am. Soc. Agron. 33: 454.
17. Hanna, W. J. 1959. Magnesium as a fertilizer element. *In* D. J. Horvath (ed.), Magnesium and agriculture. Proc. West Virginia Univ. Symp. 12–19.
18. Harmer, P. M., and E. J. Benne. 1945. Sodium as a crop nutrient. Soil Sci. 60: 137.
19. Hasler, A. 1943. Über das Verhalten des Kupfers im Boden. Mitt. Lebensmitte-lunters. u. Hyg. 34: 79.

20. Hewitt, E. J. 1963. Mineral nutrition of plants in culture media. *In* F. C. Steward (ed.), Plant physiology. Academic press, New York. 3: 97.
21. Hewitt, E. J., E. W. Bolle-Jones, and P. Miles. 1954. The production of copper, zinc and molybdenum deficiencies in crop plants with special reference to some effects of water supply and seed reserves. Plant Soil 5: 205.
22. Holm-Hansen, O., G. C. Gerloff, and F. Skoog. 1954. Cobalt as an essential element for blue-green algae. Physiol. Plant 7: 665.
23. Kittrick, J. A., and M. L. Jackson. 1954. Electron microscope observations of the formation of aluminum phosphate crystals with kaolinite as the source of aluminum. Science 120: 508.
24. Kittrick, J. A., and M. L. Jackson. Common ion effect on phosphate solubility. Soil Sci. 79: 415.
25. Leeper, G. W. 1947. The forms and reactions of manganese in the soil. Soil Sci. 63: 79.
26. Liebig, J. 1840. Organic chemistry in its applications to agriculture and physiology. L. Playfair, ed., Taylor and Walton, London.
27. Lipman, C. B. 1938. Importance of silicon, aluminum and chlorine for higher plants. Soil Sci. 45: 189.
28. Longstaff, W. H., and E. R. Graham. 1951. Release of mineral magnesium and its effect on growth and composition of soybeans. Soil Sci. 71: 167.
29. Lucas, R. E. 1948. Chemical and physical behavior of copper in organic soils. Soil Sci. 66: 119.
30. Lynd, J. Q., and L. M. Turk. 1948. Overliming injury on an acid sandy soil. J. Am. Soc. Agron. 40: 205.
31. Lyon, T. L., H. O. Buckman, and N. C. Brady. 1952. The nature and properties of soils. The Macmillan Company, New York. 1: 591.
32. Mann, P. J. G., and J. H. Quastel. 1946. Manganese metabolism in soils. Nature 158: 154.
33. Marshall, C. E. 1951. The activities of cations held by soil colloids and the chemical environment of plant roots. pp. 55–77 *In* E. Truog (ed.), Mineral nutrition of plants. University of Wisconsin Press, Madison, Wisc.
34. McAuliffe, C. D., N. S. Hall, L. A. Dean, and S. B. Hendricks. 1948. Exchange reactions between phosphates and soils: hydroxylic surfaces of soil minerals. Soil Sci. Soc. Am. Proc. 12: 119.
35. McLean, F. T., and B. E. Gilbert. 1927. The relative aluminum tolerance of crop plants. Soil Sci. 24: 163.
36. Menzel, R. G., and M. L. Jackson. 1950. Mechanism of sorption of hydroxy cupric ion by clays. Soil Sci. Soc. Am. Proc. 15: 122.
37. Millar, C. E., L. M. Turk, and H. D. Foth. 1951. Fundamentals of soil science. John Wiley & Sons, Inc., New York.
38. Miller, E. C. 1938. Plant physiology, 2nd ed., McGraw-Hill Book Co., New York.
39. Olsen, S. R. 1953. Inorganic phosphorus in alkaline and calcareous soils. Agronomy 4: 89.
40. Olsen, S. R. 1953. The measurement of phosphorus on the surface of soil

particles and its relationship to plant available phosphorus. Kansas Agr. Expt. Sta. Rept. 4: 59.
41. Osterhout, W. J. V. 1906. On the importance of physiologically balanced solutions for plants. I. Marine plants. Botan. Gaz. 42: 127.
42. Osterhout, W. J. V. 1912. Plants which require sodium. Botan. Gaz. 54: 532.
43. Piper, C. S. 1942. Investigations on copper deficiency in plants. J. Agr. Sci. 32: 143.
44. Quastel, J. H. 1963. Microbial activities of soil as they affect plant nutrition. *In* F. C. Steward (ed.), Plant physiology. 3: 671.
45. Reeve, E., and J. W. Shive. 1944. Potassium-boron and calcium-boron relationships in plant nutrition. Soil Sci. 57: 1.
46. Rogers, L. H., and C. Wu. 1948. Zinc uptake by oats as influenced by application of lime and phosphate. J. Am. Soc. Agron. 40: 563.
47. Sommer, A. L. 1926. Studies concerning essential nature of aluminum and silicon for plant growth. Univ. Calif. Publ. Agr. Sci. 5: 2.
48. Steenbjerg, F. 1950. Investigations on micro-elements from a practical point of view. *In* Trace elements in plant physiology. Lotsya 3: 87.
49. Steinberg, R. A. 1938. The essentiality of gallium to growth and reproduction of *Aspergillus niger*. J. Agr. Res. 57: 569.
50. Steinberg, R. A. 1941. Use of *Lemna* for nutrition studies on green plants. J. Agr. Res. 62: 423.
51. Steinberg, R. A. 1945. Use of microorganisms to determine essentiality of minor elements. Soil Sci. 60: 185.
52. Steinberg, R. A. 1946. Mineral requirements of *Lemna minor*. Plant Physiol. 21: 42.
53. Stiles, W. 1958. Other elements. *In* W. Ruhland (ed.), Encyclopedia of plant physiology. Springer, Berlin. 4: 599.
54. Stiles, W. 1961. Trace elements in plants. Cambridge University Press, London. 1–247.
55. Stout, P. R., and D. I. Arnon. 1939. Experimental methods for the study of the role of copper, manganese and zinc in the nutrition of higher plants. Am. J. Botan. 26: 144.
56. Ulrich, A., and K. Ohki. 1956. Chlorine, bromine and sodium as nutrients for sugar beet plants. Plant Physiol. 31: 171.
57. Wiklander, L. 1958. The soil. *In* W. Ruhland (ed.), Encyclopedia of plant physiology. Springer, Berlin. 4: 118.
58. Wilklander, L., G. Hallgren, and E. Jonsson. 1950. Studies on gyttja soils. III. Kungl. Lantbrukshögsk. Ann. 17: 425.
59. Wilson, B. D. 1926. Sulfur supplied to the soil in rainwater. J. Am. Soc. Agron. 18: 1108.
60. Woodward, J. 1699. Some thoughts and experiments on vegetation. Phil. Trans. Roy. Soc. London 21: 382.

14

Mineral salt absorption and translocation

INTRODUCTION

In a previous chapter, we discussed the occurrence and availability of the essential elements in the soil. Our next step is to determine how these elements penetrate the root tissue and how they are transported throughout the plant. Both of these problems were explained rather simply when first approached, but at present are considered complex and not completely solved.

Early workers assumed that inorganic salts were passively carried into the plant with the absorption of water. In addition, it was assumed that the translocation of the absorbed salts to different areas of the plant was dependent on the transpiration stream. Soon it was discovered that these assumptions could not adequately account for the obvious differences in the salt composition of the plant tissues and the medium in which the plant grew. A solution to this dilemma was sought in the suggestion that absorption could be explained as an osmotic phenomenon. It was thought that osmotically active substances diffused along concentration gradients from the soil solution into the plant. The osmotic concentration inside the cell was continuously kept at a low point through utilization of the absorbed substances in metabolism. The osmotic theory sufficiently explained the absorption, but did not account for the rapid translocation of the salts once they were absorbed. Again the transpiration stream was implicated, this time as only aiding in the dispersal of the salts, not their absorption. Thus, early attempts to explain salt absorption and translocation only emphasized physical mechanisms, neglecting almost entirely the participation of metabolic energy. However, during this time, a statement was made by the brilliant physiologist, Pfeffer, which contrasted sharply with prevalent theories on salt absorption and remarkably foreshadowed a popular theory today (46). Pfeffer claimed:

> . . . the nature of the plasma is such as to render it possible that a substance may combine chemically with the plasmatic elements, thus being transmitted internally, and then set free again.

This statement agrees very nicely with the carrier theory on salt absorption generally accepted today.

As is usually the case when one tries to buck the tide of popular thought, this provocative theory on absorption was not taken too seriously, and physical mechanisms and models were continuously produced to explain salt absorption. It was finally recognized, from work done in the 1930's, that salt absorption is largely dependent upon metabolic energy—that the uptake of salt is predominately active, not passive as was earlier thought.

PASSIVE ABSORPTION

Outer and apparent free space

Salt absorption takes place through the intimate contact of the root system with the soil colloids or soil solution. What are the mechanisms involved in the passage of dissolved inorganic salts from the soil solution into the plant? Passive or nonmetabolic absorption of ions has been demonstrated by numerous investigators (see review by Briggs and Robertson (9)). It has been found frequently that when a plant cell or tissue is transferred from a medium of low salt concentration to a medium of relatively high salt concentration, there is an initial rapid uptake of ions. This is followed by a slow steady uptake that is under metabolic control (Figure 14-1). The rapid initial uptake is not affected by temperature or metabolic inhibitors; that is, metabolic energy is not involved. If the above tissue is returned

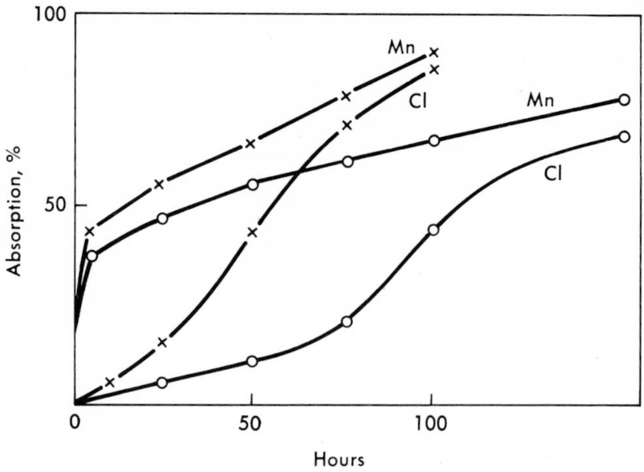

Figure 14-1 Absorption of manganese and chloride ions by parsnip tissue from a 0.001*M* solution of manganese chloride. O, after previous washing in aerated tap water for 24 hours. X, after washing for 168.5 hours. (After W. J. Rees. 1949. Ann. Botany 13: 29.)

to the low salt medium, some of the ions taken up will diffuse out into the external medium. In other words, a part of the cell or tissue immersed in the salt solution is opened to *free* diffusion of ions. Since free diffusion implies that ions can move freely in or out of the tissue, the part of the tissue opened to free diffusion will reach an equilibrium with the external medium and the ion concentration of this part will be the same as that found in the external medium. That part of a plant cell or tissue which will allow for free diffusion to take place is referred to as *outer space*.

With the establishment of the concept of "outer space," workers turned to the task of calculating the volume of plant cell or tissue involved. This may be accomplished by immersing a tissue in a solution of known concentration, allowing it to come to equilibrium, and then determining the amount of salt taken up. Assuming that the ion concentration is the same both in outer space and in the external medium and knowing the amount of salt taken up, we can calculate the volume of outer space. Under the above circumstances, active absorption must be inhibited (e.g., by metabolic inhibitors or by low temperature) or the calculated volume will be greater than the actual volume.

Hope and Stevens (26) found that bean root tips, when immersed in a KCl solution, reached equilibrium in 20 minutes. This reversible diffusion of KCl took place in the absence of metabolic energy and the volume of tissue involved was considered to include a part of the cytoplasm. In subsequent work by Hope (25) it was found that the measured volume of tissue allowing free diffusion increased when the concentration of KCl in the external solution increased, and since active transport was inhibited, we can only assume that a *passive accumulation* of ions against a concentration gradient must have occurred. The term *apparent free space* was introduced to describe the *apparent* volume allowing for the free diffusion of ions.

This brings up the question, how may ions be accumulated against a concentration gradient without the participation of metabolic energy? This may be accomplished through *ion exchange* mechanisms and through the establishment of *Donnan equilibria.*

Ion exchange

Ions adsorbed to the surfaces of the cell walls or membranes of a tissue may exchange with ions from the external solution in which the tissue is immersed. We have already encountered analogous ion exchange mechanisms between the soil solution and the soil colloids in a previous chapter. Suppose, for example, the cation, K^+, of the external solution exchanged with a hydrogen ion, H^+, adsorbed to the surface of the cell membrane. The cation would then become adsorbed to the surface of the membrane and rendered osmotically inactive. Anions could exchange with free hydroxyl ion in the same manner. Thus, ion exchange mechanisms would allow for a greater absorption of ions from the external medium than could normally be accounted for by free diffusion.

Donnan equilibrium

The *Donnan equilibrium theory* takes into account the effect of fixed or indiffusible ions. Take, for example, a membrane that is permeable to some ions and not to others and which separates the cell from the external medium. Suppose on the inner side of this membrane there is a concentration of anions to which the membrane is impermeable (fixed anions). Now, if the above membrane is freely permeable to the cations and anions in the external solution equal numbers of cations and anions from the external solution will diffuse across the membrane until an equilibrium is established. Normally, this equilibrium would also be electrically balanced. However, additional cations are needed to balance the negative charges of the "fixed" anions on the inner side of the membrane (Figure 14-2).

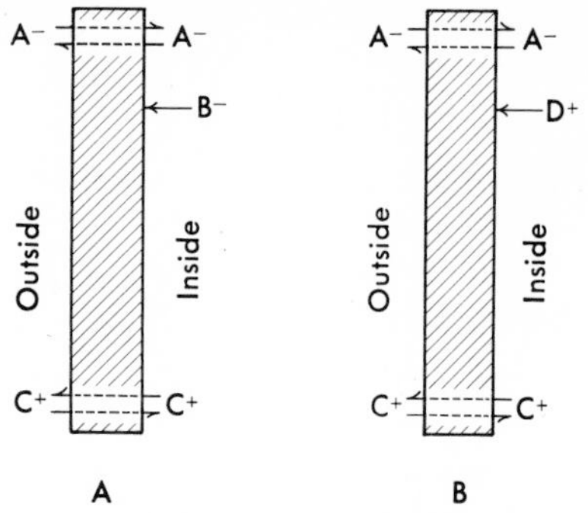

Figure 14-2 Ion diffusion across membranes. A. Membrane is impermeable to the anion, B^-, causing additional cations, C^+, to diffuse across from the outside (accumulation of cations). B. Membrane is impermeable to the cation, D^+, causing additional anions, A^-, to diffuse across from the outside (accumulation of anions).

Therefore, the cation concentration would be greater in the internal solution than in the external solution. Also, it must be remembered, because of the excess of negative charges due to fixed anions, the concentration of anions in the internal solution will be less than that of the external solution.

As shown in Figure 14-2, the Donnan equilibrium concept can also account for the accumulation of anions against a concentration gradient. In a tissue immersed in a salt solution, several equilibria may exist, causing the accumulation of ions against a concentration gradient without the participation of metabolic energy.

Mass flow

Some investigators believe that ions can move through roots along with the mass flow of water (34, 28, 29, 35). According to this theory, an increase in transpiration should cause an increase in the absorption of ions. That this is so has been generally accepted (52), but whether the effect of transpiration is direct or indirect is not clear. Some authors claim that transpiration indirectly affects ion absorption by removing ions after they have been released into the xylem ducts, causing by this dilution an increase in ion absorption activity (11, 24, 10). Opposing this viewpoint is the suggestion that ions move in mass flow with water from the soil solution through the root and eventually to the shoot. One or both of these mechanisms may be a part of the general picture of salt absorption by plants. It would be very difficult to prove or disprove either theory.

Recent work by Lopushinsky (38) with detopped tomato plants indirectly supports the concept that an increase in transpiration can increase salt absorption. By applying different degrees of hydrostatic pressure to detopped tomato root systems enclosed in pressure chambers containing nutrient solutions of radioactive P^{32} and Ca^{45}, he was able to determine that increases in the hydrostatic pressure increased the amount of phosphate and calcium moved into the root xylem. This was determined by analyzing the root exudate for P^{32} or Ca^{45} under normal root pressure conditions and under conditions of increased hydrostatic pressure (Figure 14-3). Although in the above experiments water is being pushed up the

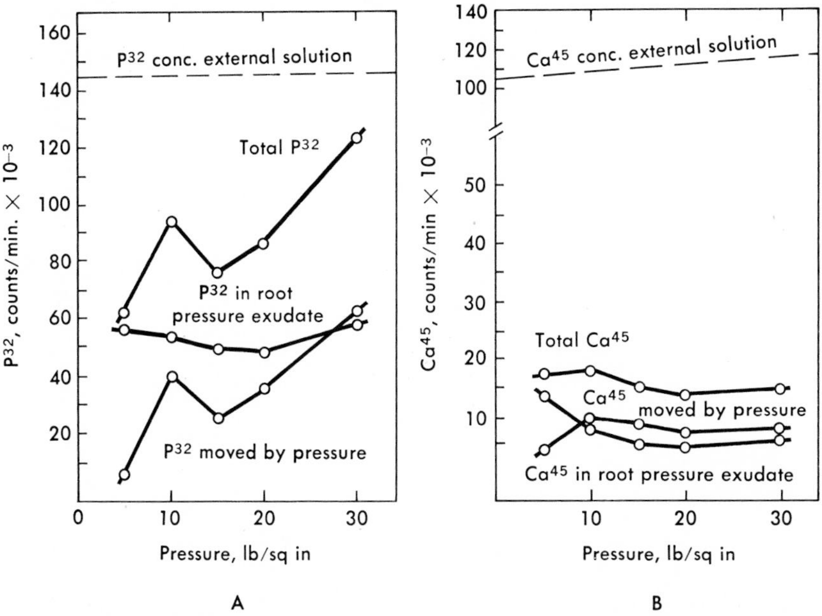

Figure 14-3 Effect of pressure on rate of (A.) P^{32} and (B.) Ca^{45} movement into the xylem of tomato roots. P^{32} or Ca^{45} in root pressure exudate represents the amount of radioactive ion moved into the root xylem in the absence of applied pressure. P^{32} or Ca^{45} moved by pressure represents the fraction of the total P^{32} or Ca^{45} that was associated with water movement under applied pressure. (After W. Lopushinsky. 1964. Plant Physiol. 39: 494.)

xylem ducts, the system is somewhat similar to one where water is being pulled up the xylem ducts as in transpiration. In both cases, the increased flow of water, either by increasing hydrostatic pressure or by increasing transpirational pull, increases the total uptake of ions.

From this discussion, we have learned that at least part of the total salt taken up by a plant may result from passive absorption. This may be accomplished through free diffusion of ions into the apparent free space of a tissue. Accumulation of ions against a concentration gradient is possible under the above circumstances due to Donnan equilibria. Accumulation may also take place against an *apparent* concentration gradient due to ion exchange mechanisms. Finally, the mass flow of ions through root tissue may be possible with the aid of transpirational "pull." All of these mechanisms occur in the absence of metabolic energy. Let us now turn to an analysis of active transport.

ACTIVE TRANSPORT

Direct analyses of the vacuolar sap of plants immersed in solutions of known salt concentration have demonstrated unequivocally that both anions and cations are accumulated by plants against concentration gradients. Furthermore, the extent of accumulation is such that known physical mechanisms, such as ion exchange and Donnan equilibria, cannot account for the extent of accumulation that occurs. Analyses of the ion accumulation in the sap of *Nitella clavata* and *Valonia macrophysa* by Hoagland (23) give an excellent picture both of the accumulation and selective properties of salt absorption mechanisms in plants (Figure 14-4).

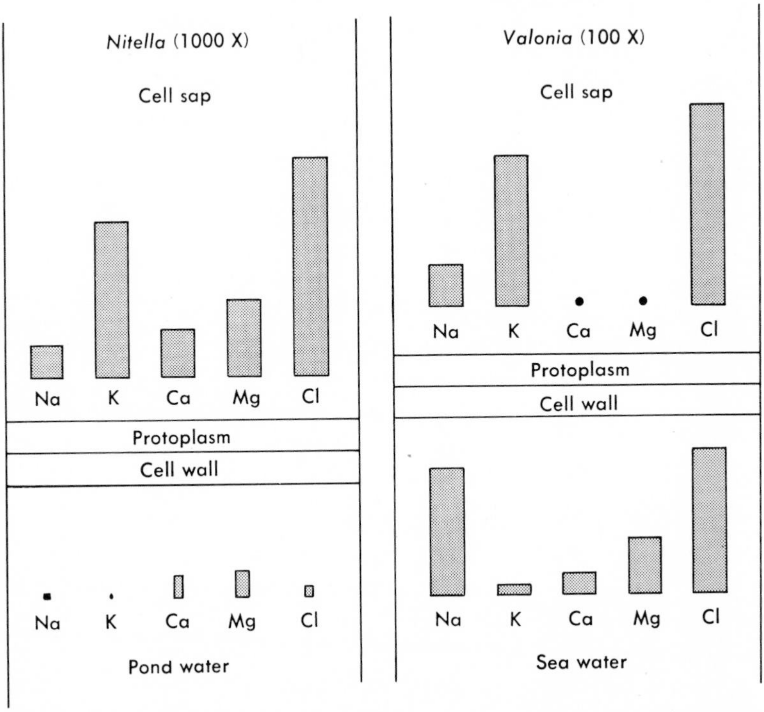

Figure 14-4 Diagram showing the relative concentrations of various ions in the cell sap of *Nitella clavata* and *Valonia macrophysa*. For comparison and to show that ions can be accumulated against a concentration gradient, the relative concentrations of these ions in the growth media is also shown. (After D. R. Hoagland. 1964. Chronica Botanica, Waltham, Mass.)

Since ion accumulation is inhibited when the metabolic activity of the plant is inhibited by low temperatures, low oxygen tension, metabolic inhibitors, etc., we can only assume that ion accumulation as it occurs in plants requires metabolic energy. The transport of ions with the aid of metabolic energy has been termed *active transport.* Various mechanisms have been devised to explain active transport, none of which have been universally accepted. All of these suggested mechanisms, however, generally accept the concept that the active transport of an ion across an impermeable membrane is accomplished through the mediation of a *carrier* compound present in the membrane.

The carrier concept

The space in a tissue or cell to which ions penetrate, through the mediation of metabolic energy, is termed *inner space.* Where outer space ends and inner space begins has not been clearly established. However, it is thought that this dividing line begins somewhere in the middle of the cytoplasm, since apparent free space volume measures have implied that part of the cytoplasm allows for free diffusion of ions. The area between outer and inner space is impermeable to free ions. Passage across this area is thought to require the intercession of specific carriers, which combine with ions in outer space and release them in inner space. This impermeable barrier is usually spoken of as a membrane and the carriers as existing within it.

The most important feature of the carrier theory is the assumption of an intermediate *carrier-ion complex,* which is capable of moving across the above mentioned impermeable membrane. The direction of movement of the complex is from outer to inner space only. Ions released into inner space cannot move out and thus are accumulated. A model giving a simplified description of the carrier concept is shown in Figure 14-5.

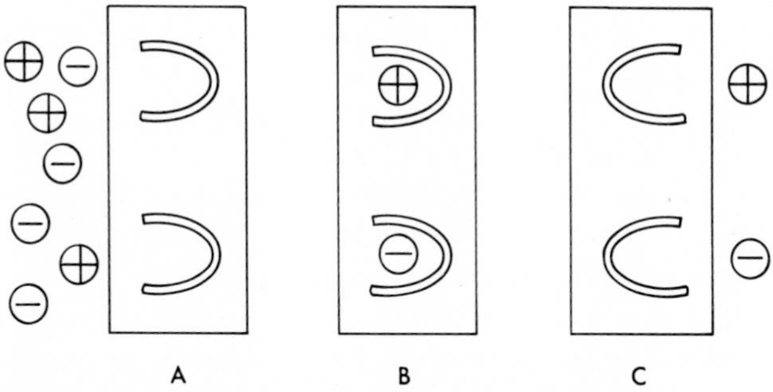

Figure 14-5 Model explaining the carrier concept. A. Membrane is impermeable to ions. B. Carrier-ion complex is formed. C. Ions are released into inner space.

The carrier concept has received impressive support by numerous investigators since its formulation by van den Honert in 1937. We will discuss three characteristics of salt absorption and active transport that appear to suggest strongly the validity of the carrier concept.

Isotopic exchange. It has been found frequently that that portion of ion absorption associated with active transport is largely nonexchangeable with ions of the same species in outer space or an external medium. Radioactive ions have been especially helpful in this observation. As Epstein (19) has pointed out in a review of the subject, the fact that not only back diffusion but also isotopic exchange of the actively absorbed ions is prevented suggests a membrane highly impermeable to free ions. Since ions are absorbed, we must attribute their movement across the impermeable membrane to the intervention of carriers. Experiments by Leggett and Epstein (36) demonstrate rather clearly what we have just described.

The above investigators studied the absorption of sulfate, labeled with S^{35}, by excised barley roots. They found, after a period of S^*O_4 absorption, that the total S^*O_4 absorbed could be separated into two fractions, (1) diffusible and (2) actively absorbed S^*O_4. The roots were allowed to absorb labeled sulfate from a solution of $K_2S^*O_4$ for a period of 60 minutes. The total amount of labeled sulfate taken up was determined for some of the root samples. Other samples were allowed to stand in water or solutions of nonradioactive $CaSO_4$ for varying periods of time up to 120 minutes. This was termed a "desorption" period, during which freely diffusible sulfate moved out of the root tissue. Immersing the roots in solutions of $CaSO_4$ allowed for any isotope exchange that might occur. It was observed that during the "desorption" period, there is a rapid loss of labeled sulfate followed by a period in which there is no further loss (Figure 14-6). The initial rapid loss, of course, is due to diffusion of S^*O_4 from those areas in the root that allow free or reversible diffusion of ions. We have previously referred to this area as outer space. That fraction of labeled sulfate remaining indicates those ions that have been actively transported to inner space. The labeled sulfate ions in inner space are not able to diffuse out during the desorption period, nor are they able to exchange for the stable isotope, SO_4 ion, in the solution of $CaSO_4$.

Saturation effects. Some support for the carrier concept comes from numerous observations demonstrating that at increasingly higher concentrations of salt in the ambient medium, absorption rates appear to approach a limit. In other words, a saturation point is asymptotically approached at which time all of the active sites on the carriers are occupied. One can immediately see the analogy between this situation and the well-known saturation effect found in enzyme reactions. The fact that a level maximum rate of absorption may be maintained over a relatively long period of time

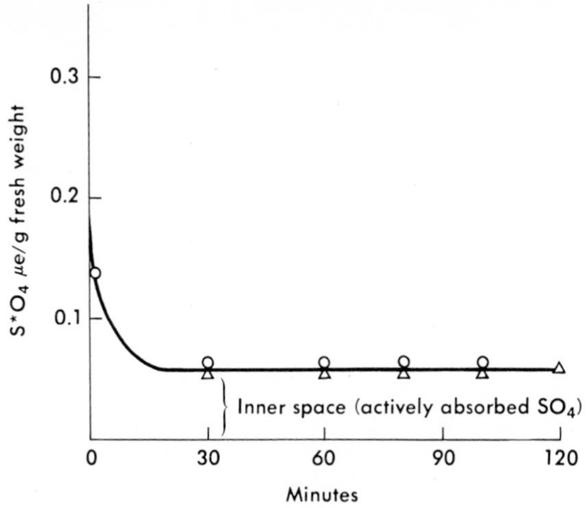

Figure 14-6 Separation of absorbed sulfate into two fractions, (1) diffusible and (2) actively absorbed sulfate. Before zero time, the excised barley roots were exposed to $K_2S^*0_4$, 0.5 meq/liter, for 60 minutes. (After J. E. Leggett and E. Epstein. 1956. Plant Physiol. 31: 222.)

suggests the participation of a *finite* number of carriers working, so to speak, at maximum efficiency. That is, the active sites on the carriers in the above situation are occupied all of the time. As soon as a carrier releases an ion to inner space, it is immediately occupied by an ion from the outer space areas in the tissue. Thus, at the saturation point the cycle is kept in continuous motion and cannot be made to proceed faster by increasing the salt concentration. An example of the effect of concentration levels on phosphate absorption by *Chlorella* cells is given in Figure 14-7.

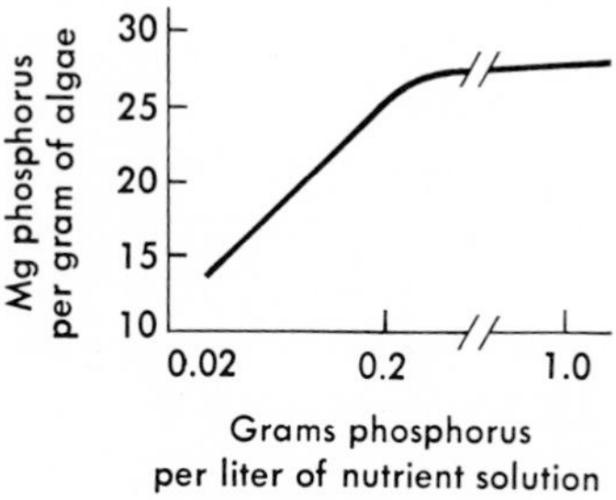

Figure 14-7 Phosphorus content of *Chlorella* grown in nutrient solutions containing different concentrations of phosphorus. (After H. J. Knauss and J. W. Porter. 1954. Plant Physiol. 29: 229.)

Specificity. The carrier concept offers a reasonable explanation of the fact that roots selectively absorb ions. That is, ions are absorbed at different rates and have different levels of accumulation in the root tissue, suggesting the presence of specific carriers. This specificity is rather rigid with ions of dissimilar chemical behavior, but weak or nonexistent with ions of similar behavior. Thus, Epstein and Hagen (20) have shown that the monovalent cations potassium, cesium and rubidium compete with each other for the same binding site. That is, the rate of absorption of rubidium can be lowered by the addition of potassium or cesium to the nutrient solution. Increasing the concentration of rubidium can overcome the inhibiting effects of the other two cations. Neither sodium nor lithium inhibit rubidium absorption, suggesting different binding sites for these ions. Selenate has been shown to inhibit sulfate absorption, but not phosphate or nitrate absorption (36).

Again, we can find a situation analogous to enzyme-substrate activity. Competitive inhibition in enzyme studies is well known and is usually explained on the basis of a mutual attraction of a substrate and an inhibitor for active sites on the enzyme. The carrier, like the enzyme, may have a binding site that attracts two or more ions, and it may also differentiate among ions such as an enzyme will among different substrates. The similarities found in the activities of carriers and enzymes is, in the author's opinion, strong support for the carrier concept in active salt absorption.

We will discuss two possible mechanisms for salt absorption that are based on the carrier concept, one in which cytochromes are involved and another in which ATP is implicated.

Cytochrome pump

Early workers observed that although salt accumulation is dependent upon metabolic energy, there appeared to be no quantitative relationship between salt absorption and respiration. However, Lundegårdh and Burström (41) claimed that such a relation exists between anion absorption and what they called "anion" or "salt" respiration. They observed that the rate of respiration increases when a plant is transferred from water to a salt solution. The amount by which respiration is increased over normal or ground respiration by the transfer of a plant or tissue from water to a salt solution is known as *salt respiration.*

The original observations of Lundegårdh and Burström have since been expanded and developed into a workable theory on active salt absorption by Lundegårdh (39, 40). Lundegårdh's theory assumes the following:

1. Anion absorption is independent of cation absorption and occurs by a different mechanism.
2. An oxygen concentration gradient exists from the outer surface to the

inner surface of a membrane, thus favoring oxidation at the outer surface and reduction at the inner surface.

3. The actual transport of the anion occurs through a cytochrome system.

Since there is a quantitative correlation between anion absorption and salt respiration and since this correlation does not exist with cation absorption, it was assumed that only anions are actively transported. The inhibition of salt respiration and consequent inhibition of anion absorption by cyanide or carbon monoxide led Lundegårdh to propose that transport of anions is mediated through *cytochrome oxidase* and that *cytochromes may be anion carriers.* A diagrammatic representation of Lundegårdh's cytochrome theory is shown in Figure 14-8.

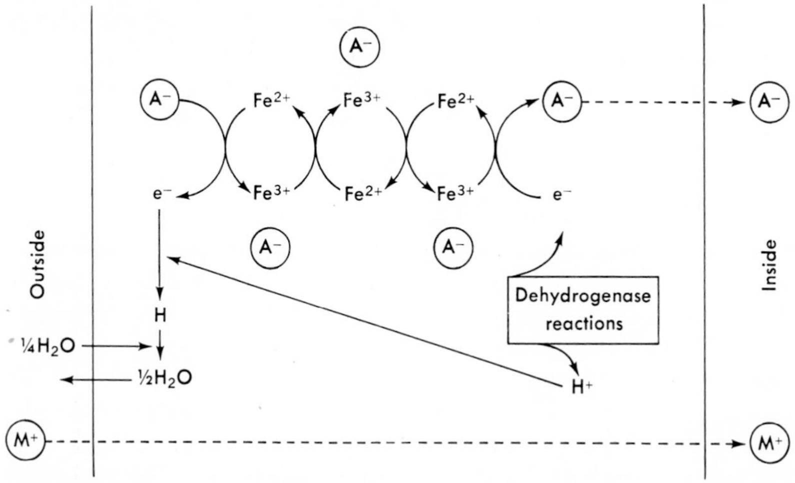

Figure 14-8 A diagrammatic representation of Lundegårdh's cytochrome theory on salt absorption. The anions (A^-) are actively absorbed via a "cytochrome pump." The cations (M^+) are absorbed passively. See text for further explanation. (After H. Lundegårdh. 1950. Physiol. Plantarum 3: 103; and 1954. Symp. Soc. Exptl. Biol. 8: 262.)

According to Lundegårdh's theory, dehydrogenase reactions on the inner surface produce protons (H^+) and electrons (e^-). The electrons produced move outward via a cytochrome chain, while anions move inward. At the outer surface of the membrane the reduced iron of the cytochrome is oxidized, losing an electron and picking up an anion. The released electron unites with a proton and oxygen to form water. At the inner surface the oxidized iron of the cytochrome becomes reduced by the addition of an electron released in a dehydrogenase reaction. The anion is released on the inside in this last reaction. Cations are absorbed passively to balance the potential difference caused by the accumulation of anions on the inner surface.

Although the cytochrome transport theory does give a clear picture of how metabolic energy might participate in ion absorption, it has not been universally accepted and has been criticized by a number of investigators. For example, Robertson et al. (51) found that 2,4-dinitrophenol (DNP), an inhibitor of oxidative phosphorylation, increases respiration but decreases salt absorption. This implies that *phosphorylation* should be included in any theory of ion accumulation. The original proposal that only anions are capable of stimulating respiration has come under considerable attack. For example, Handley and Overstreet (22) found that both potassium and sodium ions stimulated respiration. Finally, if there is only one carrier for all anions, then competition for binding sites among anions should be apparent. On the contrary, as pointed out in an earlier discussion, the anions sulfate, nitrate, and phosphate do not compete with one another.

Carrier mechanism involving ATP

The finding by Robertson et al. (51) that 2,4-dinitrophenol inhibited salt absorption presents a strong case for the participation of ATP in active salt absorption. Low concentrations of 2,4-dinitrophenol will completely retard ATP formation without affecting or increasing respiration.

A mechanism for active salt absorption that utilizes ATP has been proposed by Bennet-Clark (2). This investigator has suggested that *phospholipids* may be important in the transport of ions across membranes otherwise impermeable. In this transport *lecithin,* a phospholipid, is synthesized and hydrolyzed in a cyclic manner, picking up ions on the outer surface and releasing them on hydrolysis into inner space. The synthesis of at least one of the components of this *phosphatide cycle* requires ATP. A diagram showing the "phosphatide cycle" and how it might proceed in ion transport is given in Figure 14-9.

FACTORS AFFECTING SALT ABSORPTION

The physical and biochemical activities of living organisms are subject to the influences of their external and internal environments. Salt absorption is not an exception, being speeded up, slowed down, or kept in dynamic equilibrium by a complex of ever changing factors. The scientist has learned to study the influence of individual factors by controlling the environment and studying the effect of the one facor in question. This has been done with the process of salt absorption, and we now have an extensive, if in-

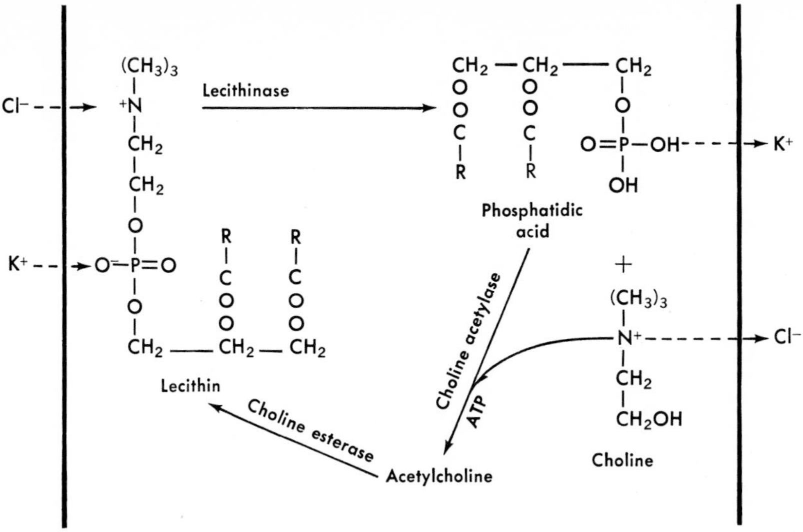

Figure 14-9 Diagrammatic representation of the phosphatide cycle. At left, ions from outer space are picked up by lecithin. On hydrolysis of the lecithin-ion complex, the ions are released to inner space. Lecithin is then resynthesized. (Redrawn from T. A. Bennet-Clark. 1956. *In* R. L. Wain and F. Wightman (eds.), Chemistry and mode of action of plant growth substances. Butterworths, London.

complete, picture of how this process might proceed in nature's everchanging environment. We will discuss the effects of temperature, pH, light, oxygen tension, interaction, and growth on salt absorption.

Temperature

In general, an increase in temperature results in an acceleration of salt absorption. However, the influence of temperature on salt absorption is confined to a relatively narrow range. In addition to accelerating salt absorption, increase in temperature past a maximum point will inhibit and eventually terminate the process (Figure 14-10). Most likely, the inhibitory effects of high temperatures are because of the denaturation of enzymes involved either directly in salt absorption or in the synthesis of some necessary component of salt absorption.

Both passive and active absorption processes are affected by temperature changes. The rate of free diffusion, for example, depends upon the kinetic energy of the diffusing molecules or ions which is, in turn, dependent upon temperature. Therefore, lowering of temperature will slow down any proc-

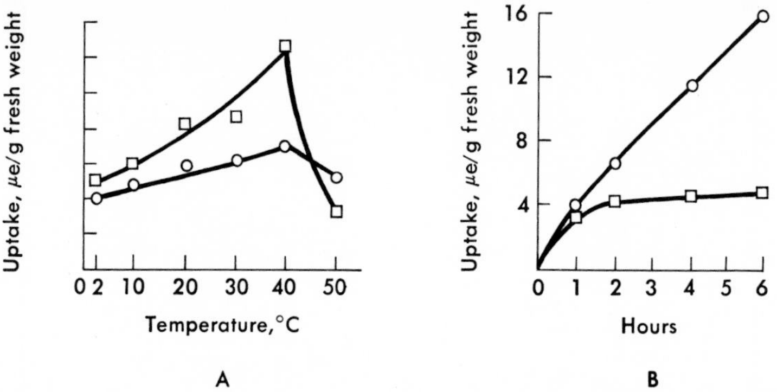

Figure 14-10 A. Effect of temperature on the uptake of potassium ions by washed carrot tissue slices in 30 minutes (○) and 2 hours (□). **B.** Uptake of potassium ions by washed carrot tissue slices over a prolonged period of time at 2°C (□) and 20°C (○). (After J. F. Sutcliffe. 1962. Mineral salts absorption in plants. Pergamon Press, New York.)

ess dependent upon free diffusion. Low temperatures will, of course, slow down the biochemical reactions found in active transport.

Hydrogen ion concentration

The availability of ions in the soil solution, discussed in a previous chapter, is profoundly affected by the hydrogen ion concentration. Ionization of electrolytes or the valence numbers of different ion species are influenced by changes in pH. For example, the monovalent phosphate ion, $H_2PO_4^-$, is the form of phosphorus most readily taken up by plants. However, as a medium approaches a more alkaline pH, production of first the bivalent phosphate (HPO_4^{2-}) and then the trivalent phosphate (PO_4^{3-}) is favored. The bivalent ion is only sparingly available to the plant, while the trivalent ion is not available at all. Since the monovalent ion is absorbed more readily than the bivalent ion, absorption of phosphate is accelerated at an acid pH. Robertson (50) has pointed out that since boron is taken up as the undissociated acid, H_3BO_3, or as the $H_2BO_3^-$ ion, it too must be absorbed more readily at a lower pH. In contrast to the above observations, with anions, increase in pH will favor the absorption of cations.

There have been numerous experiments showing little pH effect, as judged by growth (50). Marked pH effects most likely occur when ion availability is inhibited. However, if the concentration of ion is high enough, it will be difficult to show a deficiency for that ion in the plant over a physiological range of pH values. Of course, at pH values outside the physiological range, damage to plant tissues and carriers will inhibit salt absorption.

Light

The effects of light on the opening and closing of stomates and on photosynthesis indirectly affect salt uptake. Opened stomates increase the mass flow of water in the transpiration stream and thus may indirectly influence salt absorption. The energy derived from the photosynthetic process provides energy for salt uptake and the oxygen given off improves conditions for the active absorption of ions.

Oxygen tension

The active phase of salt absorption is inhibited by the absence of oxygen. Indeed, it was this observation that most strongly supported early theories on active transport. A strong influence of oxygen on the uptake of phosphate may be seen in Figure 14-11.

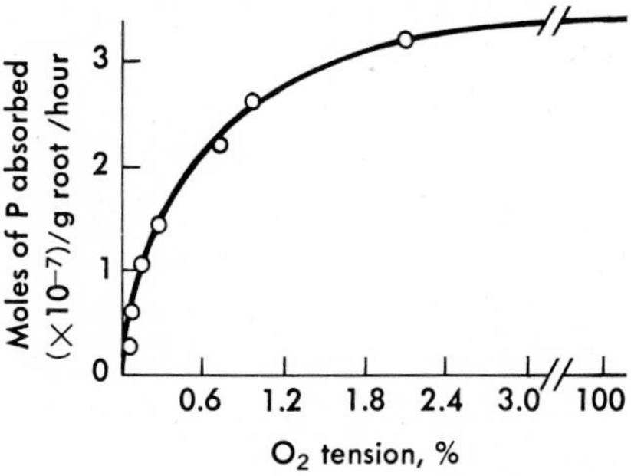

Figure 14-11 Effect of oxygen on the uptake of phosphate by excised barley roots in phosphate solutions $1 \times 10^{-4} M$ (pH 4). (After H. T. Hopkins. 1956. Plant Physiol. 13: 155.)

Interaction

It is well known that the absorption of one ion may be influenced by the presence of another ion. In a study of the uptake of KBr by excised barley roots, Viets (57) found that the absorption of potassium is affected by the presence of calcium, magnesium, and other polyvalent cations in the external medium. A dual effect by calcium on the uptake of both potassium and bromine was noted by Viets. He found that uptake of potassium and bromine is less in the absence of calcium, but decreases after the calcium concentration is increased past a maximum point (Figure 14-12). Overstreet et al. (45) also noted this effect of calcium. The absorption of magnesium is also adversely affected by the presence of calcium (44).

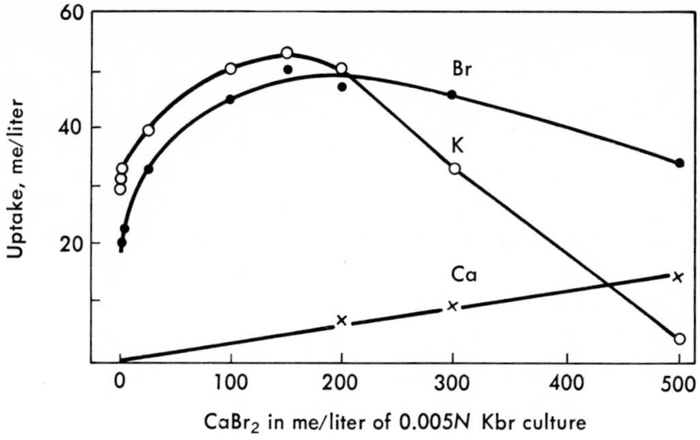

Figure 14-12 Effect of Ca on the uptake of K and Br. Note that at low concentrations of Ca, the uptake of both K and Br is increased. As the concentration of Ca is increased, however, the uptake of K and Br is inhibited. (After F. G. Viets. 1944. Plant Physiol. 19: 466.)

The interaction of several ions (K, Cs, Li, Rb, and Na) has been described by Epstein and Hagen (20) as competition for binding sites on carriers. For example, they found that potassium, rubidium, and caesium all compete with one another for a mutual binding site. Lithium and sodium, on the other hand, are not competitive, since they have different binding sites. It was later found that barium, calcium, and strontium compete with one another for a mutual binding site, which is not involved in the active uptake of magnesium (21).

It appears that interaction among ions is primarily associated with the availability and specificity of binding sites on carriers. If enough binding sites are present, interaction will not be apparent and ions with mutual binding sites will be taken up with maximum efficiency. Also, if the binding site of an ion is highly specific for that ion, its absorption should not be affected by the presence of other ions.

Growth

For a short period of time we can study the absorption of salt by plant tissues without interference from growth. However, over a prolonged period of time, salt absorption may be profoundly influenced by growth. The growth of a tissue or plant may increase surface area, number of cells, and synthesis of new binding sites or carriers, factors which will stimulate salt absorption. Also, the increased volume of water taken up by a cell as it matures may dilute the internal concentration of salt and thus increase absorption activity.

When dealing with the growth of a complete plant instead of a tissue, we must consider the different phases of development and their influence on salt absorption. For example, as a root ages, much of the surface area formally involved in salt absorption becomes heavily suberized and unable to take up salt. Vegetative development and the metabolic activity associated with vegetative development make heavy demands on many of the elements. Also, as pointed out previously, increased vegetative growth usually is accompanied by increased water movement, which may affect the passive absorption and translocation of salts. A summary of the effect of growth and metabolism on salt accumulation has been given by Steward and Sutcliffe (54) (Figure 14-13).

TRANSLOCATION

Now that the various mechanisms for the absorption and accumulation of salts have been discussed, we may ask the question, how are the salts translocated in the plant? Nutrient availability in the solid and liquid phases of the soil have been explained in two theories, (1) the *contact exchange theory,* and (2) the *carbonic acid exchange theory*. Both lines of thought have been variously defended and criticized, but still remain the best explanations for mineral salt availability to the plant from the soil (Figure 14-14).

According to the authors of the contact exchange theory (30, 31), ions may be exchanged from one adsorbent to another (clay colloid and root) without the participation of free electrolytes. That is, an ion may be adsorbed by the plant root without being first dissolved in the soil solution. These authors explain this as an overlapping of oscillation spaces of adsorbed ions. An ion adsorbed electrostatically to a solid particle, such as a plant root or clay micelle, is not held too tightly, but will oscillate within a certain small volume of space. If two adsorbents are close enough, the oscillation volume of an ion adsorbed to one particle may overlap the oscillation volume of an ion adsorbed to the other particle, and an exchange of ions may take place (Figure 14-14A).

The soil solution plays an important part in the carbonic acid exchange theory in that it provides the medium for exchange of ions between the root and clay micelles. According to this theory, respiratory CO_2 released by the root forms carbonic acid (H_2CO_3) on contact with the soil solution. In the soil solution, carbonic acid dissociates to form a cation (H^+) and an anion (HCO_3^-). The hydrogen ions diffuse to clay micelles where they may exchange with cations adsorbed to the clay surface. The cations orig-

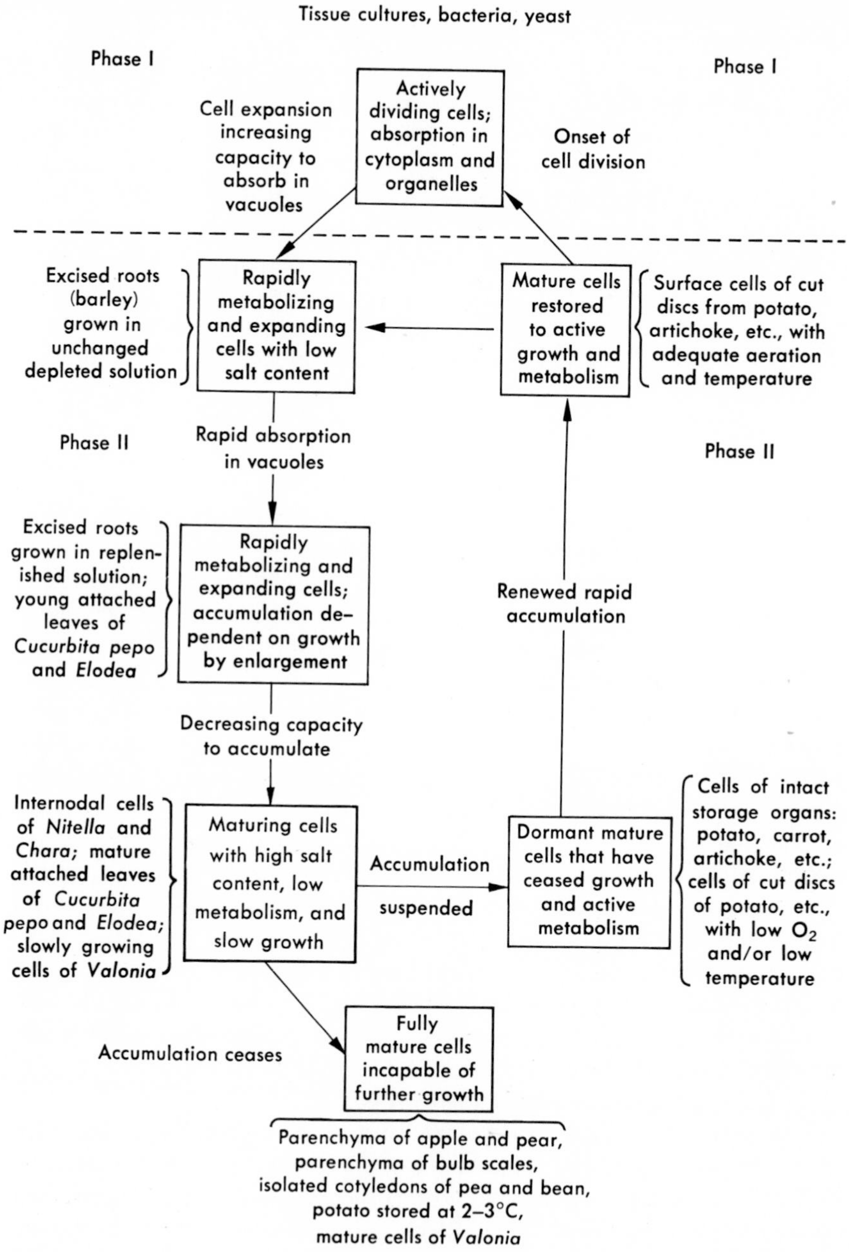

Figure 14-13 Salt accumulation in relation to growth and metabolism. In Phase I, the main emphasis is upon binding of ions of specific sites, which can multiply. In Phase II, the main emphasis is upon active secretion into vacuoles. (After F. C. Steward and J. F. Sutcliffe. 1959. *In* F. C. Steward (ed.), Plant physiology. Academic Press, New York. 2: 253.

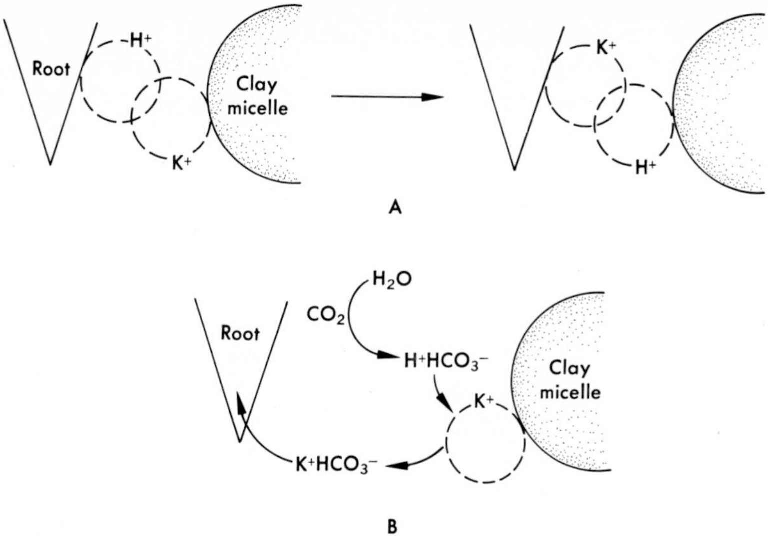

Figure 14-14 Diagrammatic representation of (A) the contact exchange theory and (B) the carbonic acid exchange theory.

inally adsorbed to the clay surface are released to the soil solution; here they are free to diffuse to the root surface where they may be absorbed in exchange for H^+ or as ion pairs with bicarbonate (Figure 14-14B).

The actual absorption of salts by roots is both passive and active. The movement of salts into apparent free space is passive, allowing for the free diffusion of ions. There is some confusion as to what area of the cell is occupied by apparent free space, some authors, such as Levitt (37), contending that it is confined to the cell walls. However, other workers have indicated that part of the cytoplasm may also be included in apparent free space. Inner space, where salts are accumulated to higher concentrations than in the external medium, is thought to comprise part of the cytoplasm and the vacuole. With the above picture in mind, it is our task now to determine how the absorbed salt moves from the outer surface of the root, across the cortex, and into the lumina of the dead conducting cells of the stele.

It is generally thought that absorbed ions move rather freely into the root as far as the *endodermis,* where further penetration may be retarded by the *Casparian strip*. Calculations of the volume of apparent free space by Butler (12) and Epstein (18) have supported the contention that metabolic energy is not required for mineral salts to reach the endodermis. If we assume that part of the cytoplasm is occupied by apparent free space, it is most probable that diffusing ions move relatively unhindered through the wet cell walls and plasmodesmata of the cortex cells to the endodermis. In this respect, all of the cytoplasm of the cortex cells may be connected via plasmodesma, these structures offering excellent pathways for the movement of salt. The complex of cytoplasm and interconnecting strands is called the *symplast*.

An explanation of how salts are transported across the endodermis and passed into the lumina of the xylem vessels, where they are accumulated against a concentration gradient, has been a perplexing problem for many years. Just as the accumulation of salts in the vacuoles of cells is an active process, so also is metabolic energy utilized in the accumulation of salts in the xylem vessel. Thus, the endodermal cells present a barrier to the passive diffusion of ions, and it is thought that the controlling feature, in this respect, is the Casparian strip. The Casparian strip is a band of suberin in the primary wall that completely circles every endodermal cell and in most cases traverses the middle lamella, thus forming a continuous suberized structure surrounding the root (Figure 14-15). Moreover, the protoplast

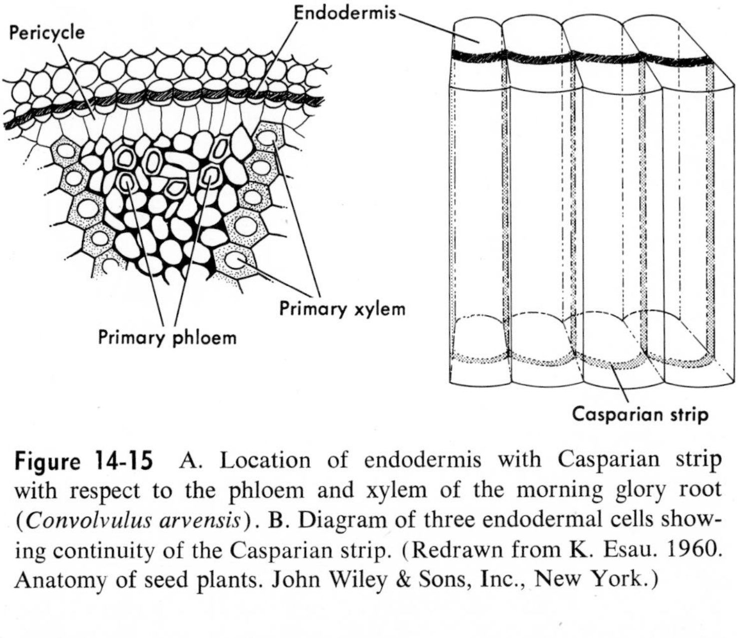

Figure 14-15 A. Location of endodermis with Casparian strip with respect to the phloem and xylem of the morning glory root (*Convolvulus arvensis*). B. Diagram of three endodermal cells showing continuity of the Casparian strip. (Redrawn from K. Esau. 1960. Anatomy of seed plants. John Wiley & Sons, Inc., New York.)

is securely attached to this band. Because of this strip, materials in solution cannot pass either between or through the walls of the endodermal cells. Also, these materials cannot pass between the protoplast and the wall because of the tight attachment of the protoplast to the Casparian strip. Therefore, the only route available is through the protoplast.

Various theories have been proposed to explain the passage of salts across the endodermis and into the xylem. One theory that appears to enjoy the most general acceptance is that proposed by Crafts and Broyer (16). These workers maintain that there is a gradient of decreasing O_2 and increasing CO_2 from the cortex to the stele. This would mean that the living cells in the immediate area of the xylem vessels would possess a low level of metabolic activity. Since energy is required to accumulate salt against a concentration gradient and to hold this salt, these cells, in contrast to the cortex cells, favor the loss of salts (15). Diffusion back through the impervious Casparian strip is impossible, thus providing for the unidirectional loss of salt into the lumina of the xylem vessels.

Circulation of mineral salts

Salts accumulated in the xylem ducts of the root are translocated to the shoot and, once there, distributed and redistributed throughout the plant. For example, mineral salts that have been deposited in the leaves of a shoot may be withdrawn prior to abscission and be translocated to other parts of the plant (e.g., reproductive areas or younger leaves). Also, there may be a general redistribution of elements that are highly mobile in the plant.

Generally, the circulation of elements takes place in the vascular tissues. Determining what vascular tissues provide passage for salts from one area of the plant to another presented a difficult task to plant physiologists before the advent of the radioactive tracer. Since the initial use of radioactive tracers, several different pathways for the translocation of salts have been discovered. We will discuss the movement of salts in the xylem, in the phloem, laterally between these two tissues, and outward from the leaf.

Translocation of salts in the xylem. Because of the evidence that has accumulated over the past three decades, there is little doubt that the salt accumulated in the xylem ducts of the root is carried upward with the transpiration stream. That salts move upward in the xylem tissues has been demonstrated in several different ways. Ringing experiments by several investigators (13, 47, 43) have shown that the upward translocation of salts is unimpeded by removal of the phloem tissue. Relatively large amounts of dissolved salts have been detected in the xylem sap by direct analysis. If salts are carried upward in the transpiration stream, one should be able to observe an increase in salt uptake with an increase in transpiration rate. This observation has been made with tomato plants by Arnon et al. (1). They found that radioactive phosphate traveled upward to the tip of the tomato plant much more rapidly under conditions favoring rapid transpiration (such as bright sunlight) than under less favorable

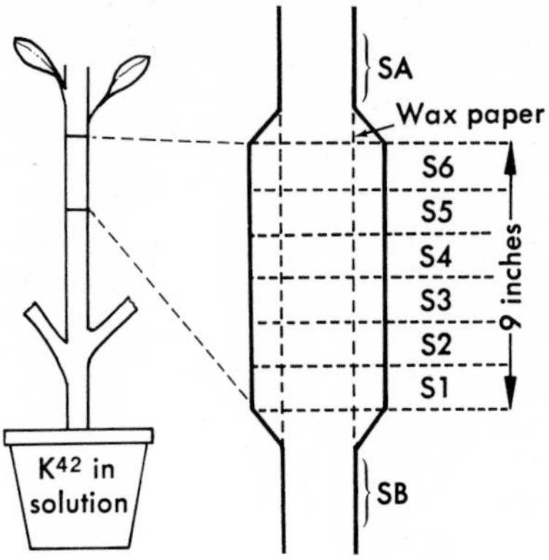

Figure 14-16 A method for detecting the upward and lateral translocation of salts. The bark of a willow plant is separated from the wood by a 9 inch strip of wax paper, still leaving the bark and wood intact. The willow is allowed to absorb K^{42} for a 5 hour period before sections of the treated and intact areas are analyzed for radioactive potassium. Results may be seen in Table 14-1. (After P. R. Stout and D. R. Hoagland. 1939. Am. J. Botan. 26: 320.)

conditions. Sutcliffe (56) has shown that if transpiration by a leaf is inhibited by covering the leaf with a polythene bag, translocation of mineral salts to that particular leaf is reduced considerably.

Very convincing evidence that the pathway of upward translocation of salts is in the xylem tissue was obtained by Stout and Hoagland (55) with the use of radioactive tracers. These authors carefully separated the bark and xylem along a 9 inch length of willow stem. A strip of impervious waxed paper was inserted between the xylem and the bark. The methods used were such that the continuity of the bark and the xylem tissue was undisturbed and the plant was left intact. The willow was allowed to absorb radioactive potassium for a 5 hour period, and then sections of the treated and intact areas of the stem were analyzed for radioactive potassium (Figure 14-16 and Table 14-1).

The data shown in Figure 14-16 and Table 14-1 clearly show that

Table 14-1 Results of experiment described in Figure 14-16.[a]

	Stripped branch		*Unstripped branch*	
Section	*K^{42} in bark, ppm*	*K^{42} in wood, ppm*	*K^{42} in bark, ppm*	*K^{42} in wood, ppm*
SA	53.0	47	64	56
S6	11.6	119		
S5	0.9	122		
S4	0.7	112	87	69
S3	0.3	98		
S2	0.3	108		
S1	20.0	113		
SB	84.0	58	74	67

[a] After P. R. Stout and D. R. Hoagland. 1939. Am. J. Botan. 26: 320.

potassium is translocated upward in the xylem tissue. In addition, analyses of sections above and below the stripped area demonstrate that lateral interchange of potassium between the phloem and xylem takes place quite readily, but that further translocation of potassium either upward or downward is retarded. If we assume that the strip of waxed paper inserted between the bark and xylem is completely impermeable to the labeled potassium being carried along in the transpiration stream, then we must assume that some, although minute, translocation takes place in the phloem tissue. This assumption is based on the detection of small amounts of radioactivity in the bark along the stripped area. Stout and Hoagland's experiment demonstrates, then, that the upward translocation of ions occurs normally in the xylem tissue and that a lateral interchange between the xylem, cambium, and phloem occurs quite readily. This interchange between the vascular tissue via the cambium has more recently been shown in cotton and bean plants (7, 6).

Lateral translocation of salts. In the above experiment we noted that, in addition to the upward translocation of salt, there is also a lateral movement between vascular tissues. Generally, the xylem tissue is separated from the phloem tissue by a layer of living cells, which constitute the *cambial tissue*. It is thought that the cambial tissue may regulate, to some extent, the amount of salt carried up in the transpiration stream. It is obvious that if the upward movement of salts was not regulated in some manner, the salt needs of certain areas of the plant would not be accommodated. The cambium is positioned in such a manner as to make it available, both metabolically and physically, for regulation of the upward, lateral, and downward movement of salt. Biddulph (4) has suggested that the active accumulation of salt by the cambial cells may act as a deterrent against an "indiscriminate" sweep of salts upward in the transpiration stream.

Discrimination between the different mineral salts carried in the transpiration stream by the cambial tissue may be accomplished. For example, if a particular element was present in high concentration in the phloem, and an equilibrium existed between the phloem and cambium, interference of the passage of that element in the transpiration stream would probably be negligible (4). On the other hand, if that element should be present in low concentration in the phloem, the active accumulation of the element and its lateral translocation into the phloem would be enhanced.

Translocation of salts in the phloem. The initial movement of salts in an upward direction occurs in the xylem tissue. However, as far back as 1935, Curtis demonstrated that upward movement of mineral salts may occur in the phloem. Curtis demonstrated that stem tip growth is impeded

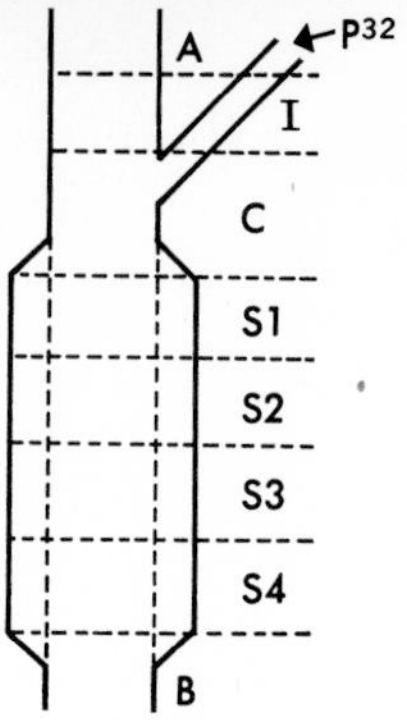

Figure 14-17 Method of detecting the movement of P^{32} downward after being introduced to a leaf. The bark immediately below a leaf petiole of a cotton plant is separated from the wood by waxed paper still leaving the bark and wood intact. Radioactive phosphorus was injected into the leaf blade just above the separated area of the stem, and after 1 hour the sections indicated in the figure were analyzed for P^{32}. The results are shown in Table 14-2. (After O. Biddulph and J. Markle. 1944. Am. J. Botan. 31: 65.)

by removing a ring of bark relatively high up on the stem. This appears to support the concept that upward translocation of mineral salts also occurs in the phloem tissue. However, because of the high position of the ring on the stem in Curtis' work, we must assume that the primary influence on stem tip growth was because of the blockage of salts moving out of the lower leaves (discussed in the next section) and being transported upward in the phloem and not because of the root absorbed salts. This assumption is based on the common observation that ringing a stem near the root level has no effect on salt nutrition.

The downward movement of salts in the phloem has been demonstrated in studies using radioactive tracers. Study of the outward movement of salts from the leaf have shown that salts entering the main vascular stream from leaf sources move primarily in a downward direction in the phloem tissue (7, 8). Data on the movement of salts in the phloem tissue are given in Figure 14-17 and Table 14-2. In support of Curtis' earlier observations, movement of salts in an upward direction was also noted in the

Table 14-2 Results of experiments described in Figure 14-17. The amount of P^{32} detected in each section is given in milligrams.[a]

	Stripped plant			*Unstripped plant*		
Section	*Bark*		*Wood*	*Bark*		*Wood*
A		1.11				
I	0.458		0.100		0.444	
C		0.610				
S1	0.554		0.064	0.160		0.055
S2	0.332		0.004	0.103		0.063
S3	0.592		0.000	0.055		0.018
S4	0.228		0.004	0.026		0.007
B		0.653			0.152	

[a] After O. Biddulph and J. Markle. 1944. Am. J. Botan. 31: 65.

above experiment. Table 14-2 also shows quite clearly that lateral transport between the vascular tissues takes place where the phloem and xylem are not separated. This implies that both tissues may be involved with the upward translocation of mineral salts moving out from leaves.

There appears, then, to be a bidirectional movement of salts in the phloem tissue. Generally, this is thought of as a simultaneous movement in both direction in the same sieve elements. However, Crafts (14) has suggested that movement of solutes (inorganic and organic) out of the leaf may occur in two different phloem channels, one toward the tip, the other toward the base of the plant. Evidence for bidirectional movement occurring in the same channel and in separate channels has been presented, and it is impossible at the present time to determine which theory is correct.

Outward movement of salts from leaves. In studies done on the mineral nutrition of leaves of deciduous plants, it has been shown that just prior to abscission there is a movement of mineral nutrients out of the leaf. Among the mineral nutrients moving out of the leaves are nitrogen, potassium, phosphorus, sulfur, chlorine, and under certain conditions, iron and magnesium. Those remaining include calcium, boron, manganese, and silicon (4). The withdrawal of mineral nutrients from leaves takes place primarily in the phloem tissue, as we have indicated in the previous section (see Figure 14-17 and Table 14-2).

A study of the path radioactive phosphorus will take when introduced to leaves at different levels on the plant has revealed that phosphorus from those leaves nearest the root system will mostly move downward toward the root, while phosphorus moving out of leaves positioned high on the plant will move mostly toward the apex (4, 33). It appears also that movement of mineral salts out of young actively growing leaves is almost nonexistent and that this characteristic greatly diminishes as the leaf matures. In many instances younger leaves will draw on the supply of mineral elements of the older more mature leaves. This is especially noticeable when there is a deficiency of elements such as nitrogen and phosphorus, which are highly mobile in the plant. The deficiency symptoms will first appear on the lower leaves.

Circulation and reutilization

Early work by Mason and Maskell (42) suggested that minerals are taken up in the transpiration stream and exported to the leaves, excess quantities being retranslocated downward in the phloem. The mineral salts could be laterally transported into the xylem tissue where upward translocation could take place again. Elements such as nitrogen, potassium, and phosphorus move readily in this circuit. Calcium, however, ascends the stem, but does not relocate in the phloem.

Biddulph (3) and Biddulph et al. (5) have demonstrated that phosphorus is highly mobile in a plant and have suggested the possibility of a continuous circulation of phosphorus. A given phosphorus atom, for example, may make several complete circuits in a plant in a single day (4). Phosphorus mobility is, perhaps, an essential feature of plant growth. Phosphorus is a necessary participant in such important metabolic schemes as photosynthesis, the synthesis of starch, glycolysis, and the synthesis of fats and proteins, etc. Phosphorus is needed, therefore, at various points in the plant where any one of these processes is occuring. Biddulph (4) has suggested that a "pool" of phosphorus in a usable form is maintained throughout the plant in a relatively uniform concentration.

Sulfur is mobile in plants, but, because of its rapid uptake into metabolic compounds, it does not circulate in the plant like phosphorus. When radioactive sulfur is taken up by roots of a bean plant, it is rapidly translocated upward in the xylem tissue to the leaves. Within 24 hours, most of the labeled sulfur will be found in the younger leaves, the older more mature leaves having lost their sulfur to the young actively growing leaves (5). Since sulfur is a constituent of protein and protein synthesis is occurring to a much greater extent in the younger leaves, compared to the older leaves, one can assume that movement to the younger leaves and metabolic capture of the sulfur at these sites is most probable. It has been suggested that sulfur makes one complete cycle before complete metabolic capture (4). Sulfur, then, is freely mobile in the plant, but is rendered immobile rather quickly in metabolic reactions.

Radioactive calcium when taken up by bean roots is carried in the transpiration stream to the different areas of the plant. However, calcium is immobile in the phloem, and once delivered by the transpiration stream, it remains stationary (5).

The mobility of iron has been studied by Rediske and Biddulph (48) in the red kidney bean plant, where it appears to be dependent primarily upon the iron concentration of the plant tissues and secondarily upon phosphorus availability and the pH of the nutrient medium. When the concentration of iron is low in the plant tissues, the mobility of iron injected into the phloem is highest. This mobility decreases with increased concentration of iron in the tissues. A pH of 4 in the nutrient solution gives high iron mobility. This mobility decreases as the pH is increased to 7. A low phosphorus content in the nutrient solution favors the mobility of iron. High phosphorus concentrations in the plant tissues renders iron immobile in the veins of the leaf.

In our discussion of the circulation of the mineral elements in the plant, we have touched upon four general directions of movement: (1) upward, (2) downward, (3) lateral, and (4) outward. The upward translocation of salts takes place primarily in the xylem tissue, although some upward movement does also take place in the phloem. Downward movement of the mineral elements takes place in the phloem tissue where, also, upward movement occurs. Movement of salts in the phloem tissue is generally spoken of as bidirectional. Lateral movement occurs between the xylem and the phloem, and this movement appears to be mediated by the cambium. Movement of salts out of leaves is a common occurrence, especially just prior to abscission. This movement occurs in the phloem tissue.

With the above account in mind, and considering the strong evidence supporting the different directions of salt movement in the plant, the theory that the circulation of mineral elements is a general phenomenon in plants is real and well documented.

BIBLIOGRAPHY

1. Arnon, D. I., P. R. Stout, and F. Sipos. 1940. Radioactive phosphorus as an indicator of phosphorus absorption of tomato plants at various stages of development. Am. J. Botan. 27: 791.
2. Bennet-Clark, T. A. 1956. Salt accumulation and mode of action of auxin; a preliminary hypothesis. pp. 284–291 *In* R. L. Wain and F. Wightman (eds.), Chemistry and mode of action of plant growth substances. Butterworths, London.
3. Biddulph, O. 1941. Diurnal migration of injected radiophosphorus from bean leaves. Am. J. Botan. 28: 348.
4. Biddulph, O. 1959. Translocation of inorganic solutes. *In* F. C. Steward (ed.), Plant physiology. Academic Press, New York. 2: 553.
5. Biddulph, O., S. F. Biddulph, R. Cory, and H. Koontz. 1958. Circulation patterns for P^{32}, S^{35}, and Ca^{45} in the bean plant. Plant Physiol. 33: 293.
6. Biddulph, O., and R. Cory. 1957. An analysis of translocation in the phloem of the bean plant using THO, P^{32} and $C^{14}O_2$. Plant Physiol. 32: 608.
7. Biddulph, O., and J. Markle. 1944. Translocation of radiophosphorus in the phloem of the cotton plant. Am. J. Botan. 31: 65.
8. Biddulph, S. F. 1956. Visual indications of S^{35} and P^{32} translocation in the phloem of the cotton plant. Am. J. Botan. 43: 143.
9. Briggs, G. E., and R. N. Robertson. 1957. Apparent free space. Ann. Rev. Plant Physiol. 8: 11.
10. Brouwer, R. 1956. Investigations into the occurrence of active and passive components in the ion uptake by *Vicia faba*. Acta Botan. Neerl. 5: 287.
11. Broyer, T. C., and D. R. Hoagland. 1943. Metabolic activities of roots and their bearing on the relation of upward movement of salts and water in plants. Am. J. Botan. 30: 261.

12. Butler, G. W. 1953. Ion uptake by young wheat plants. II. The "apparent free space" of wheat roots. Physiol. Plant 5: 617.
13. Clements, H. F., and C. J. Engard. 1938. Upward movement of inorganic solutes as affected by a girdle. Plant Physiol. 13: 103.
14. Crafts, A. S. 1951. Movement of assimilates, viruses, growth regulators, and chemical indicators in plants. Botan. Rev. 17: 203.
15. Crafts, A. S. 1961. Translocation in plants. Holt, Rinehart & Winston, New York.
16. Crafts, A. S., and T. C. Broyer. 1938. Migration of salts and water into xylem of the roots of higher plants. Am. J. Botan. 25: 529.
17. Curtis, O. F. 1935. The translocation of solutes in plants: a critical consideration of evidence bearing upon solute movement. McGraw-Hill Book Co. New York.
18. Epstein, E. 1955. Passive permeation and active transport of ions in plant roots. Plant Physiol. 30: 529.
19. Epstein, E. 1956. Mineral nutrition of plants: mechanisms of uptake and transport. Ann. Rev. Plant Physiol. 7: 1.
20. Epstein, E., and C. E. Hagen. 1952. A kinetic study of the absorption of alkali cations by barley roots. Plant Physiol. 27: 457.
21. Epstein, E., and J. E. Leggett. 1954. The absorption of alkaline earth cations by barley roots: kinetics and mechanism. Am. J. Botan. 41: 788.
22. Handley, R., and R. Overstreet. 1955. Respiration and salt absorption by excised barley roots. Plant Physiol. 30: 418.
23. Hoagland, D. R. 1944. Lectures on the inorganic nutrition of plants. Chronica Botanica, Waltham, Mass.
24. Honert, T. H. van den, J. J. M. Hooymans, and W. S. Volkers. 1955. Experiments on the relation between water absorption and mineral uptake by plant roots. Acta Botan. Néerl. 4: 139.
25. Hope, A. B. 1953. Salt uptake by root tissue cytoplasm: the relation between uptake and external concentration. Australian J. Biol. Sci. 6: 396.
26. Hope, A. B., and P. G. Stevens. 1952. Electrical potential differences in bean roots and their relation to salt uptake. Australian J. Sci. Res. B-1: 335.
27. Hopkins, H. T. 1956. Absorption of ionic species of orthophosphate by barley roots: Effects of 2,4-dinitrophenol and oxygen tension. Plant Physiol. 31: 155.
28. Hylmö, B. 1953. Transpiration and ion absorption. Physiol. Plant 6: 333.
29. Hylmö, B. 1955. Passive components in the ion absorption of the plant. I. The zonal ion and water absorption in Brouwer's experiments. Physiol. Plant 8: 433.
30. Jenny, H., and R. Overstreet. 1939. Cation interchange between plant roots and soil colloids. Soil Sci. 47: 257.
31. Jenny, H. 1951. Contact phenomena between absorbents and their significance in plant nutrition. pp. 107–132. *In* E. Truog (ed.), Mineral nutrition of plants. University of Wisconsin Press, Madison, Wisc.

32. Knauss, H. J., and J. W. Porter. 1954. The absorption of inorganic ions by *Chlorella pyrenoidosa*. Plant Physiol. 29: 229.
33. Koontz, H., and O. Biddulph. Factors regulating absorption and translocation of foliar applied phosphorus. Plant Physiol. 32: 463.
34. Kramer, P. J. 1956. Relative amounts of mineral absorption through various regions of roots. U. S. Atomic Energy Commission Report TID-7512. 287–295.
35. Kylin, A., and B. Hylmö. 1957. Uptake and transport of sulfate in wheat. Active and passive components. Physiol. Plant 10: 467.
36. Leggett, J. E., and E. Epstein. 1956. Kinetics of sulfate absorption by barley roots. Plant Physiol. 31: 222.
37. Levitt, J. 1957. The significance of "Apparent Free Space" (AFS) in ion absorption. Physiol. Plant 10: 882.
38. Lopushinsky, W. 1964. Effect of water movement on ion movement into the xylem of tomato roots. Plant Physiol. 39: 494.
39. Lundegårdh, H. 1950. The translocation of salts and water through wheat roots. Physiol. Plant 3: 103.
40. Lundegårdh, H. 1954. Anion respiration. The experimental basis of a theory of absorption, transport and exudation of electrolytes by living cells and tissues. Symp. Soc. Exptl. Biol. 8: 262.
41. Lundegårdh, H., and H. Burström. 1933. Untersuchungen über die Salzaufnahme der Pflanzen. III. Quantitative Beziehungen zwischen Atmung und Anionenaufnahme. Biochem. Z. 261: 235.
42. Mason, T. G., and E. J. Maskell. 1931. Preliminary observations on the transport of phosphorus, potassium, and calcium. Ann. Botany 45: 126.
43. Mason, T. G., E. J. Maskell, and E. Phillis. 1936. Concerning the independence of solute movement in the phloem. Ann. Botany 50: 23.
44. Olsen, C. 1942. Water culture experiments with higher green plants in nutrient solutions having different concentrations of calcium. C. r. Trav. Labor. Carlsberg, Sér. chim. 24: 69.
45. Overstreet, R., L. Jacobson, and R. Handley. 1952. The effect of calcium on the absorption of potassium by barley roots. Plant Physiol. 27: 583.
46. Pfeffer, W. 1900. The mechanism of absorption and translocation. pp. 86–175 (Chapter 4) *In* The physiology of plants. Translated and edited by A. J. Ewart. Vol. I. Oxford University Press, London.
47. Phillis, E., and T. G. Mason. 1940. The effect of ringing on the upward movement of solutes from the roots. Ann. Botany 4: 635.
48. Rediske, J. H., and O. Biddulph. 1953. The absorption and translocation of iron. Plant Physiol. 28: 576.
49. Rees, W. J. 1949. The salt relations of plant tissues. IV. Some observations on the effect of the preparation of storage tissue on its subsequent absorption of manganese chloride. Ann. Botany 13: 29.
50. Robertson, R. N. 1958. The uptake of minerals. *In* W. Ruhland (ed.), Encyclopedia of plant physiology. Springer, Berlin. 4: 243.
51. Robertson, R. N., M. J. Wilkins, and D. C. Weeks. 1951. Studies in the

metabolism of plant cells. IX. The effects of 2,4-dinitrophenol on salt accumulation and salt respiration. Australian J. Sci. Res. B4: 248.
52. Russell, R. S., and D. A. Barber. 1960. The relationship between salt uptake and the absorption of water by intact plants. Ann. Rev. Plant Physiol. 11: 127.
53. Steward, F. C. 1935. Mineral nutrition of plants. Ann. Rev. Biochem. 4: 519.
54. Steward, F. C., and J. F. Sutcliffe. 1959. Plants in relation to inorganic salts. *In* F. C. Steward (ed.), Plant physiology. Academic Press, New York. 2: 253.
55. Stout, P. R., and D. R. Hoagland. 1939. Upward and lateral movement of salt in certain plants as indicated by radioactive isotopes of potassium, sodium and phosphorus absorbed by roots. Am. J. Botan. 26: 320.
56. Sutcliffe, J. F. 1962. Mineral salts absorption in plants. Pergamon Press, New York.
57. Viets, F. G. 1944. Calcium and other polyvalent cations as accelerators of ion accumulation by excised barley roots. Plant Physiol. 19: 466.

15

Functions of the essential mineral elements and symptoms of mineral deficiency

INTRODUCTION

In the previous two chapters, we discussed the occurrence, availability, absorption, and translocation of the essential mineral elements. We have studiously avoided any mention of the different roles played by the mineral elements in the growth and development of the plant, and the deficiency symptoms that might accrue from a shortage of these elements in the culture medium. It is the author's opinion that these two aspects of mineral nutrition are best discussed together, since deficiency symptoms occur as a result of some essential function being retarded by the lack of some element necessary for that function.

NITROGEN

Function of nitrogen

Perhaps nitrogen's most important role in the plant is its presence in the structure of the protein molecule. In addition, nitrogen is found in such important molecules as *purines, pyrimidines, porphyrines,* and *coenzymes.* Purines and pyrimidines are found in the nucleic acids, RNA and DNA, essential for protein synthesis. The porphyrin structure is found in such metabolically important compounds as the chlorophylls and the cytochrome enzymes, essential in photosynthesis and respiration. Coenzymes are essential to the function of many enzymes. Other compounds in the plant contain nitrogen (e.g., some vitamins), but since the above mentioned molecules are of extreme importance to the general welfare of the plant, they are given more specific consideration.

Nitrogen deficiency symptoms

The most easily observed symptom of nitrogen deficiency is the yellowing (chlorosis) of leaves due to a drop in chlorophyll content. This symptom is usually noticed first in the more mature leaves and last in the upper, more actively growing leaves. The nitrogen deficiency symptoms appear last in the younger leaves because of the high mobility of nitrogen in the plant. The younger leaves retain their nitrogen and, in addition, obtain nitrogen translocated from older leaves. Under severe conditions of nitrogen deficiency, the lowermost leaves on plants such as tobacco or bean will be dry and yellow and, in many cases, abscise. Under these conditions, the topmost leaves are generally pale green in color.

One interesting characteristic of nitrogen deficiency found in many plants is the production of pigments other than chlorophyll when nitrogen is lacking. For example, in tomato plants a purple coloring of the leaf petioles and veins caused by *anthocyanin* formation may be observed. This response to nitrogen deficiency may also be observed on the stems of many plants.

If a plant is supplied high concentrations of nitrogen, there is a tendency to increased leaf cell number and cell size with an overall increase in leaf production (56, 50). One can assume from the above observations and from the fact that nitrogen is an essential constituent of protein, that low nitrogen availability must cause a decrease in protein synthesis, which subsequently causes a decrease in cell size and especially cell division. A decrease in leaf epidermal cell size due to nitrogen deficiency in millet and buckwheat has been noted by Lutman (45).

PHOSPHORUS

Function of phosphorus

Phosphorus is found in plants as a constituent of *nucleic acids, phospholipids,* the *coenzymes NAD and NADP,* and, most important, as a constituent of *ATP*. Phosphorus is found, of course, in other compounds of the plant, but these are considered most important. Heavy concentrations of phosphorus are found in the meristematic regions of actively growing plants, where it is involved in the synthesis of nucleoproteins. For example, not only is phosphorus found in the nucleic acid moiety of the nucleoprotein molecule, but it is also involved, through ATP, in the activation of amino acids for the synthesis of the protein moiety of this compound. It is thought that phospholipids, along with protein, may be important constituents of cell membranes. The coenzymes NAD and NADP are important in oxidation-reduction reactions in which hydrogen transfer takes place. Such important plant processes as *photosynthesis, glycolysis, respiration,* and *fatty acid synthesis,* to name a few, are dependent upon the action of these coenzymes. The significance of ATP as an energy transfer compound has been treated elsewhere in this book. Suffice it to say, there is no question as to the essentiality of phosphorus to the plant.

Phosphorus deficiency symptoms

Many of the symptoms of phosphorus deficiency can be confused with nitrogen deficiency. Also, the symptoms are not as pronounced as those found for nitrogen. Similar to nitrogen, phosphorus deficiency may cause premature leaf fall and purple or red anthocyanin pigmentation. Unlike nitrogen, plants lacking phosphorus may develop dead necrotic areas on the leaves, petioles, or fruits; they may have a general overall stunted appearance, and the leaves may have a characteristic dark to blue-green coloration. Because of the high mobility of phosphorus in the plant and because of the tendency of younger leaves to deplete older leaves of mobile elements under deficiency conditions, the older leaves are usually the first to exhibit deficiency symptoms. Symptoms of zinc and phosphorus deficiencies may sometimes be confused. For example, lack of either one of these elements may cause a distortion in the shape of the leaves of some plants (30).

Anatomical studies by Lyon and Garcia (46) on the stems of phosphorus-deficient tomato plants produced some interesting observations. Generally, they found large amounts of pith and small amounts of vascular tissue. Central pith cells had disintegrated, and those that remained were large, succulent, and thin-walled with abnormally large intercellular spaces. Phloem and xylem elements were thin-walled, and development of these vascular tissues was at a minimum.

A series of papers by Eaton (13, 14, 16) on phosphorus deficiency in sunflower, soybean, and black mustard demonstrated that a deficiency of this element causes an accumulation of carbohydrates.

CALCIUM

Function of calcium

One well-known role played by calcium in the plant is its function as a constituent of cell walls in the form of *calcium pectate*. The middle lamella of plant cell walls is composed primarily of calcium and magnesium pectates. The partial removal of calcium from the middle lamella with ethylenediamine tetraacetic acid (EDTA), a chelating agent, stimulates growth of the *Avena coleoptile* (4). It has been assumed that this stimulation is a result of increased plasticity caused by the removal of pectate-bound calcium. However, it may also be caused by an increase in cell permeability because of removal of calcium.

It is thought that calcium is important in the formation of cell membranes and lipid structures. For example, the calcium salt of lecithin, a lipid compound, may be involved in the formation or organization of cell membranes (30). Also, it has been noted that calcium in small amounts is necessary for normal mitosis. In this respect, Hewitt (30) has suggested that calcium may be involved in chromatin or mitotic spindle organization. Abnormal mitosis may also develop because of an effect of calcium deficiency on chromosome structure and stability. This suggestion is supported by the close correlation between calcium deficiency and chromosome abnormalities (33, 67, 68, 18) and by the suggestion that nucleoprotein particles are held together by divalent cations (48). A possible role for calcium as an activator of the enzyme phospholipase in cabbage leaves has been investigated (8). In addition to the above mentioned enzyme, calcium may be an activator for the enzymes arginine kinase, adenosine triphosphatase, adenyl kinase, and potato apyrase (49).

Florell (20, 21) found that the number of mitochondria in wheat roots is reduced under calcium-deficiency conditions. Calcium deficiency in cotton plants results in increased levels of carbohydrates in the leaves and decreased levels in the stems and roots (37). Joham (37) interprets this as a decrease in carbohydrate translocation due to calcium deficiency, an effect similar to that found in boron-deficient plants.

Calcium deficiency

The easily observed symptoms of calcium deficiency are quite striking. Meristematic regions found at stem, leaf, and root tips are greatly affected and eventually die, thus terminating growth in these organs. Roots may become short, stubby, and brown as in calcium-deficient tomato plants (38). Chlorosis generally occurs along the margins of younger leaves, these areas usually becoming necrotic. Malformation or distortion of the younger leaves is also characteristic of calcium-deficient plants, a hooking of the leaf tip being the most easily detected symptom. Deficiency symptoms generally appear first in the younger leaves and the growing apices, probably as a consequence of the immobility of calcium in the plant.

Cell walls may become rigid or brittle in calcium-deficient plants (38, 9). A study of calcium deficiency in *Pinus taeda* by Davis (9) demonstrated that cell enlargement, vacuolation, and differentiation occur closer to the shoot apex in deficient plants than in normal plants, an observation more recently made in tomato root tips by Kalra (38). Vacuolation of cells occurring closer to the root apex of calcium-deficient rape and buckwheat plants was also observed by Lutman (45).

MAGNESIUM

Function of magnesium

Two very essential roles played by magnesium in the plant may be found in the important processes *photosynthesis* and *carbohydrate metabolism*. Magnesium is a constituent of the chlorophyll molecule without which photosynthesis would not occur. Many of the enzymes involved in carbohydrate metabolism require magnesium as an activator. Generally, ATP is also involved in these reactions (Table 15-1). Magnesium is also an activator for those enzymes involved in the synthesis of the nucleic acids (DNA, RNA) from nucleotide polyphosphates. Both the reactions mentioned above and those requiring magnesium in carbohydrate metabolism involve *phosphate transfer*. It has been suggested that magnesium may participate in this type of group transfer as an intermediate carrier (54). In this respect, Calvin (7) has stressed that coenzymes, such as ATP or ADP, could become linked to the enzyme surface through a chelate complex involving the enzyme magnesium and the pyrophosphate group (Figure 15-1). In many cases, manganese can partially substitute for magnesium as an activator in the above enzyme systems.

Another possible function of magnesium has been postulated by T'so et al. (69). Microsomal particles containing RNA, protein, and magnesium

Table 15-1 Some of the enzymes involved in carbohydrate metabolism which require Mg^{2+} as an activator.

Enzyme	*Reaction*
glucokinase	glucose + ATP → glucose-6-P
fructokinase	fructose + ATP → fructose-1-P
galactokinase	galactose + ATP → galactose-1-P
hexokinase	hexose + ATP → hexose-6-P
triosekinase	glyceraldehyde + ATP → phosphoglyceraldehyde
gluconolactonase	6-phosphogluconolacton → 6-phosphogluconate
6-phosphogluconic dehydrogenase	6-phosphogluconate → ribulose-5-P
phosphopentokinase	ribulose-5-P + ATP → ribulose-1,5-diP
enolase	2-phosphoglycerate + ATP → phosphoenolpyruvate
pyruvic kinase	phosphoenolpyruvate + ADP → pyruvate
carboxylase	pyruvate → acetaldehyde
phosphoglyceric kinase	1,3-diphosphoglycerate + ADP → 3-phosphoglycerate

were isolated from homogenates of pea seedlings by the above investigators. Treatment of the particles with the chelating agent EDTA caused their dissociation into subunits. It was suggested that magnesium may bind these subunits together and dissociation caused by EDTA may be because of the removal of the magnesium ion from the microsomal particle by the chelating agent. If the above postulation is true, magnesium may be assigned two roles in protein synthesis: (1) an activator in some of the enzyme systems involved in the synthesis of nucleic acids and (2) an important binding agent in microsomal particles where protein synthesis takes place.

Figure 15-1 Chelate complex involving the pyrophosphate group of ADP (or ATP), magnesium, and an enzyme. (Redrawn from A. Nason and W. D. McElroy. 1963. *In* F. C. Steward (ed.), Plant physiology. Academic Press, New York. 3: 451.)

Magnesium deficiency symptoms

Since magnesium is a constituent of the chlorophyll molecule, the most common symptom of magnesium deficiency in green plants is extensive interveinal chlorosis of the leaves. Yellowing is apparent first in the basal leaves, and as the deficiency becomes more acute, eventually reaches the younger leaves. The base to tip order of appearance of deficiency symptoms indicates that magnesium, like nitrogen and phosphorus, is mobile in the plant. Chlorosis is often followed by the appearance of anthocyanin pigments in the leaves. At a more acute stage in the deficiency, that is, following chlorosis and pigmentation, necrotic spotting may be observed.

Anatomical studies by Lyon and Garcia (46) of tomato plants that were provided with an abundant or deficient supply of magnesium resulted in some interesting observations. An abundant supply of magnesium caused to some extent a depression of internal phloem development and an increase in the size of parenchymatous cells adjacent to the endodermis. Under low magnesium conditions, more extensive chlorenchyma development was observed, the cells being smaller but greater in number and rather densely packed with chloroplasts. Also smaller pith cells were observed under deficient conditions.

POTASSIUM

Function of potassium

Although a deficiency in potassium may affect such varied processes as respiration, photosynthesis, chlorophyll development, and water content of leaves, a specific role for potassium in plants is, as yet, unknown (54). The highest concentrations of potassium are found in the meristematic regions of the plant (54), an observation that seems in keeping with the findings of Webster (72, 74, 73) that potassium is essential as an activator for enzymes involved in the synthesis of certain peptide bonds. The accumulation of carbohydrates, often observed during the early stages of potassium deficiency, may be due to impaired protein synthesis (16). That is, the carbon skeletons that would normally go into protein synthesis are accumulated as carbohydrates. In addition to its role as an activator in protein metabolism, potassium also can act as an activator for several enzymes involved in carbohydrate metabolism.

Apical dominance in several plants appears to be lacking or weak under potassium-deficient conditions (30). This may be caused by damage to the apical bud as a result of potassium deficiency.

Potassium deficiency symptoms

The external symptoms of potassium deficiency are easily recognized on the leaves of the plant. A mottled chlorosis first occurs, followed by the development of necrotic areas at the tip and margin of the leaf. Because of the mobility of potassium, these symptoms generally appear first on the more mature leaves. Also, in many cases, there is a tendency for the leaf tip to curve downward and, as in the case of the French bean and potato, marginal regions may roll inward toward the upper surface (30). Generally, a plant deficient in potassium is stunted in growth with a pronounced shortening of the internodes.

Potassium deficiency in tomato plants causes disintegration of pith cells and results in an increase in the differentiation of secondary phloem parenchyma into sieve tubes and companion cells (47).

SULFUR

Function of sulfur

The content of sulfur in plants varies considerably and may reach a very high concentration in the brassicaceous plants (members of the cabbage tribe of the mustard family) (25). Its most obvious function is its participation in protein structure in the form of the sulfur-bearing amino acids cystine, cysteine, and methionine. Sulfur is taken up by the plant as the sulfate ion (SO_4^{2-}) and is subsequently reduced via an activation step involving the compound 3′-phosphoadenosine-5′-phosphosulfate (PAPS) and ATP.

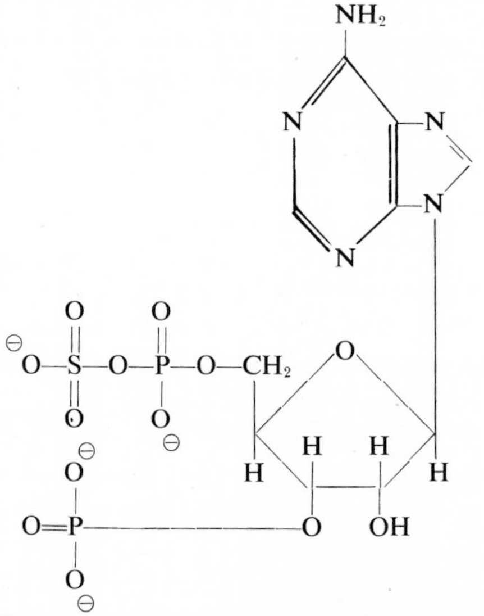

3′-Phosphoadenosine-5′-phosphosulfate (PAPS)

PAPS, first described by Robbins and Lipmann (61), is synthesized in two distinct steps, an activation of sulfate by ATP and the enzyme sulfurylase to form adenosine-5′-phosphosulfate (APS), followed by the conversion of APS to PAPS by a specific kinase (61, 3).

$$SO_4^{2-} + ATP \xrightarrow[Mg^{2+}?]{\text{Sulfurylase}} APS + P{-}P$$

$$APS + ATP \xrightarrow[Mg^{2+}?]{\text{Kinase}} PAPS + ADP$$

The activated sulfate is eventually reduced and incorporated into cystine, cysteine, and methionine and finally into the protein structure.

When speaking of the function of sulfur in the plant, one must not forget the sulfur-bearing vitamins *biotin, thiamine,* and *coenzyme A*. Thus, the function of sulfur is, in part, involved in the metabolic activities of these vitamins. Another function of sulfur may be found in sulfhydryl groups, which are present in many enzymes and, in many cases, are necessary for enzyme activity. Also sulfur cross links in the protein molecule supplement peptide and hydrogen bonding in stabilizing protein structure.

Sulfur deficiency symptoms

The visible symptoms of sulfur deficiency resemble somewhat those of nitrogen deficiency. As in nitrogen-deficient plants, there is a general chlorosis, followed by the production of anthocyanin pigments in some species (15). Unlike nitrogen deficiency, sulfur-deficient plants show chlorosis of the younger leaves first. Under severe conditions, however, all of the leaves may undergo some loss of green color (25).

In a series of studies of sulfur deficiency in tomato, sunflower, black mustard, and soybean, Eaton (10, 11, 12, 15) found that starch, sucrose, and soluble nitrogen were accumulated under deficiency conditions, but that reducing sugars were lower than normal. Eaton suggested that the increase in soluble nitrogen resulted from protein synthesis being inhibited and proteolytic activity being increased.

IRON

Function of iron

Iron has a number of important functions in the overall metabolism of the plant. Although iron is frequently taken up in the ferric state (Fe^{3+}), it is generally accepted that the *ferrous* state (Fe^{2+}) is the metabolically active form of iron in the plant. Although it appears to be essential for the synthesis of chlorophyll, its chemical role both in the synthesis and degradation of chlorophyll is still uncertain (54). Several authors are of the opinion that iron functions in the synthesis of chloroplastic protein and may in this way impair the machinery for chlorophyll synthesis (22). In a previous chapter we discussed the synthesis of chlorophyll and pointed out protoporphyrin-9 as one of the intermediates in this biosynthesis. Granick (27) is of the opinion that this compound represents a focal point in the biosynthesis of both cytochromes and chlorophyll and that the synthetic path taken is dependent upon what metal, magnesium or iron, is incorporated into the porphyrin structure. In a more recent investigation, it was found that the addition of iron to iron-deficient *Euglena* cells considerably increases the rate of chlorophyll synthesis (59) (Figure 15-2).

Iron has been identified as a component of various flavoproteins (metalloflavoproteins) active in biological oxidations. Iron is also found in the

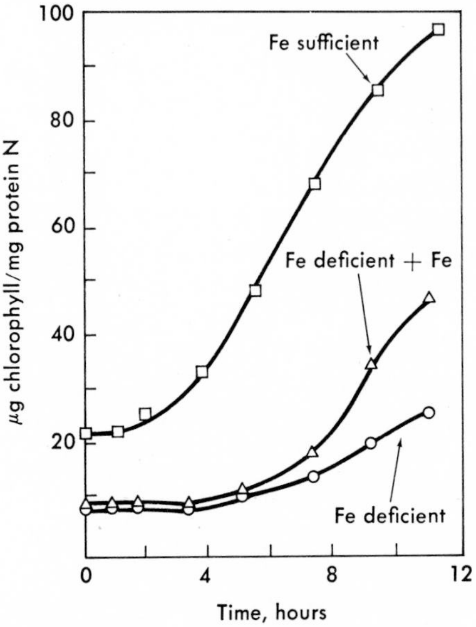

Figure 15-2 Time course of chlorophyll synthesis. Cells grown under low (50 ft – c) light intensity with $3 \times 10^{-5}M$ iron (□) and low iron ($1.8 \times 10^{-7}M$) (○,△). After harvest the cells were resuspended in $10^{-3}M$ phosphate buffer, pH 6, with (△) and without (○) $3 \times 10^{-5}M$ iron added and incubated under high light intensity; samples taken at various intervals for chlorophyll analysis. (After C. A. Price and E. F. Carell. 1964. Plant Physiol. 39: 862.)

iron-porphyrin proteins, which include cytochromes, peroxidases, and catalases. The description and function of these enzymes are discussed in another section of this book.

Iron deficiency symptoms

The most easily observed symptom of iron deficiency in plants is extensive chlorosis in the leaves. Generally, the younger leaves are most affected, the most mature leaves sometimes showing no chlorosis at all. Primarily, this is because of the relative immobility of iron in the plant. Thus, the younger leaves cannot withdraw iron from the older leaves. One feature of iron-induced chlorosis is its characteristic interveinal nature, the surface of the leaf usually showing a fine reticulate network of green veins setting off chloratic areas. Total chlorosis of the younger leaves is rare. However, secondary and tertiary veins may undergo chlorosis under severe deficiency conditions.

Several attempts have been made to find a good correlation between iron deficiency and chlorophyll content. However, only limited success has been achieved with this line of investigation. For example, some workers have found a good correlation between iron and chlorophyll content (35, 66, 71), while on the other hand, some investigators have found that the chlorotic leaves may contain as much and even more iron than their normal counterparts (43, 34, 75). Jacobson and Oertli (36), in a study of iron deficiency in sunflower, found that good correlation may be achieved if iron is supplied at a uniform rate. However, if a plant is subjected to a brief period of iron deficiency and then supplied adequate iron, a correlation between chlorophyll and iron does not exist, probably because of an enhanced iron uptake. The above authors found that chlorosis is incompletely reversible in sunflower leaves. Thus, if a chlorotic plant is restored to a normal iron supply, the chlorotic leaves of that plant are likely to accumulate as much or more iron than would be found under normal conditions. Jacobson and Oertli (36) have proposed that lack of iron may inhibit formation of the chloroplasts through inhibition of protein synthesis, a fact that might explain incomplete recovery from chlorosis.

MANGANESE

Function of manganese

It appears that manganese is an essential factor in *respiration* and *nitrogen metabolism;* in both processes it functions as an *enzyme activator*. However, in many cases, especially with reactions in respiration, manganese can be replaced by other divalent cations, such as Mg^{2+}, Co^{2+}, Zn^{2+}, and Fe^{2+}. The most frequent replacement of manganese is by magnesium. Manganese appears to be essential, however, for some reactions in the metabolism of the plant. For example, malic dehydrogenase, an enzyme of the Krebs cycle, requires manganese as an activator. Another enzyme of the Krebs cycle, oxalosuccinic decarboxylase, requires the presence of manganese as an activator, although in this case, the manganese requirement may be partially substituted for by cobalt. From the very extensive work done on the enzymes of the Krebs cycle, one can draw the conclusion that manganese is the predominant metal ion of Krebs cycle reactions.

That manganese plays an important role in nitrate reduction has been known for some time (6). More recently, however, this role has been clarified to some extent. Manganese acts as an activator for the enzymes nitrite reductase and hydroxylamine reductase (63, 52). The preference of ammonia over nitrate as a nitrogen source by manganese-deficient cells (54) supports the above-mentioned role of manganese. Manganese is also thought to be involved in the destruction or oxidation of indole-3-acetic acid (IAA), a natural auxin of plants (26, 40).

A decrease in the rate of photosynthesis in algae at an early stage of manganese deficiency suggests a direct role for manganese in photosynthesis (76). According to Eyster et al. (19), the sensitivity of chlorophyll to light destruction increases under conditions of manganese deficiency, leading ultimately to chlorosis in *Chlorella pyrenoidosa*. They also found that the Hill reaction was suppressed under deficiency conditions. It appears from work on the alga *Ankistrodesmus braunii* that the site of manganese activity is in the oxygen-producing step in photosynthesis (41, 42). Photoreduction in photosynthesis is not impaired by manganese deficiency.

Manganese deficiency symptoms

Manganese deficiency is characterized by the appearance of chlorotic and necrotic spots in the interveinal areas of the leaf. These symptoms may appear first on the young leaves of some species, while on other species they may appear first on the older leaves. A brown necrosis of the cotyledons of pea and bean seeds may also be observed (57, 29). Manganese deficiency also appears to have a marked effect on the chloroplast. Eltinge (17) found that the chloroplasts of tomato leaves are the first part of the plant affected by manganese deficiency. The chloroplasts lose chlorophyll and starch grains, becoming yellow-green in color, vacuolated, and granular and finally disintegrating.

COPPER

Function of copper

There is little doubt as to the necessity of copper for normal plant metabolism. Copper acts as a component of phenolases, laccase, and ascorbic acid oxidase, and its role as a part of these enzymes probably represents the most important function of copper in plants (54). Work by Neish (55) and Green et al. (28) suggested that copper may function in photosynthesis. For example, Neish found that the chloroplasts of clover contain most of the copper of the plant. Green and his associates found that the rate of photosynthesis by *Chlorella pyrenoidosa* could be decreased by adding to the culture medium organic compounds capable of forming complexes with copper. In addition, Loustalot et al. (44) found that CO_2 absorption is decreased in copper-deficient tung trees.

Copper deficiency symptoms

The most easily recognized symptoms of copper deficiency are those found in a disease of fruit trees called "exanthema" and a condition known as "reclamation" found in cereals and leguminous plants. A description of these afflictions does not serve the purpose of this book. However, it may be said that copper deficiency generally causes a necrosis of the tip of young leaves that proceeds along the margin of the leaf, giving it a withered appearance. Under more severe conditions, the leaves may be lost, and the whole plant may appear wilted.

ZINC

Function of zinc

Zinc is involved in the biosynthesis of the plant auxin *indole-3-acetic acid* (IAA). Skoog (65) observed that there is a marked decrease in auxin content of zinc-deficient tomato plants, while on addition of zinc to the deficient plants, there is a significant increase in the IAA content. Both of these responses (increase and decrease in auxin content) precede growth response to the absence or addition of zinc, suggesting that deficiency symptoms could, in part, be associated with the decrease in the plant auxin concentration. In later work, it was observed that the content of *tryptophan* parallels the content of auxin in the plant, both when zinc is deficient and when it is supplied to deficient plants. It was concluded that zinc reduces auxin content through its involvement in the synthesis of tryptophan, a precursor of auxin (70). In support of this hypothesis, Nason (51) found that the activity of the enzyme tryptophan synthetase is low in zinc-deficient *Neurospora*. This enzyme catalyzes the reaction of serine with indole to form tryptophan.

Zinc participates in the metabolism of plants as an activator of several enzymes. Carbonic anhydrase was the first zinc-containing enzyme to be discovered (39). This enzyme catalyzes the decomposition of carbonic acid to carbon dioxide and water. Other enzymes dependent on the presence of zinc are alcohol dehydrogenase and pyridine nucleotide dehydrogenases (53, 32). An accumulation of inorganic phosphorus in zinc-deficient tomato plants (60) suggests that zinc may act as an activator for some phosphate-transferring enzyme, such as hexose kinase or triose-phosphate dehydrogenase. Another striking characteristic of zinc deficiency is the accumulation of soluble nitrogen compounds, such as amino acids and amides (58). One can assume from this observation that zinc must play an important role in protein synthesis.

Zinc deficiency symptoms

Generally, the first sign of zinc deficiency is an interveinal chlorosis of the older leaves, starting at the tips and margins. White necrotic spotting soon follows as in cotton (5). Smaller leaves and shortened internodes, resulting in stunted growth, are characteristic of more severe zinc deficiency. Perhaps the most easily recognized symptom of zinc deficiency is the distorted appearance of the plant leaves. They are generally smaller in size, distorted in shape, and twisted in appearance and may be clustered on short branches known as *rosettes*. The effect of zinc deficiency on leaves is sometimes referred to as "little leaf" disease. The absence of zinc also may have an adverse effect on the production of seeds in beans and peas and the development of fruit in citrus.

BORON

Function of boron

Although symptoms of boron deficiency are quite striking, its role in plant metabolism has not, as yet, been clarified. Gauch and Dugger (23, 24) have built a strong case for the involvement of boron in *carbohydrate transport* within the plant. They have drawn attention to the fact that the borate ion will complex readily with polyhydroxy compounds such as sugar. They propose that sugar is transported more readily across cell membranes as a borate complex. As an alternative proposal, they suggest that the borate ion may be associated with the cell membrane where it could complex with a sugar molecule and facilitate its passage across the membrane. Gauch and Dugger have also drawn attention to the fact that common features of boron deficiency in plants are the death of stem and root tips and the abscission of flowers, areas of the plant high in metabolic activity. They suggest that symptoms of boron deficiency are actually symptoms of sugar deficiency. Since areas of the plant that are high in metabolic activity also need higher quantities of sugar, these areas are the first to be affected under conditions of boron deficiency. The above-mentioned role of boron in sugar translocation has been strongly supported by experiments using C^{14}-labeled sucrose (64). These experiments showed that the uptake and translocation of sugar is retarded in boron-deficient plants. Photosynthesis in the presence of $C^{14}O_2$ also supports the Gauch and Dugger theory of boron-facilitated translocation of sugars (64). The translocation of labeled photosynthate is much less efficient in boron-deficient plants.

Although many roles for boron in plant metabolism have been submitted, its function in the translocation of sugar is the only one enjoying general acceptance. For example, boron has been implicated in cellular differentiation and development, in nitrogen metabolism, fertilization, active salt absorption, hormone metabolism, water relations, fat metabolism, phosphorus metabolism, and photosynthesis (54). However, convincing evidence of boron participation in these processes is still forthcoming. Indeed, one could say that all of the above processes could be indirectly affected by the effect of boron on sugar translocation.

Boron deficiency symptoms

The first visible symptom of boron deficiency is the death of the shoot tip. This usually causes the growth of lateral shoots, the tips of which also die. The leaves may have a thick coppery texture, sometimes curling and becoming quite brittle. Generally, flowers do not form and root growth is stunted. Storage or fleshy organs react in a striking manner to boron deficiency. A general disintegration of internal tissues results in abnormalities, such as heart rot of sugar beet, internal cork formation in apples, and water core in turnip.

MOLYBDENUM

Function of molybdenum

Molybdenum has long been implicated in gaseous nitrogen fixation and nitrate assimilation. The essential functions of molybdenum in nitrogen metabolism will be covered in the next chapter, which is devoted entirely to nitrogen metabolism.

Several investigators have observed that molybdenum deficiency always leads to a drop in the concentration of ascorbic acid in the plant (31, 1). Normal levels of ascorbic acid are restored on addition of molybdenum. Arnon (2) has suggested that ascorbic acid may have a protective role in the chloroplast. For example, isolated chloroplasts retain their phosphorlyating activity for a much longer time when washed with a 0.01*M* solution of ascorbic acid. Hewitt (30), citing unpublished work by Hewitt and Hucklesby, drew attention to the fact that chloroplast disorganization occurs with the appearance of "whiptail" symptoms, a common disease of molybdenum deficiency. There is also some evidence that molybdenum is involved in the phosphorus metabolism of the plant. However, the mechanism of action of molybdenum in phosphorus metabolism has not been explained.

Molybdenum deficiency symptoms

Visible symptoms of molybdenum deficiency may start with chlorotic interveinal mottling of the lower leaves, followed by marginal necrosis and infolding of the leaves. Under more severe conditions, mottled areas may become necrotic, causing the leaf to wilt. Flower formation is inhibited, and if flowers do form, they abscise before setting fruit.

One condition due to molybdenum deficiency, known as whiptail, is typically demonstrated in cauliflower plants. The leaves first show an interveinal mottling, and the leaf margins may become gray and flaccid and finally brown. The leaf tissues wither, leaving only the midrib and a few small pieces of leaf blade, giving the appearance of a whip or tail.

BIBLIOGRAPHY

1. Agarwala, S. C., and E. J. Hewitt. 1954. Molybdenum as a plant nutrient. IV. The interrelationships of molybdenum and nitrate supply in chlorophyll and ascorbic acid fractions in cauliflower plants grown in sand culture. J. Hort. Sci. 29: 291.
2. Arnon, D. I. 1959. Chloroplasts and photosynthesis. *In* The photochemical apparatus—its structure and function. 11: 181.
3. Bandurski, R. S., L. G. Wilson, C. L. Squires. 1956. The mechanism of "active sulfate" formation. J. Am. Chem. Soc. 78: 6408.
4. Bennet-Clark, T. A. 1956. Salt accumulation and mode of action of auxin; a preliminary hypothesis. *In* R. L. Wain and F. Wightman (eds.), Chemistry and mode of action of plant growth substances. Butterworths, London. 284–291.

5. Brown, L., and C. C. Wilson. 1952. Some effects of zinc on several species of *Gossypium* L. Plant Physiol. 27: 812.
6. Burström, H. 1939. Über die Schwermetallkatalyze der Nitratassimilation. Planta 29: 292.
7. Calvin, M. 1954. Chelation and catalysis. pp. 221–256 *In* W. D. McElroy and H. B. Glass (eds.), Mechanism of enzyme action. Johns Hopkins Press, Baltimore, Md.
8. Davidson, F. M., and C. M. Long. 1958. The structure of the naturally occurring phosphoglycerides. 4. Action of cabbage leaf phospholipase. Biochem. J. 69: 458.
9. Davis, D. E. 1949. Some effects of calcium deficiency on the anatomy of *Pinus taeda.* Am. J. Botan. 36: 276.
10. Eaton, S. V. 1935. Influence of sulfur deficiency on the metabolism of the soybean. Botan. Gaz. 97: 68.
11. Eaton, S. V. 1941. Influence of sulfur deficiency on metabolism of the sunflower. Botan. Gaz. 102: 533.
12. Eaton, S. V. 1942. Influence of sulfur deficiency on metabolism of black mustard. Botan. Gaz. 104: 306.
13. Eaton, S. V. 1949. Effects of phosphorus deficiency on growth and metabolism of sunflowers. Botan. Gaz. 110: 449.
14. Eaton, S. V. 1950. Effects of phosphorus deficiency on growth and metabolism of soybean. Botan. Gaz. 111: 426.
15. Eaton, S. V. 1951. Effects of sulfur deficiency on the growth and metabolism of the tomato. Botan. Gaz. 112: 300.
16. Eaton, S. V. 1952. Effects of phosphorus deficiency on growth and metabolism of black mustard. Botan. Gaz. 113: 301.
17. Eltinge, E. T. 1941. Effects of manganese deficiency upon the histology of *Lycopersicon esculentum*. Plant Physiol. 16: 189.
18. Eversole, R. A., and E. L. Tatum. 1956. Chemical alteration of crossing over frequency in *Chlamydomonas*. Proc. Natl. Acad. Sci. 42: 68.
19. Eyster, C., T. E. Brown, H. Tanner, and S. L. Hood. 1958. Manganese requirement with respect to growth, Hill reaction and photosynthesis. Plant Physiol. 33: 235.
20. Florell, C. 1956. The influence of calcium on root mitochondria. Physiol. Plant. 9: 236.
21. Florell, C. 1957. Calcium, mitochondria and anion uptake. Physiol. Plant 10: 781.
22. Gauch, H. G. 1957. Mineral nutrition of plants. Ann. Rev. Plant Physiol. 8: 31.
23. Gauch, H. G., and W. M. Dugger. 1953. The role of boron in the translocation of sucrose. Plant Physiol. 28: 457.
24. Gauch, H. G., and W. M. Dugger. 1954. The physiological role of boron in higher plants: a review and interpretation. Univ. Maryland Agr. Expt. Sta. Tech. Bull. A-80.
25. Gilbert, F. A. 1951. The place of sulfur in plant nutrition. Botan. Rev. 17: 671.

26. Goldacre, P. L. 1961. The indole-3-acetic acid oxidase-peroxidase of peas. pp. 143–147 *In* R. M. Klein (ed.), Plant growth regulation. Iowa State University Press, Ames, Iowa.
27. Granick, S. 1950. Iron metabolism in animals and plants. Harvey Lectures Ser. 44: 220.
28. Green, L. F., J. F. McCarthy, and C. G. King. 1939. Inhibition of respiration and photosynthesis in *Chlorella pyrenoidosa* by organic compounds that inhibit copper catalysis. J. Biol. Chem. 128: 447.
29. Hewitt, E. J. 1945. Marsh spot in beans. Nature 155: 22.
30. Hewitt, E. J. 1963. The essential nutrient elements: requirements and interactions in plants. *In* F. C. Steward (ed.), Plant physiology. Academic Press, New York. 3: 137.
31. Hewitt, E. J., S. C. Agarwala, and E. W. Jones. 1950. Effect of molybdenum status on the ascorbic acid content of plants in sand culture. Nature 166: 1119.
32. Hoch, F. L., and B. L. Vallee. 1958. The metabolic role of zinc. pp. 337–363 *In* C. A. Lamb, O. G. Bentley, and J. M. Beattie, (eds.), Trace elements. Academic Press, New York.
33. Hyde, B. B., and R. L. Paliwal. 1958. Studies on the role of cations in the structure and behaviour of plant chromosomes. Am. J. Botan. 45: 433.
34. Iljin, W. S. 1952. Metabolism of plants affected with lime-induced chlorosis (calciose). III. Mineral elements. Plant Soil 4: 11.
35. Jacobson, L. 1945. Iron in the leaves and chloroplasts of some plants in relation to chlorophyll content. Plant Physiol. 20: 233.
36. Jacobson, L., and J. J. Oertli. 1956. The relation between iron and chlorophyll contents in chlorotic sunflower leaves. Plant Physiol. 31: 199.
37. Joham, H. E. 1957. Carbohydrate distribution as affected by calcium deficiency in cotton. Plant Physiol. 32: 113.
38. Kalra, G. S. 1956. Responses of the tomato plant to calcium deficiency. Botan. Gaz. 118: 18.
39. Keilin, D., and T. Mann. 1940. Carbonic anhydrase. Biochem. J. 34: 1163.
40. Kenten, R. H. 1955. The oxidation of indole-3-acetic acid by waxpod bean root sap and peroxidase systems. Biochem. J. 59: 110.
41. Kessler, E. 1955. On the role of manganese in the oxygen-evolving system in photosynthesis. Arch. Biochem. Biophys. 59: 527.
42. Kessler, E., W. Arthur, and J. E. Brugger. 1957. The influence of manganese and phosphate on delayed light emission, fluorescence, photoreduction and photosynthesis in algae. Arch. Biochem. Biophys. 71: 326.
43. Lindner, R. C., and C. P. Harley. 1944. Nutrient interrelations in lime-induced chlorosis. Plant Physiol. 19: 420.
44. Loustalot, A. J., F. W. Burrows, S. G. Gilbert, and A. Nason. 1945. Effect of copper and zinc deficiencies on the photosynthesis activity of the foliage of young tung trees. Plant Physiol. 20: 283.
45. Lutman, B. F. 1934. Cell size and structure in plants as affected by inorganic elements. Univ. Vermont Agr. Expt. Sta. Bull. 383.

46. Lyon, C., and C. R. Garcia. 1944. Anatomical responses of tomato stems to variations in the macronutrient anion supply. Botan. Gaz. 105: 394.
47. Lyon, C., and C. R. Garcia. 1944. Anatomical responses of tomato stems to variations in the macronutrient cation supply. Botan. Gaz. 105: 441.
48. Mazia, D. 1954. The particulate organization of the chromosome. Proc. Natl. Acad. Sci. 40: 521.
49. McElroy, W. D., and A. Nason. 1954. Mechanism of action of micronutrient elements in enzyme systems. Ann. Rev. Plant Physiol. 5: 1.
50. Morton, A. G., and D. J. Watson. 1948. A physiological study of leaf growth. Ann. Botan. 12: 281.
51. Nason, A. 1950. Effect of zinc deficiency on the synthesis of tryptophane by *Neurospora* extracts. Science 112: 111.
52. Nason, A. 1956. Enzymatic steps in the assimilation of nitrate and nitrite in fungi and green plants. pp. 109–136 *In* W. D. McElroy and H. B. Glass (eds.), Inorganic nitrogen metabolism. Johns Hopkins Press, Baltimore, Md.
53. Nason, A., N. O. Kaplan, and H. A. Oldewurtel. 1953. Further studies of nutritional conditions affecting enzymatic constitution in *Neurospora.* J. Biol. Chem. 201: 435.
54. Nason, A., and W. D. McElroy. 1963. Modes of action of the essential mineral elements. *In* F. C. Steward (ed.), Plant physiology. Academic Press, New York. 3: 451.
55. Neish, A. C. 1939. Studies on chloroplasts. II. Their chemical composition and the distribution of certain metabolites between the chloroplasts and the remainder of the leaf. Biochem. J. 33: 300.
56. Njoku, E. 1957. The effect of mineral nutrition and temperature on leaf shape in *Ipomoea caerulea.* New Phytologist 56: 154.
57. Piper, C. S. 1942. Investigations on copper deficiency in plants. J. Agr. Sci. 32: 143.
58. Possingham, J. V. 1956. The effect of mineral nutrition on the content of free amino acids and amides in tomato plants. I. A comparison of effects of deficiencies of copper, zinc, manganese, iron and molybdenum. Australian. Biol. Sci. 9: 539.
59. Price, C. A., and E. F. Carell. 1964. Control by iron of chlorophyll formation and growth in *Euglena graciles.* Plant Physiol. 39: 862.
60. Reed, H. S. 1946. Effects of zinc deficiency on phosphate metabolism of the tomato plant. Am. J. Botan. 33: 778.
61. Robbins, P. W., and F. Lipmann. 1956. Identification of enzymatically active sulfate as adenosine-3′-phosphate-5′-phosphosulfate. J. Am. Chem. Soc. 78: 2652.
62. Robbins, P. W., and F. Lipmann. 1956. The enzymatic sequence in the biosynthesis of active sulfate. J. Am. Chem. Soc. 78: 6409.
63. Sadana, J. C., and W. D. McElroy. 1957. Nitrate reductase from *Achromobacter fischeri.* Purification and properties: function of flavines and cytochrome. Arch. Biochem. Biophys. 67: 16.

64. Sisler, E. C., W. M. Dugger, and H. G. Gauch. 1956. The role of boron in the translocation of organic compounds in plants. Plant Physiol. 31: 11.
65. Skoog, F. 1940. Relationships between zinc and auxin in the growth of higher plants. Am. J. Botan. 27: 939.
66. Smith, P. F., W. Reuther, and A. W. Specht. 1950. Mineral composition of chlorotic orange leaves and some observations on the relation of sample preparation technique to the interpretation of results. Plant Physiol. 25: 496.
67. Steffensen, D. 1953. Induction of chromosome breakage at meiosis by a magnesium deficiency in *Tradescantia*. Proc. Natl. Acad. Sci. 39: 613.
68. Steffensen, D. 1955. Breakage of chromosomes in *Tradescantia* with a calcium deficiency. Proc. Natl. Acad. Sci. 41: 155.
69. T'so, P. O. P., J. Bonner, and J. Vinograd. 1957. Physical and chemical properties of microsomal particles from pea seedlings. Plant Physiol. Suppl. 32: XII.
70. Tsui, C. 1948. The role of zinc in auxin synthesis in the tomato plant. Am. J. Botan. 35: 172.
71. Wallihan, E. F. 1955. Relation of chlorosis to concentration of iron in citrus leaves. Am. J. Botan. 42: 101.
72. Webster, G. C. 1953. Peptide bond synthesis in higher plants. I. Arch. Biochem. Biophys. 47: 241.
73. Webster, G. C. 1956. Effect of monovalent ions on the incorporation of amino acids into protein. Biochem. Biophys. Acta 20: 565.
74. Webster, G. C., and J. E. Varner. 1954. Mechanism of enzymatic synthesis of gamma-glutamyl-cysteine. Federation Proc. 13: 1049.
75. Weinstein, L. H., E. R. Purvis, A. N. Meiss, and R. L. Uhler. 1954. Absorption and translocation of ethylenediamine tetraacetic acid by sunflower plants. J. Agr. Food Chem. 2: 421.
76. Wiessner, W. 1962. Inorganic micronutrients. pp. 267–286 *In* R. A. Lewin (ed.), Physiology and biochemistry of algae. Academic Press, New York.

16
Nitrogen metabolism

INTRODUCTION

We will devote one chapter to the discussion of nitrogen metabolism—yet one chapter is a small allotment when one considers the complexity and importance of this subject. With the exception of carbon, hydrogen, and oxygen, nitrogen is the most prevalent element in the living organism and is found in such essential compounds as proteins, nucleic acids, some of the plant growth regulators, and in many of the vitamins. As a component of these and many other compounds, nitrogen is involved in most, if not all, of the biochemical reactions that compose life.

The large quantities of nitrogen present in the plant, the importance of nitrogen in the structure and metabolism of the plant, and the need of the plant for a continuous supply of nitrogen dramatically point out one of nature's most paradoxical situations. Since nitrogen composes 80% of the earth's atmosphere, the plant world may literally be said to be submerged in a sea of nitrogen, yet nitrogen in this form is *unavailable* to most plants. Indeed, nitrogen is one of the most inert elements, requiring excessive temperatures and pressures in order to react with other elements or compounds. Although some forms of combined or fixed nitrogen may be contributed to the soil without the participation of living organisms (e.g., nitrogen oxides produced through electric discharge during lightning storms), a much greater quantity is fixed through the mediation of soil microorganisms. What, then, are the forms of nitrogen available to the plant, and how is atmospheric or molecular nitrogen converted to these forms? In the following pages we will discuss the forms and absorption of available nitrogen, the incorporation of reduced nitrogen into keto acids to form amino acids, the synthesis of protein, and finally the degradation of protein and amino acids.

NITROGEN NUTRITION

With the exception of those species capable of fixing molecular nitrogen, most plants absorb nitrogen in a fixed form from the soil. The forms of nitrogen available to the plant may be divided into four groups: *nitrate nitrogen, ammonia nitrogen, organic nitrogen,* and *molecular nitrogen.* Very few plants (certain bacteria and algae) are capable of utilizing all four forms of nitrogen (38). Although most plants utilize the nitrate form of nitrogen, several plants can assimilate ammonia and certain forms of organic nitrogen. The utilization of molecular nitrogen is confined to a certain few groups found in the lower forms of plant life. However, the list of plant species capable of utilizing molecular nitrogen is growing every day.

Nitrate and ammonia nitrogen

The roots of most higher plants absorb nitrogen from the soil in the form of nitrate (NO_3^-). Nitrogen in this form, however, is not directly used by the plant, but must be reduced to ammonia before it may be incorporated into the nitrogenous compounds of the plant. The reduction of nitrate to ammonia requires the energy of respiration. Thus, the carbohydrates of the plant not only provide the carbon skeletons needed for the incorporation of ammonia but also provide, through their breakdown in respiration, the energy needed for nitrate reduction. In this respect, many investigators have observed that under conditions of high nitrate reduction and assimilation in the dark, carbohydrate levels in the plant are significantly lowered. The lowering of carbohydrate levels under these conditions in the light is not as impressive because of the compensating effects of photosynthesis.

The relationship between the carbohydrate status of the plant and nitrate reduction and assimilation is diagrammatically shown in Figure 16-1.

Through work with bacteria and fungi, as well as higher plant parts,

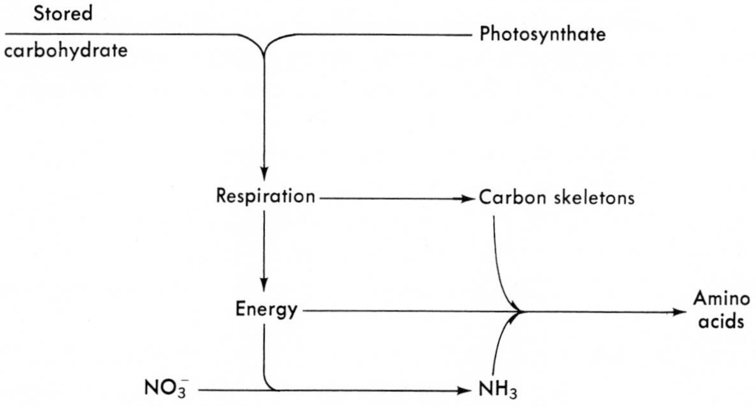

Figure 16-1 The relation between the carbohydrate status of the plant and nitrate reduction and assimilation.

several intermediates in nitrate reduction to ammonia have been identified. It is assumed that the first step in nitrate reduction is the conversion of nitrate to *nitrite* (NO_2^-). This assumption has been strongly supported by the identification of nitrite in plant tissues and by the isolation of an enzyme capable of catalyzing this reduction, *nitrate reductase,* from soybean leaves and *Neurospora* (8, 20). Since the formation of nitrite requires the transfer of two electrons to nitrate, it was thought that the next intermediate should be a compound requiring the transfer of two electrons to nitrite. *Hyponitrite* (HNO) qualifies for this position, although it has never been identified in plant tissue. Support for the participation of hyponitrite as an intermediate in nitrate reduction has been found in enzyme studies. Enzyme systems, which presumably include *nitrite reductase,* have been prepared from both *Neurospora* and soybean leaves that are capable of catalyzing the reduction of nitrite to ammonia (20). Subsequent investigations have shown that hyponitrite is a product of nitrite reduction (19). Finally, Frear (11) has shown that plant preparations are capable of reducing labeled hyponitrite to *ammonia.* Verhoeven (32) has suggested that hyponitrite has not been detected because of its great instability, causing its conversion to other compounds as quickly as it is formed.

In agreement with the two electron transfer concept, hydroxylamine (NH_2OH) has been proposed as the next compound in the sequence of intermediates leading from nitrate to ammonia. Hydroxylamine has been shown to be formed in both the higher and lower forms of plant life. For example, an enzyme has been found in *Neurospora* that will catalyze the conversion of hyponitrite to hydroxylamine (19). The final step in our sequence is the conversion of *hydroxylamine* to ammonia, a step also requiring the addition of two electrons. The enzyme catalyzing this reaction, *hydroxylamine reductase,* has been found in *Neurospora* (49) and in higher plants (11). The above-discussed sequence in the reduction of nitrate to ammonia proceeds as follows (the oxidation number for each compound is given under the formula name of that compound):

NO_3 →	NO_2 →	HNO →	NH_2OH →	NH_3
Nitrate	Nitrite	Hyponitrite	Hydroxylamine	Ammonia
+5	+3	+1	−1	−3

Because of the widespread occurrence in plants of the above intermediates (with the exception of hyponitrite) and the detection of enzymes in different plant tissues that catalyze their reduction, it is thought that this inorganic sequence is an important pathway for nitrate reduction in plants. Whether or not nitrogen has to be reduced to the ammonia level before reacting with organic compounds of the plant still needs to be determined. However, evidence has accumulated indicating that the nitrogen of hydroxylamine may be taken up in some organic compounds before its reduction to ammonia.

If we assume that nitrate must be reduced to ammonia before nitrogen can enter the metabolic system, then we should observe a more rapid assimilation of nitrogen when ammonia instead of nitrate is utilized as a nitrogen source. Quite a number of investigations have shown that ammonia assimilation is indeed rapid compared to nitrate assimilation. Healthy plants with an adequate supply of respirable carbohydrates will incorporate ammonia nitrogen so fast into the metabolic system that even during periods of high nitrogen uptake only traces of free ammonium may be found in the plant tissues (27). In contrast, free nitrate may be found at relatively high amounts in the plant tissues. As with nitrate reduction and assimilation, ammonia assimilation is dependent, in part, upon the carbohydrate status of the plant. Because of the rapid assimilation of ammonia, however, the carbohydrate supplies of a plant utilizing ammonia as a sole nitrogen source may be depleted to a dangerously low point (30, 21, 23). For example, with the tomato plant a soft, succulent, nonfruitful, highly vegetative growth may result as a consequence of a high depletion of carbohydrate.

Nitrate reductase. A discussion of the enzyme activity involved in each step of nitrate reduction is beyond the scope of this book. However, since an impressive amount of information has accumulated about the enzyme nitrate reductase, we will briefly discuss the nature of this enzyme and the cofactors involved in the reaction it catalyzes.

Nitrate reductase is a metalloflavoprotein that catalyzes the reduction of nitrate to nitrite and has been isolated in a highly purified form from soybean leaves and *Neurospora* (8, 20). The enzyme system includes a reduced pyridine nucleotide (NADPH or NADH) as an electron donor, flavin adenine dinucleotide (FAD) as a prosthetic group, and molybdenum as an activator. Electrons are passed from reduced pyridine nucleotide to FAD, giving reduced FAD ($FADH_2$). The electrons are, in turn, passed from $FADH_2$ to oxidized molybdenum, resulting in reduced molybdenum, which in turn passes electrons to nitrate, reducing it to nitrite (21, 22) (Figure 16-2).

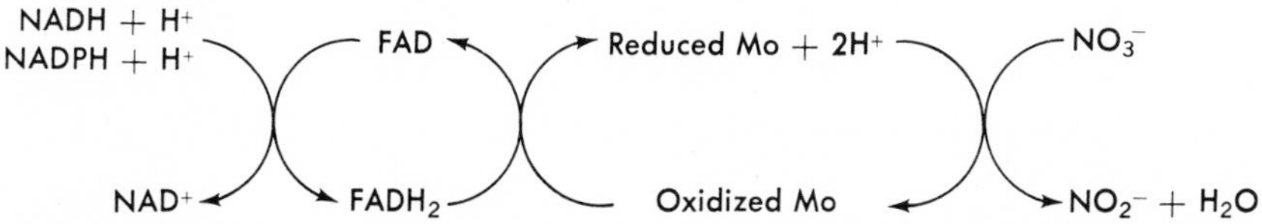

Figure 16-2 The sequence of electron transport in nitrate reduction catalyzed by nitrate reductase. (After D. J. D. Nicholas and A. Nason. 1955. Plant Physiol. 30: 135.)

In summary, then, nitrate reductase is a metalloflavoprotein that catalyzes the reduction of nitrate. This reduction involves a stepwise transfer of electrons from reduced pyridine nucleotide to nitrate. FAD and molybdenum act as intermediate electron carriers in this transfer.

Organic nitrogen

Many plants are capable of using organic as well as inorganic nitrogen as a nitrogen source for growth. Many of the amino acids and amides will provide available nitrogen for plant growth. Also, urea provides a good source of organic nitrogen. With a possible few exceptions, these compounds are the only organic nitrogen compounds capable of providing available nitrogen in the quantities needed to support normal plant growth. Much of the soil nitrogen is bound in organic form, primarily as proteins. The breakdown of proteins releases free amino acids, which may either be oxidized, releasing their nitrogen in the form of ammonium, which is usually oxidized to nitrate before being absorbed by the plant, or the amino acids may be used directly by the plant. Many of the soil microorganisms can readily assimilate amino acids and compete with higher plants for this nitrogen source.

Amino acid assimilation by intact plants has had only limited attention. However, a good deal of work has been done on the assimilation of amino acids by plant tissues grown in aseptic cultures. Early work by White (40) demonstrated that certain amino acids can act as nitrogen sources for the growth of excised tomato roots. Since White's pioneer work, the uptake of amino acids by various plant tissue has been demonstrated.

Foliar application of urea ($NH_2\text{—}\overset{\overset{\textstyle O}{\|}}{C}\text{—}NH_2$) has proved to be a very effective method of relieving nitrogen shortages in many plants (39, 16). It is thought that the first step in the utilization of urea nitrogen is the rapid hydrolysis of urea by the enzyme urease to yield ammonia and carbon dioxide (16).

$$NH_2\text{—}\overset{\overset{\textstyle O}{\|}}{C}\text{—}NH_2 \xrightarrow{\text{urease}} 2NH_3 + CO_2$$

This conclusion has been supported by the work of Webster et al. (39). They incubated young bean leaves with C^{14}-labeled urea ($NH_2\text{—}\underset{\underset{\textstyle O}{\|}}{C^{14}}\text{—}NH_2$) and C^{14}-labeled sodium carbonate ($NaHC^{14}O_3$) and found that the carbon of urea and the carbon of sodium carbonate have similar patterns of incorporation into amino acids. This strongly suggests that urea is hydrolyzed to ammonia and carbon dioxide before its nitrogen is incorporated into the organic compounds of the plant.

The above scheme for utilization of urea nitrogen does not appear to have universal acceptance. For example, the enzyme urease could not be detected in *Chlorella pyrenoidosa* or *Chlorella ellipsoidea* (36, 15). It has, therefore, been suggested by several authors that urea might in some cases be assimilated directly without prior hydrolysis to ammonia and carbon dioxide. One possible route for the incorporation of the intact urea molecule would be its condensation with ornithine (an amino acid) to form the amino acid arginine (4, 15, 36). However, convincing evidence for this pathway of urea incorporation still needs to be demonstrated.

Molecular nitrogen

By far, the most abundant supply of nitrogen on earth is that found in the atmosphere in molecular form. However, only a relatively few plants are capable of assimilating or "fixing" this plentiful supply of nitrogen, and these are confined to the lower plant forms such as certain groups of bacteria and blue-green algae. Although higher plants are not able to utilize molecular nitrogen directly, some are able to utilize gaseous nitrogen indirectly through the mediation of microorganisms in the soil. The direct use of molecular nitrogen is termed *asymbiotic* nitrogen fixation, and the indirect use of molecular nitrogen, *symbiotic* nitrogen fixation. We will discuss them in that order.

Asymbiotic nitrogen fixation. Nitrogen fixation by living organisms was recognized in the latter half of the nineteenth century. Jodin, in 1862, was able to determine a loss of atmospheric nitrogen and oxygen in a closed system containing a nonsterile solution and a source of carbon. In 1885, Berthelot demonstrated that the content of fixed nitrogen in nonsterile soil samples could be shown, by chemical analysis, to increase over a period of time. However, credit for actually showing that a living organism is involved in nitrogen fixation must be given to Winogradsky who, in 1894, isolated the nitrogen-fixing anaerobic bacterium *Clostridium pastorianum.*

Not long after the isolation of *C. pastorianum* by Winogradsky, two other even more important free-living, nitrogen-fixing organisms were isolated by Beijerinck in 1901. In contrast to the anaerobic *C. pastorianum,* the two bacteria isolated by Beijerinck, *Azotobacter chroococcum* and *Azotobacter agile,* are aerobic. Since that time, several nitrogen-fixing species of *Azotobacter* have been found. We will discuss briefly the requirements, inhibition, and biochemistry of molecular nitrogen fixation.

(a) *Environmental conditions.* Other than those environmental 'conditions necessary for good growth, the process of nitrogen fixation places no special requirements on the organism. One possible exception to this statement may be found in the quantities of certain mineral elements needed for the most efficient nitrogen fixation. It has been established by many workers that the elements molybdenum, iron, and calcium are required in higher quantities when molecular nitrogen rather than ammonia nitrogen is used, suggesting their participation in the nitrogen-fixing process. The effects of different concentrations of these three elements on the growth of *Azotobacter vinelandii* are shown in Figure 16-3 and Table 16-1.

Table 16-1 Requirement of molybdenum for molecular nitrogen fixation by *Azotobacter vinelandii.* All values are given as μg fixed N per millimeter.[a]

	N_2		NH_4^+	
Experiment	*With Mo*	*Without Mo*	*With Mo*	*Without Mo*
I	205	50	201	200
II	212	58	279	301

[a] After Esposito (1955), as reported by P. W. Wilson. 1958. *In* W. Ruhland (ed.), Encyclopedia of plant physiology. Springer, Berlin 8:9.

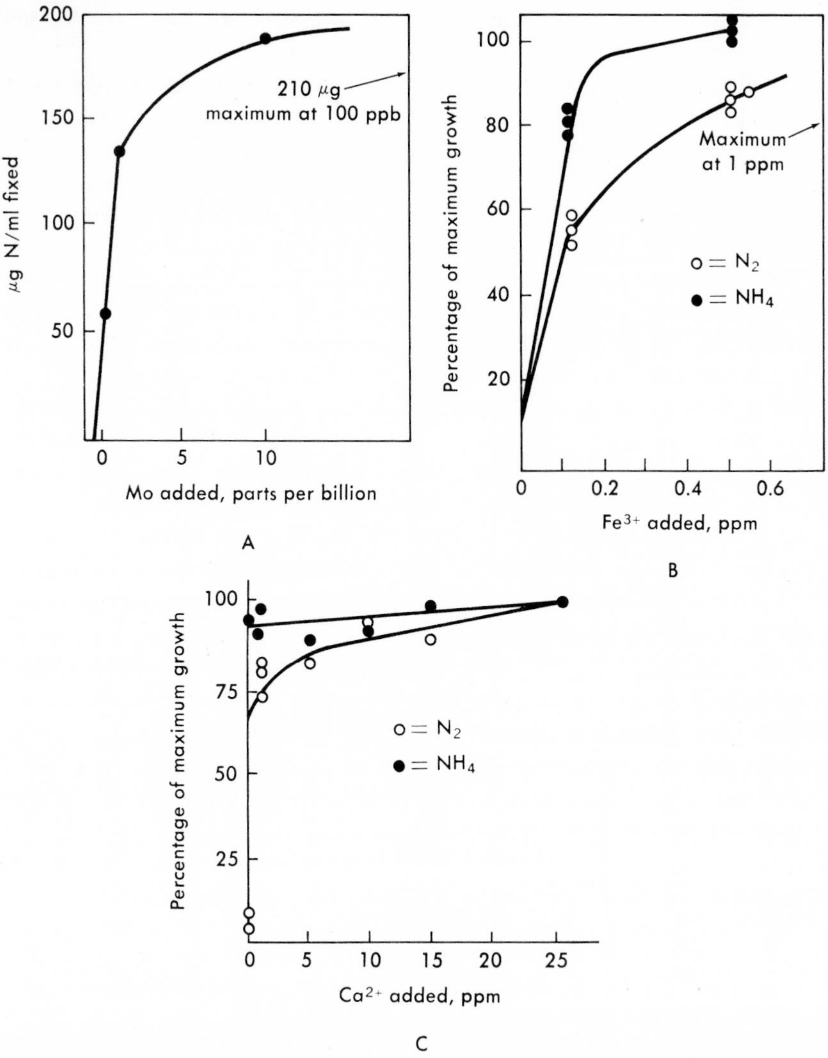

Figure 16-3 Effect of (A) Mo, (B) Fe^{3+}, and (C) Ca^{2+} on growth of *Azotobacter vinelandii.* Note that the elements molybdenum, iron, and calcium are required in higher quantities when molecular nitrogen rather than ammonia nitrogen is used. (After Esposito, 1955. Redrawn from P. W. Wilson. *In* W. Ruhland (ed.), Encyclopedia of plant physiology. Springer, Berlin 8:9.)

The most extensive work on the requirements of higher levels of molybdenum, iron, and calcium for nitrogen fixation has been done with molybdenum. Wilson (43) has pointed out that a requirement for molybdenum has been determined for every nitrogen-fixing organism studied. However, convincing evidence for the actual participation of molybdenum in the mechanism of nitrogen fixation has not been established (26).

(b) *Inhibition of nitrogen fixation.* Inhibition of nitrogen fixation may be conveniently separated into three general situations: (1) inhibition of cellular metabolism, (2) inhibition with molecular hydrogen, and (3) inhibition with combined nitrogen. Since healthy growth is associated with nitrogen fixation, it is not surprising that inhibitors of cellular metabolism also inhibit nitrogen fixation. A special case can be made for carbon monoxide (CO), an inhibitor of respiration. It appears that nitrogen fixation is far more sensitive to carbon monoxide poisoning than is respiration (44). This observation suggests that carbon monoxide may inhibit nitrogen fixation directly rather than indirectly through respiration.

Unlike carbon monoxide, molecular hydrogen acts as a specific inhibitor of nitrogen fixation. We mean by this that inhibition is only observed when the sole source of nitrogen is molecular nitrogen not when other forms of combined nitrogen are fed (45, 46). Two explanations for this inhibition have been suggested: (1) hydrogen may compete physically with nitrogen for an active site on the surface of some enzyme involved in nitrogen fixation, or (2) inhibition may be related to the function of the enzyme *hydrogenase* in nitrogen fixation.

The second explanation has received the most attention, since there is a good deal of indirect evidence linking hydrogenase, an enzyme using molecular hydrogen as a substrate, with nitrogen fixation. For example, the hydrogenase content of *Azotobacter* and *Rhodospirillum* increases considerably when these organisms are fed molecular nitrogen instead of combined nitrogen (18, 12).

Generally, the fixation of nitrogen is inhibited by ammonia or compounds easily converted to ammonia, such as nitrate and nitrite. These compounds do not interfere with the mechanism of nitrogen fixation, but merely are preferred over molecular nitrogen as nitrogen sources. In other words, if both molecular nitrogen and combined nitrogen are present, the combined nitrogen will be used in preference to the gaseous nitrogen. However, both forms of nitrogen may be used simultaneously and generally are.

(c) *Pathway of nitrogen fixation.* Our knowledge of the pathway of nitrogen fixation is still rather meager. Experiments employing the radioactive isotope N^{15} have shown beyond doubt, however, that ammonia occupies a key position in this pathway. The question of what intermediates are present between molecular nitrogen and ammonia has been difficult to answer. Webster (38) has pointed out that the initial step in nitrogen fixation may be an oxidation, reduction, or hydrolysis of the nitrogen molecule. Oxidation of nitrogen might yield nitrous oxide (N_2O) or nitrous dioxide (N_2O_2); reduction could yield hydrazine ($H_2N—NH_2$), and hydrolysis could yield, as an intermediate product, HO—NH—NH—OH. No matter what the initial reaction may be, oxidation, reduction, or hydrolysis of the nitrogen molecule, most investigations have shown that the intermediates formed are ultimately reduced to the ammonia level before entering the metabolic system (Figure 16-4).

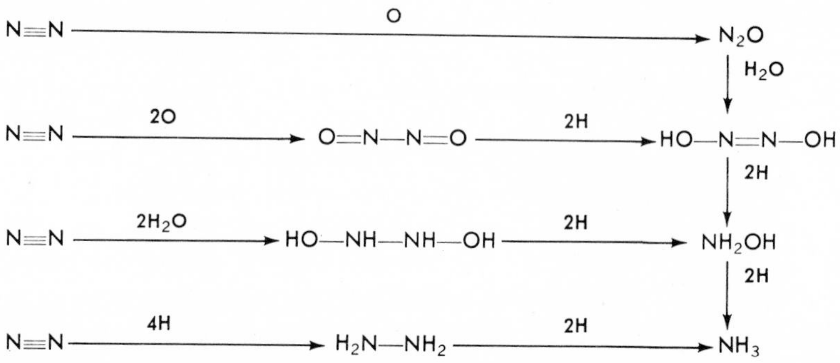

Figure 16-4 Various possible pathways of nitrogen fixation. (After *Nitrogen Metabolism in Plants* by George C. Webster (Row, Peterson, 1959). Used by permission of Harper & Row Publishers.)

Symbiotic nitrogen fixation. A relatively large group of plants, the legumes, are capable of fixing atmospheric nitrogen through a symbiotic association with soil bacteria of the genus *Rhizobium*. Neither organism alone is able to fix nitrogen. The actual site of nitrogen fixation is in the nodules formed on the roots of the legume plant as a result of the penetration of *Rhizobium* (Figure 16-5).

Aside from the actual symbiotic fixation of nitrogen, the penetration of these bacteria and the resulting stimulation of root cell growth is an interesting aspect of this association. The accumulation of soil bacteria in the vicinity of plant roots, especially roots of legume plants, is a common observance. This is most likely because of the excretion of certain growth factors into the soil by the plant roots. The bacteria, then, either penetrate the relatively soft root hair tip or invade damaged or broken root hairs and progress in an "infection thread" through the cortex tissue to the immediate area of the endosperm and pericycle. Cell divisions commence in this area, and the nodule grows rapidly, pushing its way to the surface of the root. One rather remarkable observation, first made by Wipf and Cooper (47),

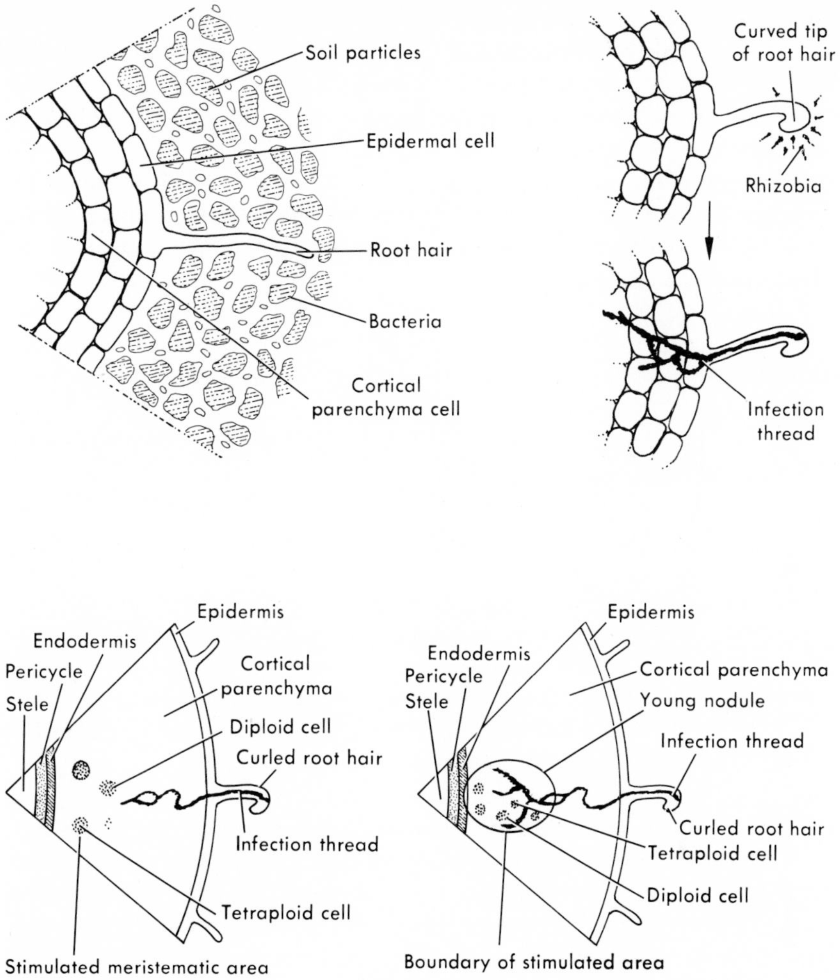

Figure 16-5 Penetration of *Rhizobia* into the root hair of a legume plant. Note that the root hair curls at the tip, an infection thread is formed, and finally, a nodule forms. (After P. W. Wilson. 1940. The biochemistry of symbiotic fixation. University of Wisconsin Press, Madison, Wisc.)

is that the nodule cells contain double the number of chromosomes found in the normal somatic cells of the plant. Wipf and Cooper (48), in a later study of nodule formation in pea and vetch, showed that successful nodule formation only occurs when the root nodule bacteria invade cells containing double the normal somatic compliment of chromosomes. These cells are stimulated into meristematic activity by the invasion and form the nodule. If there are no cells with double the normal chromosome number in the area of the root penetrated by the infection thread, no nodule will form.

The factor or factors causing the profuse growth of the cells that form the nodules is at present unknown. The fact that *Rhizobium* are known to produce the plant hormone indole acetic acid (IAA) led Thimann (29) to suggest it as the stimulant. This theory has enjoyed only limited acceptance, due primarily to the fact that many other soil microorganisms are able to produce IAA, but are not able to cause nodule formation. However, recent work by Tanner and Anderson (28) supports the IAA theory. They suggested that the well-known inhibition of nodule formation by combined nitrogen may be caused, in part, by the effect of combined nitrogen in reducing the formation of IAA by *Rhizobium*.

(a) *Hemoglobin of nodules.* The dissection of a root nodule will reveal the presence of a red pigment that is remarkably similar in properties to the hemoglobin of red blood cells. The red pigment of the nodules is appropriately called hemoglobin and appears to be a product of the *Rhizobium*-legume complex since the pigment is not present in either organism cultured alone (1). Data from investigations of several workers have strongly suggested that the hemoglobin of nodules is involved in nitrogen fixation. The facts that nodules lacking hemoglobin are unable to fix nitrogen and that a correlation between hemoglobin concentration and rate of nitrogen fixation is apparent from numerous investigations (34) bring one to the conclusion that hemoglobin and symbiotic nitrogen fixation are intimately involved. Figure 16-6 illustrates the agreement between hemoglobin content and nitrogen content during different stages of growth of soybean.

(b) *Transfer of fixed nitrogen to the host plant.* Although it is not specifically known how the transfer of symbiotically fixed nitrogen from the nodule to the host plant takes place, it is generally thought that either lysis of the bacterial cells occurs, releasing soluble nitrogenous compounds into the cytoplasm of the root cell, or the bacterial cells excrete soluble nitrogenous products into the cytoplasm of the root cell. It is rather difficult to ascertain which theory is correct, or if both situations occur. Whatever the method of release of fixed nitrogen, efficient transfer of this nitrogen is assured by the radial differentiation of vascular tissues connecting the nodule with the main vascular strands of the host plant.

Nitrogen converters in the soil

Oxidation of ammonia to nitrate in the soil may occur through the mediation of two groups of bacteria, *Nitrosomonas* and *Nitrobacter*. The energy needed for the growth of these organisms is obtained through the oxidation

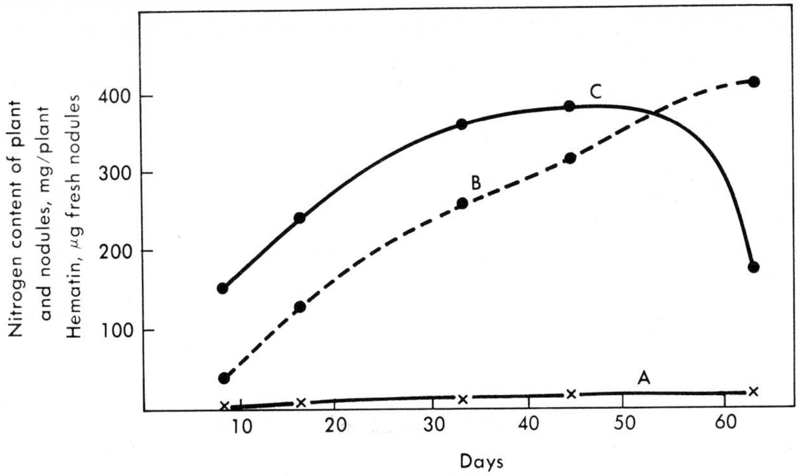

Figure 16-6 Nitrogen content of plant and hematin content of nodules at different stages of growth of soybean. A. Nitrogen in nodules, milligrams per plant. B. Nitrogen, milligrams per total plant minus nodules. C. Hematin, micrograms per gram fresh nodules. (After A. I. Virtanen et al. 1947. Acta Chem. Scand. 1: 861. Redrawn from A. I. Virtanen and J. K. Miettinen. 1963. *In* Plant physiology. Academic Press, New York. 3: 539.)

of ammonia or of nitrite. In other words, *Nitrosomonas* and *Nitrobacter* are *autotrophic* bacteria requiring only inorganic materials for growth. With only one major difference, this type of growth is similar to that found in green plants. In green plants, light provides the energy for growth, while with the bacteria of nitrification, oxidation of ammonia or of nitrite provides this energy. Both of these organisms were isolated in 1891 by Winogradsky. He demonstrated that *Nitrosomonas* could convert ammonia only as far as nitrite and that *Nitrobacter* was needed for the further conversion of nitrite to nitrate. The conversion of ammonia to nitrite and then to nitrate is called *nitrification.*

$$NH_4^+ \xrightarrow{\text{Nitrosomonas}} NO_2^- \xrightarrow{\text{Nitrobacter}} NO_3^-$$

The conversion of nitrate to nitrous oxide (N_2O) and nitrogen gas also takes place through the mediation of a wide variety of soil organisms. This process is known as *denitrification.* The process of denitrification, which ends in the release of nitrogen gas to the atmosphere, completes nature's complex nitrogen cycle. Small amounts of fixed nitrogen are contributed to the soil from electrically produced nitrogen oxides, which are washed down from the atmosphere during rain storms. Much greater amounts of fixed nitrogen are contributed by the molecular nitrogen-fixing organisms. The fixed nitrogen is taken up by plants and converted to the many different organic nitrogen compounds of the plant. This organic nitrogen also contributes to the nitrogen development of animals, which are unable to convert inorganic nitrogen to the organic nitrogen and must, therefore, ingest preformed organic nitrogen compounds as essential components of their diet. As a result of death, the organic nitrogen of animals and plants is eventually returned to the soil where, through microbial decomposition, ammonia is produced. The ammonia is rapidly converted to nitrate by the process of nitrification. Nitrate is then either available to the plant or converted to nitrogen gas in the process of denitrification. An outline of this cycle is shown in Figure 16-7.

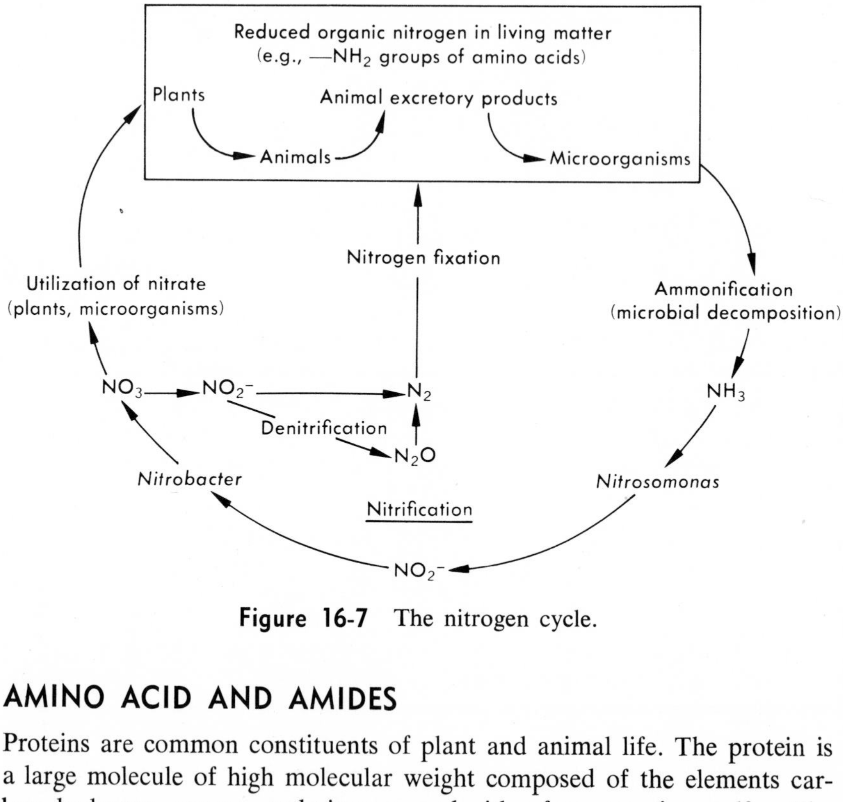

Figure 16-7 The nitrogen cycle.

AMINO ACID AND AMIDES

Proteins are common constituents of plant and animal life. The protein is a large molecule of high molecular weight composed of the elements carbon, hydrogen, oxygen, and nitrogen, and with a few exceptions sulfur. The acid hydrolysis of the protein molecule reveals that it is composed of smaller repeating units called amino acids. With the exception of two secondary amino acids, the amino acids found in protein have the following general structure.

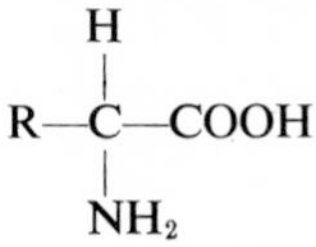

This structure depicts a primary amino acid in which the amino group (—NH_2) is attached to the carbon (α-carbon) adjacent to the carboxyl group (—COOH). Individual differences between the primary amino acids are found in the R group, which may be quite different from one amino acid to the next. For example, the three amino acids glycine, valine, and leucine have R groups that are quite different. The structures for these amino acids are given with the R groups circled.

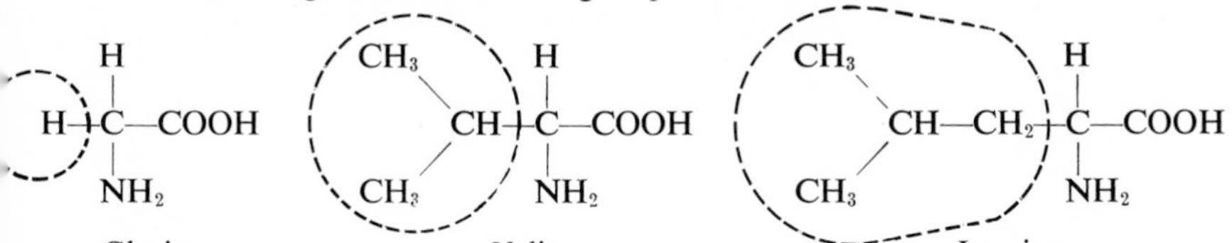

Glycine Valine Leucine

The amino acids found in plant protein as a result of extensive investigations by numerous workers are *glycine, alanine, valine, leucine, isoleucine, serine, threonine, phenylalanine, tyrosine, tryptophan, cystine, cysteine, methionine, proline, hydroxyproline, aspartic acid, glutamic acid, histidine, arginine,* and *lysine*. The structures of these amino acids are shown in Table 16-2.

Amino acid synthesis

Amino acids are generally considered to be the initial products of nitrogen assimilation. Evidence obtained by following the assimilation of inorganic nutrients containing N^{15} has shown that, in most cases, the initial recipients of the nitrogen of these compounds are the free α-keto acids in the cytoplasm. The α-keto acid is similar to the amino acid with the exception of an oxygen attached to the α-carbon instead of an amino group. We will discuss two ways by which nitrogen can be incorporated into α-keto acids.

Reductive amination. Experiments with radioactive nitrogen have shown that during the early stages of nitrogen assimilation, *glutamate* is by far the most labeled compound. Confronted with this evidence, the investigator is very likely to conclude that there is a direct incorporation of ammonia into *α-ketoglutarate,* the corresponding keto acid of glutamate. The reaction is reversible and proceeds as shown on page 378.

Table 16-2

Name	*Formula*	*Type*
glycine	$NH_2—CH_2—COOH$	aliphatic
alanine	$CH_3—CH(NH_2)—COOH$	aliphatic
valine	$(CH_3)_2CH—CH(NH_2)—COOH$	aliphatic
leucine	$(CH_3)_2CH—CH_2—CH(NH_2)—COOH$	aliphatic
isoleucine	$CH_3—CH_2—CH(CH_3)—CH(NH_2)—COOH$	aliphatic
serine	$CH_2(OH)—CH(NH_2)—COOH$	aliphatic
threonine	$CH_3—CH(OH)—CH(NH_2)—COOH$	aliphatic
phenylalanine	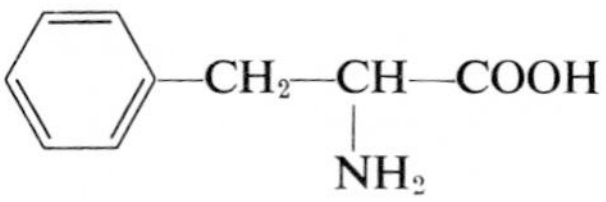	aromatic
tyrosine	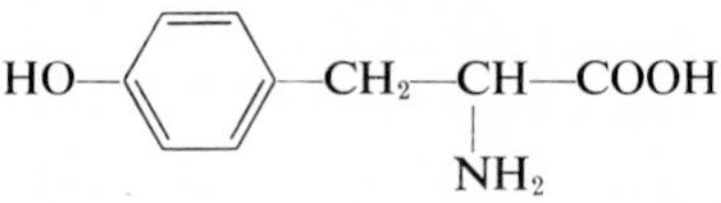	aromatic
tryptophan	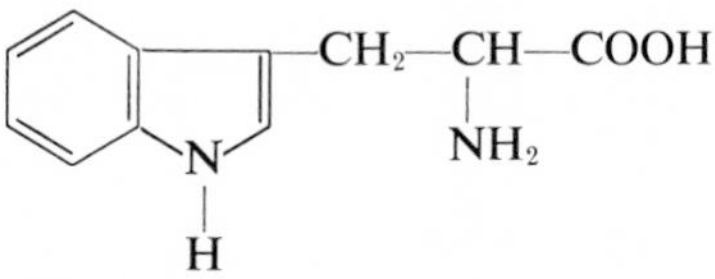	aromatic

Table 16-2 *(continued)*

Name	*Formula*	*Type*
cystine	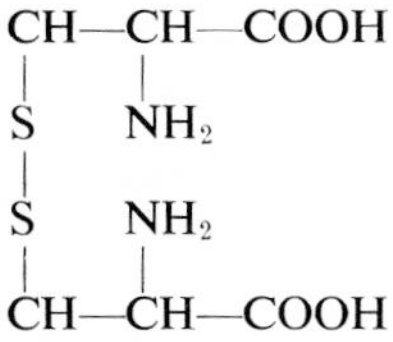	S-containing amino acids
cysteine	$HS—CH_2—CH(NH_2)—COOH$	S-containing amino acids
methionine	$CH_3—S—CH_2—CH_2—CH(NH_2)—COOH$	S-containing amino acids
proline	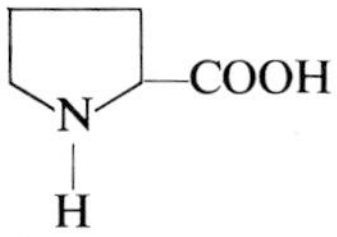	secondary amino acids
hydroxyproline	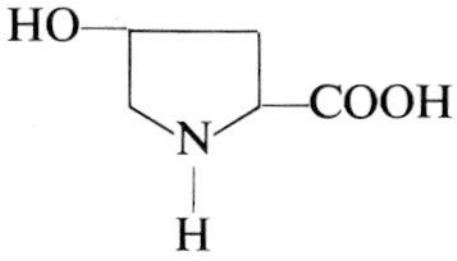	secondary amino acids
aspartic acid	$HOOC—CH_2—CH(NH_2)—COOH$	acidic amino acids
glutamic acid	$HOOC—CH_2—CH_2—CH(NH_2)—COOH$	acidic amino acids
histidine	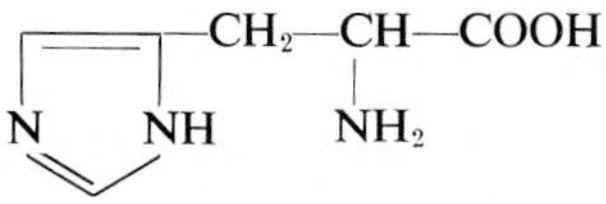	basic amino acid
arginine	$H_2N—C(=NH)—NH—CH_2—CH_2—CH_2—CH(NH_2)—COOH$	basic amino acids
lysine	$H_2N—CH_2—CH_2—CH_2—CH_2—CH(NH_2)—COOH$	basic amino acids

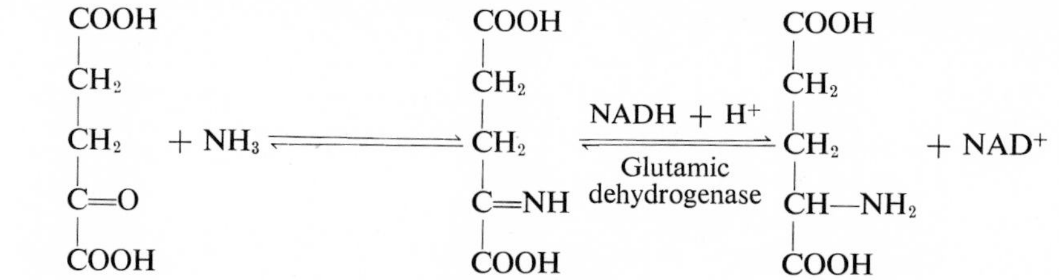

α-Ketoglutarate α-Iminoglutarate Glutamate

The first reaction probably proceeds spontaneously, but the second reaction is catalyzed by the enzyme *glutamic dehydrogenase* and requires the presence of reduced nicotinamide-adenine-dinucleotide ($NADH + H^+$). Because of the central importance of glutamate in the synthesis of other amino acids and because of the high proportion of glutamate formed in this manner by the plant, this reaction is of utmost importance to the nitrogen metabolism of the plant. It represents, so to speak, the major "port of entry" into the metabolic system for inorganic nitrogen. The widespread occurrence of glutamic dehydrogenase in plants strongly supports the above statement.

Reductive amination as a means for the synthesis of amino acids other than glutamate is of limited importance. There is some indirect evidence for the direct amination of oxaloacetate and pyruvate to form aspartate and alanine, respectively. Virtanen and Tarnanen (35) have reported the presence of the enzyme *aspartase* in several plant species. This enzyme catalyzes the reversible amination of fumarate to form aspartate. However, it is doubtful that this reaction is of much importance in amino acid synthesis.

We have, then, four ways by which ammonia nitrogen can gain entrance into organic compounds to form amino acids. These are as follows:

$$\alpha\text{-Ketoglutarate} + NH_3 \rightleftharpoons \text{Glutamate}$$

$$\text{Oxaloacetate} + NH_3 \rightleftharpoons \text{Aspartate}$$

$$\text{Fumarate} + NH_3 \rightleftharpoons \text{Aspartate}$$

$$\text{Pyruvate} + NH_3 \rightleftharpoons \text{Alanine}$$

Of these four pathways, only the amination of α-ketoglutarate appears of any real importance in the assimilation of nitrogen by plants.

Transamination. There is little doubt that the most important reaction in amino acid synthesis is *transamination,* which involves the transfer of an amino group of an amino acid to the carbonyl group of a keto acid. When $N^{15}H_3$ is fed to plants, glutamic acid labeling is quite high in comparison with other amino acids, suggesting a key role for glutamate in this reaction. After inorganic nitrogen has gained entry primarily through the amination of α-ketoglutarate, the product, glutamate, is available for transamination reactions with keto acids to form the corresponding amino acids. Wilson et al. (41) demonstrated the formation of 17 different amino acids through transamination reactions with glutamate.

The enzymes catalyzing transamination reactions are called *transaminases*. When a specific transaminase is referred to, however, the substrate and product prefix the generic term. Thus, the enzyme catalyzing the transfer of an amino group of glutamic acid (substrate) to the carbonyl group of oxaloacetate to form aspartate (product) is called *glutamic-aspartic transaminase*.

Although transamination reactions involving glutamic acid are by far the most prevalent in the plant, other transamination reactions have been found. For example, a transamination reaction involving aspartic acid and alanine has been found in higher plants. However, for the most part transamination reactions involve α-ketoglutarate or glutamate as an essential component (17).

It has definitely been established that transamination reactions involve the participation of *pyridoxal phosphate* or *pyridoxamine phosphate* as a coenzyme. Apparently, pyridoxal phosphate, which is tightly bound to the enzyme, accepts an amino group from the amino acid to form pyridoxamine phosphate, releasing the corresponding keto acid product. Pyridoxamine phosphate then passes the amino group to another keto acid, forming a new amino acid and regenerating pyridoxal phosphate. The reaction should proceed as follows:

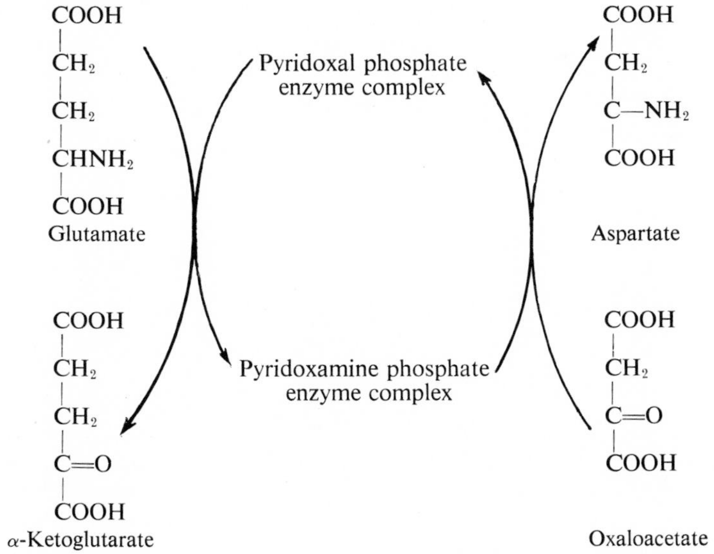

Before leaving the synthesis of amino acids for a discussion on proteins, we should first mention the amides *asparagine* and *glutamine.* These compounds have been found in relatively high quantities in many plants and appear to function in the transport and storage of nitrogen. In the synthesis of glutamine, the hydroxyl group of one of the carboxyl groups of glutamic acid is replaced by an $—NH_2$ group. The enzyme catalyzing this reaction, *glutamine synthetase,* is activitated by the metal cofactor, Mg^{2+}. In addition, ATP is required.

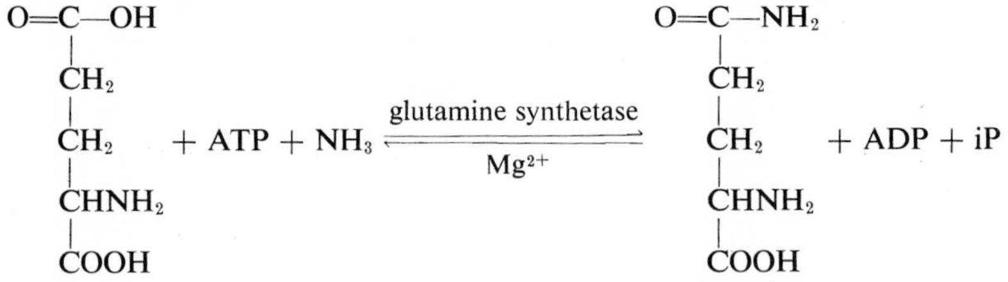

Glutamate Glutamine

It is thought that the synthesis of asparagine from aspartate takes place in the same manner, requiring a metal activator and ATP. However, the enzyme *asparagine synthetase,* which would catalyze this reaction, has not as yet been isolated from plant tissues.

THE PROTEINS

As mentioned before, proteins are composed of repeating units, the amino acids. These are linked together by bonds connecting the carboxyl group of one amino acid with the amino group of another. This type of linkage, which is repeated many times in the protein molecule, is called the *peptide bond.* A diagrammatic representation of the peptide bond is given below.

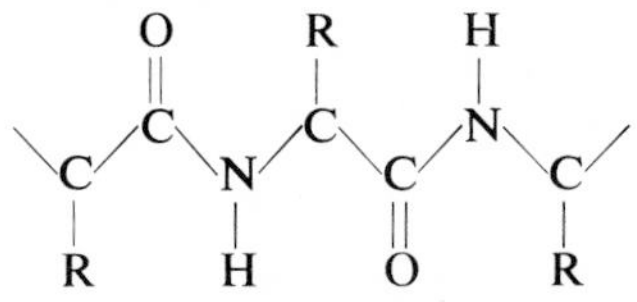

Peptide bond

A compound composed of two amino acids linked together by a peptide bond is called a *dipeptide*—of three amino acids, a *tripeptide,* etc. When a large number of amino acids are linked together in this fashion, the resulting compound is called a *polypeptide.* When we consider that a protein may be made up of 20 different amino acids, each one of which may be present many times and in different sequences, we get an idea of the complexity and size of the protein molecule. Proteins may range in size from the molecular weight of insulin, which is 6000, to a molecular weight of several million.

Protein structure

Generally, it is considered that the biological properties of a protein molecule are related to its structure. The peptide bond and the definite sequence of amino acids give the protein its *primary structure.* Also important in the primary structure of a protein is the *disulphide bond.* Since many proteins contain more than one polypeptide chain, a connection between them other than a peptide bond is a necessary feature of the protein molecule. The disulphide (—S—S—) bond in the amino acid cystine is important in this respect. These features of the primary structure of proteins may be seen in Figure 16-8, which shows the proposed structure of beef insulin, a small animal protein.

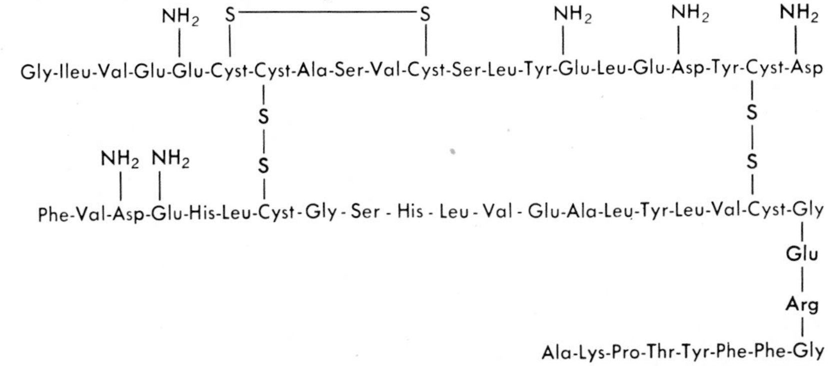

Figure 16-8 Composition and sequence of amino acids in beef insulin.

Evidence from numerous investigations indicates that peptide and disulphide bonds are not the only links involved in protein structure. For example, dissociation of many proteins may occur under mild conditions that would not disturb the peptide or disulphide bond. Available evidence indicates that the polypeptide chains have a coiled or helical structure. This arrangement is maintained by noncovalent links called *hydrogen bonds,* which occur as a result of the hydrogen atom sharing electrons with two oxygen atoms. The helical structure of the polypeptide chain constitutes the *secondary structure* of the protein molecule. In addition to hydrogen bonds, *salt links* and *van der Waals forces* also help maintain the helical structure.

It has also been determined that the helix itself may be folded into different specific patterns. The folding of the helix in such a manner is usually referred to as the *tertiary structure* of the protein molecule and is maintained primarily by hydrogen bonding. Salt links and van der Waals forces, however, are also involved. The different bonds that may occur in the protein molecule are shown in Figure 16-9.

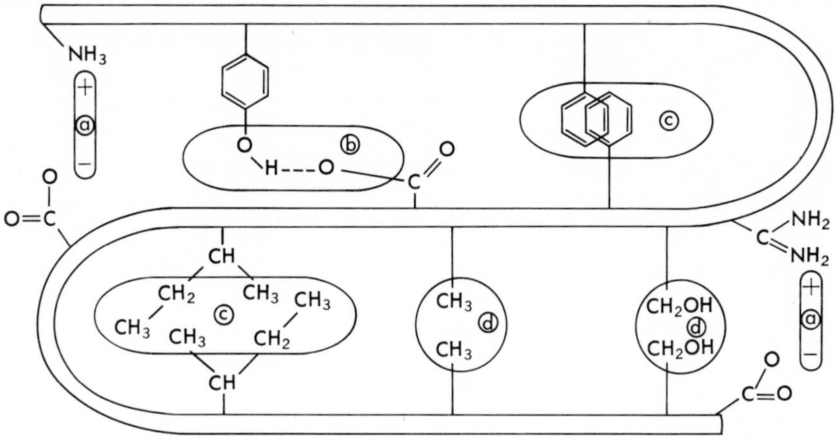

Figure 16-9 Some of the different bonds that may be found in a protein molecule. A. Electrostatic interaction. B. Hydrogen bonding between tyrosine residues and carboxylate groups on side chains. C. Interaction of nonpolar side chains caused by the mutual repulsion of solvent. D. van der Waals interactions. (After C. B. Anfinsen. 1959. The molecular basis of evolution. John Wiley & Sons, Inc., New York.)

It is now thought that the secondary and tertiary structure of the protein molecule are intimately associated with the molecule's biological function. Indeed, in many instances where these features are disrupted, certain specific functions (e.g., enzyme activity) are irreversibly lost. This may occur when proteins are exposed to relatively high temperatures, changes in pH, ultraviolet radiation, etc. All of these conditions cause what is referred to as *denaturation*. Loss of many of the properties of the protein molecule—such as solubility, specific activity, crystallizability—follow its denaturation. In many cases, these properties cannot be recovered on return to normal conditions.

Protein classification

Because of the similar general structure found in the many different proteins, it is easy to separate them from other nitrogenous compounds into their own general group. However, because of this similarity it is rather difficult to establish a classification for proteins themselves. Indeed, the classification that exists at the present time is considered unsatisfactory by many. A classification based on specific structural characteristics is next to impossible because of our scanty knowledge of the secondary and tertiary structures of proteins. Therefore, a classification has been attempted that is based in part on solubility properties and in part on known chemical and physical differences.

Simple proteins. Simple proteins are compounds that, on hydrolysis, yield only amino acids. Classification of the simple proteins is primarily based on solubility properties. The simple proteins can be divided into six major groups, *albumins, globulins, glutelins, prolamines, histones,* and *protamines.*

(a) *Albumins.* The albumins are soluble in water and in dilute salt solutions. They can be coagulated by exposure to heat. The β-amylase of barley is a good example of an albumin (6).

(b) *Globulins.* The globulins are either insoluble or sparingly soluble in water. They are soluble in dilute salt solutions. The globulins will also coagulate when exposed to heat. Many examples of globulins may be found in the storage proteins of seeds.

(c) *Glutelins.* The glutelins are insoluble in neutral solutions, but are soluble in weak acid or basic solutions. These proteins are chiefly found in the cereal grains. Glutenin is an example of a glutelin protein from wheat. Another example would be oryzenin from rice.

(d) *Prolamines.* The prolamines are insoluble in water, but are soluble in 70–80% ethanol. They are not soluble in absolute ethanol. On hydrolysis, these proteins yield relatively large quantities of proline and ammonia—thus, the term prolamine. Examples of plant prolamines are zein of maize, gliadin of wheat, and rye and hordein of barley.

(e) *Histones.* The histones are rich in basic amino acids, such as arginine and lysine, and are soluble in water. These have been found in cell nuclei and may be associated with nucleic acids.

(f) *Protamines.* Like the histones, the protamines are rich in basic amino acids and are soluble in water. Also, like histones, they are found in the nucleus and are probably associated with the nucleic acids. The amino acids tyrosine and tryptophan are not found in these proteins. Also protamines contain no sulfur.

Conjugated proteins. In addition to amino acids, the conjugated protein is associated with a nonamino acid component. This additional component is usually referred to as a *prosthetic group.* The conjugated proteins may be divided into five major groups: *nucleoproteins, glycoproteins, lipoproteins, chromoproteins,* and *metalloproteins.* It is obvious from these terms used to describe the different groups, that the conjugated proteins are named in accordance with their associated prosthetic group.

(a) *Nucleoproteins.* On hydrolysis, the nucleoprotein yields a simple protein plus a nucleic acid. The nucleic acids will be discussed later in this chapter. There is some evidence that nucleoproteins do not really exist, but are artifacts of isolation. At least a chemical association between nucleic acids and proteins has not, as yet, been shown.

(b) *Glycoproteins.* As the name implies, glycoproteins are proteins containing small amounts of carbohydrates as prosthetic groups. It is thought that some of the proteins of the cell membrane may be glycoproteins.

(c) *Lipoproteins.* The lipoproteins are soluble in water and contain lipids, such as lecithin and cephalin, as prosthetic groups. Lipoproteins are common components of membranes. They have been found in the cell membrane (in fact, the cell membrane is thought of as a lipo-protein complex), in the nucleus, and in the lamellae of the chloroplast.

(d) *Chromoproteins.* The chromoproteins comprise a rather diverse group of compounds, which includes flavoproteins, carotenoid proteins, chlorophyll proteins, and hemoglobins. The one property they all have in common is a pigment group for a prosthetic group.

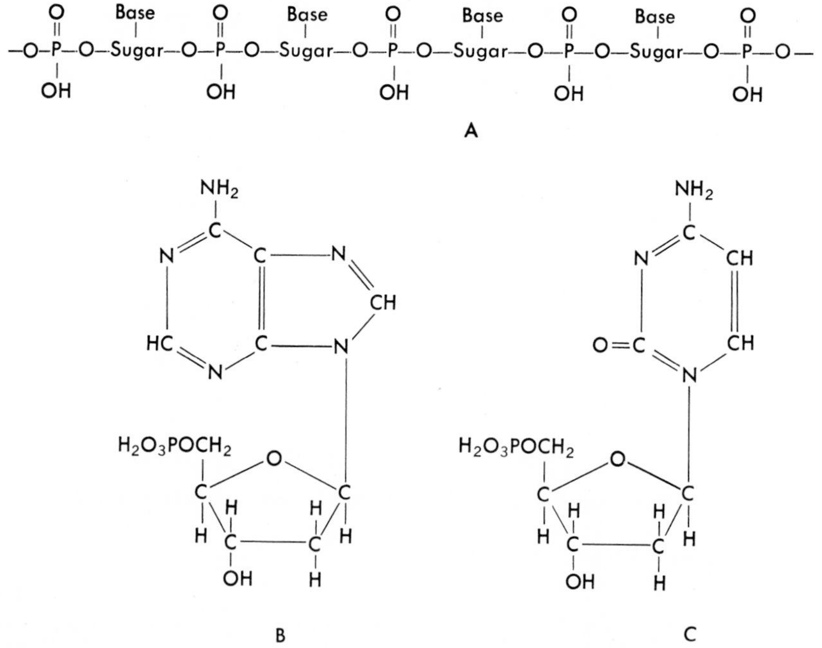

Figure 16-10 A. Sequence of the DNA molecule showing the sugar-phosphate linkages. B. Purine nucleotide, adenylic acid. C. Pyrimidine nucleotide, cytidylic acid.

(e) *Metalloproteins.* Many of the enzymes belong to the metalloprotein group, these enzymes requiring a metal as an activator. We encountered this particular type of protein many times in the discussion of the respiratory enzymes.

NUCLEIC ACIDS

Before discussing the subject of protein synthesis, we must first acquaint ourselves with the nucleic acids: *ribose nucleic acid* (RNA) and *deoxyribose nucleic acid* (DNA). The nucleic acids are large polymeric molecules, composed of repeating units called *nucleotides,* which, in turn, are composed of three components: a *purine* or *pyrimidine* base, a *pentose* or *deoxypentose sugar,* and *phosphoric acid.* The nucleotides are bound together by sugar-phosphate linkages (Figure 16-10).

Separation of the nucleic acids into two large groups is determined by the sugar component present, a factor that has also influenced the naming of these groups. Thus, ribose nucleic acid (RNA) contains ribose, and deoxyribose nucleic acid (DNA) contains deoxyribose. The difference between these two sugars can be found in the second carbon.

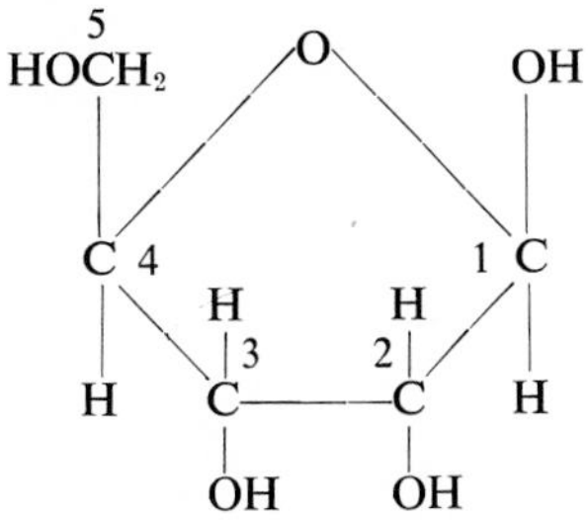

Ribose

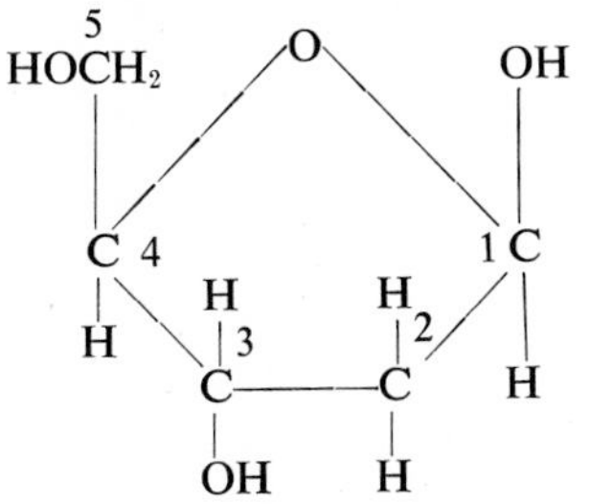

2-Deoxyribose

Numerous investigations have unequivocally established that two types of nitrogenous bases occur in nucleic acids—the purines and pyrimidines. *Adenine* and *guanine* are the two purines commonly found, while *thymine, cytosine,* and *uracil* are the pyrimidines that are generally present. As with the sugar moiety, here also there is a difference between DNA and RNA. The pyrimidine thymine is found only in DNA, while the pyrimidine uracil is confined to the RNA molecule. The structures of the different nitrogenous bases found in the nucleic acids are as shown.

DNA appears to be confined to the chromosomes. RNA has a more varied distribution, being found in the chromosomes, nucleolus, and the cytoplasm. Apparently, the biological functions of DNA and RNA are the transmission of hereditary characteristics and the biosynthesis of pro-

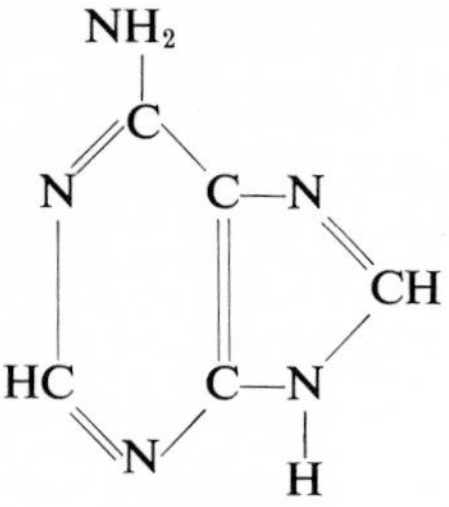

Adenine

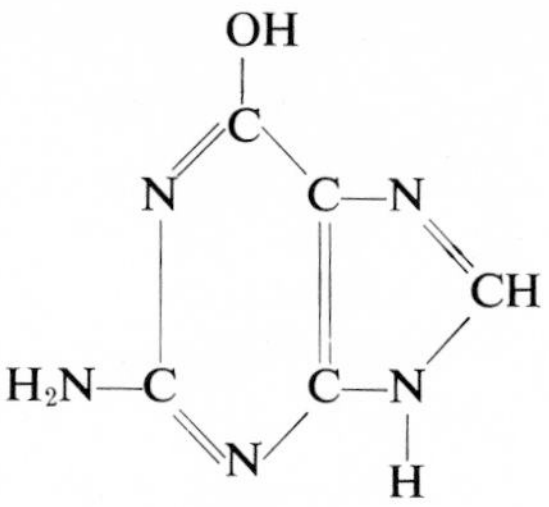

Guanine

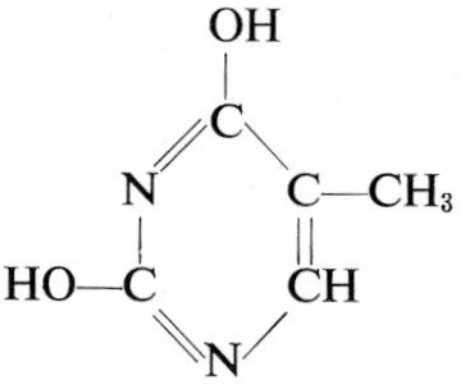

Thymine

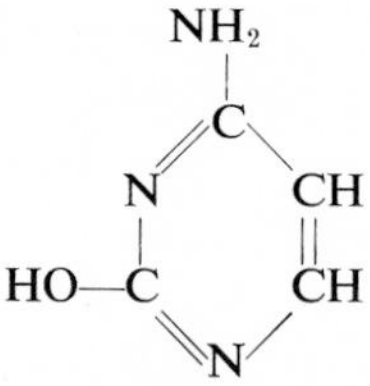

Cytosine

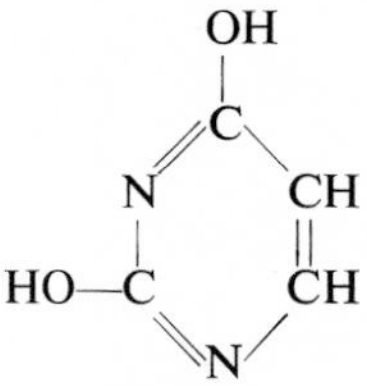

Uracil

teins. DNA is primarily associated with the transmission of "genetic information," while RNA is connected with the protein system.

The molecular structure and nucleotide sequence of the nucleic acids has been studied intensively. Evidence accumulated from x-ray diffraction studies indicates that the DNA molecule is a double helical structure, the two strands being entwined and complementary (Figure 16-11) (37).

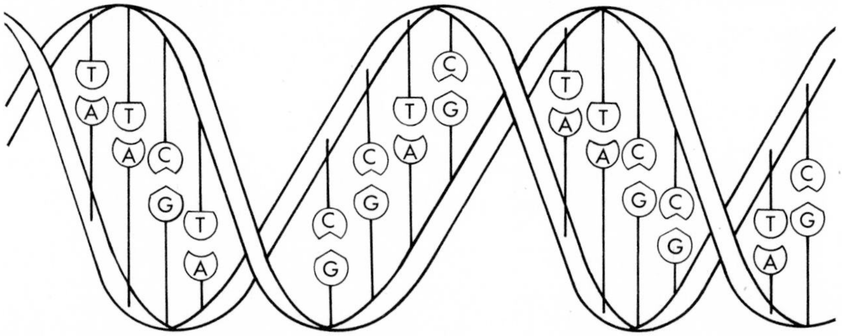

Figure 16-11 A schematic representation of the Watson-Crick model of the DNA molecule. The letters A, T, G, and C stand for the nitrogen bases adenine, thymine, guanine, and cytosine, respectively.

The two strands are linked together through hydrogen bonding between base pairs. Chemical analyses of the DNA molecule indicate that there is a 1:1 relationship between adenine and thymine and between guanine and cytosine. This observation and others suggest that base pairing between the two helical strands occurs between purines and pyrimidines, not between two purines or between two pyrimidines. However, the ratio of adenine-thymine to guanine-cytosine can differ from one DNA molecule to another. It is thought that the DNA molecule is a self-replicating molecule. Presumably, under the appropriate conditions and with the necessary enzymes, the two chains can unwind from the double helix, draw from a base pool, and duplicate each other. The structure of RNA has not been studied as intensively as the structure of DNA, but it is now known that RNA is also a helical structure and is composed of a sequence of nucleotides spaced in much the same manner as found in DNA. Uracil replaces thymine in the RNA molecule. However, just as adenine pairs with thymine in DNA, so also does it pair with uracil in RNA. In addition, recent discoveries suggest that DNA can direct the synthesis of RNA by acting as a template. This observation suggests that genetic information can be passed from DNA to a newly synthesized RNA molecule, which in turn will direct the synthesis of specific protein. If the above observations are correct, they explain how an ordered sequence of amino acids can be incorporated into a protein molecule.

Protein synthesis

The process of protein synthesis can be divided into three steps: (1) activation of amino acids, (2) attachment of the activated amino acid to RNA (soluble RNA), and (3) formation of polypeptides on the ribosome.

Activation of amino acids. The first step in protein synthesis, amino acid activation, entails the selection of specific amino acids from a heterogeneous pool in the cytoplasm. The selection of amino acids is accomplished through the aid of highly specific enzymes, each amino acid having at least one activating enzyme. In the presence of ATP the activating enzyme catalyzes the formation of an energy-rich, enzyme-bound amino acid adenylate (E—AA—AMP) and the release of pyrophosphate (PP).

Amino acid-RNA complex. The activation of an amino acid is followed by its attachment to RNA. The RNA molecule that complexes with the activated amino acid is a special type of RNA. It is a relatively small molecule, containing anywhere from 70 to 100 nucleotides, and is generally referred to as *soluble RNA* (sRNA). There is evidence suggesting a specific sRNA molecule for each amino acid (25, 3), leading one to assume that the transfer of amino acids from the enzyme-bound active complex to sRNA is an additive rather than a competitive process. It is thought that the point of attachment between sRNA and the activated amino acid is at the second or third carbon of the ribose sugar of a terminal adenylic acid.

Polypeptide formation. Peptide formation takes place at or on the surface of ribosomes. Just as a special type of RNA is utilized in the formation of the amino acid-RNA complex, there is also a special type of RNA involved in the formation of polypeptides. This type is referred to as *messenger RNA* (*mRNA*). It is assumed that DNA acts as a template directing the synthesis of mRNA. When the mRNA is completely formed, migration to the ribosome takes place where it will act as a template for protein synthesis. The sRNA-amino acid complexes are transferred to the mRNA of the ribosome where an ordered polymerization of the amino

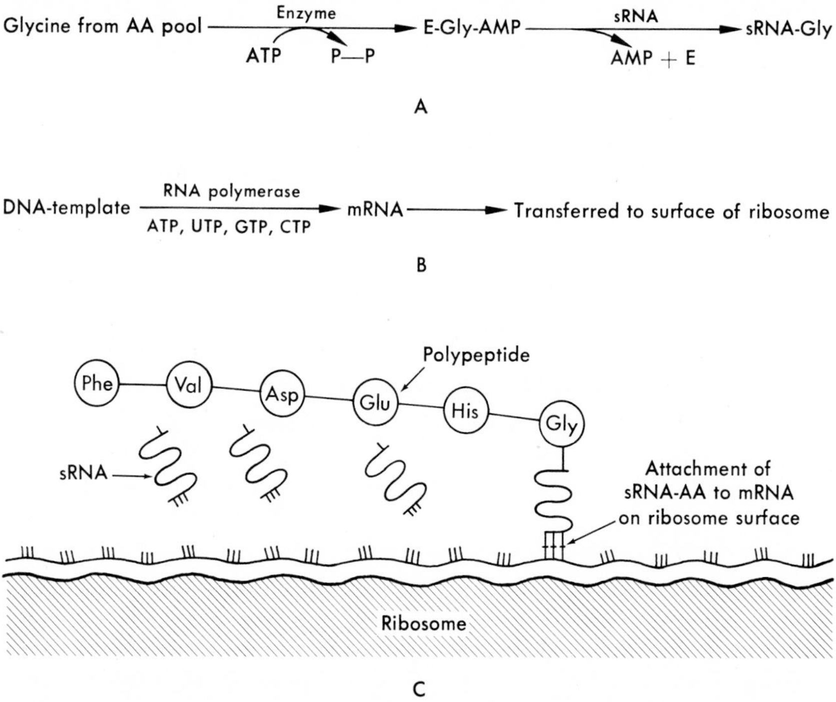

Figure 16-12 Polypeptide formation. A. Under the control of a specific enzyme, an amino acid (in this case, glycine) is selected from an amino acid pool in the cytoplasm. The activated amino acid attaches to sRNA to form an sRNA-AA complex. B. mRNA is formed on a DNA template in the presence of RNA polymerase and the four triphosphates ATP, UTP, GTP, and CTP. The mRNA is then transferred to the surface of a ribosome. C. The sRNA-AA complex attaches to the mRNA on the surface of the ribosome, and an ordered polymerization takes place.

acids takes place, resulting in the synthesis of new protein. An outline of the different steps in protein synthesis is given in Figure 16-12.

Protein degradation

Protein metabolism in plants is in a continuous state of flux between synthesis and breakdown. Proteolytic enzymes, such as *proteases* and *peptidases,* have been found in various plant organs, suggesting that protein degradation may be controlled in part by the activity of these enzymes. Webster (38) has suggested that protein degradation may also occur as a reversal of protein synthesis. He points out that one desirable result of protein being degraded in this manner would be the considerable amount of ATP that would be synthesized. Whether the principal pathway of protein degradation takes place via the reversal of protein synthesis or through the activity of proteolytic enzymes is not yet known. Most likely both pathways for protein breakdown are active in plants.

Protein degradation has been studied principally in germinating seeds and in detached leaves. During germination, a massive breakdown of storage protein occurs in the cotyledon or endosperm, paralleled by a rapid synthesis of protein by the embyro. An accumulation of amino acids and amides in the embryo also has been observed. Apparently, the physiological factors leading to germination set in motion the degradation of storage protein, the migration of the products of this degradation (amino acids) to the embryo, and the synthesis of new protein from these amino acids.

Studies of nitrogen metabolism during the germination of peas (5) and barley (10) show that storage proteins are among the first compounds to disappear. Development of oat and barley embryos is retarded when they are excised from their storage parts and grown in a nutrient medium. Development of the embryos is revived to some extent if amino acids are added to the culture medium (9, 13). In a study of the protein metabolism of intact and excised corn embryos, Oaks and Beevers (24) produced evidence suggesting that the large quantities of preformed amino acids being transferred from the endosperm to the developing embryo restrict the synthesis of new amino acids within the embryo. When the corn embryo is excised from its storage parts and grown on a nutrient medium containing glucose and inorganic nitrogen, the level of protein nitrogen is considerably less than that of the intact embryo grown for the same period of time. This suggests that the embryo possesses only a limited ability to incorporate inorganic nitrogen and synthesize new amino acids. However, it was found (24) that the ability to incorporate inorganic nitrogen and synthesize new amino acids and proteins develops in the excised embryo grown for a period of time on a medium low in soluble amino acids.

When a leaf is detached from its parent plant and grown on a nutrient medium, there is a marked decrease in protein level, paralleled by an increase in amino acids and amides. The amides asparagine and glutamine account for a significant proportion of the nitrogen liberated by protein breakdown in the excised leaf. The amide accumulation is far in excess of the quantity of amides that could possibly be present in the leaf protein before detachment, suggesting a synthesis of these compounds during protein breakdown (38). Actually, amide formation represents a protective mechanism of the plant during periods of extensive protein breakdown. If it were not for the incorporation of ammonia to form amides, toxic levels of ammonia would soon result from protein breakdown. After a period of time the accumulated amino acids and amides are also metabolized, resulting in the liberation of large quantities of ammonium ions.

The mechanisms of protein synthesis and especially protein breakdown are not clearly understood and represent a challenge of vital importance to the scientist specifically and to man in general. A study of protein metabolism has a practical as well as an academic interest. For example, an understanding of the mechanisms involved in the synthesis and breakdown of proteins in the plants may enable the scientist to block or retard protein breakdown and possibly raise protein levels in plants used for food. This would certainly be welcomed by those countries of the world whose populations live on a diet consisting almost wholly of carbohydrates. Perhaps a future can be envisioned where protein levels in crop plants will be almost completely under the control of man.

BIBLIOGRAPHY

1. Allen, E. K., and O. N. Allen. 1958. Biological aspects of symbiotic nitrogen fixation. *In* W. Ruhland (ed.), Encyclopedia of plant physiology. Springer, Berlin. 8: 48.
2. Anfinsen, C. B. 1959. The molecular basis of evolution. John Wiley & Sons, Inc. New York.
3. Berg, P., and E. J. Ofengand. 1958. An enzymatic mechanism for linking amino acids to RNA. Proc. Natl. Acad. Sci. 44: 78.
4. Bollard, E. G. 1959. Urease, urea and unreides in plants. Symp. Soc. Exptl. Biol. 13: 304.
5. Danielson, C. E. 1951. The breakdown of high molecular reserve proteins of peas during germination. Acta Chem. Scand. 5: 551.

6. Davies, D. D., J. Giovanelli, and T. Rees. 1964. Plant biochemistry. Blackwell Scientific Publications, Oxford.
7. Esposito, R. G., and P. W. Wilson. 1956. Trace metals in the nutrition of *Azotobacter vinelandii* O. Biochim. Biophysics Acta 22: 186.
8. Evans, H. J., and A. Nason. 1953. Pyridine nucleotide-nitrate reductase from extracts of higher plants. Plant Physiol. 28: 233.
9. Folkes, B. F. 1959. The position of amino acids in the assimilation of nitrogen and the synthesis of proteins in plants. *In* S.E.B. Symposia 13: 126.
10. Folkes, B. F., and E. W. Yemm. 1958. The respiration of barley plants. X. Respiration and the metabolism of amino acids and proteins in germinating grain. New Phytologist 57: 106.
11. Frear, D. S., and R. C. Burrell. 1955. Spectrophotometric method for determining hydroxylamine reductase activity in higher plants. Anal. Chem. 27: 1664.
12. Gest, H., J. Judis, and H. D. Peck. 1956. Reduction of molecular nitrogen and relationships with photosynthesis and hydrogen metabolism. pp. 298–315 *In* W. D. McElroy and B. Glass (eds.), Inorganic nitrogen metabolism. Johns Hopkins Press, Baltimore, Md.
13. Harris, G. P. 1954. Amino acids as sources of nitrogen for the growth of isolated oat embryos. New Phytologist 55: 253.
14. Hattori, A. 1957. Studies on the metabolism of urea and other nitrogenous compounds by nitrogen-starved cells. J. Biochem. (Tokyo) 44: 253.
15. Hattori, A. 1958. Studies on the metabolism of urea and other nitrogenous compounds in *Chlorella ellipsoidea*. II. Changes in levels of amino acids and amides during the assimilation of ammonia and urea by nitrogen-starved cells. J. Biochem. (Tokyo) 45: 57.
16. Hinsvark, O. N., S. H. Wittwer, and H. B. Tukey. 1953. The metabolism of foliar-applied urea. I. Relative rates of $C^{14}O_2$ production by certain vegetable plants treated with labeled urea. Plant Physiol. 28: 70.
17. Loomis, W. D., and P. K. Stumpf. 1958. Transamination and transamidation. *In* W. Ruhland (ed.), Encyclopedia of plant physiology. 8: 249.
18. Lee, S. B., and P. W. Wilson. 1943. Hydrogenase and nitrogen fixation of *Azotobacter*. J. Biol. Chem. 151: 377.
19. Medina, A., and D. J. D. Nicholas. 1957. Hyponitrite reductase in *Neurospora*. Nature 179: 533.
20. Nason, A., and H. J. Evans. 1954. Triphosphopyridine nucleotide-nitrate reductase in *Neurospora*. J. Biol. Chem. 202: 655.
21. Nicholas, D. J. D., and A. Nason. 1954. Mechanism of action of nitrate reductase from *Neurospora*. J. Biol. Chem. 211: 183.
22. Nicholas, D. J. D., and A. Nason. 1955. Role of molybdenum as a constituent of nitrate reductase from soybean leaves. Plant Physiol. 30: 135.
23. Nightingale, G. T., L. G. Schermerhorn, and W. R. Robbins. 1928. The growth status of the tomato as correlated with organic nitrogen and carbohydrates in roots, stems and leaves. N. J. Agr. Exptl. Sta. Bull. 461.
24. Oaks, A., and H. Beevers. 1964. The requirement for organic nitrogen in *Zea mays* embryos. Plant Physiol. 39: 37.

25. Schweet, R. S., F. C. Bovard, E. Allen and F. Glassman. 1958. The incorporation of amino acids into ribonucleic acid. Proc. Natl. Acad. Sci. 44: 173.
26. Stiles, W. 1961. Trace elements in plants, 3rd ed., University Press, Cambridge.
27. Street, H. E., and D. E. G. Sheat. 1958. The absorption and availability of nitrate and ammonia. *In* W. Ruhland (ed.), Encyclopedia of plant physiology. Springer, Berlin. 8: 150.
28. Tanner, J. W., and J. C. Anderson. 1964. External effect of combined nitrogen on nodulation. Plant Physiol. 39: 1039.
29. Thimann, K. V. 1939. The physiology of nodule formation. Trans. Third Comm. Intern. Soc. Soil Sci. New Brunswick, N. J. 24–28.
30. Tiedjens, V. A. 1934. Factors affecting assimilation of ammonia and nitrate nitrogen particularly in tomato and apple. Plant Physiol. 9: 31.
31. Tiedjens, V. A., and M. A. Blake. 1932. Factors affecting the use of nitrate and ammonium nitrate by apple trees. N. J. Agr. Exptl. Sta. Bull. 547.
32. Verhoeven, W. 1956. Some remarks on nitrate and nitrite metabolism in microorganisms. pp. 61–86 *In* W. D. McElroy and B. Glass (eds.), Inorganic nitrogen metabolism. Johns Hopkins Press, Baltimore, Md.
33. Virtanen, A. I., J. Erkama, and H. Linkola. 1947. On the relation between nitrogen fixation and leghaemoglobin content of leguminous root nodules. II. Acta Chem. Scand. 1: 861.
34. Virtanen, A. I., and J. K. Miettinen. 1963. Biological nitrogen fixation. F. C. Steward (ed.), *In* Plant physiology. Academic Press, New York. 3: 539.
35. Virtanen, A. I., and J. Tarnanen. 1932. Die enzymatische Spaltung and Synthese der Asparaginsäune. Biochem. Z. 250: 193.
36. Walker, J. B. 1952. Arginosuccinic acid from *Chlorella pyrenoidosa*. Proc. Natl. Acad. Sci. 38: 561.
37. Watson, J. D., and F. H. C. Crick. 1953. Molecular structure of nucleic acids. Nature 171: 737.
38. Webster, G. C. 1959. Nitrogen metabolism in plants. Row, Peterson and Co., New York.
39. Webster, G. C., J. E. Varner, and A. N. Gansa. 1955. Conversion of carbon-14-labeled urea into amino acids in leaves. Plant Physiol. 30: 372.
40. White, P. R. 1937. Amino acids in the nutrition of excised tomato roots. Plant Physiol. 12: 793.
41. Wilson, D. G., K. W. King, and R. H. Burris. 1954. Transamination in plants. J. Biol. Chem. 208: 863.
42. Wilson, P. W. 1940. The biochemistry of symbiotic nitrogen fixation. University of Wisconsin Press, Madison, Wisc.
43. Wilson, P. W. 1958. Asymbiotic nitrogen fixation. *In* W. Ruhland (ed.), Encyclopedia of plant physiology. Springer, Berlin 8: 9.
44. Wilson, P. W., and C. J. Lind. 1943. Carbon monoxide inhibition of *Azotobacter* in microrespiration experiments. J. Bacter. 45: 219.

45. Wilson, P. W., and W. W. Umbreit. 1937. Mechanism of symbiotic nitrogen fixation, III. Hydrogen as a specific inhibitor. Arch. Mikrobiol. 8: 440.
46. Wilson, P. W., W. W. Umbreit, and S. B. Lee. 1938. Mechanism of symbiotic nitrogen fixation. IV. Specific inhibition by hydrogen. Biochem. J. 32: 2084.
47. Wipf, L., and D. C. Cooper. 1938. Chromosome numbers in nodules and roots of red clover, common vetch and garden peas. Proc. Natl. Acad. Sci. 24: 87.
48. Wipf, L., and D. C. Cooper. 1940. Somatic doubling of chromosomes and nodular infection in certain *Leguminosae*. Am. J. Botan. 27: 821.
49. Zucker, M., and A. Nason. 1955. A pyridine nucleotide-hydroxylamine reductase from *Neurospora*. J. Biol. Chem. 213: 463.

Part SIX

Plant growth hormones

17

The natural growth hormones

INTRODUCTION

It is now recognized that most, if not all, of the physiological activity of the plant is regulated by a variety of chemical substances called *hormones*. The presence of growth-regulating hormones in plants was first suggested by Julius von Sachs in the latter half of the nineteenth century when he proposed that there were "organ-forming substances" in plants, which were produced in the leaves and translocated downward in the plant. This famous scientist's astute observations remarkably foreshadowed the intensive study of plant growth regulation performed during the twentieth century.

While Sachs was formulating his theories on growth regulation, another famous scientist was studying the tropisms of plants. Charles Darwin, known more for his theory on evolution, studied the effect of gravity and unilateral light on the movement of plants. He suggested, as did Sachs, that plant growth might be under the control of special substances. He was able to demonstrate that the effects of light and gravity on the bending of both roots and shoots are mediated by the tip, and that this influence can be transmitted to other parts of the plant. He concluded that "when seedlings are freely exposed to a lateral light some influence is transmitted from the upper to the lower part causing the latter to bend." With respect to geotropism of roots, he concludes "that it is the tip alone which is acted on, and that this part transmits some influence to the adjoining parts, causing them to curve downwards." The above quotes were taken from Darwin's delightful book *The Power of Movement in Plants*.

For his experimental plant, Darwin used canary grass (*Phalaris canariensis*). This plant in its early stages of growth puts forth a tubular leaf (coleoptile), which encases the primary leaf. Darwin found that if he exposed the tip of the coleoptile to a unilateral source of light, the coleoptile would bend toward the light. If the tip of the coleoptile was covered, so as to exclude all light from that area, the coleoptile was insensitive to light and did not bend.

Actual proof of the material nature of plant growth regulators was demonstrated by Boysen-Jensen (27, 28, 29); when he decapitated a coleoptile a few millimeters from the tip, put a block of gelatin on the stump, replaced the tip, and illuminated the coleoptile unilaterally above the incision, curvature toward the light progressed as in the intact coleoptile. He also demonstrated that one could interfere with the normal phototropic bending of the plant by making a transverse slit halfway through the coleoptile below the tip on the dark side of a unilaterally illuminated grass seedling and inserting a piece of mica in the slit. Inserting the piece of mica on the illuminated side of the seedling produced no such interference, giving evidence that the stimulus for bending passes down the dark side of the seedling.

Although Boysen-Jensen demonstrated that some substance, which originates in the tip, is responsible for the bending of unilaterally illuminated coleoptiles toward the light, he did not claim originally that this substance is a growth regulator. Paal (81) decapitated coleoptiles, replaced the tip asymmetrically, and discovered that the coleoptile bent away from the side with the tip, even in the dark. Paal's experiment strongly suggested that there was a material substance emanating from the tip, which could stimulate growth of cells below the tip.

The next logical steps were to isolate this substance from the plant and to demonstrate that it could stimulate growth when introduced into the plant. This task was accomplished by the Dutch botanist, F. W. Went. He placed freshly cut coleoptile tips on small blocks of agar for a measured period of time and then placed the agar blocks asymmetrically on decapitated coleoptiles for 2 hours in the dark. The coleoptiles exhibited a curvature similar to that obtained when coleoptile tips were placed asymmetrically on coleoptile stumps. He then developed a method for determining the amount of active substance in coleoptile tips; that is, he developed a bioassay for auxin. Went found that the degree of curvature of coleoptile tips is proportional, within limits, to the amount of active substance in the agar blocks (Figure 17-1). Because of the use of the *Avena*

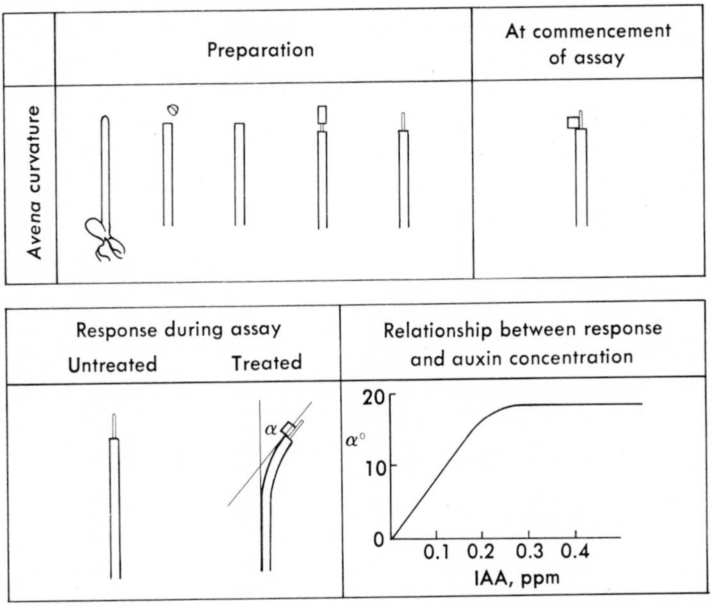

Figure 17-1 Diagrammatic representation of the *Avena* curvature test. (Redrawn from L. J. Audus. 1959. Plant growth substances. Interscience Publishers, New York.)

plant for this bioassay, it subsequently became known as the *Avena curvature test.*

Application of the *Avena* test to a great variety of substances led to the finding that human urine is rich in growth substance. Starting with 33 gallons of human urine, Kögl and Haagen-Smit (64) concentrated the hormone activity by employing a series of purification processes. The activity of the products of each purification step was determined by the *Avena* curvature test. After distillation in high vacuum, the final step yielded 40 mg of crystals that had a specific activity 50,000 times that of the original urine. The final product was given the name *auxin-A* (auxentriolic acid).

Using approximately the same purification methods, another active substance was isolated from corn germ oil by Kögl, Erxleben, and Haagen-Smit (63). This substance was found to be very similar in structure and activity to auxin-A and was given the name *auxin-B* (auxenolonic acid). In the same year, still another substance was isolated from human urine. Repeating the isolation from urine on a larger scale and with the use of a charcoal absorption method for removing the active substance, Kögl, Haagen-Smit, and Erxleben (65) isolated the compound *heteroauxin* (other auxin) or, as it is known today, *indole-3-acetic acid*. This is usu-

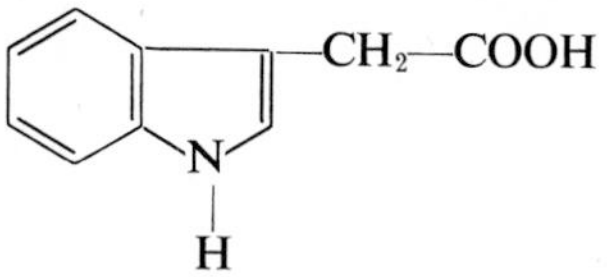

Indole-3-acetic acid (IAA)

ally abbreviated as IAA. This was not a new compound, but had been discovered and isolated from fermentations in 1885 by E. and H. Salkowski. However, at this time the biological activity of the compound was not suspected.

Today, there is considerable doubt as to the existence of auxin-A and auxin-B. Since their first isolation by Kögl and his colleagues, auxins A and B have never been isolated again. In contrast, IAA has been isolated in the crystalline form many times from different sources by a number of different investigators.

DEFINITIONS

Since the discovery and chemical characterization of auxin, there has been an immense amount of research in the field of plant growth regulation. Needless to say, this prodigious amount of work brought forth a number of synthetic as well as natural compounds that were similar to IAA in their physiological activity. In most cases the synthetic compounds were chemical analogues of the natural auxin. Also, many compounds were discovered that counteracted the effect of growth regulators. Because of the number of biologically active compounds being introduced and the confusion in terminology that arose, a committee formed by the American Society of Plant Physiologists suggested the following definitions (99).

1. *Plant regulators* are organic compounds other than nutrients, which in small amounts promote, inhibit, or otherwise modify any physiological process in plants.
2. *Plant hormones* (synonym: *phytohormones*) are regulators produced by

plants, which in low concentrations regulate plant physiological processes. Hormones usually move within the plant from a site of production to a site of action.

3. *Growth regulators* (synonym: *growth substances*) are regulators that affect growth.
4. *Growth hormones* are hormones that regulate growth.
5. *Flowering regulators* are regulators that affect flowering.
6. *Flowering hormones* are hormones that initiate the formation of floral primordia or promote their development.
7. *Auxin* is a generic term for compounds characterized by their capacity to induce elongation in shoot cells. They resemble indole-3-acetic acid in physiological action. Auxins may, and generally do, affect other processes besides elongation, but elongation is considered critical. Auxins are generally acids with an unsaturated cyclic nucleus or derivatives of such acids.
8. *Auxin precursors* are compounds which in the plant can be converted into auxins.
9. *Antiauxins* are compounds that inhibit competitively the action of auxins.

DISTRIBUTION OF AUXIN IN THE PLANT

The highest concentrations of auxin are found in the growing tips of the plant, that is, in the tip of the coleoptile, in buds, and in the growing tips of leaves and roots. However, auxin is also found widely distributed throughout the plant, undoubtedly transported from the meristematic regions. This was clearly illustrated by Thimann (93) in his determination of the auxin content in different areas of the *Avena* seedling (Figure 17-2).

Figure 17-2 Auxin distribution in an etiolated *Avena* seedling. (After K. V. Thimann. 1934. J. Gen. Physiol. 18: 23. Redrawn from A. C. Leopold. 1955. Auxins and plant growth. University of California Press, Los Angeles.)

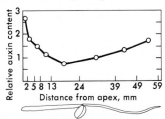

The concentration of auxin drops as one progresses from the tip to the base of the coleoptile, the highest content being found at the tip and the lowest at the base. Continuing from the base of the coleoptile along the root, there is a steady increase in auxin content until a high point is reached at the tip of the root. The concentration of auxin found at the tip of the root is, however, nowhere near the concentration found at the tip of the coleoptile. Since Thimann's early work, several studies on auxin distribution have been made roughly confirming the widespread occurrence of auxin in the plant (98, 100).

Thimann's work on the distribution of auxin, and later the work of others, disclosed that auxin is present in the plant in two different forms, one that is easily extracted by diffusion methods and another that is much more difficult to extract, necessitating the use of organic solvents. The easily extracted auxin is called *free auxin* and that which is hard to extract, *bound auxin*. It is now generally accepted that bound auxin is the form that is active in growth and that free auxin is excess auxin in equilibrium with the bound auxin. Yet a third form of auxin has been postulated (11) that requires more drastic measures for removal from plant material than simple diffusion methods or direct extraction with some organic solvent. For example, spinach leaves heated in weak alkaline solution or treated with enzymes that break up protein (where auxin may be bound) give up a much higher content of auxin than would have been found if only direct extraction procedures had been performed. It would appear, then, that auxin may be found in the plant in two or more active forms, possibly forming different protein complexes.

So far, it has been suggested that auxin in the plant is present in a "free" nonactive form and a "bound" active form, and that a dynamic equilibrium exists between the two. There may be several different forms of the bound auxin. One can conclude from the above information that growth, its initiation and regulation, may be controlled by the conditions of different equilibria between free and bound auxin at various growth centers in the plant. Most likely, auxin is transported in the free form from its place of origin to its site of activity.

TRANSLOCATION OF AUXIN

The transport of auxin in plants is a subject that plant physiologists have occupied themselves with for many years and have not completely solved. Experiments by Darwin (p. 398) and by Boysen-Jensen (p. 398) demonstrating the transport of an active stimulus from the tip to the base of the coleoptile, led other investigators to assume that the movement of this stimulus was polar. The actual proof of polar transport was given in a series of experiments by Went in 1928 (104). He showed that if one placed a cylindrical section of a coleoptile (cut from the center of the coleoptile) between two agar blocks, the top block containing auxin, translocation of the auxin into the bottom block would take place only if the section was oriented in the normal manner. If the section was inverted, no diffusion would take place. In each experiment the amount of auxin in each block was determined by the *Avena* curvature test. This very simple but ingenious technique clearly demonstrated that the translocation of auxin in the coleoptile takes place in only one direction, from tip to base (basipetal). Figure 17-3A gives a diagrammatic representation of this experiment.

Experiments by Beyer (14) in the same year confirmed the results of

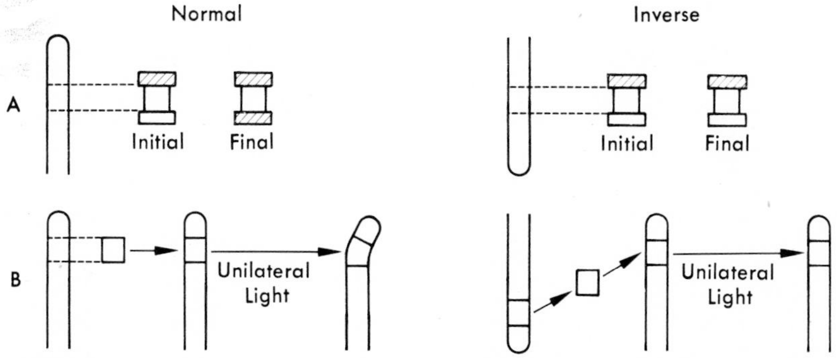

Figure 17-3 Schematic representation of two experiments illustrating polar transport of auxin in the *Avena* coleoptile. In experiment A the shaded agar blocks contain auxin. (Experiment A is after F. W. Went. 1935. Botan. Rev. 1: 162. Experiment B is after A. Beyer. 1928. Z. Botan. 20: 321. Redrawn from F. W. Went and K. V. Thimann. 1937. Phytohormones. The Macmillan Co., New York.)

Went. Beyer showed that if a section of a coleoptile is removed and then replaced in the exact same manner, a phototropic response can be obtained. If, however, the section is put back in an inverted manner, no phototropic response can be obtained (Figure 17-3B).

The translocation of auxin in plant tissues occurs at such high rates as to exclude diffusion as the principal method of auxin transport in the plant. The actual mechanism involved in the transport of auxin is still a matter of controversy. One group of investigators believes that a difference in electrical potential between the tip and the base of the coleoptile controls auxin transport (73, 85). The base of the *Avena* coleoptile is more electropositive than the tip; the dark side of a unilaterally illuminated coleoptile is more electropositive than the lighted side, and in a horizontally placed coleoptile the lower side is the more electropositive. In each of these situations the translocation of auxin is toward the highest positive charge. One very serious objection to this theory, however, is that when a transverse external field is applied to the coleoptile, initial curvature is toward the positive pole of the applied charge (85). This is opposite to the direction natural tropisms take, which is toward the negatively charged side.

Gregory and Hancock (51) have suggested that transport of auxin may be controlled to some extent by the metabolism of the cell; that is, metabolic energy is involved. They found that a lack of oxygen inhibits the transport of auxin. This is also true for metabolic inhibitors (78).

That the transport of auxin is strictly basipetal has recently been criticized by Jacobs (62). He found that in *Coleus* stem sections the ratio of basipetal to acropetal (base to tip) transport of auxin is 3:1. Although acropetal movement is only $\frac{1}{3}$ that of basipetal movement, it is real and significant. Also, auxin produced in the leaves is transported in the phloem tissues to other parts of the plant (11), a type of transport that is definitely not polar.

It appears that in young actively growing tissues auxin transport is usually polar, but in mature differentiated tissues both polar and nonpolar movement may be found. Vascular transport of auxin can take place when unphysiological concentrations are applied to plant material. Excess auxin, when in contact with open vascular strands, may be carried upward in the xylem tissue and downward in the phloem.

PHYSIOLOGICAL EFFECTS

Since the discovery of auxin and its identification as a growth hormone, an enormous amount of literature has accumulated describing its effect on the growth of the plant. In some cases auxin is stimulatory, in others inhibitory, and in still other cases a necessary participant in the growth activity of another plant hormone (e.g., kinins and gibberellins). Needless to say, a discussion on all of the physiological aspects of auxin activity is beyond the scope of this book. We will discuss only the involvement of auxin in (a) cell elongation, (b) apical dominance, (c) root initiation, (d) parthenocarpy, (e) abscission, (f) callus formation, and (g) respiration.

Cell elongation

In an earlier discussion in this book, we studied the osmotic conditions that prevail in the living cell. We learned that the cell membrane and vacuolar membrane are differentially permeable and that osmotically active solutes are present in the cell sap and cytoplasm. It was also mentioned that an osmotic equilibrium exists in the cell, where the turgor pressure developed is balanced by an equal and opposite wall pressure. It is thought that the modification by auxin of the conditions responsible for this equilibrium, such as wall resistance and osmotic concentration, stimulates cell elongation.

Most of the studies of the effects of auxin on cell elongation have employed excised plant material (e.g., oat coleoptile sections or excised root sections) having no endogenous auxin supply. Plant material used in this manner presents an ideal situation for measuring the influence of auxin on cell elongation. The effect of exogenously applied auxin may be measured without fear of any contaminating influence by endogenous auxin.

In a study of IAA-induced cell elongation in oat coleoptile sections, Bonner (21) found that cell elongation takes place to a small extent in the absence of exogenously applied IAA (Figure 17-4). With the use of

Figure 17-4 Growth of *Avena* coleoptile sections in an auxin medium and in the absence of auxin. The initial length of the sections was 5.0 mm. (Reproduced from *Plant Growth Regulation,* edited by R. M. Klein, © 1961 by the Iowa State University Press.)

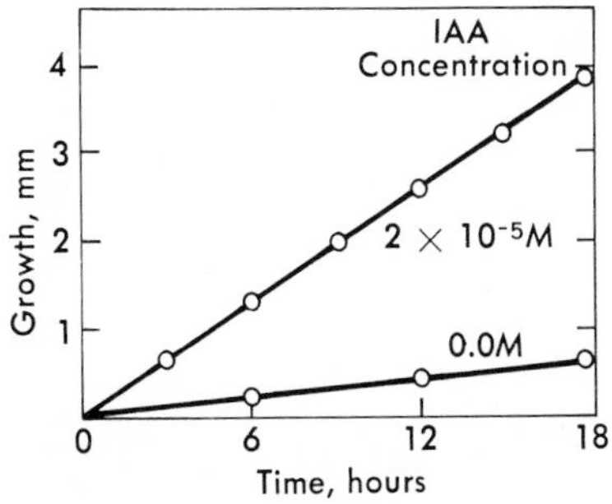

competitive inhibitors of IAA, it was determined that noninduced elongation is not due to any residual IAA that might be present in the coleoptile section.

It should also be noted in Figure 17-4 that the response of the coleoptile section to optimal concentrations of IAA is very large, causing in some cases a tenfold increase in rate of elongation over the rate in the absence of IAA (21).

We have already mentioned that the action of auxin on cell elongation must involve some modification of the osmotic system of the cell. How then would this be accomplished? The theories proposed from major studies on this problem have suggested that auxin may (1) increase the osmotic content of the cell, (2) increase permeability of the cell to water, (3) cause a reduction in wall pressure, or (4) cause an increase in wall synthesis.

Increase in osmotic solutes. The amount of solute present in the cell sap increases in a cell treated with IAA (35). However, the osmotic concentration or concentration of osmotically active solutes does not change (12, 31, 35) and might even decrease (58).

Since the osmotic pressure does not increase, it is hard to believe that an auxin-induced increase in amount of osmotically active solutes alone is responsible for an increase in cell extension. In fact, the increase in solutes may be an effect rather than the cause of an increase in cell elongation.

However, strong support for osmotic pressure playing a major role in cell elongation has been given by Ordin et al. (80). They found that oat coleoptile sections failed to respond to IAA treatment when placed in an isotonic solution. Oat coleoptile section growth was found to be quite sensitive, however, if the osmotic pressure of the external solution was dropped below the isotonic condition (Figure 17-5).

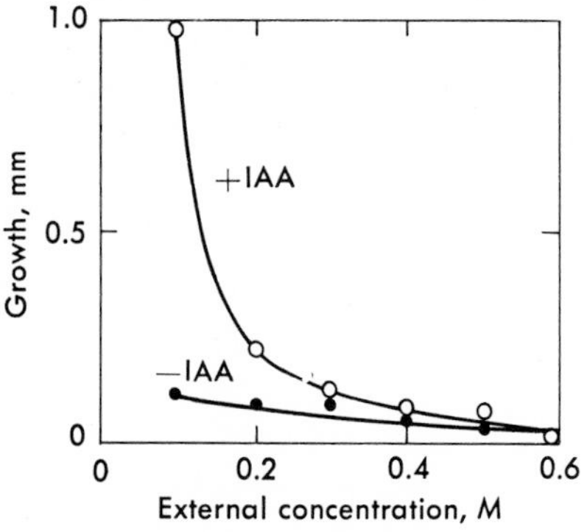

Figure 17-5 Growth of *Avena* coleoptile sections as a function of osmotic concentration. Osmotic solutes were made up of sucrose (0.09*M*) and varied amounts of mannitol. (After L. Ordin, T. H. Applewhite, and J. Bonner. 1956. Plant Physiol. 31: 44. Adopted by permission from *Plant Growth Regulation,* edited by R. M. Klein, © 1961 by Iowa State University Press.)

Increased permeability to water. Northen (79) observed that auxin decreases the viscosity of cytoplasm, leading him to propose that auxin may bring about the decomposition of cytoplasmic protein. This decomposition would release osmotically active particles into the cytoplasm, raising its osmotic pressure, which in turn would increase the diffusion of water into the cell.

In a recent review (35) the suggestion that auxin induces an increase in permeability to water by the cell has been criticized on the grounds that direct measurements of the uptake of isotopically labeled water demonstrate no influence by auxin.

Reduction in wall pressure. We have already discussed that there is an increase in the quantity but not the concentration of osmotically active particles in auxin-treated cells; that is, no change in osmotic pressure or turgor pressure is noted despite quite an increase in cell size. To allow for this, some of the properties of the cell wall must be modified by the action of auxin.

Reduction in wall pressure has received the strongest support as the method by which auxin induces cell elongation. How this is done is not clearly understood. In the first stages of cell elongation, the cell wall may actually get thinner (30), implying a stretching of the cell wall without an accompanying cell wall synthesis. However, at the end of a period of cell elongation the wall in many cases is thicker (11), suggesting that new cell wall material may be synthesized after the initial stages of extension growth.

It has been noted that elastic stretching (reversible stretching) of a cell increases in auxin-treated tissue only if irreversible elongation also occurs (35). In the absence of elongation auxin has no effect on the elastic properties of the cell wall, implying that the increase in elasticity may be a consequence of cell elongation, not of auxin.

That auxin increases wall plasticity (irreversible stretching) has been convincingly demonstrated with the *Avena* coleoptile. It has been shown that cell wall plasticity increases before and during auxin-induced cell elongation (92). It has been proposed that this may be because of the rupturing of Ca bonds in the cell wall. Experimental support for this proposal has been received from studies by Thimann and Schneider (97) and Cooil and Bonner (36). See Figure 17-6.

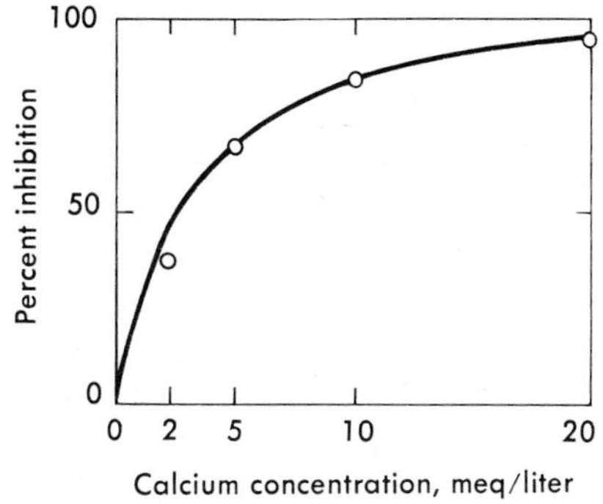

Figure 17-6 Inhibitory effect of calcium on IAA-induced growth of *Avena* coleoptile sections. Presumably, this is because of calcium increasing cell wall resistance. (After B. Cooil and J. Bonner. 1957. Planta 48: 696. Adopted by permission from *Plant Growth Regulation,* edited by R. M. Klein, © 1961 by the Iowa State University Press.)

Increase in wall synthesis. Although new wall synthesis does occur during auxin-induced cell elongation, there is no convincing evidence that this is the cause of cell elongation rather than a consequence of it. However, the fact that auxin will increase the rate of respiration suggests an increase in energy output that might be utilized in the synthesis of new wall material. Again, one doesn't know which comes first, the increase in respiration or the increase in cell elongation.

From the above discussion one very prominent feature may be observed, that the mode of action of auxin in cell elongation has not been elucidated. In a recent review on the subject, Cleland and Burstrom (35) had this to say:

> It must be concluded that we do not know as yet how auxin regulates elongation. The evidence, at present, suggests that in most tissues auxin acts

through a series of steps which may involve metabolism and that the end result is a change in cell wall pressure.

Apical dominance

Long before the discovery of hormonal regulation in plant growth, the peculiar dominance of apical over lateral growth seen in a great many species of plants had been noted by botanists. They had observed that the apical or terminal bud of many vascular plants was very active in growth, while the lateral buds remained inactive. The same phenomenon was observed in the new shoot growth of many tree species. In fact, the characteristic growth patterns of many plant species reflect the influence of apical dominance. Plants that grow tall and unbranched reflect a strong influence, while plants that are short and shrubby give evidence of a weak influence of apical dominance.

The strong influence of the apical bud on the growth of lateral buds is easily demonstrated by removing it from the plant. In the absence of the apical bud, active growth begins in the lateral bud. However, in a short time the lateral bud nearest the apical bud will establish dominance over the remaining buds, causing them to become inactive again.

The first hint that apical dominance might be because of auxin produced at the terminal bud and transported downward through the stem was given in studies by Skoog and Thimann (89). Removal of the terminal bud of the broad bean and its replacement with a block of agar resulted, as might be expected, in lateral bud growth. Replacement of the terminal bud with agar blocks containing IAA, however, suppressed lateral bud growth in much the same manner as the terminal bud (Figure 17-7).

Previous to the experiments of Skoog and Thimann, it had been noted that the apical bud contained a much higher auxin content than the lateral buds. This fact undoubtedly led to the experiments with the broad bean. However, physiologists to this day have been unable to explain why lateral bud growth should be inhibited by a much smaller amount of auxin than is found in the apical bud, which, to make the problem more complex, grows vigorously in the presence of this relatively high concentration of auxin.

Although the problem of apical dominance did not lend itself to easy solution, it did cause a great deal of speculation in the botanical world. Many theories were proposed with varying degrees of acceptance until Thimann, in 1937 (95), suggested that lateral buds respond to auxin in much the same manner as roots and shoots, that is, to minimum, optimum, and maximum concentrations. Concentrations of auxin above that which will give the maximum concentration will cause inhibition (Figure 17-8).

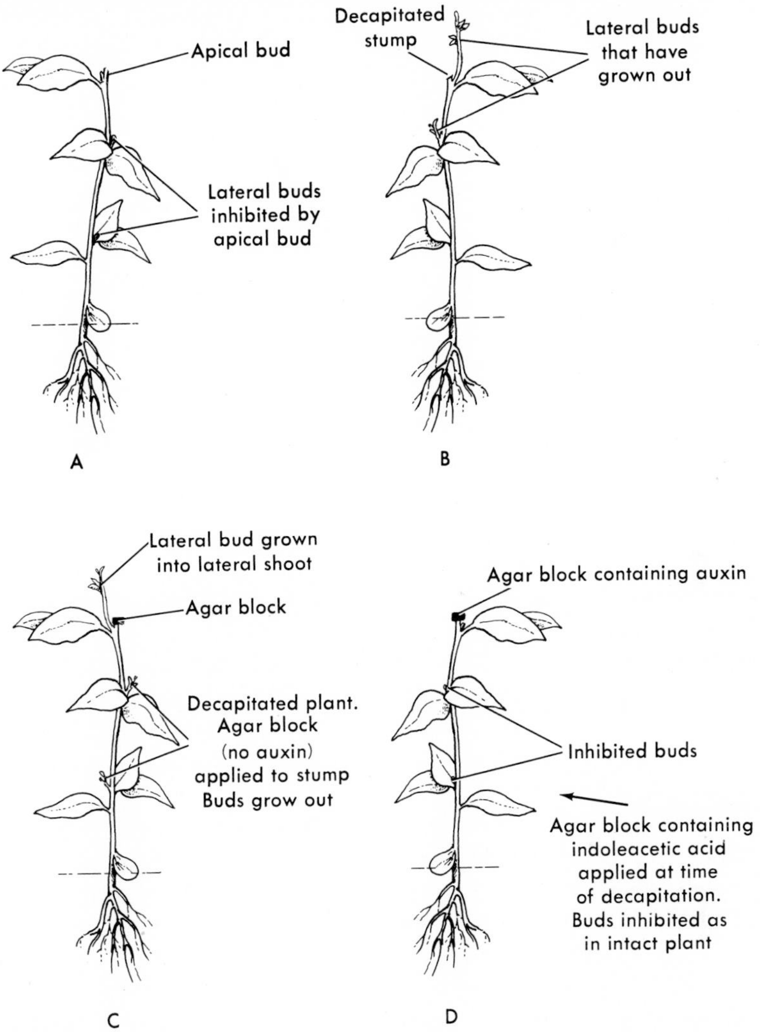

Figure 17-7 A. Normal plant. B. Plant with apical bud removed, removing the suppression of lateral bud growth. C. Plant with apical bud removed and replaced with an agar block. No suppression of lateral bud growth results. D. Plant with apical bud removed and replaced with agar block containing IAA. Suppression of lateral bud growth results. (Redrawn from *Principles of Plant Physiology* by James Bonner and Arthur W. Galston. Copyright by W. H. Freeman and Company, 1952.)

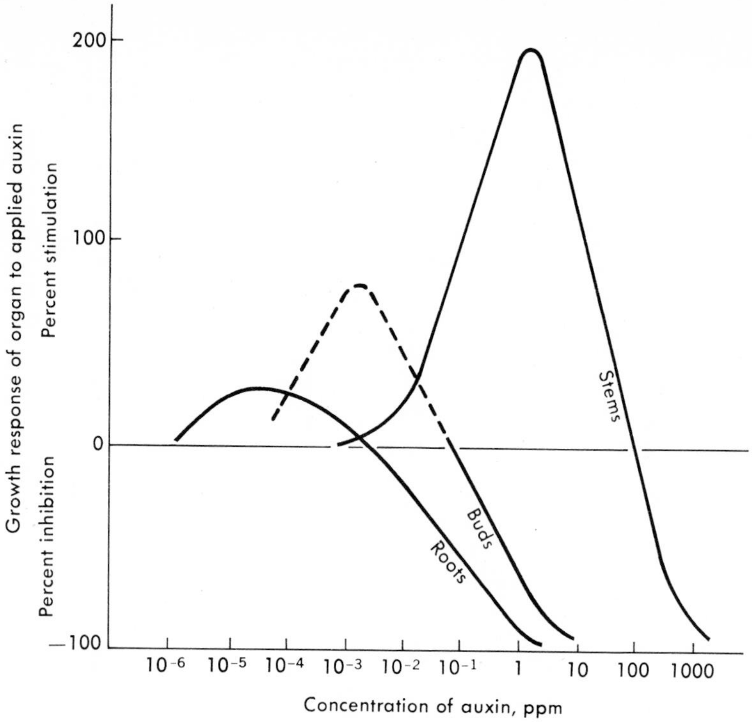

Figure 17-8 Dose response curves showing the effect of different concentrations of IAA on the growth of three plant organs. (After L. J. Audus. 1959. Plant growth substances. Interscience Publishers, New York.)

Thimann claimed that lateral buds are more sensitive than stems to auxin and that the concentration of auxin that stimulates stem growth is inhibitory to lateral bud growth. This theory received general acceptance, although it still failed to explain why the apical bud should be less sensitive to auxin merely because of its location on the stem.

The apical bud is not the only source of auxin. Young developing leaves also produce auxin, and it has been shown that auxin from this source may inhibit lateral bud growth (84).

Presently, the above explanation of apical bud dominance has been receiving an increasing amount of criticism from a number of different investigators. For example, studies done on the lilac (*Syringa vulgaris*) have demonstrated that the auxin-poor mature leaves of this plant have a much greater influence on lateral bud inhibition than the auxin-rich terminal bud (32). In addition, lateral bud inhibition not only occurs below the mature leaves on the stem, but above them also. Because of the upward movement of the auxin influence on the stem, Champagnat

(32) has claimed that auxin may not be involved in apical dominance. But, as we discussed earlier, nonpolar movement of auxin has been demonstrated in several cases, making it very possible for an influence of auxin to be felt in an upward direction from its origin as well as in a downward direction.

The most provocative criticism of Thimann's theory on apical dominance has been given by Gregory and Veale (52). They investigated the nutritional aspects of apical dominance with surprising results. It was found that the influence of auxin on lateral bud growth is controlled by the "nutritional status" of the plant. If the nitrogen needs of a flax plant are completely supplied during its growth, then, at the optimal period of growth, lateral bud inhibition by applied auxin cannot be demonstrated. However, in flax plants grown under conditions of inadequate nitrogen supply, the influence of applied auxin on lateral bud growth is easily demonstrated.

Root initiation

As already discussed, removal of the tip of a shoot greatly reduces the shoot's growth rate. In contrast, the removal of the tip of a root does not appreciably affect the growth rate (109). In fact, removal of less than 1 mm of the tip results in a very small but significant stimulation of growth rate (33). Replacement of the tip will again retard root growth (33, 34). Coleoptile tips have been found to act in the same manner as the root tip, retarding root growth when substituted for a root tip. There is little doubt that both the root tip and the coleoptile tip secrete a substance inhibitory to root growth. This substance has now been identified as IAA (65).

The question arises, is the action of auxin fundamentally different in roots as compared to stems? It has, more recently, been found that the action of auxin in roots is similar to that in stems, but that the concentrations of auxin stimulatory to stem growth are inhibitory to root growth. In other words, roots are much more sensitive to auxin than stems (Figure 17-8), and real stimulation of root elongation may be achieved if low enough concentrations are used.

The application of relatively high concentrations of IAA to roots not only retards root elongation, but causes a noticeable increase in the number of branch roots. Application of IAA in lanolin paste to the severed end of a young stem stimulates the rate of formation and number of roots initiated. This discovery is not only of scientific interest, but also has opened the door to commercial application of IAA to promote root formation in cuttings of economically useful plants. Figure 17-9

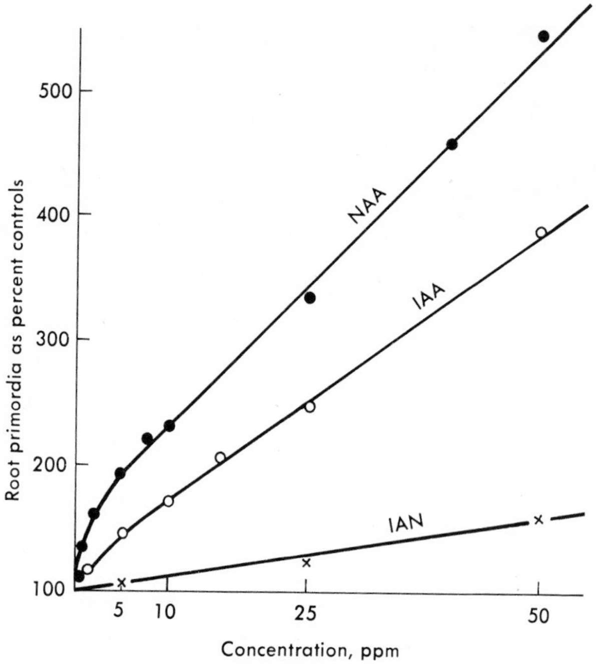

Figure 17-9 Dose response curves illustrating the effect of three auxins on the promotion of root primordia formation in bean seedlings. NAA = α-naphthaleneacetic acid, and IAN = indole-3-acetonitrile. (After L. C. Luckwill. 1956. J. Hort. Sci. 31: 89. Redrawn from L. J. Audus. 1959. Plant growth substances. Interscience Publishers, New York.)

illustrates the effect of IAA and two synthetic auxins on root formation in bean seedlings.

Parthenocarpy

With pollination and the subsequent fertilization of the ovule of a flower, the complex growth patterns leading to fruit set begin. Growth of the ovary wall and in some cases the tissues associated with the receptacle is greatly accelerated. Most of this acceleration of growth is due to cell enlargement, a phenomenon we have now learned to associate with auxin.

It appears from the above description of fruit set that pollination and fertilization are in some way connected with development of the fruit—perhaps with the release of a stimulus of some kind. Fruit development in the absence of pollination does, however, occur and in fact is relatively common in the plant world. The development of fruit in this manner is called *parthenocarpic development,* and the fruit that is formed is called *parthenocarpic fruit.*

The fact still remains that in the great majority of cases fruit development does not occur if fertilization does not take place. In what manner, then, does fertilization of the ovule trigger off responses leading to fruit set? As far back as 1902, Massart (75) had demonstrated that swelling of the ovary wall of orchids could be stimulated by dead pollen grains. Following Massart's work, Fitting (41) observed that water extracts of pollen are capable of inhibiting floral abscission and stimulating ovary wall swelling in orchids. Due to either a lack of interest or the complexity of the investigation, the problem of parthenocarpic fruit development lay dormant at this level for over 20 years. In 1934, the problem was again opened by Yasuda (113), who succeeded in causing the development of parthenocarpic fruit with the application of pollen extracts to cucumber flowers. An analysis of the materials present in such extracts showed that auxins were present (92). Finally, Gustafson (53) demonstrated that parthenocarpic development of fruit could be induced by application of IAA in lanolin paste to the stigma of the flower.

It was later found (76) that immediately after pollination, there is a sharp rise in the auxin content of tobacco ovaries. In the absence of pollination, no increase in auxin content is observed (Figure 17-10).

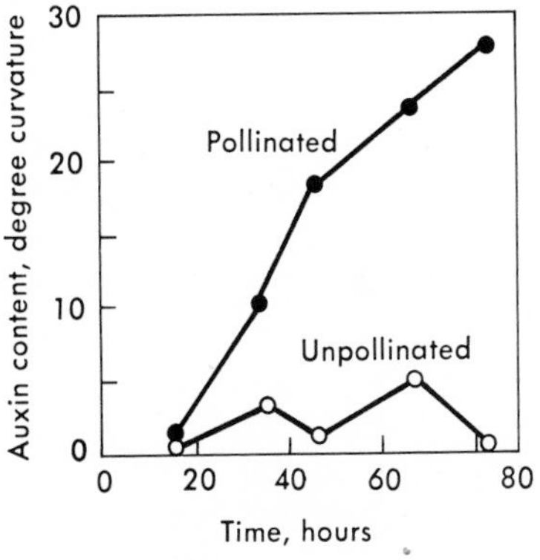

Figure 17-10 Increase in diffusible auxin content in tobacco ovary due to pollination. (After R. M. Muir. 1942. Am. J. Botany 29: 716. Redrawn from A. C. Leopold. 1955. Auxins and plant growth. University of California Press, Los Angeles.)

Muir (77) also observed that growth of the pollen tube increases considerably the amount of extractable auxin in the style of tobacco plants, leading him to suggest that an enzyme may be released by the pollen tubes which catalyzes the production of auxin. This suggestion was later given support by Lund (74) who found that pollen tubes secrete an enzyme capable of converting tryptophan to auxin.

It is obvious from the above discussion that auxins play an important role in the development of fruit. It appears that pollination, growth of the pollen tube, and fertilization all contribute to the "gush" of auxin responsible for fruit development. Although significant, the amount of auxin found in pollen grains is not sufficient to account for the high concentration of auxin found in the ovary after fertilization (49). However, as we have already suggested, an enzyme may be released by the growth of the pollen tube which is involved in the synthesis of auxin, perhaps from a precursor such as tryptophan.

Natural parthenocarpic fruit development is quite common in the plant world, leading some to suggest that auxins are not involved after all in the development of fruit. However, Gustafson (54) found that in the ovaries of species capable of natural parthenocarpy, the auxin content is a great deal higher than that found in the ovaries of species needing fertilization to produce fruit.

Abscission

The controlling influence of natural auxins on the abscission of leaves was first suspected when Laibach (66) showed that a substance contained in the extract of orchid pollinia is capable of preventing abscission. Support of this observation was given by LaRue (69) when he demonstrated the delaying effects of various synthetic auxins on the abscission of *Coleus* leaves. Since that time, a great deal of confirmatory work has been performed, clearly establishing indole-3-acetic acid (IAA) as the primary controlling factor in the abscission of plant organs (5).

Before the abscission of a plant organ, a layer of tissue is usually formed at the base of the organ, this tissue being easily distinguished from the surrounding tissues. This layer of tissue is referred to as the *abscission zone*. Cells in the abscission zone appear to be thin-walled and are almost completely lacking in lignin and suberin (86). In most cases, a series of cell divisions precede separation, although separation in the absence of cell division has been found in several species (5). The indication is that cell division is not essential to separation, but important in the forming of scar tissue, which acts as a protective layer over the wound left by abscission (46).

In a review on the subject of abscission, Addicott and Lynch (5) have listed three types of dissolution phenomenon that may cause abscission. In some cases, the middle lamella dissolves between two layers of cells, the primary walls remaining intact. The middle lamella and the primary wall may both dissolve, and in a few examples, whole cells have dissolved.

Botanists have sought to answer the question, what are the factors leading up to the abscission of a plant organ? It is a well-known fact that removal of a leaf blade will cause, in a short period of time, the abscission of the petiole. As discussed before, one of the sites of auxin production is the leaf blade from which auxin is transported through the petiole into the stem. Auxin, therefore, has been suspected as a controlling factor in abscission. This was clearly illustrated by Shoji et al. (87). They found that auxin content is high in the immature bean leaf blade, compared to the petiole, but that as the leaf ages, the auxin content of the blade falls to a point comparable to that found in the petiole (Figure 17-11). At this point, the leaves are yellow and ready to abscise.

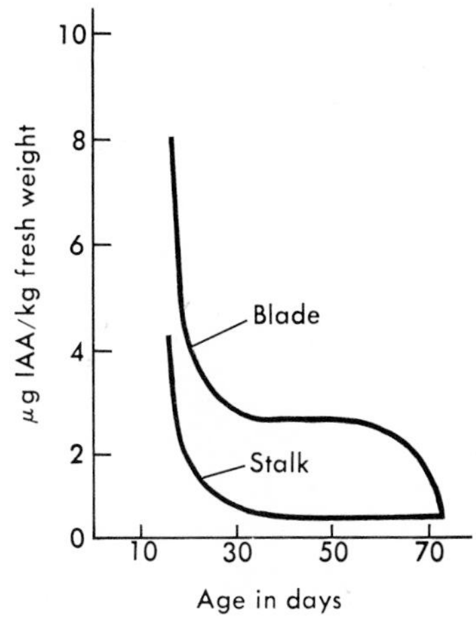

Figure 17-11 Decrease in diffusible auxin content in bean leaf blades and petioles with age. (After K. Shoji et al. 1951. Plant Physiol 26: 189.)

In a remarkable series of experiments, Addicott and Lynch (4) demonstrated that the most important factor controlling abscission is the condition of the *auxin gradient* across the abscission zone. Application of IAA in lanolin paste to either the proximal or distal (away from the stem) end of debladed bean leaf petioles has a profound effect on the rate of abscission of those petioles. Proximal application accelerates the rate of abscission and distal application retards it (Figure 17-12). It was concluded that a critical auxin concentration gradient across the abscission zone, rather than the concentration itself, may be necessary to prevent abscission. According to this theory, abscission does not occur when the gradient is steep, that is, when the endogenous auxin concentration is high on the distal side and low on the proximal side of the abscission zone. Abscission occurs when the gradient becomes slight or neutral and is accelerated when the gradient is reversed. These relationships are shown diagrammatically in Figure 17-13. It is interesting to note that Rossetter and Jacobs (84) found that the intact leaves of *Coleus* speed abscission of nearby debladed

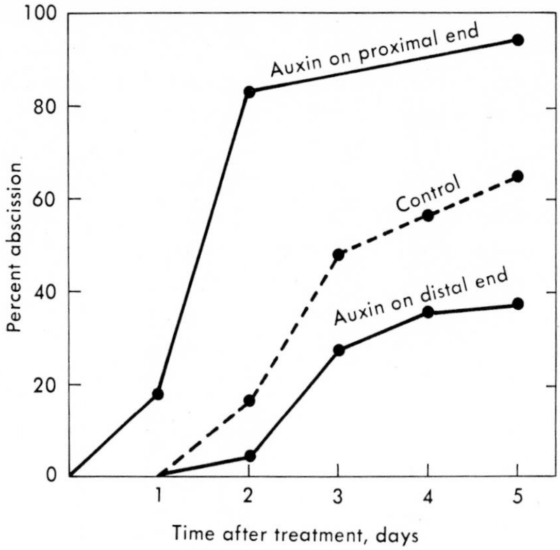

Figure 17-12 Effect of proximal and distal applications of auxin (105 mg/liter) on the rate of abscission of debladed bean leaf petioles. (After F. T. Addicott and R. S. Lynch. 1951. Science 114: 688.)

petioles, suggesting that the intact leaves act as sources of proximal auxin for nearby petioles.

Respiration

James Bonner (18) was the first investigator to recognize that auxin has a stimulatory effect on respiration. His work led him to suggest that auxin activity only takes place in the presence of oxidative metabolism. Since Bonner's pioneer work, many studies have confirmed that auxin stimulates respiration and that there is a correlation between increased growth due to auxin treatment and increase in respiration. In Figure 17-14, a striking similarity can be seen between the response of growth and the response of respiration to different concentrations of IAA. The optimal response for both curves occurs at almost the same concentration of IAA.

Physiologists are still faced with the problem of explaining how auxin induces a stimulation of respiration. An attractive approach to the problem has been made by French and Beevers (42). They demonstrated that respiration may be increased by substances that have no effect or an inhibitory effect on growth. Dinitrophenol (DNP), a substance which

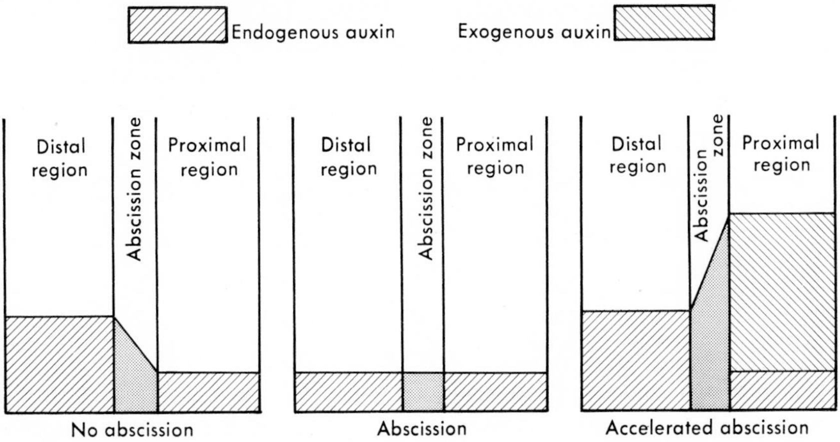

Figure 17-13 Relations between the auxin gradient across the abscission zone and abscission. (After F. T. Addicott and R. S. Lynch. 1955. Ann. Rev. Plant Physiol. 6: 211.)

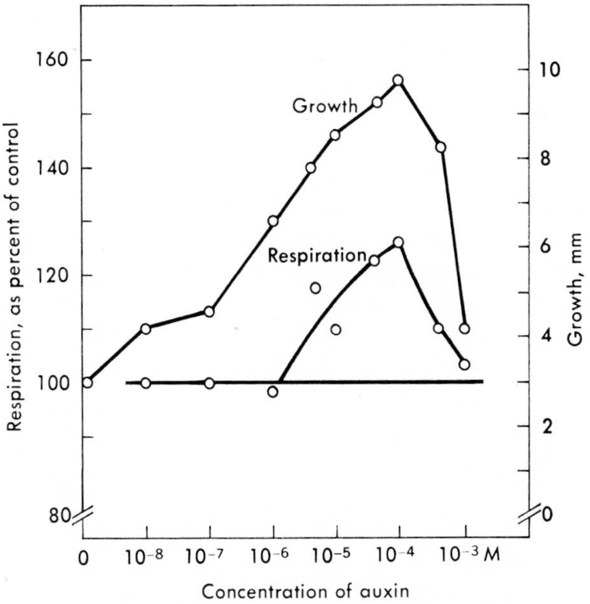

Figure 17-14 The effect of different concentrations of auxin on the rate of growth and respiration of corn coleoptile sections. (After R. C. French and H. Beevers. 1953. Am. J. Botany 40: 660.)

inhibits oxidative phosphorylation (formation of ATP from ADP in respiration), increases the rate of respiration while inhibiting growth. Since the rate of respiration is normally limited by the supply of ADP, treatment of living tissues with DNP should cause an increased supply of ADP and thus stimulate respiration. It is thought that auxin may also increase the supply of ADP by causing ATP to be rapidly used up in the expanding cell, thus increasing the supply of ADP. This would appear to give auxin an indirect role in the stimulation of respiration rather than the direct role that was earlier postulated.

Callus formation

Although we have been stressing that auxin activity manifests itself in the plant primarily as a stimulant of cell elongation, it also may be active in cell division. For example, application of 1% IAA in lanolin paste to a debladed petiole of a bean plant will cause a yellow swelling where the auxin is applied. This swelling is caused by the development of callus tissue made up of rapidly dividing parenchyma cells. If a succulent stem is cut a few millimeters below a mature leaf and the wound treated with IAA in lanolin paste, this same proliferation of parenchyma cells is observed. After a period of time, young adventitious roots will develop. Thus, IAA not only causes a proliferation of cells, but also under some conditions may cause a dedifferentiation of these cells, that is, cause the formation of adventitious roots.

Also, in many tissue cultures where callus growth is quite normal, the addition of auxin is necessary for the continued growth of such callus. The amount of callus tissue formed is related to the concentration of IAA applied, higher concentrations causing greater development of the callus tissue (Figure 17-15).

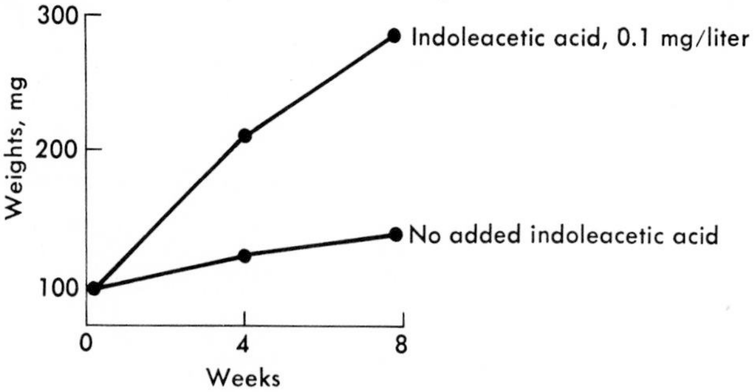

Figure 17-15 Callus growth with and without the addition of IAA. (After R. S. de Ropp. 1950. Am. J. Botany 37: 358.)

BIOASSAYS

When dealing with biologically active substances, such as plant growth hormones, it is essential that a means for measuring their activity be obtained. In most cases, the material used to measure the activity of a growth regulator responds specifically to that compound or to a group of compounds with similar activity. Also, there is always a correlation between the response of the testing material and the concentration of growth regulator. *Bioassay* is the term used to describe the employment of living material to test the effect of biologically active substances.

Although several bioassays for auxin activity have been devised since the discovery of auxins in plants, only a very few have found general use. We will concern ourselves with four bioassays, which have found general application to the study of growth regulators. These are (1) *Avena curvature test,* (2) *Avena section test,* (3) *split pea stem curvature test,* and (4) *cress root inhibition test.*

Avena curvature test

Earlier in this chapter, we discussed very briefly the *Avena* curvature test and its founder, F. W. Went. This was the first bioassay for auxin and probably the best one. The sensitivity and reliability achieved by the *Avena* curvature test gives it extensive use even now, more than 35 years after its discovery.

The measurement of auxin activity by the *Avena* curvature test depends upon the strict, rapid polar transport of auxin in the *Avena* coleoptile. Because of this property, auxin applied to one side of the coleoptile will diffuse down that side rapidly. However, it will not to any significant extent diffuse laterally. The differential growth that is caused by the transport of auxin down only one side of the coleoptile produces a curvature that is proportional, within limits, to the amount of auxin applied.

The procedure for the *Avena* curvature test is as follows:

1. *Avena* seedlings are germinated and grown in the dark. There is a reduction in sensitivity of the coleoptile to auxin when it is exposed to blue light. Inconvenient elongation of the first internode may be reduced by exposing the seedling two days after germination to 2–4 hours of red light.
2. After a height of 15–30 mm has been reached, 1 mm of the apical tip of the coleoptile is removed, thus removing the natural source of auxin.
3. A second decapitation is necessary after a 3-hour period to remove tissue that has regenerated and now produces auxin (2–4 mm are removed).
4. The primary leaf, which has been exposed by the second decapitation,

is then gently pulled; Its connection should be broken at the base of the coleoptile so that it will extend a few millimeters out of the coleoptile. Note that we now have vertical support (tip of the primary leaf) for the agar block that will be placed on the coleoptile.

5. An agar block containing auxin may now be placed on one side of the severed end of the coleoptile. Auxin will be transported in a polar fashion down that side of the coleoptile to which the auxin-agar block has been applied.
6. After 90 minutes, the shadows of the seedlings are projected onto a strip of bromide paper and photographed. This gives the investigator a permanent record.
7. Curvature is measured by recording the angle made by a vertical line and a line drawn parallel to the curved portion of the stem.

The *Avena* curvature test is diagrammatically shown in Figure 17-1.

Within a certain range of concentrations of IAA, there is a linear relationship between the concentration and the amount of curvature obtained. As shown in Figure 17-16, this range for IAA reaches an optimum peak at around 0.2 mg/liter.

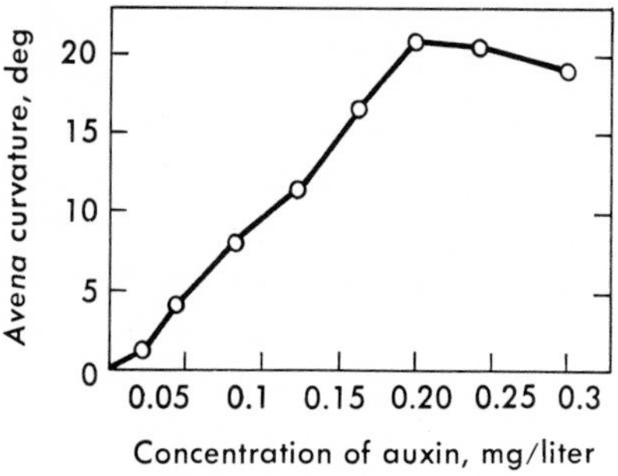

Figure 17-16 Linear response of the *Avena* coleoptile to increasing concentration of IAA. (After F. W. Went and K. V. Thimann. 1937. Phytohormones. The Macmillan Co., New York.)

Avena section test

The *Avena* section test is based only on the ability of auxin to stimulate cell elongation. Transport of auxin or differential growth caused by auxin are not involved here.

This test, utilizing sections of the oat coleoptile, was first used by Bonner in 1933 (18). Since then, this bioassay has found wide use, both for its simplicity and its applicability. The *Avena* section test, unlike the *Avena* curvature test, measures the effect of growth regulators over a very wide range of concentrations. In addition, unlike the *Avena* curvature test, the test is not hindered by problems of transport of the growth regulator. Some growth regulators are not transported as readily as IAA and therefore could not be used in the *Avena* curvature test. However, the *Avena* curvature test is much more sensitive to low concentrations of auxin than the section test, thus having a major advantage in this respect. This becomes particularly advantageous in plant extraction procedures where only very small quantities of auxin are present. In order to detect the presence of auxin under these conditions, the *Avena* curvature test would have to be employed.

The procedure for the *Avena* section test is as follows:

1. *Avena* seeds (caryopsis) of a pure strain (e.g., victory) are germinated and grown in the dark at 25°C and a relative humidity of about 85%. Only weak red light may be used in the growth room.
2. When the coleoptiles are about 25–30 mm in length, they are harvested; the apical 4 mm are removed, and a section 3–5 mm in length is cut from each coleoptile cylinder.
3. All sections are soaked in distilled water for a minimum of one hour and then distributed at random to petri dishes containing 20 ml of test solution.
4. After a 12, 24, or 48 hour incubation period at 25°C, the sections are measured with the aid of a dissecting microscope equipped with an ocular micrometer. If determination of growth rate is desired, the sections are measured after a 12 hour incubation period. If growth is to be determined, 24 or 48 hour incubation periods are usually used.

The *Avena* section test is diagrammatically shown in Figure 17-17.

In the *Avena* section test, the growth response of the sections is found to be directly proportional to the logarithm of the concentration of growth regulator used (see dose response curve in Figure 17-17). This contrasts with the *Avena* curvature test in which the growth response is directly proportional to the amount of auxin used. The *Avena* curvature test, therefore, is a much more sensitive test, but is confined to a short concentration range.

The split pea stem curvature test

This test, first described by Went (105), like the *Avena* curvature test, depends upon a differential growth response. A stem section of a pea seedling of a pure strain (e.g., Alaska) is slit longitudinally and floated on the test solution. At first a negative curvature occurs (curvature outward) because of the uptake of water by the inner cortical cells. The epidermal cells respond to auxin with considerable growth in length and a negligible growth in width, while the cortical cells respond to auxin with more growth in width than in length. Consequently, after an incubation period with a physiological concentration of auxin, a positive curvature results. Within

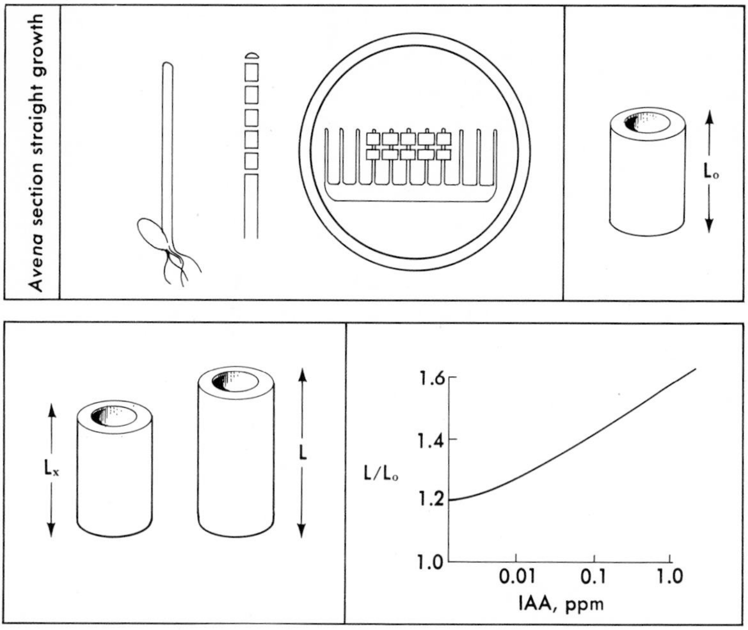

Figure 17-17 Diagrammatic representation of the *Avena* section test. L_0 = length of freshly cut segment; L_x = length of untreated segment after floating in water for length of test period; L = length of treated segment after floating in test solution for length of test period. (After L. J. Audus. 1959. Plant growth substances. Interscience Publishers, New York.)

a certain range, the response of the slit halves of the stem is roughly proportional to the logarithm of the concentration of auxin used.

The procedure for the split pea stem curvature test is as follows:

1. Pea seeds are germinated and grown in the dark for 8 days. The seedlings are exposed to 3 hours of red light per day to increase sensitivity to auxin.
2. The stems are harvested, decapitated, and a section $\frac{1}{2}$ inch long between the second and third internode is removed.
3. The sections are soaked in distilled water for an hour to remove any endogenous auxin that might be present in the stem section.
4. The stem section is then slit longitudinally a standard 3 cm and placed in a petri dish containing 25 ml of auxin solution. Five or six sections to a petri dish is the usual procedure.
5. After an incubation period of 6 hours, curvature of the slit stem tips is read.

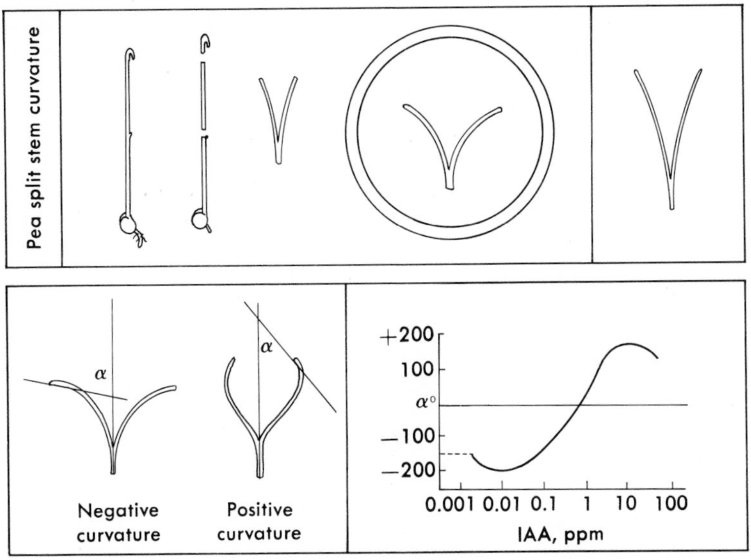

Figure 17-18 Diagrammatic representation of the split pea stem curvature test. (After L. J. Audus. 1959. Plant growth substances. Interscience Publishers, New York.)

The split pea stem curvature test is diagrammatically shown in Figure 17-18.

As in the *Avena* section test, transport of auxin is not involved in the pea stem test. Therefore, the effect of growth regulators that are not easily transported in plant tissues can be measured by the pea stem test.

Cress root inhibition test

Earlier in this chapter, we mentioned that roots are much more sensitive to auxin than stems and are, in fact, inhibited by concentrations of auxin that normally stimulate stem growth. However, at very low concentrations of auxin, root growth may be stimulated. The value, then, of the root test is that the effect of extremely low concentrations of auxin, such as found in plant extracts, may be measured.

The procedure for the cress root inhibition test is as follows:

1. Seeds are sterilized and then germinated on most filter paper.
2. When the roots of the seedling have reached a desired length, they are placed in petri dishes containing 15 ml of test solution.
3. Growth of the root is measured after 48 hours.

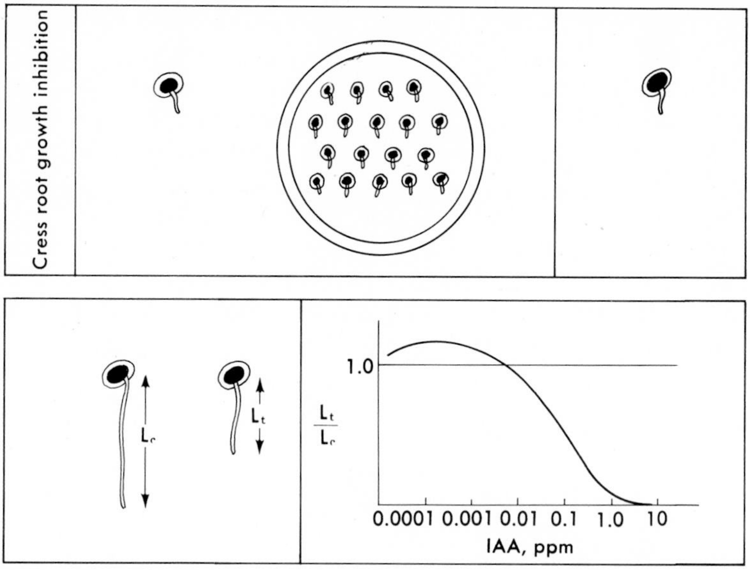

Figure 17-19 Diagrammatic representation of the cress root inhibition test. L_C = length of control seedling root at the termination of the test period. L_T = length of treated seedling root at the termination of the test period. (After L. J. Audus. 1959. Plant growth substances. Interscience Publishers, New York.)

The cress root inhibition test is diagrammatically shown in Figure 17-19.

Many other bioassays for auxin activity have been devised, some for specific use and others for more general application. However, the above-mentioned assays are the ones most generally used. Of the four assays described, the *Avena* curvature test is the best for quantitative determinations, but is restricted to compounds that are transported rapidly in a polar manner. The *Avena* section test and split pea stem curvature test are applicable to a wide range of concentrations, but cannot be used for quantitative determinations of low concentrations of auxin such as found in plant extracts. The cress root inhibition test is even more sensitive than the *Avena* curvature test, being able to detect concentrations of IAA as low as 1/100,000 mg. However, small differences in auxin concentration cannot be detected by the root test, its response being roughly proportional to the logarithm of the auxin concentration.

BIOSYNTHESIS OF AUXIN

In the earlier years of auxin study, Bonner (17) found that the mould *Rhizopus suinus* increased its output of natural auxin if grown in a medium containing peptone. *R. suinus,* at that time, was one of the best sources of natural auxin. This increase in auxin supply undoubtedly occurred through the oxidation of the amino acids of peptone. Three years later, it was demonstrated that this mould could convert the amino acid *tryptophan* to IAA (94). To this day, tryptophan is considered to be the primary precursor of IAA.

The synthesis of auxin during lengthy extraction procedures was a source of error in early work with IAA. It was soon discovered that boiling the plant material (55) or extracting at low temperatures (112) effectively limited the synthesis of IAA. The above discoveries gave support to the suggestion by Skoog and Thimann (90) that the production of auxin is an enzymatic process. Finally, an enzymatic system capable of converting tryptophan to IAA was isolated by Wildman et al. (111) from spinach leaves.

Detailed studies on the presence of an enzyme capable of converting tryptophan to IAA in *Avena* coleoptiles have demonstrated a close agreement between the distribution of IAA and the enzyme (110). The enzyme is present in greatest amount at the tip and is progressively less concentrated toward the base of the coleoptile.

The biosynthetic pathways by which tryptophan might be converted to IAA are illustrated schematically in Figure 17-20. Gordon and Nieva (48) found that if leaf discs or crude extracts of pineapple leaves are incubated with tryptophan, tryptamine, or indolepyruvic acid, IAA is formed. They proposed that IAA could be formed from tryptophan via two different pathways: by the deamination of tryptophan to form indolepyruvic acid, followed by decarboxylation to form indole acetaldehyde or by the decarboxylation of the tryptophan to form tryptamine, followed by deamination to form indoleacetaldehyde. By either pathway, indoleacetaldehyde is formed and thus must be considered the immediate precursor of IAA in plants. Indoleacetaldehyde is readily oxidized to form IAA. Its conversion to the auxin has been demonstrated on several occasions, using crude enzyme preparations from different plants (68, 10, 13).

Gordon (47), in a recent review on the subject of auxin biosynthesis, suggested that auxin may be formed by different pathways during the development of the plant. In other words, the biochemistry of auxin formation in germinating seeds may be different from auxin formation in leaves, coleoptile tips, etc. He draws a parallel in this respect to the glycolytic pathway. There are many examples where glucose oxidation follows different pathways during the ontogeny of the plant.

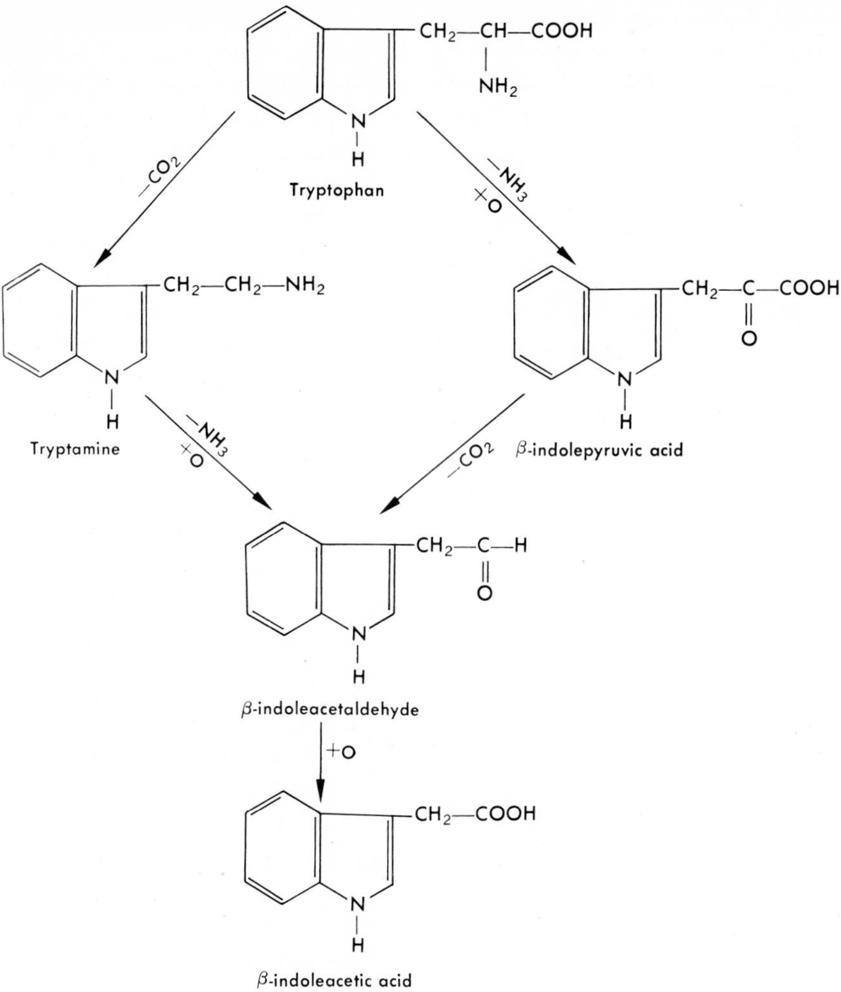

Figure 17-20 Possible pathways of auxin synthesis from tryptophan.

OTHER PLANT HORMONES

Traumatic acid

The formation of wound callus on plants that have been damaged in one manner or another (e.g., in pruning) is a common observation. It was postulated as early as the latter half of the nineteenth century that damaged tissue may cause the production of a substance which, upon diffusion into nearby undamaged cells, would stimulate meristematic activity (11). Haberlandt (57) demonstrated that extracts of damaged cells are capable of inducing meristematic activity when applied to undamaged cells.

Subsequent investigations, notably those of Wehnelt (102) and Bonner and English (24), led to the isolation of a compound that is very active in inducing meristematic activity in undamaged green bean pods. This hormone, a straight chain dicarboxylic acid, was given the name *traumatic acid*. Its structure is as follows:

$$HOOCCH{=}CH(CH_2)_8COOH$$

The effect of traumatic acid on inducing cells to divide does not appear to be general. In fact, most plant tissues do not respond to traumatic acid, suggesting that it may be a specific wound hormone for bean-pod tissue (40).

Calines

Evidence has been accumulating that the effect of auxin on root stem and leaf growth are not isolated reactions, but involve other natural hormones. These hormones, it is postulated, have to be present in the correct concentration in order for auxin to initiate any growth effects. Indirect evidence has been presented for the existence of three of these hormones: *rhizocaline* (root-caline), *caulocaline* (stem-caline), and *phyllocaline* (leaf-caline).

It has been observed that the presence of leaves and buds on cuttings is necessary for a good rooting response to auxin. Indeed, in some cases it is essential that a certain number of leaves be present for rooting to occur. In an attempt to explain the above phenomenon, two schools of thought have developed: (1) that leaves produce a compound that in combination with auxin will cause roots to develop, and (2) that leaves do not provide a specific root hormone, but merely provide nutrients that are necessary for the growth of the roots.

Bouillenne and Went (26) were the first to suggest the existence of a special root-forming hormone produced by the leaves and transported in a polar manner down the stem. They called this hormone *rhizocaline*. Later work by Cooper (37) supported these observations. He found that lemon cuttings respond to auxin treatments by forming lateral roots. However, if the portion of the stem containing these roots is removed and auxin applied a second time, there is no rooting response, even though the leaves should still be providing nutrients. Cooper suggested that there is a limited supply of rhizocaline and that this is used up in the first application of auxin. In subsequent years, there have been several studies supporting the "rhizocaline theory." However, the isolation of rhizocaline has not been accomplished, leaving us only with indirect evidence as to its existence.

On the other hand, van Overbeek et al. (101) have convincingly demonstrated that rooting of cuttings of red hibiscus is strongly dependent upon nutrients produced in the leaves. They have shown that the effect of leaves on root formation can be completely replaced by sugar and nitrogenous compounds (Figure 17-21).

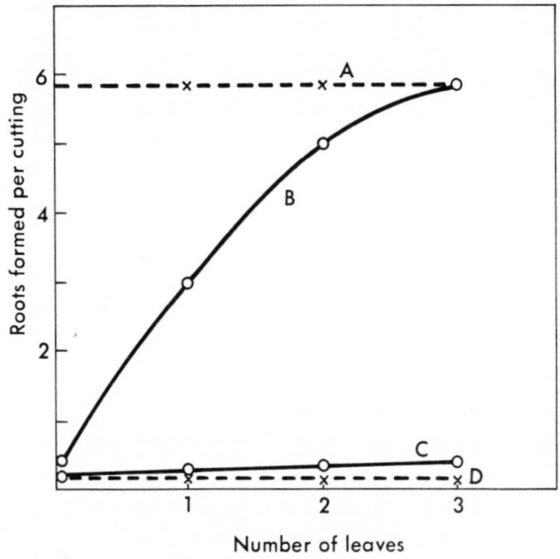

Figure 17-21 Promotion by leaves of auxin-stimulated root formation on cuttings of red hibiscus. Curve A represents a treatment with auxin, sucrose, and $(NH_4)_2SO_4$. Curve B represents a treatment with auxin. Curve C represents a treatment with sucrose and $(NH_4)_2SO_4$. Curve D represents the control. The stimulating effect of leaves can be entirely replaced by 4% sucrose and 0.1% $(NH_4)_2SO_4$. (After van Overbeek et al. 1946. Am. J. Botany 33: 100.)

The existence of a stem-forming hormone was first postulated by Went (107) who called it *caulocaline*. Its synthesis takes place in the plant roots from where it is translocated to its site of activity in the stem. However, conflicting evidence has been presented by studies demonstrating the growth of isolated stem parts in the light on simple inorganic media (71, 88). Went (108) has explained the findings of these studies as exceptional cases where caulocaline is synthesized in the stem.

Phyllocaline, also named by Went (108), stimulates mesophyll development in leaves. Its synthesis takes place only in the presence of light; that is, it is photochemically produced (50). Its actual site of synthesis has not been identified, but at least in one study, cotyledons have been suspected. Bonner et al. (16) have shown that the growth of isolated discs of leaf mesophyll in a sucrose medium is stimulated considerably by the addition of pea cotyledon extract. Whether this is a result of a combination of growth factors contained in the extract or due to one specific compound, we do not know. Again, until phyllocaline is isolated, we can only speculate as to its existence.

Vitamins

Vitamins are organic compounds which in low concentration have catalytic and regulatory functions in cell metabolism. Most higher plants are capable of synthesizing all of the vitamins necessary for their normal growth, while in animals this ability is lacking. Therefore, vitamins are necessary constituents of the diet of most animals.

Since plants are capable of synthesizing vitamins, it is difficult to study their effect on the plant. For example, in animal study, merely removing the vitamin from the diet is all that is necessary for observing the effects of a vitamin deficiency. However, in most cases, the physiological role of a vitamin in a plant can be deduced from its metabolic function in animals. Direct experimental proof, of course, is desired, and recently methods for producing and detecting vitamin deficiency in plants have been developed.

One method for studying the role of vitamins in plants is to isolate and grow in tissue culture an organ (e.g., root) of the plant that is incapable of synthesizing a certain vitamin. Under normal conditions, the missing vitamin would be translocated from its site of production to the organ in which it is lacking. Isolation of this organ in tissue culture allows an investigator to study the role of that vitamin in the development of the organ.

Another method for creating vitamin deficiencies in plants is to remove from the environment those conditions necessary for the normal synthesis of the vitamin. For example, many vitamins require light for their normal synthesis (2); growth in the dark, therefore, induces vitamin deficiencies.

Vitamin A. *Vitamin A* has not, as yet, been found in plants. However, the precursors of vitamin A, the carotenoids, are found in all parts of the plants and are synthesized in situ in the organ in which they are found (20). We discussed the functions of carotenoids in plants in the first chapter on photosynthesis.

The synthesis of carotenoids can take place in the dark, but is greatly accelerated by light (2). Transport of vitamin A has not been convincingly demonstrated, and since it is produced in all parts of the plant, its translocation from one organ to another would be of little significance. The structure of vitamin A is given.

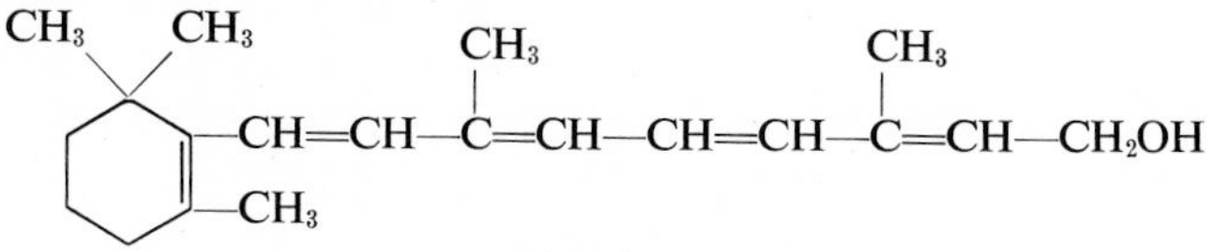

Vitamin A

Thiamine (vitamin B_1). The significance of thiamine to cellular metabolism may be found in its role as a coenzyme in the decarboxylation of α-keto acids (e.g., pyruvate and α-keto glutarate). Vitamin B is generally found in two forms, a "free" form which is *thiamine* and a "bound" form called *thiamine pyrophosphate*. In cereal grains in which there is a plentiful supply of thiamine, the free form dominates (82), this possibly being the form in which the vitamin is stored. The active form of the vitamin, however, is thiamine pyrophosphate, which is synthesized in the transfer of pyrophosphate from ATP to thiamine. The structures of thiamine and thiamine pyrophosphate are given.

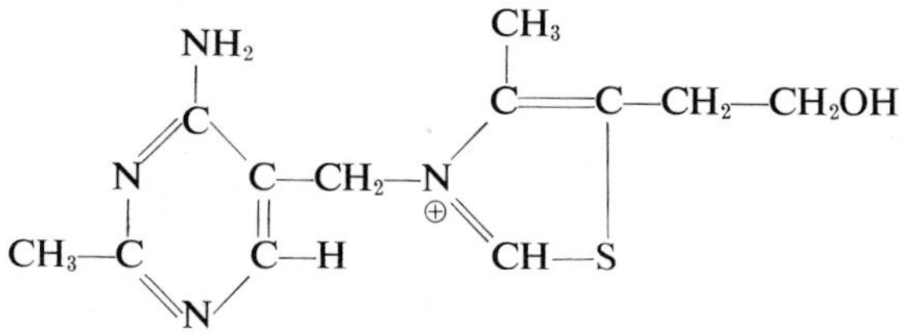

Thiamine

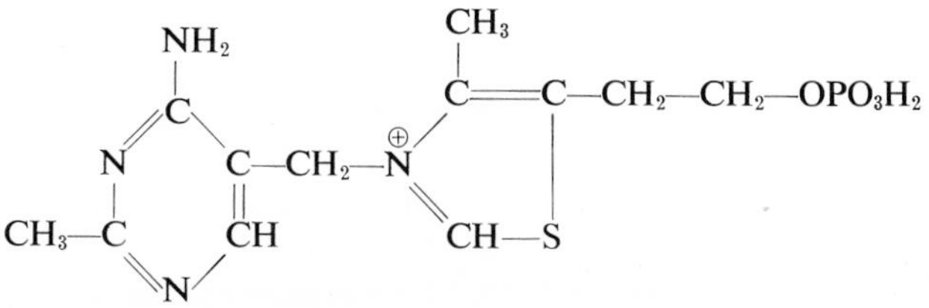

Thiamine pyrophosphate

Thiamine is found in highest concentrations in the actively growing regions of the plant (19). Evidence has been presented that the synthesis of thiamine takes place in the leaves (19) and that it is often light-dependent (22).

Thiamine deficiency effects can best be demonstrated in sterile cultures of excised roots in which normal growth will not occur unless thiamine is added to the culture. Apparently, the root systems of most plants do not synthesize a sufficient amount of thiamine to meet their needs. Girdling experiments with tomato plants have shown that thiamine is translocated from the leaves to the roots in the phloem system (25).

Riboflavin (vitamin B_2). *Riboflavin* is of general occurrence in plants (2) where it is found primarily in a bound form. Riboflavin functions as a constituent of the coenzymes *flavin mononucleotide* (FMN) and *flavin adenine dinucleotide* (FAD), which are involved in biological oxidations. We have already encountered FMN in the discussion of photosynthesis which described its participation in cyclic electron transport. The structure of riboflavin is given.

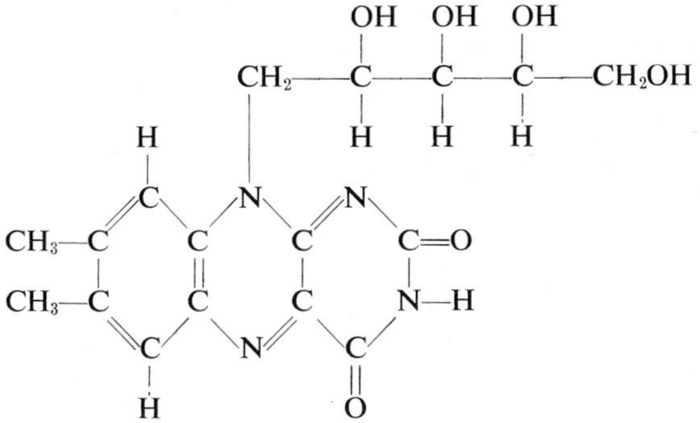

Riboflavin

Since riboflavin is synthesized in sufficient amounts by all parts of the plant, deficiency symptoms are very difficult to demonstrate. Isolated reports of growth stimulations due to addition of riboflavin have not been confirmed. However, it has been reported that riboflavin may be involved in an auxin-inactivating mechanism (45).

Nicotinic acid (niacin). The biological importance of *nicotinic acid* was realized when it was discovered that it is generally found in the form of NADP and NAD, important coenzymes in many hydrogen transfer processes. Nicotinic acid is widely distributed in plants (56) and as with riboflavin is found in unusually high concentrations in wheat grains (59). The structure of nicotinic acid is given below.

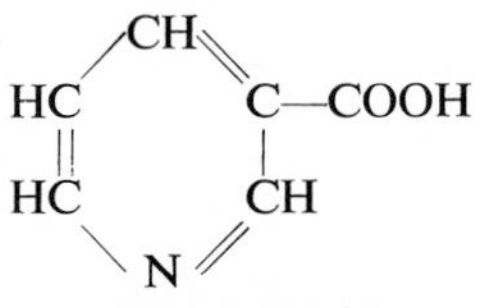

Nicotinic acid

Deficiency effects are easily demonstrated in excised root tissue cultures since nicotinic acid is not synthesized in sufficient enough quantities in most root systems to sustain normal growth. Meristematic activity, cell dimensions, and the number of cell columns all may be reduced in isolated root tissue cultures as a result of a nicotinic acid deficiency (3).

The fact that tryptophan has been suggested as a precursor of both nicotinic acid (61) and IAA (94) has led to investigations of possible interactions between the auxin and nicotinic acid. Galston (44) found that nicotinic acid has a synergistic effect on IAA stimulation of root initiation. In addition, he found that IAA is antagonistic to bud growth stimulation due to nicotinic acid. Undoubtedly, these interactions are due to the fact that both compounds have a common precursor in tryptophan.

Pyridoxine, pyridoxal, and pyridoxamine (vitamin B_6 complex). Of the three compounds listed above as members of the B_6 complex, no one can be considered the vitamin, since all three are active in plant nutrition. However, it has been suggested that *pyridoxine* is converted to *pyridoxal* and *pyridoxamine,* which are then phosphorylated to give *pyridoxal phosphate* and *pyridoxamine phosphate,* respectively. The phosphate derivatives, especially pyridoxal phosphate, represent the functional form of pyridoxine. The structures for the three components of the B_6 complex and their phosphate derivatives are shown.

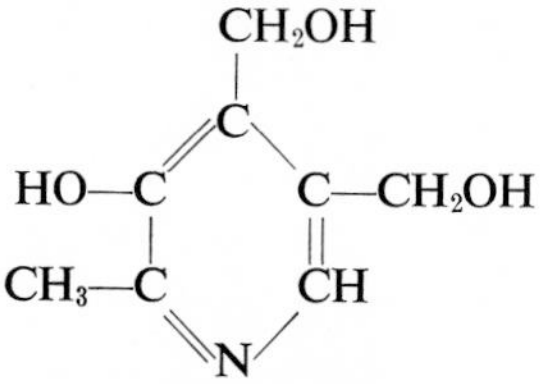

Pyridoxine

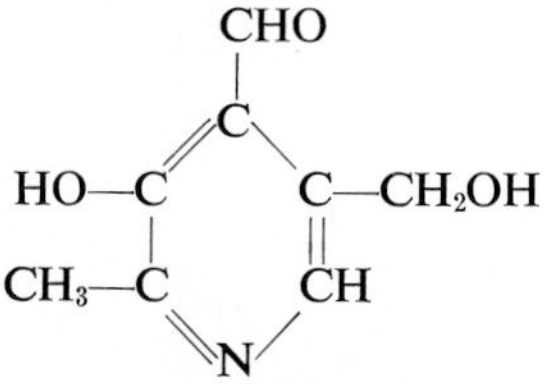

Pyridoxal

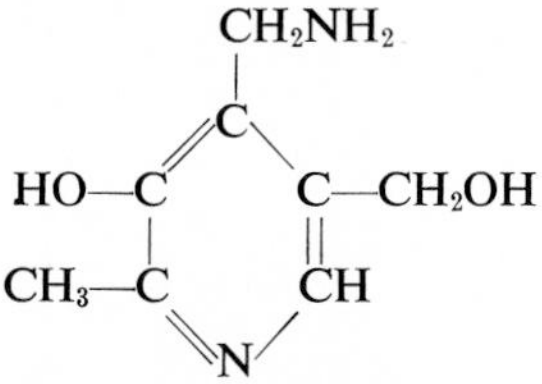

Pyridoxamine

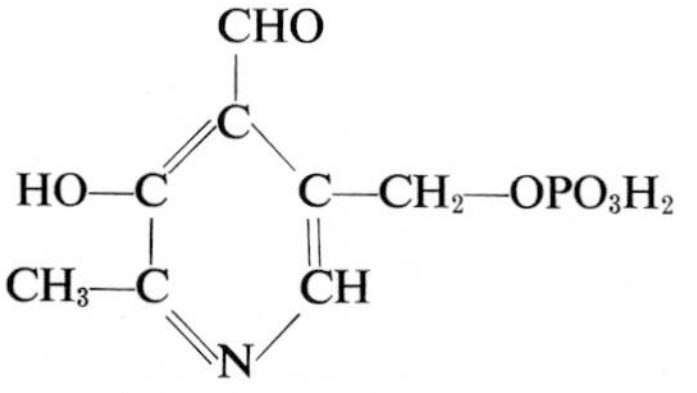

Pyridoxal phosphate

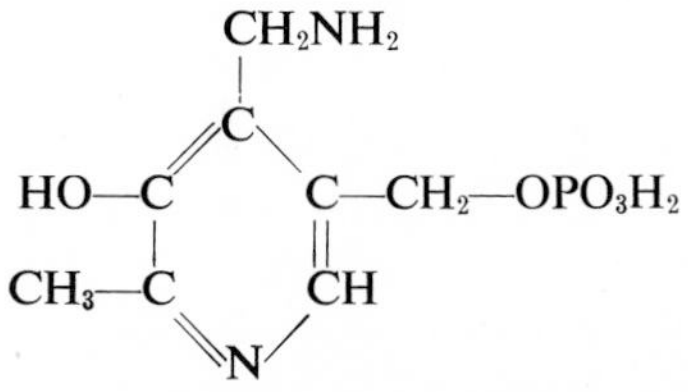

Pyridoxamine phosphate

Vitamin B_6 is distributed generally throughout the plant, occurring in stems, leaves, roots, seeds, and fruits (22). However, there is suggestive evidence that most of the vitamin that is found in the roots has been translocated from the leaves since vitamin B_6 is a necessary growth factor for most root tissue cultures. In addition, steam girdles applied to both petioles and stems cause an accumulation of vitamin B_6 above the girdles. These experiments also demonstrate that vitamin B_6 moves in the phloem tissue and generally in the direction of nutrient transport.

A decrease in meristematic activity of isolated roots due to vitamin B_6

deficiency has been noted by Almestrand (6, 7). Desoxypyridoxine, an antagonist of pyridoxine, causes a depressed growth in tomato root culture, which is reversed on further addition of pyridoxine (15).

The most important physiological function of vitamin B_6 may be found in the participation of pyridoxal phosphate as a coenzyme in amino acid metabolism. Transamination and decarboxylation reactions are the most prevalent in this function of the vitamin. It also has been suggested that vitamin B_6 may participate in the synthesis of tryptophan and nicotinic acid.

Pantothenic acid. *Pantothenic acid* has been found in most plant parts and, according to Bonner and Dorland (23), is synthesized in most of these parts. The highest concentrations of pantothenic acid have been found in the aleurone layer of wheat grains (59).

Pantothenic acid is very seldom found in the free form. Practically all of it may be found in the form of coenzyme A. Coenzyme A is involved in transacylation reactions, which are of extreme importance to carbohydrate and fat metabolism. The structure of pantothenic acid is shown.

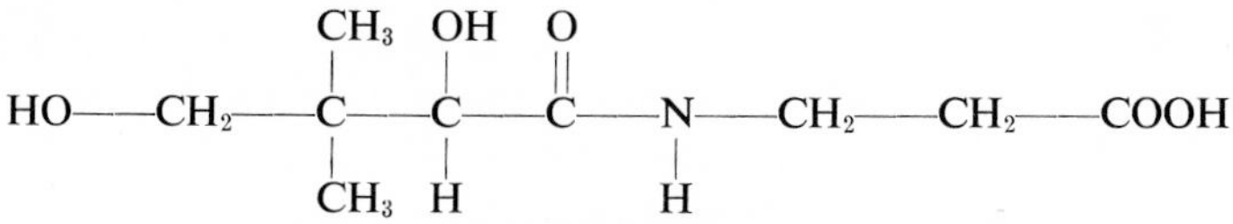

Pantothenic acid

Convincing evidence of any growth restrictions due to pantothenic acid deficiency in plant tissues has not as yet been demonstrated. Utilization of acetic acid as a carbon source by excised tomato flowers is inhibited by a pantothenic acid deficiency (70). It has also been suggested that pantothenic acid may be implicated in the photoperiodic responses of plants (67).

Biotin. *Biotin* has been detected in all parts of the higher plants (22, 91). The action of biotin in higher plants is relatively unknown, most of our knowledge of its activity in cellular metabolism coming from work done on microorganisms. The vitamin appears to be active in the metabolism of aspartic acid, decarboxylation reactions involving Krebs cycle intermediates, and oleic acid synthesis (43). The structure of biotin is given.

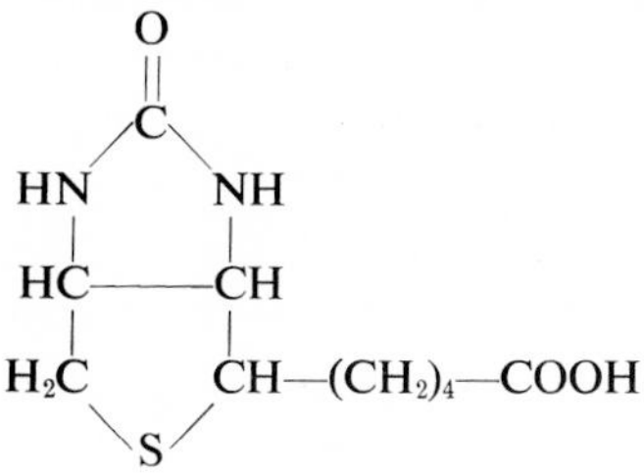

Biotin

Ascorbic acid (vitamin C). *Ascorbic acid* is found in all parts of the plant, the highest concentrations being detected in green leaves and certain fruits (2). It is found mostly as ascorbic acid, but small amounts of its oxidized form, *dehydroascorbic acid,* are also generally found. Translocation of the vitamin in plants has not been convincingly demonstrated. The structures of the reduced and oxidized forms of ascorbic acid are given.

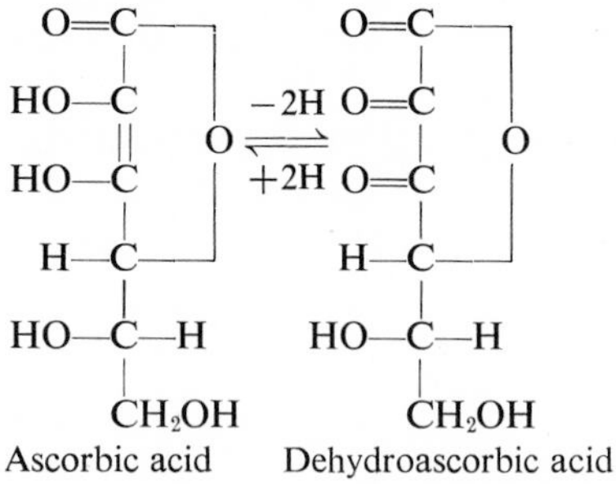

Ascorbic acid is readily oxidized to dehydroascorbic acid, which in turn can be reduced again by a copper-containing enzyme, ascorbic acid oxidase, present only in plants. Because of its reversible oxidation-reduction potential, ascorbic acid has been suggested as a catalyst in photosynthetic phosphorylation (9), as an important regulator of the oxidation-reduction state of protoplasm, and as an influence on the oxidative state and activity of SH-enzymes (2).

Vitamin C may also be involved in the transfer of hydrogen from NADPH to oxygen by undergoing a cyclic oxidation-reduction reaction coupled with the oxidized and reduced states of glutathione (GSSG to GSH) (1). The electron path is as follows:

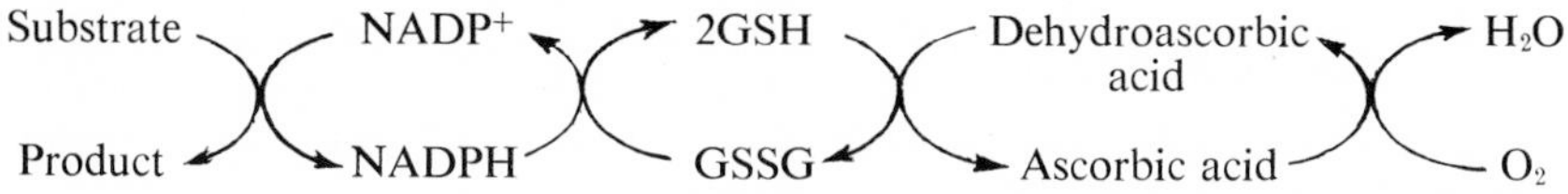

Vitamin K. The occurrence of *vitamin K* in higher plants is well established (60). The highest concentrations of the vitamin are found in the chloroplast (38), where it is active as a catalyst in cyclic electron transport in photosynthesis (8). Other than its function in electron transport, the biochemical role of vitamin K in plants has not been elucidated.

Ferreting out the role of the different vitamins in the cellular metabolism of plants is more of an academic pursuit than a necessity. As a rule, normal green plants do not suffer from vitamin deficiencies since they synthesize their own. Those organs of the plant that do not synthesize a sufficient amount of a vitamin for their needs have it translocated to them from another organ. For this reason, plant organs such as roots isolated in tissue culture sometimes need the addition of certain vitamins.

BIBLIOGRAPHY

1. Aberg, B. 1958. Ascorbic acid. *In* W. Ruhland (ed.), Encyclopedia of plant physiology. Springer, Berlin. 6: 479.
2. Aberg, B. 1961. Vitamins as growth factors in higher plants. *In* W. Ruhland (ed.), Encyclopedia of plant physiology. Springer, Berlin. 14: 418.
3. Addicott, F. T. 1941. Effects of root-growth hormones on the meristem of excised pea roots. Botan. Gaz. 102: 576.
4. Addicott, F. T., and R. S. Lynch. 1951. Acceleration and retardation of abscission by indole-acetic acid. Science 114: 688.
5. Addicott, F. T., and R. S. Lynch. 1955. Physiology of abscission. Ann. Rev. Plant Physiol. 6: 211.
6. Almestrand, A. 1950. Growth factor requirements of isolated wheat roots. Physiol. Plant 3: 293.
7. Almestrand, A. 1951. The effects of pyridoxine on the growth of isolated grass roots. Physiol. Plant 4: 224.
8. Arnon, D. I. 1959. Chloroplasts and photosynthesis. *In* The photochemical apparatus—its structure and function. 11: 181.
9. Arnon, D. I., F. R. Whatley, and M. B. Allen. 1955. Vitamin K as a cofactor of photosynthetic phosphorylation. Biochem. Biophys. Acta 16: 607.
10. Ashby, W. C. 1951. Effects of growth regulating substances and aldehydes on growth of roots. Botan. Gaz. 112: 237.
11. Audus, L. J. 1959. Plant growth substances. Interscience Publishers, New York.
12. Beck, W. A. 1941. Production of solutes in growing epidermal cells. Plant Physiol. 16: 637.
13. Bentley, J. A., and S. Housley. 1952. Studies on plant growth hormones. II. J. Exptl. Botan. 3: 406.
14. Beyer, A. 1928. Beiträge zum Problem der Reizleitung. Z. Botan. 20: 321.
15. Boll, W. G. 1954. Inhibition of growth of excised tomato roots by desoxypyridoxin and its reversal by pyridoxin. Science 120: 991.
16. Bonner, D. M., A. J. Haagen-Smit, and F. W. Went 1939. Leaf growth hormones. I: A bio-assay and source for leaf growth factors. Botan. Gaz. 101: 128.
17. Bonner, J. 1932. The production of growth substances by *Rhizopus suinus*. Biol. Zbl. 52: 565.
18. Bonner, J. 1933. The action of the plant growth hormone. J. Gen. Physiol. 17: 63.
19. Bonner, J. 1942. Transport of thiamin in the tomato plant. Am. J. Botan. 29: 136.

20. Bonner, J. 1950. Plant biochemistry. Academic Press, New York.
21. Bonner, J. 1961. On the mechanics of auxin-induced growth. *In* Plant growth regulation. Intern. Conf. Plant Growth Reg. 4th. The Iowa State University Press, Ames, Iowa.
22. Bonner, J., and H. Bonner. 1948. The B vitamins as plant hormones. Vitamins Hormones 6: 225.
23. Bonner, J., and R. Dorland. 1943. Some observations concerning riboflavin and pantothenic acid in tomato plants. Am. J. Botan. 30: 414.
24. Bonner, J., and J. English, Jr. 1938. A chemical and physiological study of traumatin, a plant wound hormone. Plant Physiol. 13: 331.
25. Bonner, J., and A. W. Galston. 1952. Principles of plant physiology. W. H. Freeman & Company, San Francisco.
26. Bouillenne, R., and F. W. Went. 1933. Recherches experimentales sur la néoformation des racines dans les plantules et les boutures des plantes supérieures. Ann. Jard. Botan. Buitenzorg. 43: 25.
27. Boysen-Jensen, P. 1910. Über die Leitung des phototropischen Reizes in Avenakeimpflanzen. Ber. D. Botan. Ges. 28: 118.
28. Boysen-Jensen, P. 1911. La transmission de l'irritation phototropique dans l'Avena. K. Danske Vidensk. Selsk. 3: 1.
29. Boysen-Jensen, P. 1913. Über die leitung des phototropischen Reizes in der *Avena*-koleoptile. Ber. D. Botan. Ges. 31: 559.
30. Brown, R., and J. F. Sutcliffe. 1950. The effects of sugar and potassium on extension growth in the root. J. Exptl. Botan. 1: 88.
31. Burström, H. 1942. Die osmotischen Verhältnisse während das Streckungswachstum der Wurzel. Ann. Agr. Coll., Sweden.
32. Champagnat, P. 1955. Les corrélations entre feuilles et bourgeons de la pousse herbacée du lilas. Rev. Gen. Botan. 62: 325.
33. Cholodny, N. 1926. Beiträge zur Analyse der geotropischen Reaktion. Jahrb. wiss Botan. 65: 447.
34. Cholodny, N. 1931. Zur Physiologie des pflanzlichen Wuchshormons. Planta 14: 207.
35. Cleland, R. E., and H. Burstrom. 1961. Theories of the auxin action on cellular elongation. A summary. *In* W. Ruhland (ed.), Encyclopedia of Plant Physiology. Springer, Berlin. 14: 807.
36. Cooil, B., and J. Bonner. 1957. The nature of growth inhibition by calcium in the *Avena* coleoptile. Planta 48: 696.
37. Cooper, W. C. 1935. Hormones in relation to root formation on stem cuttings. Plant Physiol. 10: 789.
38. Dam, H., E. Hjorth, and I. Kruse. 1948. On the determination of vitamin K in chloroplasts. Physiol. Plant 1: 379.
39. Darwin, C. 1881. The power of movement in plants. D. Appleton and Company, New York.
40. Davies, E. A. 1949. Effects of several plant growth-regulators on wound healing of sugar maple. Botan. Gaz. 111: 69.
41. Fitting, H. 1909. Die Beeinflussing der Orchideenblüten durch die Bestäubung und durch andere Umstände. Z. Botan. 1: 1.

42. French, R. C., and H. Beevers. 1953. Respiratory and growth responses induced by growth regulators and allied compounds. Am. J. Botan. 40: 660.
43. Fruton, J. S., and S. Simmonds. 1959. General biochemistry. John Wiley & Sons, Inc., New York.
44. Galston, A. W. 1949. Indoleacetic-nicotinic acid interactions in the etiolated pea plant. Plant Physiol. 24: 577.
45. Galston, A. W., and R. S. Baker. 1949. Studies on the physiology of light action. II. The photodynamic action of riboflavin. Am. J. Botan. 36: 773.
46. Gawadi, A. G., and G. S. Avery. 1950. Leaf abscission and the so-called abscission layer. Am. J. Botan. 37: 172.
47. Gordon, S. A. 1961. The biogenesis of auxin. *In* W. Ruhland (ed.), Encyclopedia of plant physiology. Springer, Berlin. 14: 620.
48. Gordon, S. A., and F. S. Nieva. 1949. The biosynthesis of auxin in the vegetative pineapple. I and II. Arch. Biochem. Biophys. 20: 356.
49. Gorter, C. J. 1961. Morphogenetic effects of synthetic auxins. *In* W. Ruhland (ed.), Encyclopedia of plant physiology. Springer, Berlin. 14: 807.
50. Gregory, F. C. 1928. Studies in the energy relation of plants. II. The effect of temperature on increase in area of leaf surface and in dry weight of *Cucumis sativus*. Ann. Botan. 42: 469.
51. Gregory, F. G., and C. R. Hancock. 1955. The rate of transport of natural auxin in woody shoots. Ann. Botan. N. S. 19: 451.
52. Gregory, F. G., and J. A. Veale. 1957. A re-assessment of the problem of apical dominance. Symp. Soc. Exptl. Biol. 11: 1.
53. Gustafson, F. G. 1936. Inducement of fruit development by growth-promoting chemicals. Proc. Natl. Acad. Sci. 22: 628.
54. Gustafson, F. G. 1939. The cause of natural parthenocarpy. Am. J. Botan. 26: 135.
55. Gustafson, F. G. 1941. Extraction of growth hormones from plants. Am. J. Botan. 28:947.
56. Gustafson, F. G. 1954. Synthesis of B vitamins by excised parts of white lupine seedlings grown in sterile culture. Arch. Biochem. 52: 190.
57. Haberlandt, G. 1913. Zur Physiologie der Zellteilung. S. B. preuss. Akad. Wiss. 318.
58. Hackett, D. P. 1952. The osmotic change during auxin-induced water uptake by potato tissue. Plant Physiol. 27: 279.
59. Hinton, J. J. C., F. G. Peers, and B. Shaw. 1953. The B-vitamins in wheat: the unique aleurone layer. Nature (London) 172: 993.
60. Hoffmann-Ostenhof, O. 1955. Ein-und zweikerniges Chinone. *In* K. Paech and M. V. Tracey (eds.), Modern methods of plant analysis. 3: 359.
61. Hurt, W. W., B. T. Scheer, and H. S. Deuel. 1949. The synthesis of niacin from tryptophan in rat liver slices. Arch. Biochem. 21: 87.
62. Jacobs, W. P. 1961. The polar movement of auxin in the shoots of higher plants: its occurrence and physiological significance. *In* Plant growth

regulation. Intern. Conf. Plant Growth Reg. 4th. The Iowa State University Press, Ames, Iowa.
63. Kögl, F., H. Erxleben, and A. Haagen-Smit. 1934. Über die Isolirung der Auxine "a" und "b" aus pflanzlichen Materialen. IX. Mitteilung. Z. Physiol. Chem. 225: 215.
64. Kögl, F., and A. Haagen-Smit. 1931. Über die Chemic des Wuchsstoffs. Proc. Kon. Akad. Wetensch. Amsterdam 34: 1411.
65. Kögl, F., A. Haagen-Smit, and H. Erxleben. 1934. Über ein neues Auxin (Heteroauxin) aus Harn. XI. Mitteilung. Z. Physiol. Chem. 228: 90.
66. Laibach, F. 1933. Wuchsstoffversuche mit levenden Orchideen pollinien. Ber. dtsch. botan. Ges. 51: 336.
67. Langston, R., and A. C. Leopold. 1954. Effect of photoinduction upon some B-vitamins in barley. Physiol. Plant 7: 397.
68. Larson, P. 1949. Conversion of indole acetaldehyde to indoleacetic acid in excised coleoptiles and in coleoptile juice. Am. J. Botan. 36: 32.
69. LaRue, C. D. 1936. The effect of auxin on the abscission of petioles. Proc. Natl. Acad. Sci., Washington 22: 254.
70. Leopold, A. C., F. S. Guernsey, and R. Langston. 1953. Pantothenic acid and acetic acid utilization in tomato fruit-set. Plant Physiol. 28: 748.
71. Loo, S. 1945. Cultivation of excised stem tips of asparagus *in vitro*. Am. J. Botan. 32: 13.
72. Luckwill, L. C. 1956. Two methods for the bioassay of auxins in the presence of growth inhibitors. J. Hort. Sci. 31: 89.
73. Lund, E. J. 1947. Bioelectric fields and growth. University of Texas Press, Austin.
74. Lund, H. A. 1956. Growth hormones in the styles and ovaries of tobacco responsible for fruit development. Am. J. Botan. 43: 562.
75. Massart, J. 1902. Sur la pollination sans fécondation. Bull. Jard. Botan. Brux. 1: 89.
76. Muir, R. M. 1942. Growth hormones as related to the setting and development of fruit in *Nicotiana tabacum*. Am. J. Botan. 29:716.
77. Muir, R. M. 1947. The relationship of growth hormones and fruit development. Proc. Natl. Acad. Sci. 33: 303.
78. Niedergang-Kamien, E., and A. C. Leopold. 1957. Inhibitors of polar auxin transport. Physiol. Plant 10: 29.
79. Northen, H. T. 1942. Relation of dissociation of cellular protein by auxin to growth. Botan. Gaz. 103: 668.
80. Ordin, L., T. H. Applewhite, and J. Bonner. 1956. Auxin-induced water uptake by *Avena* coleoptile sections. Plant Physiol. 31: 44.
81. Paal, A. 1919. Über phototropische Reizleitung. Jabrb. Wiss. Botan. 58: 406.
82. R. A. Peters, and J. A. O'Brien. 1955. Thiamine and its derivatives. *In* K. Paech and M. V. Tracey (eds.), Modern methods of plant analysis. 4: 345.
83. deRopp, R. S. 1950. Am. J. Botan. 37: 358.

84. Rossetter, F. N., and W. P. Jacobs. 1953. Studies on abscission. The stimulating role of nearby leaves. Am. J. Botan. 40: 276.
85. Schrank, A. R. 1951. Electrical polarity and auxins. *In* F. Skoog (ed.), Plant growth substances. University of Wisconsin Press, Madison, Wisc.
86. Scott, F. M., M. R. Schroeder, and F. M. Turrell. 1948. Development of abscission in the leaf of Valencia orange. Botan. Gaz. 109: 381.
87. Shoji, K., F. T. Addicott, and W. A. Swets. 1951. Auxin in relation to leaf blade abscission. Plant Physiol. 26: 189.
88. Skoog, F. 1944. Growth and formation in tobacco tissue cultures. Am. J. Botan. 31: 19.
89. Skoog, F., and K. V. Thimann. 1934. Further experiments on the inhibition of the development of lateral buds by growth hormone. Proc. Natl. Acad. Sci. 20: 480.
90. Skoog, F., and K. V. Thimann. 1940. Enzymatic liberation of auxin from plant tissues. Science 92: 64.
91. Strong, F. M. 1955. Riboflavin, folic acid and biotin. *In* K. Paech and M. V. Tracey (eds.), Modern methods of plant analysis. 4: 643.
92. Tagawa, T., and J. Bonner. 1957. Mechanical properties of the *Avena* coleoptile as related to auxin and to ionic interactions. Plant Physiol. 32: 207.
93. Thimann, K. V. 1934. Studies on the growth hormone of plants. VI. The distribution of the growth substance in plant tissues. J. Gen. Physiol. 18: 23.
94. Thimann, K. V. 1935. On the plant growth hormone produced by *Rhizopus suinus*. J. Biol. Chem. 109: 279.
95. Thimann, K. V. 1937. On the nature of inhibitions caused by auxin. Am. J. Botan. 24: 407.
96. Thimann, K. V., and J. B. Koepfli. 1935. Identity of the growth-promoting and root-forming substances of plants. Nature 135: 101.
97. Thimann, K. V., and C. L. Schneider. 1938. The role of salts, hydrogen ion concentration and agar in the response of the *Avena* coleoptile to auxin. Am. J. Botan. 25: 270.
98. Thimann, K. V., and F. Skoog. 1934. Inhibition of bud development and other functions of growth substance in *Vicia Faba*. Proc. Roy. Soc. (London) B, 114: 317.
99. Tukey, H. B., F. W. Went, R. M. Muir, and J. van Overbeek. 1954. Nomenclature of chemical plant regulators. Plant Physiol. 29: 307.
100. van Overbeek, J., E. S. deVásquez, and S. A. Gordon. 1947. Free and bound auxin in the vegetative pineapple plant. Am. J. Botan. 34: 266.
101. van Overbeek, J., S. A. Gordon, and L. E. Gregory. 1946. An analysis of the function of the leaf in the process of root formation in cuttings. Am. J. Botan. 33: 100.
102. Wehnelt, B. 1927. Untersuchungen über das Wundhormon der Pflanzen. Jb. wiss. Botan. 66: 773.
103. Went, F. W. 1926. On growth-accelerating substances in the coleoptile of *Avena sativa*. Proc. Kon. Akad. Wetensch. Amsterdam 35: 723.

104. Went, F. W. 1928. Wuchsstoff und Wachstum. Rec. Trav. Botan. Neerl. 25: 1.
105. Went, F. W. 1934. On the pea test method for auxin, the plant growth hormone. K. Akad. Wetenschap. Amsterdam Proc. Sect. Sci. 37: 547.
106. Went, F. W. 1935. Auxin, the plant growth hormone. Botan. Rev. 1: 162.
107. Went, F. W. 1938. Specific factors other than auxin affecting growth and root formation. Plant Physiol. 13: 55.
108. Went, F. W. 1951. The development of stems and leaves. *In* F. Skoog (ed.), Plant growth substances. University of Wisconsin Press, Madison, Wisc.
109. Went, F. W., and K. V. Thimann. 1937. Phytohormones. The Macmillan Co., New York.
110. Wildman, S. G., and J. Bonner. 1948. Observations on the chemical nature and formation of auxin in the *Avena* coleoptile. Am. J. Botan. 35: 740.
111. Wildman, S. G., M. G. Ferri, and J. Bonner. 1947. The enzymatic conversion of tryptophan to auxin by spinach leaves. Arch. Biochem. Biophys. 13: 131.
112. Wildman, S. G., and R. M. Muir. 1949. Observation on the mechanism of auxin formation in plant tissues. Plant Physiol. 24: 84.
113. Yasuda, S. 1934. The second report on the behaviour of the pollen tubes in the production of seedless fruits caused by interspecific pollination. Jap. J. Genet. 9: 118.

18

The synthetic growth hormones

INTRODUCTION

A natural consequence of the discovery of auxin activity was the isolation and characterization of the auxin molecule. As soon as this was accomplished, an intensive search began for compounds chemically similar to IAA and with similar activity. Before long, the results of this search brought forth other indole derivatives, such as indole-3-propionic acid, indole-3-butyric acid (36), and indolepyruvic acid (11), all of which demonstrate physiological activity similar to that of IAA. Other compounds, similar in activity but not in chemical structure to IAA were also discovered. Of these, the more important ones are α- and β-naphthylacetic acids, phenylacetic acid (36), naphthoxyacetic acid (12), and phenoxyacetic acid (35). The structures of the above-mentioned compounds are given.

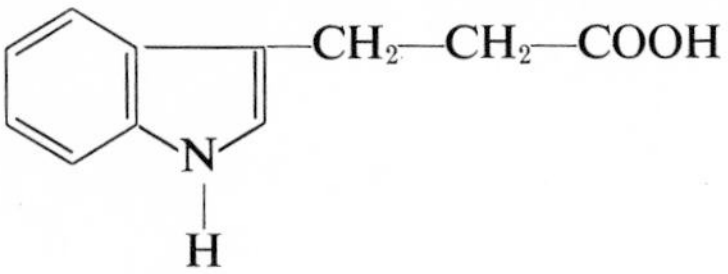

Indole-3-propionic acid

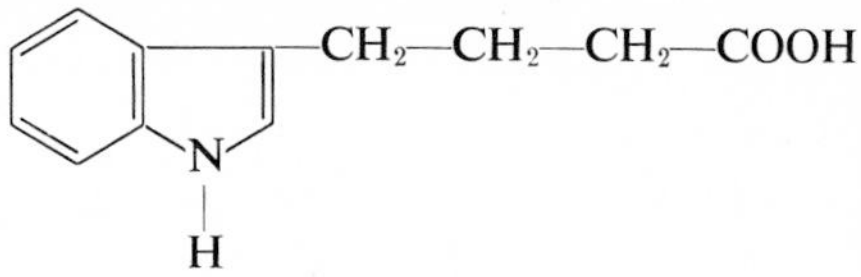

Indole-3-butyric acid

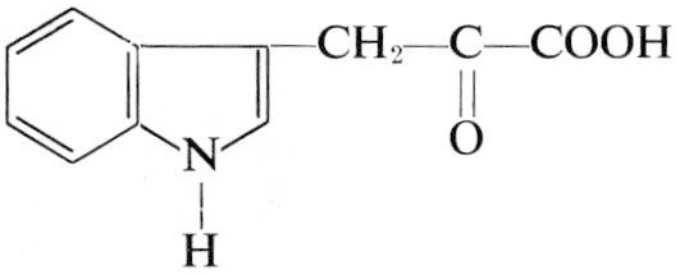

Indolepyruvic acid

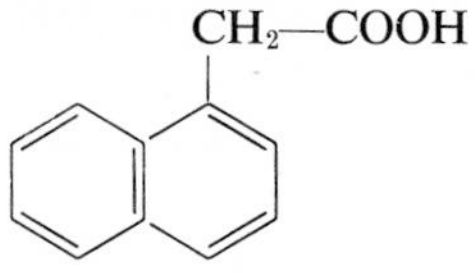

α-Naphthaleneacetic acid

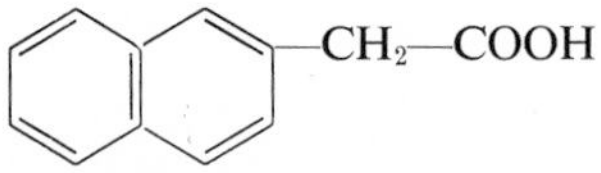

β-Naphthaleneacetic acid

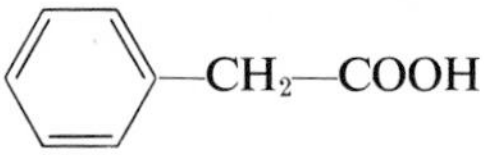

Phenylacetic acid

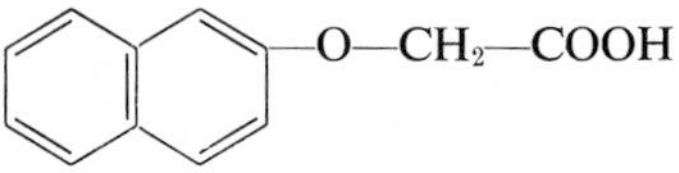

Naphthoxyacetic acid

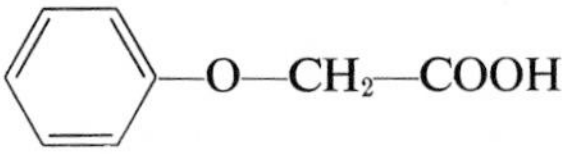

Phenoxyacetic acid

MOLECULAR STRUCTURE AND AUXIN ACTIVITY

The chemical characterization of physiologically active compounds never fails to generate interest in the relationship between the structure of the compound and its physiological activity. It was interest such as this that led to the listing of certain minimal requirements needed by a compound for auxin activity (13). These requirements are:

1. An unsaturated ring system.
2. An acid side chain.
3. Separation of the carboxyl group (—COOH) from the ring (several exceptions).
4. A particular spatial arrangement between the ring system and the acid side chain.

The above requirements are minimal for auxin activity. However, the degree of substitution in the ring and side chain, nature of the ring (indole, phenyl, anthracene, etc.), and length of the side chain all are factors that will influence auxin activity (34).

Nature of the ring system

After IAA had been isolated and characterized, it was soon found that the nitrogen of the indole ring was not essential for auxin activity. When either a carbon or an oxygen atom was substituted for nitrogen, activity, although considerably diminished, was still observed (30). One might have anticipated this due to the fact that ring sizes ranging from the small phenyl ring to the relatively large anthracene ring have been found in compounds having auxin activity. Nitrogen is not found in the phenyl or anthracene ring.

There seems to be considerable evidence supporting the requirement that the ring be unsaturated. Activity decreases with hydrogenation of the double bonds of the ring, with complete cessation of activity occurring in the saturated ring (1).

It was not until the auxin activity of the phenoxyacetic acid series was discovered (35) that the profound effect of the substitution of various groups onto the ring or side chain was truly appreciated. The nature of the group substituted and the location of the substitution was found to influence the activity of the compound. A striking example of this may be seen in the substitution of the chlorine atom at various positions on the phenyl ring of phenoxyacetic acid.

This was clearly demonstrated by Muir et al. (19) when they experimented with the substitution of halogens and methyl groups in the 2, 4, and 6 positions of the phenyl ring. They found that substitution of both the 2 and the 6 positions with chlorine atoms resulted in complete loss of activity. However, substitution of the 3 or 4 position alone increased activity. Chlorine atoms attached to the 2 and 4 positions of the phenyl ring of the phenoxyacetic acid molecule gave the greatest auxin activity. Indeed, 2,4-dichlorophenoxyacetic acid (2,4-D) is one of the most widely used synthetic auxins at the present time. The effects of various substitutions of the chlorine atom onto the phenyl ring of the phenoxyacetic acid molecule are shown in Figure 18-1. The fact that there is a complete loss of activity when both the 2 and the 6 positions are chlorinated, led these investigators to hypothesize that the position on the phenyl ring adjacent to the point of attachment of the side chain is involved in the growth reaction.

Nature of the acid side chain

According to the work of Koepfli et al. (13) and others, the position and length of the acid side chain has a striking influence on auxin activity. Side chains that have the carboxyl group separated from the ring by a carbon

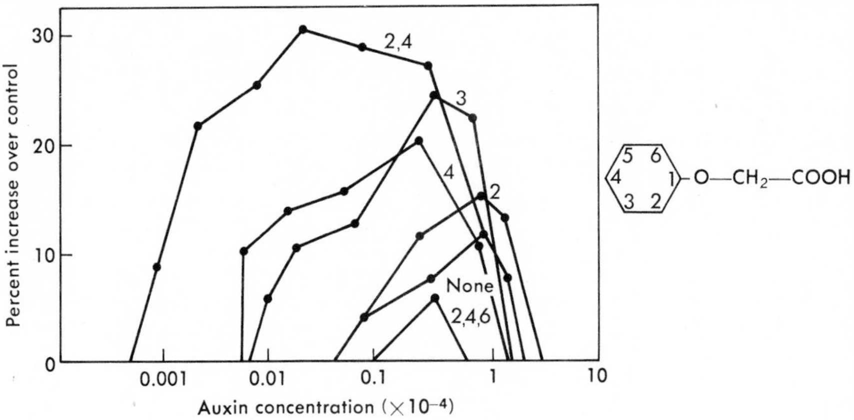

Figure 18-1 Effect of different concentrations of chlorinated phenoxyacetic acids in the *Avena* straight growth test. The number or numbers on the curves represent the position or positions of chlorine substitution on the phenyl ring. (After R. M. Muir et al. 1949. Plant Physiol. 24: 359.

or a carbon and oxygen give optimal activity. For example, the acid side chains of IAA and 2,4-D, two highly active auxins, fulfill these requirements.

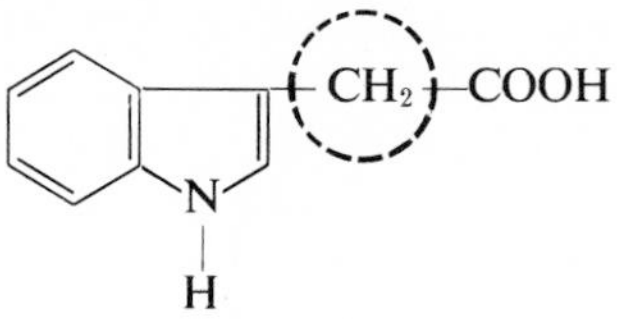

IAA

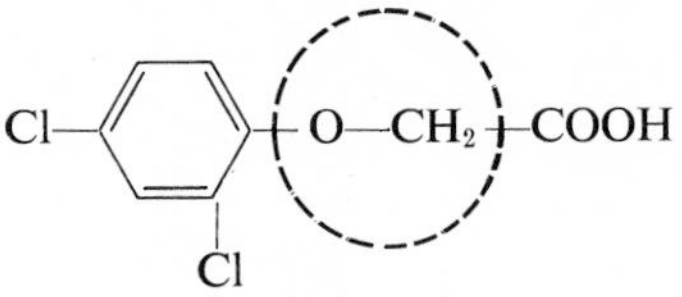

2,4-D

As the length of the side chain in the phenoxyacetic acid series is increased, there is a falling off of activity. This drop is erratic, activity falling much lower when the side chain contains an odd number of carbons. That is, 2,4-dichlorophenoxybutyric acid (4 carbons) is more active than 2,4-dichlorophenoxypropionic acid (3 carbons). A possible explanation for the above phenomenon may be found in the work of Synerholm and Zimmerman (28) and Fawcett et al. (5). Apparently, side chains containing an odd number of carbons are metabolized in living tissue to the inactive phenol, whereas the even-numbered chains are broken down to the active phenoxyacetic acid (Figure 18-2).

Substitution of different groups onto the side chain also affects activity. Thus, substitution of a methyl group on the α-carbon of the side chain of phenylacetic acid does not take away auxin activity. However, substitution

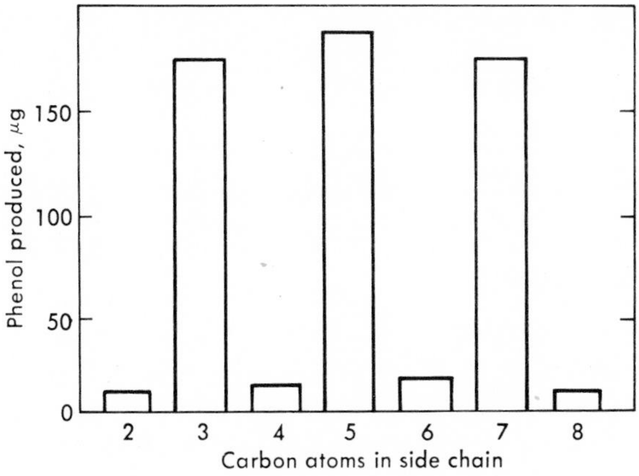

Figure 18-2 Amount of phenol produced on breakdown of even-numbered and odd-numbered side chains of phenoxy acids when exposed to flax plants. (After C. H. Fawcett et al. 1952. Nature 170: 887. Redrawn from A. C. Leopold. 1955. Auxins and plant growth. University of California Press, Los Angeles.)

of two methyl groups on the α-carbon eliminates auxin activity entirely (13). Later, when we discuss the mechanism of auxin action, we will

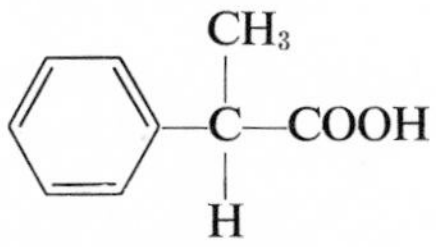

Phenylisopropionic acid

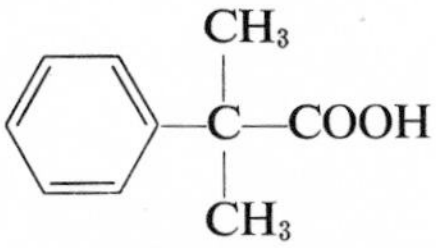

Phenylisobutyric acid

learn why the substitution of "bulky methyl" groups on the acid side chain inhibits auxin activity.

Hydroxyl substitution in the side chain also can eliminate auxin activity. For example, substitution of a hydroxyl group or an alcohol group on the α-carbon of phenyl acetic acid produces two inactive derivatives (31).

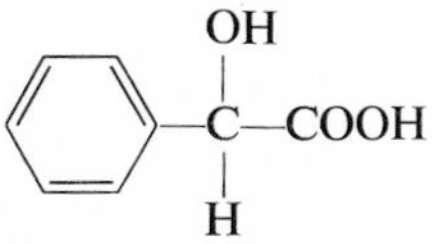

α-Hydroxyphenylacetic acid

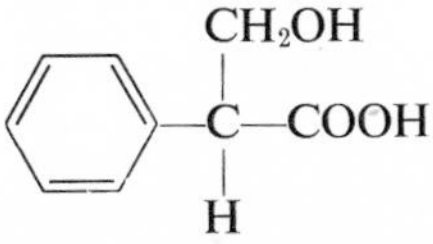

α-Hydroxymethylphenylacetic acid

Earlier, it was thought that separation of the carboxyl group from the side chain was essential for auxin activity (13). However, many exceptions to this rule have been found (2). For example, 2,3,6-trichlorobenzoic acid exhibits a strong auxin activity.

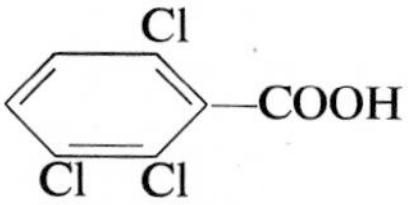

2,3,6-Trichlorobenzoic acid

Spatial arrangement

The spatial relationship between the ring and side chain is an important factor in the activity of an auxin molecule. For example, *cis*-cinnamic acid demonstrates good auxin activity in the *Avena* straight growth test, and its *trans* isomer does not. Veldstra (32) suggested, after a study of the rela-

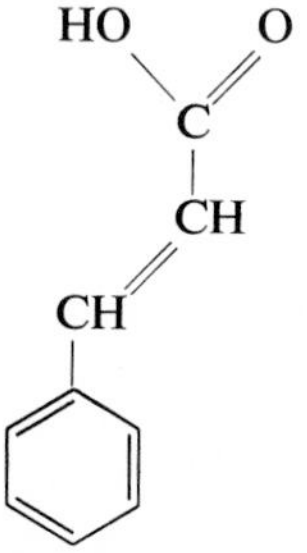

trans-Cinnamic acid

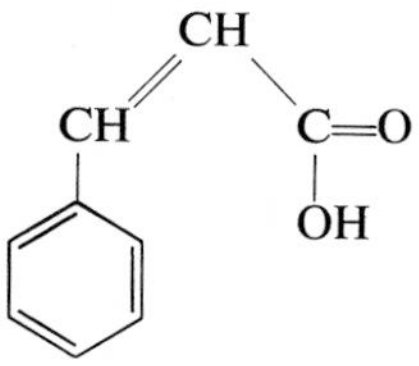

cis-Cinnamic acid

tion between structure and activity, that in order for a molecule to have auxin activity the —COOH group and the ring should lie in different planes. This theory was supported by observation of the activity of *cis* and *trans* forms of tetrahydronaphylideneacetic acid (31) and the above *cis* and *trans* forms of cinnamic acid.

ANTIAUXINS

If one assumes that the chemical configuration of a compound is responsible for its effect on physiological processes, then we must also recognize that there can be an interference with such action by similar, but not identical, compounds (18). Many antiauxins have been discovered, and, generally, these compounds are similar to auxin in molecular structure, but, in combination with auxin, inhibit its activity.

Actually, the term antiauxin should define only those compounds that will compete with auxin for a reactive site in the growing cell (1). What do we mean by a reactive site? Because of the relationship of molecular structure and configuration with degree of physiological activity, most theories on auxin action are based on the attachment of the auxin molecule to some substance in the cell (e.g., protein). This complex (bound auxin) can then induce auxin activity. True antiauxins, then, are compounds which, because of their molecular similarity to auxin, would become attached to reactive sites, thus neutralizing them for action in growth. However, if true competition for reactive sites is involved here, increasing applications of auxin should eventually swamp the reactive sites with auxin molecules and overcome the antiauxin effect.

There is general agreement that in order for an auxin molecule to be active, it must make a *two-point* attachment at a reactive site. In addition, it is thought that the two points of attachment are made through a position on the unsaturated ring and by the carboxyl group of the side chain. In the phenoxyacetic acids, the position on the ring through which attachment is made is the *ortho* position.

Based on the two-point attachment theory, McRae and Bonner (17) have drawn up a rigorous classification for true antiauxins. Using 2,4-D, a synthetic auxin, as a representative molecule, they have shown where "analogs" of the 2,4-D molecule containing some, but not all, of the structural properties of the auxin are capable of competing for reactive sites. The antiauxin makes a one-point instead of the two-point attachment necessary for growth action. McRae and Bonner have listed three ways by which a modification of the 2,4-D molecule can lead to antiauxin activity.

1. Elimination of the essential carboxyl group.
2. Elimination of the essential reactive *ortho* group.
3. Elimination of proper spatial relationships between the ring and the carboxyl group as by introduction of bulky groups in the side chain.

These relationships are shown diagrammatically in Figure 18-3.

Although not as popular as the two-point attachment theory, a three-point attachment theory has been proposed as necessary for auxin activity (27). According to this theory, an auxin molecule in order to be active must contain the following necessary structural properties: an unsaturated ring, a carboxyl group, and at least one α-hydrogen. A further stipulation is that all three must be correctly oriented in space with each other. Figure 18-4 gives a diagrammatic representation of the three-point attachment theory. In Figure 18-4, the importance of spatial relationship is shown. Of the isomers of 2,4-dichlorophenoxy-α-propionic acid, only the "+" form is active (31). The "−" form is not properly oriented, thus failing to accomplish the three-point attachment necessary for auxin activity.

Contact is made by the auxin with the reactive site simultaneously at three positions on the auxin molecules. If only one site or even two posi-

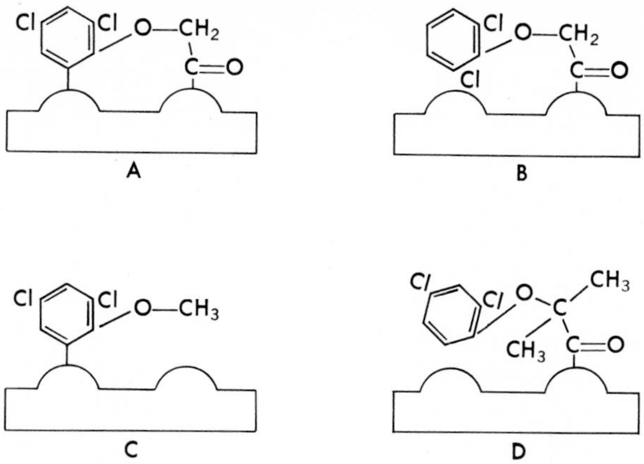

Figure 18-3 Diagrammatic representation of the two-point attachment theory as it applies to auxin and anti-auxin activity. A. Auxin activity. B. *Ortho* position blocked. C. Carboxyl group missing. D. bulky methyl group blocks attachment at the *ortho* position. (After D. H. McRae and J. Bonner. 1953. Physiol. Plantarum 6: 485.)

tions are occupied, no activity ensues. In fact, molecules that occupy only one or two of the positions on the reactive site can be considered antiauxins.

A type of antiauxin which has not, as yet, been considered is the compound having weak auxin activity. A weak auxin can make the necessary two-point (or three-point) attachment and initiate a stimulation of growth. However, this stimulation is small, and at the same time active sites in volved with the weak auxin cannot be occupied by a strong auxin. An example of a weak auxin having antiauxin characteristics is phenylbutyric acid.

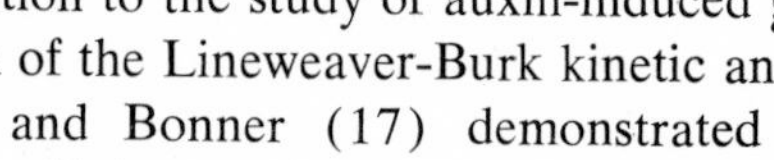

Phenylbutyric acid

KINETICS OF AUXIN ACTION

A valuable contribution to the study of auxin-induced growth reactions has been the application of the Lineweaver-Burk kinetic analysis of competitive inhibition. McRae and Bonner (17) demonstrated that auxin-induced growth reactions could be treated by the methods of classical enzyme kinetics.

It is generally accepted that in enzyme reactions, an intermediate complex is formed between the substrate and enzyme and that this complex is

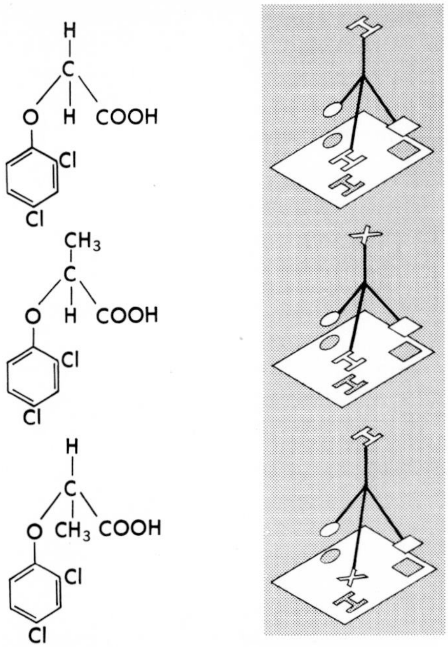

Figure 18-4 Diagrammatic representation of the three-point attachment theory. A. Acetic three-point contact, active response. B. Propionic (+)-isomer three-point contact, active response. C. Propionic (−)-isomer two-point contact, no response. (After M. S. Smith and R. L. Wain. 1952. Proc. Roy. Soc. 139: 118. Redrawn from L. J. Audus. 1959. Plant growth substances. Interscience Publishers, New York.)

formed at an active site on the enzyme. The complex is converted to the enzyme and reaction products.

$$E + S \rightleftharpoons ES \rightarrow E + P$$

Using the above scheme, McRae and Bonner demonstrated that stimulation of straight growth of *Avena* coleoptile sections by auxin could be mathematically analyzed. In their scheme, enzyme (E) is the auxin receptor, substrate (S) is the auxin applied, complex (ES) is the receptor-auxin attachment, and the product in this case is growth. Let us rewrite the above equation using A for auxin, R for receptor, RA for the intermediate complex, and G for growth.

$$R + A \rightleftharpoons RA \rightarrow R + G$$

Now, in classical enzyme study, a competitive inhibitor is thought of as a compound that will compete with the normal substrate of an enzyme for active sites on that enzyme. The formation of an enzyme-inhibitor complex may be illustrated in the following manner.

$$E + I \rightleftharpoons EI$$

The fact that the formation of EI is reversible is important since this allows for competition by the substrate with the inhibitor for active sites. Therefore, by increasing the substrate, inhibition by a competitive inhibitor may be overcome.

The effect of a competitive inhibitor may be observed in a decrease in the rate of an enzyme reaction. However, if the substrate concentration is increased until all active sites on the enzyme are "swamped," then maximum velocity (V_{max}) or rate will be obtained. This maximum velocity will be identical to that of the same reaction without a competitive inhibitor. In other words, increasing the concentration of a substrate decreases the amount of inhibition, and, conversely, decreasing the substrate concentration increases inhibition.

We have mentioned that antiauxins compete with auxins for active sites on an auxin receptor or growth center. This situation, of course, is analogous to the concept of competitive inhibition in enzyme study.

Now, using the Lineweaver-Burk plotting method, one can measure the velocity of an auxin reaction (in this case, rate of growth) and, at the same time, calculate the effect of an antiauxin on this velocity. By plotting the reciprocal of the velocity ($1/V$) of the auxin reaction against the reciprocal of the concentration of auxin ($1/[A]$) applied, one obtains a straight line relationship. Maximum velocity (V_{max}) may be obtained by extending this line to the ordinate, the intercept being $1/V_{max}$ (Figure 18-5).

Also illustrated in Figure 18-5 is the effect of a competitive inhibitor.

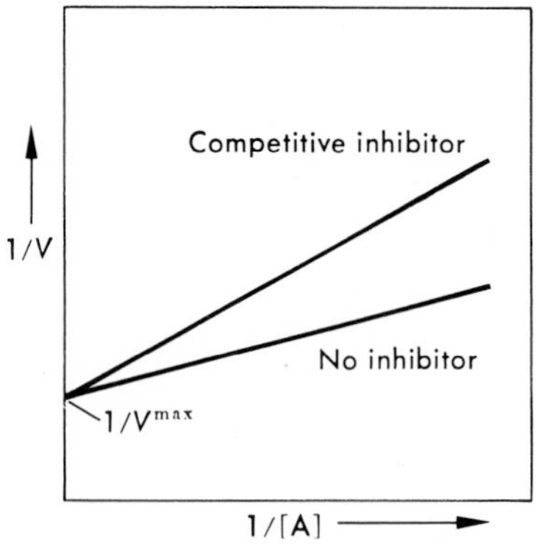

Figure 18-5 Reciprocal plot for an enzyme reaction with no inhibitor and a competitive inhibitor. Note that the intercept is the same for both conditions, but that the slope is increased by the presence of a competitive inhibitor.

Note that the concentration of inhibitor will affect the slope of the line, but not the intercept.

A mathematical analysis of the interaction of 2,4-D and the antiauxins 4-chlorophenoxyisobutyric acid, 2,6-dichlorophenoxyacetic acid, and 2,4-dichloroanisole has been undertaken (Figure 18-6). The compound 4-

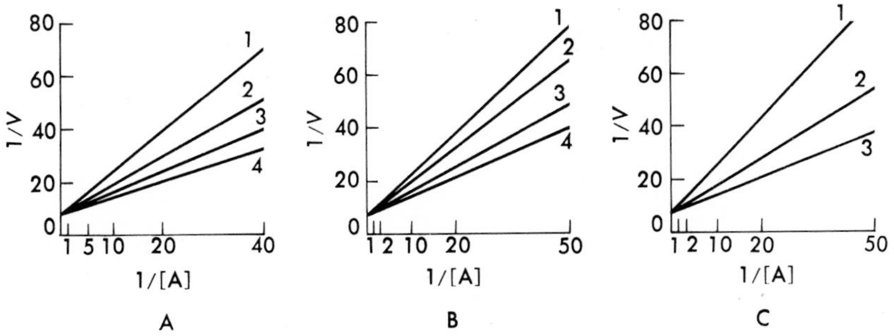

Figure 18-6 Counteraction of 2,4-D stimulation of section growth by the antiauxins (A) 2,4-dichlorophenoxyisobutyric acid, (B) 2,6-dichlorophenoxyacetic acid, and (C) 2,4-dichloroanisole. In A, curves 1, 2, 3, and 4 refer to 2,4-dichlorophenoxyisobutyric acid concentrations of 1.0, 0.5, 0.1, and 0.0 mg/liter, respectively. In B, curves 1, 2, 3, and 4 refer to 2,6-dichlorophenoxyacetic acid concentrations of 1.0, 0.5, 0.1, and 0.0 mg/liter, respectively. In C, curves 1, 2, and 3 refer to 2,4-dichloroanisole concentrations of 5.0, 1.0, and 0.0 mg/liter, respectively. (After D. H. McRae and J. Bonner. 1952. Plant Physiol. 27: 834; and 1953. Physiol. Plantarum 6: 485.)

chlorophenoxyisobutyric acid is an antiauxin because of bulky methyl groups in the side chain interfering with attachment of the carboxyl group to the auxin receptor. 2,6-Dichlorophenoxyacetic acid owes its antiauxin properties to blockage of the reactive *ortho* positions on the ring by chlorine atoms. 2,4-Dichloroanisol has no carboxyl group and therefore cannot make the necessary two-point attachment.

INACTIVATION OF AUXIN

Just as the production and subsequent physiological effects of auxin have a profound influence on plant development, the inactivation of auxin appears also to be of significance in this respect. For example, the inactivation of auxin is important in phototropisms, control of cell elongation, and in the aging of plant tissues. We will discuss the mechanisms involved in the destruction of auxin and the influence of its destruction on cell elongation and ageing. Discussions on phototropisms will be left to a later chapter.

MECHANISMS OF AUXIN INACTIVATION

A preponderance of literature has developed on the mehanisms of auxin inactivation since the isolation by Tang and Bonner (29) of an enzyme capable of oxidizing IAA. This enzyme was named *IAA oxidase*. Since that time, other natural means of auxin inactivation have been discovered. However, two systems for the destruction of auxin in the plant appear to dominate, and these are (a) enzymatic oxidation and (b) photooxidation.

Enzymatic oxidation

Enzyme systems that oxidize IAA have been found in several plant tissues. However, as is generally true, one system is usually studied in much more detail than the others, and in this case it is the enzyme system present in extracts of etiolated pea epicotyls. It appears that in this system a flavoprotein must be present, which gives rise to hydrogen peroxide. The oxidation of IAA by hydrogen peroxide is catalyzed by a peroxidase to yield some inactive product, probably indolealdehyde (Figure 18-7). In the inactivation of IAA by this system, 1 mole of O_2 is consumed for every mole of IAA inactivated and CO_2 released.

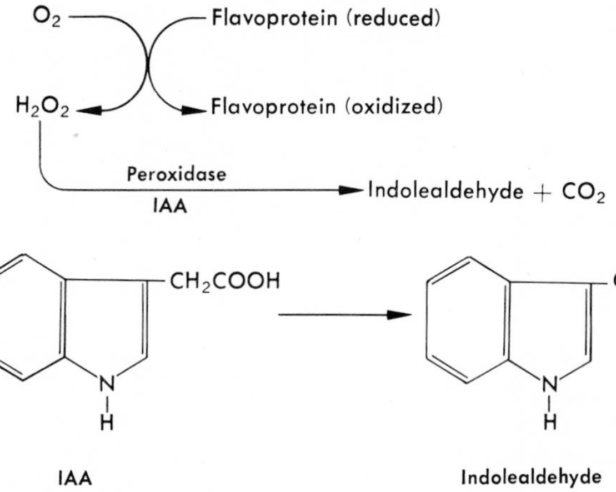

Figure 18-7 Schematic representation of the IAA oxidase system.

In addition to indolealdehyde, other breakdown products have been suggested (21, 15). However, it is generally accepted that the logical end product of IAA oxidation is indolealdehyde. As mentioned before, IAA oxidase systems have been found in many plants, and in several cases these have differed from the original IAA oxidase system found in the pea plant (3, 24). Perhaps in these, different end products of IAA oxidation are obtained.

An inverse relationship between IAA oxidase activity and IAA content in the plant has been found (8). That is, where IAA content is high, IAA oxidase activity is low and vice versa. Meristematic regions that have a high auxin content have been found to be low in IAA oxidase activity. The root, which is generally thought to be low in auxin content, has been found to be high in IAA oxidase activity (8). In fact, Galston (6) has found (at least in the pea plant) that as cells age, their IAA oxidase activity increases, and their auxin content drops.

Increased capacity to inactivate IAA has been demonstrated by young plant tissues treated with synthetic IAA or analogs of the IAA molecule. It appears, then, that IAA is capable of inducing the formation of the enzyme that destroys it (8, 6). This is particularly interesting since IAA, which initiates growth, also puts into action the mechanisms leading to the termination of growth. Galston (6), a leading figure in research on plant growth, has this to say:

> It seems possible that the decreased sensitivity to auxin of older cells is a consequence of their higher IAA oxidase activity, which in turn is a consequence of prior induction by IAA. According to this scheme, the administration of IAA to a young cell not only initiates growth, but also sets in motion a chain of events leading to the diminution and eventual culmination of growth.

Photooxidation

It has long been known that IAA can be inactivated by ionizing radiation. Skoog (25, 26) demonstrated that rapid inactivation of pure IAA takes place when it is subjected to x- and gamma-radiation. He also noted that little, if any, inactivation takes place in a nitrogen atmosphere, suggesting that inactivation is due to oxidation by peroxides formed during irradiation (9). There is some evidence that only a small amount of IAA is inactivated or oxidized in this manner, most of the detrimental effect of this type of irradiation to IAA being of an indirect nature. For example, Gordon (10) has claimed that the major effect of ionizing radiation on auxin metabolism may be found in the destructive effect of the radiation on the enzyme system converting tryptophan to IAA.

Ultraviolet light also inactivates IAA. This might have been predicted because of the ring structure of the IAA molecule, which absorbs to some extent in ultraviolet (maximum absorption at about 280 mμ). Here, there is a direct effect on the IAA molecule due to the absorption of ultraviolet light. Determinations of auxin content before and after irradiation with ultraviolet light have shown that this type of irradiation reduces auxin levels in plants (20, 4).

It is a well-known fact that IAA does not absorb wavelengths in the visible portion of the spectrum. Yet, when an oat coleoptile is subjected to unilateral light, it bends toward the light. This is true for the majority of plants; that is, they will bend toward a source of light. It has been generally accepted that the reason for this is that auxin is destroyed on the illuminated side, causing the plant to bend toward the light. The cells on the dark side elongate normally, while the cells on the illuminated side do not.

Visible light, then, must have a destructive effect on IAA. Since the IAA molecule is not involved directly, there must be present a photoreceptor (probably a pigment) capable of absorbing visible wavelengths of light and then causing the photodegradation of IAA. As in the action of IAA oxidase, 1 mole of oxygen is consumed for every mole of IAA inactivated, and 1 mole of CO_2 is released (9).

If one follows the action spectrum for the curvature of an oat coleoptile, he will find that maximum curvature occurs at about 450 mμ. Although indirect, one can consider this an action spectrum for the destruction of IAA since this is what causes the curvature. If the destruction of IAA by visible light involves a pigment absorbing in the visible region, then the absorption spectrum for that pigment should follow very closely the action

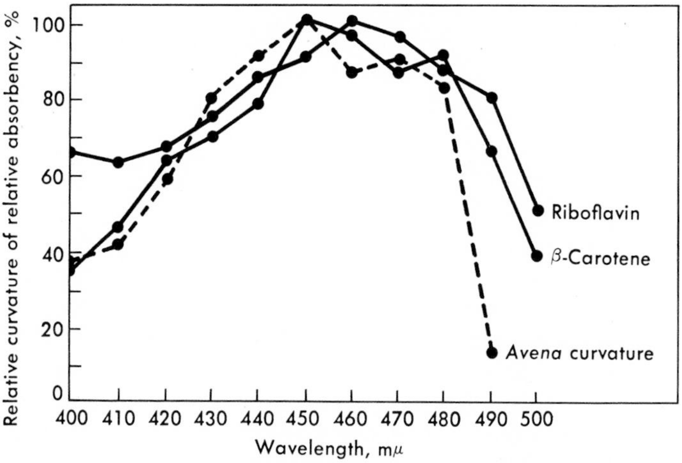

Figure 18-8 Absorption spectra of β-carotene and riboflavin presented with the action spectrum for curvature of the *Avena* coleoptile. (After A. W. Galston and R. S. Baker. 1949. Am. J. Botany 41: 373.)

spectrum for the destruction of IAA. Two pigments have been found in plant cells that have absorption spectra closely resembling that of the action spectrum for *Avena* coleoptile curvature (Figure 18-8). These are *β-carotene* and *riboflavin*. Note in Figure 18-8 that there is a close relationship between maximum effect (curvature) and maximum absorption. However, the question of which pigment is the one involved in the destruction of IAA is still unanswered.

There is considerable evidence supporting riboflavin as the photoreceptor in auxin inactivation. Perhaps the most damaging evidence against β-carotene is that plants containing no β-carotene will respond positively to a unilateral source of light (33). In fact, β-carotene has been assigned a protective rather than a destructive role by some investigators. Interfering with light absorption and acting as an alternate substrate for oxidation are two possible ways protection by β-carotene might be accomplished (22, 23).

BIBLIOGRAPHY

1. Audus, L. J. 1959. Plant growth substances. Interscience Publishers, New York.
2. Bentley, J. A. 1950. Growth-regulating effect of certain organic compounds. Nature 65: 449.
3. Briggs, W. R., G. Morel, T. A. Steeves, I. M. Sussex, and R. H. Wetmore. 1955. Enzymatic auxin inactivation by extracts of the fern, *Osmunda cinnamomea L.* Plant Physiol. 30: 143.
4. Burkholder, P. A., and E. S. Johnston. 1937. Inactivation of plant growth substance by light. Smithsonian Inst. Misc. Collections 95: 20.
5. Fawcett, C. H., M. A. Ingram, and R. L. Wain. 1952. β-Oxidation of ω-phenoxyalkylcarboxylic acids in the flax plant. Nature 170: 887.
6. Galston, A. W. 1956. Some metabolic consequences of the administration of indoleacetic acid to plant cells. *In* R. L. Wain and F. Wightman (eds.), The chemistry and mode of action of plant growth substances. Butterworths Scientific Publications, London 219.
7. Galston, A. W., and R. S. Baker. 1949. Studies on the physiology of light action. II. The photodynamic action of riboflavin. Am. J. Botan. 36: 773.
8. Galston, A. W., and L. Y. Dalberg. 1954. The adaptive formation and physiological significance of indoleacetic acid oxidase. Am. J. Botan. 41: 373.
9. Galston, A. W., and W. S. Hillman. 1961. The degradation of auxin. *In* W. Ruhland (ed.), Encyclopedia of plant physiology. Springer, Berlin. 14: 647.
10. Gordon, S. A. 1956. The biogenesis of natural auxins. *In* R. L. Wain and F. Wightman (eds.), The chemistry and mode of action of plant growth substances. Butterworths Scientific Publications, London 65.

11. Haagen-Smit, A., and F. W. Went. 1935. A physiological analysis of the growth substance. Proc. Kon. Nederl. Akad. Wetensch. Amsterdam 38: 852.
12. Irvine, V. C. 1938. Studies in growth-promoting substances as related to x-radiation and photoperiodism. Univ. Colo. Studies 26: 69.
13. Koepfli, J. B., K. V. Thimann, and F. W. Went. 1938. Phytohormones: structure and physiological activity. J. Biol. Chem. 122: 763.
14. Leopold, A. C. 1955. Auxins and plant growth. University of California Press. Los Angeles.
15. Manning. D. T., and A. W. Galston. 1955. On the nature of the enzymatically catalyzed oxidation products of indoleacetic acid. Plant Physiol. 30: 225.
16. McRae, D. H., and J. Bonner. 1952. Diortho-substituted phenoxyacetic acids as anti-auxins. Plant Physiol. 27: 834.
17. McRae, D. H., and J. Bonner. 1953. Chemical structure and antiauxin activity. Physiol. Plant 6: 485.
18. Muir, R. M., and C. Hansch. 1955. Chemical constitution as related to growth regulator action. Ann. Rev. Plant Physiol. 6: 157.
19. Muir, R. M., C. H. Hansch, and A. H. Gallup. 1949. Growth regulation by organic compounds. Plant Physiol. 24: 359.
20. Popp, H. W., and H. R. C. McIlvaine. 1937. Growth substances in relation to the mechanism of the action of radiation on plants. J. Agr. Res. 55: 931.
21. Ray, P. M., and K. V. Thimann. 1955. Steps in the oxidation of indoleacetic acid. Science 122: 187.
22. Reinert, J. 1952. Über die Bedeutung von Carotin und Riboflavin für die Lichtreizaufnahme bei Pflanzen. Naturwiss 39: 47.
23. Reinert, J. 1953. Über die Wirkung von Riboflavin und Carotin bein Phototropismus von Avena-Koleoptilen und bei anderen pflanzlichen Lichtreizreaktionen. Z. Botany 41: 103.
24. Segueira, L., and T. A. Steeves. 1954. Auxin inactivation and its relation to leaf drop caused by the fungus *Omphalia flavida*. Plant Physiol. 29: 11.
25. Skoog, F. 1934. The effect of x-rays on growth substance and plant growth. Science 79: 256.
26. Skoog, F. 1935. Effect of x-irradiation on auxin and plant growth. J. Cell Comp. Physiol. 7: 227.
27. Smith, M. S., and R. L. Wain. 1952. The plant growth-regulating activity of *dextro* and *laevo* α(2-naphthoxy) propionic acid. Proc. Roy. Soc. 139: 118.
28. Synerholm, M. E., and P. W. Zimmerman. 1947. Preparation of a series of 2,4-dichlorophenoxyaliphatic acids. Contr. Boyce Thompson Inst., 14: 369.
29. Tang, Y. W., and J. Bonner. 1947. The enzymatic inactivation of indoleacetic acid. Arch. Biochem. Biophys. 13: 11.
30. Thimann, K. V. 1935. On an analysis of activity of two growth-promoting substances on plant tissues. Proc. Kon. Acad. Wet., Amsterdam 38: 896.
31. Thimann, K. V. 1951. The synthetic auxins: relation between structure and

activity. *In* F. Skoog (ed.), Plant growth substances. University of Wisconsin Press, Madison, Wisc.
32. Veldstra, H. 1944. Researches on plant growth substances IV. The relation between structure and activity. Enzymologia 11: 97.
33. Wallace, R. H., and A. E. Schwarting. 1954. A study of chlorophyll in a white mutant strain of *Helianthus annuus*. Plant Physiol. 29: 431.
34. Went, F. W., and K. V. Thimann. 1937. Phytohormones. The Macmillan Co., New York.
35. Zimmerman, P. W., and A. E. Hitchcock. 1942. Substituted phenoxy and benzoic acid growth substances and the relation of structure to physiological activity. Contr. Boyce Thompson Inst. 12: 321.
36. Zimmerman, P. W., A. E. Hitchcock, and F. Wilcoxon. 1936. Several esters as plant hormones. Contr. Boyce Thompson Inst. 8: 105.

19

The gibberellins and kinetin

GIBBERELLINS

If it were not for the bakanae disease, which had devastating effects on the rice economy of Japan, the existence of gibberellins in plants might still be unknown. Japanese farmers noted that plants affected with this disease were taller, thinner, and paler than their normal counterparts and sometimes were devoid of fruit (41). Crop losses as high as 40% were reported. Needless to say, the Japanese scientists were interested in the cause of the disease and its control.

In the early part of the twentieth century, an extensive program of research into the cause of bakanae disease was initiated. Japanese pathologists first demonstrated the connection between the bakanae disease and the fungus called *Fusarium moniliforme* Sheld [*Gibberella fujikuroi* (Saw.) Wr.]. It was then postulated by Sawada (46) that the disease may be caused by something secreted by the fungus. This postulation was given experimental support by Kurosawa (27), who demonstrated that sterile filtrates of the fungus are capable of causing the symptoms of bakanae disease in otherwise normal rice seedlings. Finally, in 1938, Yabuta and Sumiki were able to isolate the crystalline gibberellin. Since that time, gibberellins and gibberellin-like substances have been found in higher plants (35, 55, 52).

Chemistry of the gibberellins

Several compounds have now been isolated with biological activity similar to that of the original gibberellin isolated from the fungus *G. fujikuroi*. So far, nine different gibberellins have been found, all having very similar chemical structures (51). The chemical structures of these compounds, sometimes referred to as the gibberellin A series, are given in Figure 19-1. All of these compounds possess the same general carbon skeleton and all are able to promote either stem elongation or cell division or both in plants. However, their relative effectiveness in these promotions are often quite different (Figure 19-2).

Physiological effects

Because of the widespread distribution of gibberellins in plants and because of the different specific responses of individual flowering plants to exogenously applied gibberellins, they should be regarded as natural plant growth hormones. Indeed, they have been compared to IAA in their biological activity, although in some cases they act in a different manner (Table 19-1) and in other cases in a similar manner (18). Gibberellins

Table 19-1 Summation of some differences between auxins and gibberellins.[a]

Activity	*Auxin*	*Gibberellin*
transport polar	yes	no
promote root initiation	yes	no
inhibit root elongation	yes	no
delay leaf abscission	yes	no
inhibit lateral buds	yes	no
induce callus formation	yes	no
promote epinastic responses	yes	no
promote growth of intact plants, especially of the dwarf type, and of monocotyledonous leaves	no	yes
promote seed germination and the breaking of dormancy	no	yes
promote bolting and flowering in nonvernalized biennials and in long-day plants	no	yes

[a] After A. W. Galston and W. H. Purves. 1960. Ann. Rev. Plant Physiol. 11: 239.

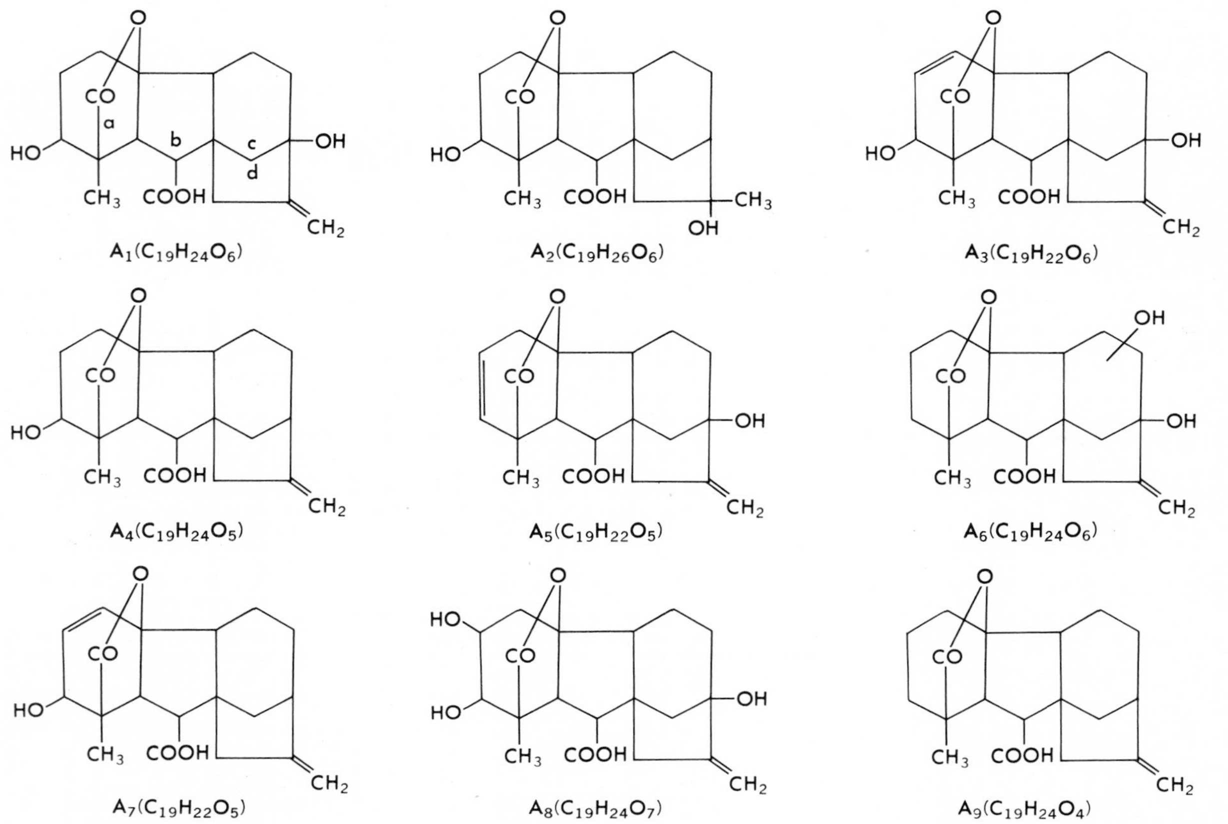

Figure 19-1 Chemical structures of nine known gibberellins. (After Cross et al., 1961. Advan. Chem. Ser. 28: 3; and MacMillan et al., 1961. Advan. Chem. Ser. 28: 18.)

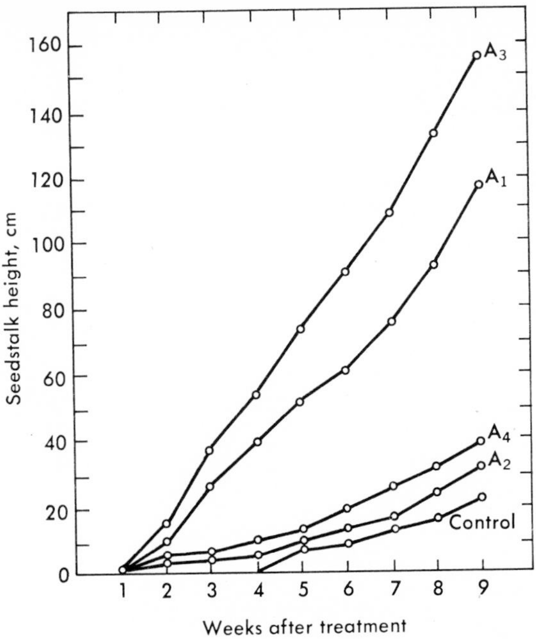

Figure 19-2 Effect of four different gibberellins (A_1, A_2, A_3, and A_4) on rate of seedstalk elongation in Grand Rapids leaf lettuce. (Reproduced from *Plant Growth Regulation,* edited by R. M. Klein, © 1961 by Iowa State University Press.)

act similarly to IAA in that they promote cell elongation and induce parthenocarpy. Both, in some cases, induce cell division.

We will cover in the following discussion the influence of gibberellins on genetic dwarfism, bolting and flowering, light-inhibited plants, and parthenocarpy.

Genetic dwarfism. One of the most striking properties of the gibberellins is their ability to overcome genetic dwarfism in certain plants. Usually in such cases, dwarfism is caused by the mutation of a single gene. Possibly, the mutation of this gene may cause a block in a metabolic pathway leading to the synthesis of gibberellin or some growth site involved in the biological activity of gibberellin. Generally, this type of dwarfism causes a shortening of the internodes rather than a decrease in the number of internodes. For this reason, when gibberellin is applied to single gene dwarf mutants, such as *Pisum sativum, Vicia faba,* and *Phaseolus multiflorus,* they elongate to become indistinguishable from their respective normal counterparts (7). Gibberellin applied to the normal plant in the above ex-

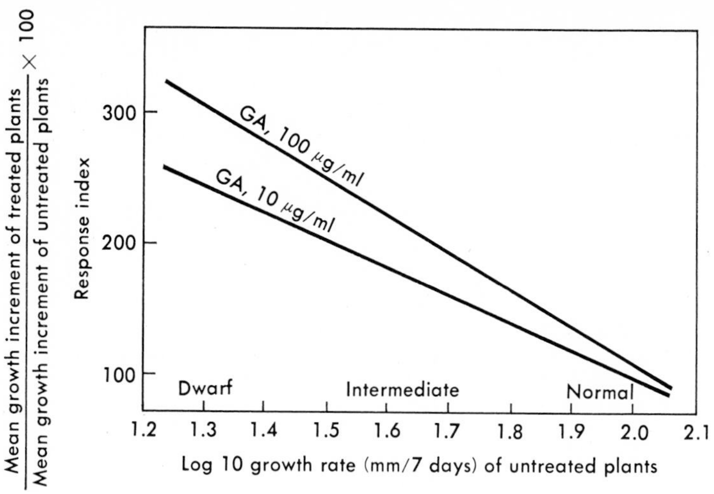

Figure 19-3 Relation between growth rate and response of pea varieties to gibberellic acid. (After P. W. Brian and H. G. Hemming. 1955. Physiol. Plantarum 8: 669.)

ample has no effect. Figure 19-3 illustrates the influence of gibberellin on dwarf, intermediate, and normal pea plants. Note the lack of response of the normal plants and the excellent response of the dwarf pea plants. Note, also, that the response increases with an increase in the concentration of gibberellin applied.

It is thought by many investigators that the condition of dwarfism corrected by application of gibberellin is due to a lack of endogenous gibberellin or concentrations of gibberellin so low as to have no effect. This could be caused, for example, by the lack of an enzyme involved in a sequence of reactions leading to the synthesis of gibberellin. The application of exogenous gibberellin alleviates the shortage of endogenous gibberellin.

Also, there are some who believe that an excess of some natural inhibitor is present in dwarf plants, which retards growth, and that gibberellin counteracts the effect of this inhibitor. Supporting evidence has been given for both theories.

Bolting and flowering. In addition to their role in internode elongation, gibberellins function in many plants as a controlling factor in a balance between internode growth and leaf development. For example, in many plants leaf development will be profuse, while internode growth will be retarded, a form of growth called a "rosette." Just before the reproductive stage, there is a striking stimulation of internode elongation, the stem sometimes elongating from five to six times the original height of the plant.

Usually this type of plant is a rosetted "long-day" plant, requiring a certain minimum number of hours of daylight to bolt and flower or a rosetted "cold-requiring" plant, needing a cold treatment to bolt and flower. If the long-day plant is kept under short-day conditions and the cold-requiring plant is not given a cold treatment, the rosette form of growth is maintained.

Treatment of these plants with gibberellin during conditions that would normally maintain the rosette form will cause the plant to bolt and flower (28). It is even possible to separate bolting from flowering by controlling the amount of gibberellin applied; that is, a plant will bolt but not flower if a smaller dosage of gibberellin is applied (41).

The separation of bolting and flowering in gibberellin treatment of rosetted plants has led some investigators to suggest that flowering is only an indirect result of gibberellin treatment. The stimulated elongation of the stem necessitates the production of the many compounds needed to maintain such internodal growth. Some of these compounds, by either their concentration or presence, may ultimately lead to the differentiation of floral primordia. In addition, gibberellin treatment of short-day plants under photoperiods unsuitable for flowering does not promote flowering (47). In fact, in at least one case, gibberellin treatment of short-day plants under conditions favorable to flowering actually reduced flowering (22).

It appears that the reason a plant either remains in the rosette form or bolts and flowers is related to the amount of native gibberellin present in the plant. For example, there is some evidence that native gibberellin-like substances are found in greater amounts in the bolted plant than in the nonbolted form. In addition, higher concentrations of gibberellin-like substances have been found in the bolted cold-requiring plant *Chrysanthemum morifolium* Ram. cv. Shuokan and in the long-day plant *Rudbeckia speciosa* Wenderoth than in the nonbolted forms (21, 39).

Light inhibited stem growth. Anyone comparing the stem growth of an etiolated plant (dark-grown) with that of a light-grown plant will immediately conclude that light has an inhibitory effect on stem elongation. Application of gibberellins to certain plants growing in the light will greatly increase their stem growth. With the above facts in mind, we are presented with the question, is there a relationship or interaction between endogenous gibberellin and light absorbed by the plant?

The reversal of light-induced inhibition of stem elongation by application of gibberellin suggests that endogenous gibberellin is the limiting factor in stem growth. The most obvious conclusion is that light causes inhibition of stem growth by lowering the level of available gibberellin in the plant. This inhibition is overcome by applying exogenous gibberellin to the plant. However, investigation along this line of reasoning has put this very simple solution in doubt.

Lockhart (29), a proponent of the theory that light lowers the level of available gibberellin in the plant, has shown that increase in the level of available gibberellin increases the plasticity of young cell walls. In previous discussions, we have mentioned the importance of cell wall plasticity in cell elongation. Lockhart has also demonstrated that plasticity of the cell wall is decreased in the light-grown cells (Figure 19-4). He concludes

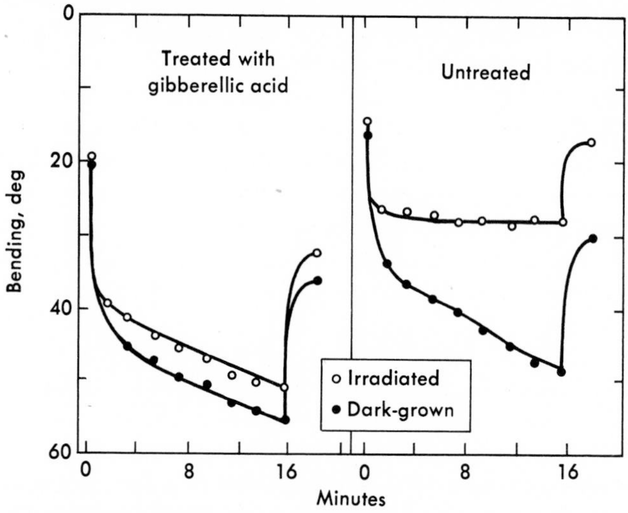

Figure 19-4 Plasticity of the cell wall of elongating cell in dark-grown and irradiated Alaska pea stems. The irradiation treatment consisted of a 3 hour exposure to red light. Gibberellic acid was applied 3 hours prior to irradiation. Plasticity is here measured as the amount of residual bending after a weight is removed. Note that plasticity was not decreased by irradiation when gibberellic acid was applied. (Reproduced from *Plant Growth Regulation,* edited by R. M. Klein, © 1961 by Iowa State University Press.)

that exposure to light lowers the level of endogenous gibberellin, which in turn decreases the plasticity of the cell walls, thus inhibiting stem growth. Application of exogenous gibberellin counteracts light-induced decrease in plasticity (Figure 19-4). However, some investigators have found that in at least one plant, gibberellin-stimulated stem elongation is partly because of increased cell division. This, of course, would have nothing to do with increase or decrease in cell wall plasticity.

In the work of Mohr and Appuhn (36) and Mohr (37), another argument may be found against the theory that light inhibition of stem elongation is caused by light-induced lowering of the gibberellin level in plants. Stem elongation of mustard seedlings grown in the dark may also be stimulated by application of gibberellin. In fact, the concentration of gibberellin needed for maximum response is the same for both dark- and light-grown mustard seedlings. This could not be so if light lowered the endogenous level of available gibberellin in the plant.

Whether gibberellin-induced elongation and light-induced inhibition of stem growth act independently of each other is still as yet unsolved. Certainly, there seems to be arguments for both conclusions.

Parthenocarpy. In a previous discussion, we described how application of auxins could cause fruit to develop parthenocarpically. In the early years of this discovery, it was thought that auxin activity after fertilization was the primary mechanism of fruit development. In fact, substitution of exogenous auxin for fertilization became a highly valuable venture into the economics of fruit growing.

However, auxins are not the only natural growth hormones capable of inducing parthenocarpy. Gibberellins have been found very reliable in producing parthenocarpic fruit-set and, in many cases, show higher activity than the native auxin in this respect. In fact, there are several examples where auxin has proven ineffective and gibberellins active. For example, pome and stone fruit have been generally unresponsive to auxin treatment (57). Yet, gibberellins have induced parthenocarpy in both pome (14, 30) and stone (12, 44) fruits. There is little doubt that native gibberellins and gibberellin-like substances play a major role in the development of fruit under natural conditions. Whether this is a direct action by gibberellins or an interaction with the native auxin of the plant has not been conclusively shown. A comparison between gibberellin-induced parthenocarpic fruit and fruit developed normally after fertilization is given in Figure 19-5.

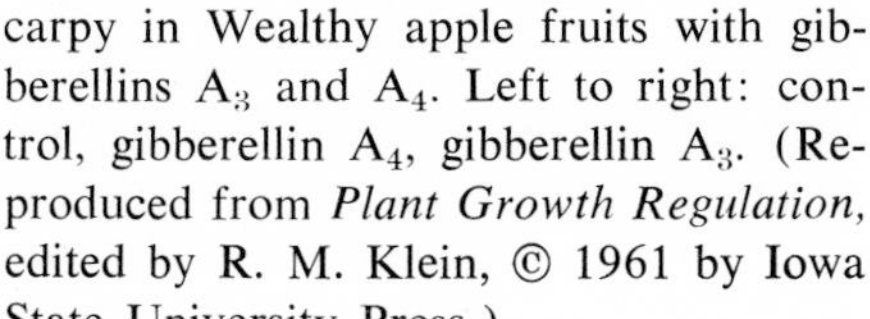

Figure 19-5 Inducement of parthenocarpy in Wealthy apple fruits with gibberellins A_3 and A_4. Left to right: control, gibberellin A_4, gibberellin A_3. (Reproduced from *Plant Growth Regulation*, edited by R. M. Klein, © 1961 by Iowa State University Press.)

Biosynthesis of gibberellins

Precise knowledge of the biosynthetic pathway or pathways leading to the synthesis of gibberellin is lacking. The outlines, however, of at least one pathway that might lead to the synthesis of gibberellins has been presented and has received experimental support from labeling studies (4, 5). In this scheme, acetate and mevalonate are thought to be precursors.

By growing the fungus *F. moniliforme* on media containing acetate labeled in the carboxyl carbon and mevalonate labeled in the number 2 carbon, Birch et al. (4) were able to show that the pattern of labeling in gibberellin A_3 extracted from the fungus was as they had predicted. The postulated path and labeling patterns of the synthesis of gibberellin A_3 from acetate-1-C^{14} and mevalonate-2-C^{14} are given in Figure 19-6 (41).

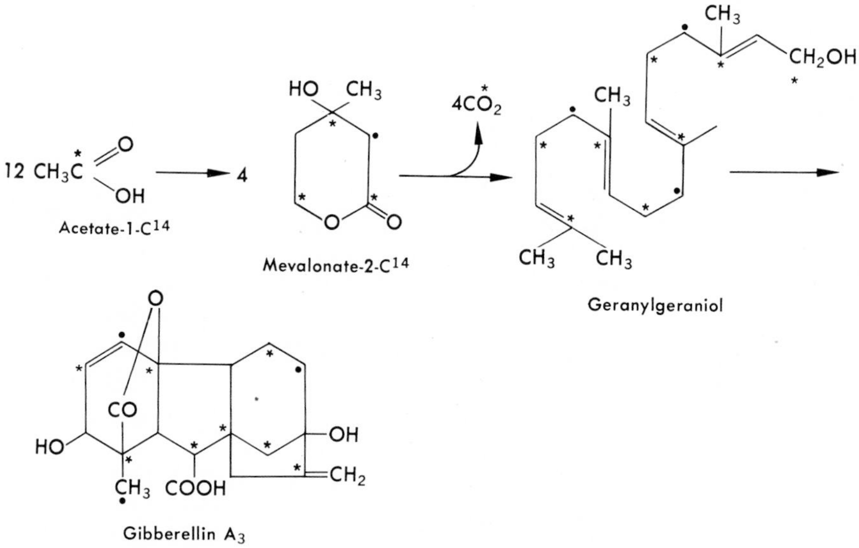

Figure 19-6 Suggested route for the biosynthesis of the gibberellin carbon skeleton. * Predicted labeling from acetate-1-C^{14}. • Predicted labeling from mevalonate-2-C^{14}. (After B. O. Phinney and C. A. West. 1961. *In* W. Ruhland (ed.), Encyclopedia of plant physiology. Springer, Berlin. 14: 1185.

Gibberellin and auxin interaction

We have learned that gibberellins are active in many of the same plant growth systems that auxins are active in (e.g., cell elongation, fruit-set, flowering, etc.). The question arises, do gibberellins act through an auxin-mediated system? That is, does gibberellin promote the synthesis, transport, action, or inactivation of auxin in the plant? An answer to the above question may possibly be found in a study of the effects of gibberellin on dwarf garden pea internodes. Application of gibberellin to the intact plant will cause the internodes to elongate considerably. However, when these same internodes are removed from the plant (excised) and placed in a buffered solution, they will not respond to gibberellin unless IAA is also added (8, 9). The excised internode is separated from the apical meristem from which it received its supply of auxin, but the addition of exogenous IAA to the buffered solution relieves this shortage. In addition, decapitated plants do not respond to applications of gibberellic acid (2).

However, there have been several studies demonstrating that gibberellins and auxins are quite different (Table 19-2) and that they act independently

Table 19-2 Some differences in activities of gibberellin and auxin.[a]

Test	*IAA*	GA_1
Avena standard	+	−
pea split stem	+	−
tomato epinasty	+	−
callus formation	+	−
bud inhibition	+	−
root formation	+	−

[a] After J. Kato. 1953. Mem. Coll. Sci. Univ. Kyoto B 20: 189. and 1958. Physiol. Plant 11: 10.

of each other. For example, etiolated pea stem sections respond to both gibberellin and IAA when these growth regulators are applied separately. When applied simultaneously, their effect is merely additive (43, 26), indicating independent action. In fact, Hillman and Purves (23) found that gibberellic acid could promote pea stem section elongation in the presence of inhibitory levels of IAA, again indicating independent action. However, a synergistic effect (more than additive) may be obtained when green, instead of etiolated, pea stem sections are used (17).

Competitive inhibitors of IAA activity (antiauxin) have been found to be noncompetitive with gibberellin in pea stem section elongation (26). That is, increasing the concentration of gibberellin could not overcome the inhibitory effect of the antiauxin.

Many investigators believe that gibberellin may have an influence on IAA-oxidase that results in an "auxin-saving" mechanism. That is, the auxin level in the plant is raised because of an influence of gibberellin on

IAA-oxidase. In support of this hypothesis, Galston and McCune (17) have found that gibberellin treatment of dwarf pea and corn plants lowers peroxidase activity in both plants. This would have the effect of protecting endogenous IAA from oxidation. In a previous chapter, we discussed the essential role of peroxidase as a constituent of the IAA-oxidase system. However, the findings by Hillman and Purves (23) that gibberellin will promote etiolated pea stem section elongation in the presence of inhibitory concentrations of IAA seems to contradict any suggestion that gibberellin acts through an auxin-saving or protecting mechanism in the plant.

It appears from the above discussion that gibberellin and auxin act both independently and together, depending upon the species of plant, the conditions under which the plant is growing, and the type of response being measured. The study of whether or not auxins and gibberellins interact is still far from conclusive. There still is a lot of work to be done on this aspect of plant growth regulation.

KINETIN

Up to now, we have been concerned with growth hormones, synthetic and natural, whose primary function is to promote cell elongation. We have mentioned that IAA and gibberellin do promote an increase in the number of cells in certain circumstances, but this is the exception rather than the

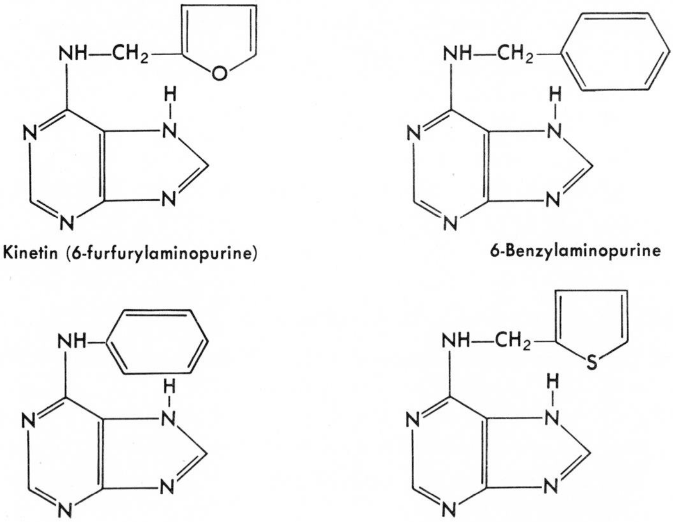

Figure 19-7 Structural formulas for kinetin and three analogs. All four compounds are active in the promotion of cell division.

rule. The only growth regulator we have discussed so far, concerned primarily with cell division, was traumatic acid (wound hormone). However, in addition to traumatic acid, there exists in plants several compounds capable of promoting cell division. For example, coconut milk was found to be very active as a stimulant of cell division by van Overbeek et al. (54). Subsequently, this finding was supported by several investigations on a variety of plant tissues, confirming that coconut milk is, indeed, an active promoter of cell division (11, 38, 3).

Perhaps the most exciting discovery in the search for compounds that will induce cells to multiply is *kinetin* (6-furfurylaminopurine), a compound isolated from yeast DNA by Miller et al. (34). Actually, kinetin is formed from deoxyadenosine, a degradation product of DNA (20). Subsequent to its discovery, many analogs of kinetin, active in promoting cell division, were synthesized. In order to group this type of substance under one title, the generic term *kinin* has been given to all compounds with biological activity similar to that of kinetin (33). Kinetin and three analogs of kinetin, all active in cell division, are given in Figure 19-7.

Physiological effects

Shortly after the discovery of kinetin, there followed a great number of papers describing its effects on many different plant growth systems. Most of these were concerned, directly or indirectly, with kinetin's ability to promote cell division and cell enlargement. We will discuss the effects of kinetin on cell division, cell enlargement, root initiation and growth, shoot initiation and growth, and breaking of dormancy.

Cell division. The stimulation of cell division in plant tissue cultures was the first effect of kinetin to be observed (33, 49). In the tobacco pith cultures used by these investigators, it was noted that, in addition to kinetin, IAA is also needed for continuous growth. Although either growth regulator, when used alone, produces a small response, it is not continuous and in a relatively short period of time subsides. It has been suggested by Miller (32) that the small response invoked by kinetin or IAA used alone on tobacco pith cultures is due to small amounts of endogenous kinetin-like substances and IAA already present. However, when IAA and kinetin are applied together in the right ratio of concentrations, the results are striking and growth of the culture can be maintained indefinitely. The ability of kinetin in the presence of IAA to promote cell division is shown in Figure 19-8.

In order that cell division may take place, an ordered sequence (DNA synthesis, mitosis, and cytokinesis) must take place. Is there a specific influence of IAA or kinetin alone on any step in this sequence? The answer

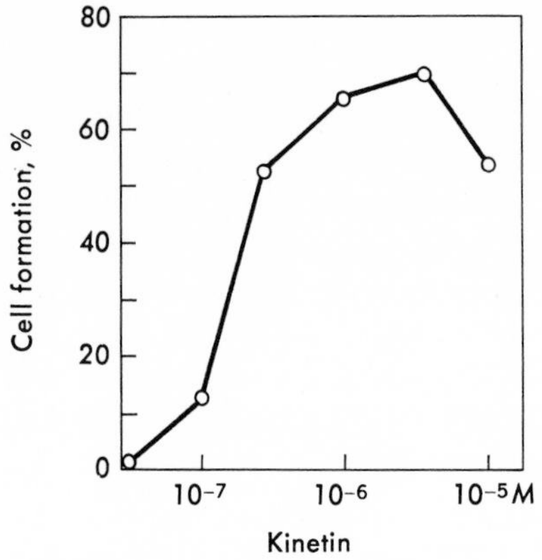

Figure 19-8 The effect of kinetin in promotion of cell division in tobacco-pith-tissue cultures. Two mg/liter of IAA was also present in the culture medium. (After F. Skoog and C. O. Miller. 1957. *In* Biological action of growth substances. Symp. Soc. Exptl. Biol. 11: 118.)

is apparently, yes. Das et al. (13) found that both IAA and kinetin, when used alone, stimulate DNA synthesis in tobacco pith cultures. The above authors also found that both growth regulators are needed for mitosis, although IAA appears to dominate in this step. In addition, they suggested that when either kinetin or IAA is present in high concentration, the other may become limiting for at least one of the three steps needed to complete cell division. In a later paper, these authors stated that of the three steps in cell division, IAA is involved in the first two (DNA duplication and mitosis), but that the last step (cytokinesis) is controlled by kinetin (40). Here again, as with our discussions on gibberellins and IAA, we are presented with the importance of balance between growth hormones in plant growth and development.

How kinetin induces cell division is still an unsolved question. The adenine moiety of the kinetin molecule appears essential for this process, many different substituted side chains being applicable. Strong (50) has suggested that the side chain may influence some physical property (such as solubility) bearing on the efficiency of the growth regulator to induce cell division.

Cell enlargement. Not only does kinetin promote cell division, but it also induces cell enlargement, an effect usually associated with IAA and gibberellins. Treatment of leaf discs cut from etiolated leaves of *Phaseolus vulgaris* (bean) causes significant cell enlargements (31, 42). This effect of kinetin occurs in the absence of IAA. Cell enlargement after kinetin treatment has also been observed in tobacco pith cultures (19) and tobacco roots (1). Since kinetin-induced cell enlargement has been clearly shown, it should not be considered solely a cell division factor.

Root initiation and growth. Although relatively few studies have been made of kinetin effects on the root system, it appears that kinetin is able both to stimulate and to inhibit root initiation and development. Kinetin in the presence of casein hydrolysate and IAA stimulates root initiation and development in tobacco stem callus cultures (49). Increase in dry weight and elongation of the roots of lupin seedlings was found by Fries (16) to be promoted by kinetin. This is shown in Figure 19-9. In Figure 19-9, it can be seen that all concentrations of kinetin increase the dry

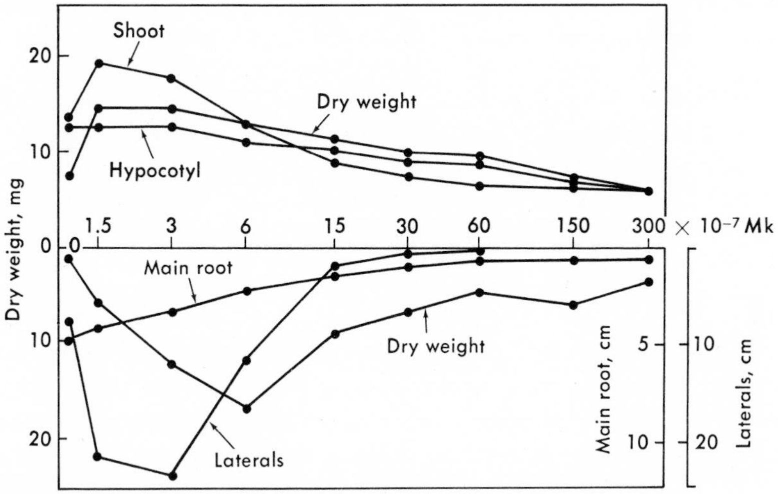

Figure 19-9 Effect of kinetin (K) on different growth systems in the intact lupin seedling. The graph is divided, the lower half representing main and lateral root growth and the upper half representing hypocotyl and shoot growth. Note that the mid-line of the graph gives the amount of kinetin used in molar concentrations $\times 10^{-7}$ (After N. Fries. 1960. Physiol. Plantarum 13: 468.)

weight of the root system even though at the higher concentration root elongation is inhibited.

Shoot initiation and growth. In the original work with tobacco callus cultures and kinetin, it was found that the callus tissue can be kept in an undifferentiated state as long as the proper balance of IAA and kinetin is maintained. However, if the ratio of kinetin to IAA is increased, either by the addition of more kinetin or the use of less IAA, leafy shoots are initiated (see review by Miller (32). Torrey (53) observed that kinetin initiated bud primordia on root segments of *Convolvulus arvensis* (bindweed), this effect being much more marked when the segments were grown in the dark.

Five day old bean seedlings soaked in kinetin solutions and then allowed to grow for an additional 46 hours respond with an increase in fresh weight of the epicotyl, increase in leaf expansion, and increase in the elongation of stems and petioles (31). There have been several additional demonstrations of kinetin-induced promotions of shoot initiation and growth. However, the above studies serve to illustrate that kinetin is active in the initiation and development of the aerial portions of the plant.

Breaking of dormancy. Earlier, we discussed apical dominance, the inhibition of lateral bud growth by auxin emanating from the apical bud. The controlling features of this phenomenon are not clearly understood and may involve not only IAA but other factors, which may interact with the auxin. This has been suggested in a study by Wickson and Thimann (56) on the interaction of IAA and kinetin in apical dominance. They found that the growth of the lateral buds of pea stem sections in culture solutions containing IAA is inhibited, as might be expected. The growth of lateral buds on stem sections in nutrient solutions not containing IAA, of course, is uninhibited. However, the addition of kinetin along with IAA stimulates the growth of these buds (Figure 19-10). Kinetin alone has little effect.

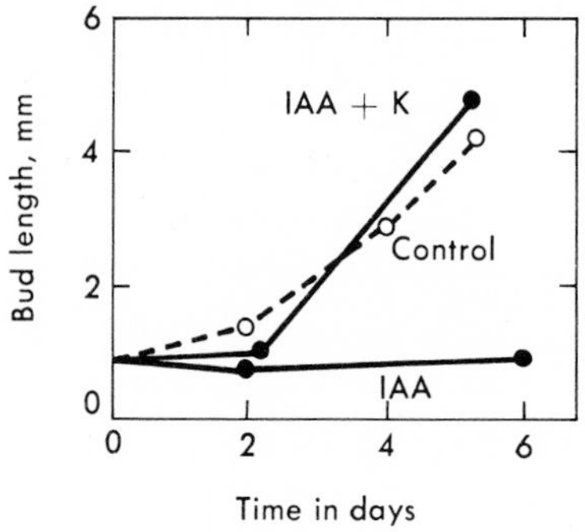

Figure 19-10 Effect of kinetin-IAA interaction on bud growth of stem sections of *Pisum sativum* var. Alaska. Note that IAA inhibition is overcome by kinetin (K). Concentrations used: 1 ppm IAA and 4 ppm kinetin. (After M. Wickson and K. V. Thimann. 1958. Physiol. Plantarum 11: 62.)

These investigators also demonstrated that the effect of kinetin on apical dominance can also be observed in entire shoots; that is, the apical bud is present. They found, as in the classical studies of apical dominance, that removal of the apical bud stimulates the growth of the lateral buds. On the other hand, if the apical bud remains, the lateral buds are completely inhibited. However, if the intact shoot is soaked in a kinetin solution, inhibition of the lateral buds by the apical bud is overcome to a large extent (Figure 19-11). In addition to the above study, there have been several other investigations demonstrating the stimulatory effects of kinetin on lateral bud growth (see review by Miller (32)). It appears that apical dominance may be controlled by a balance of concentrations between endogenous kinetin-like substances and IAA (56).

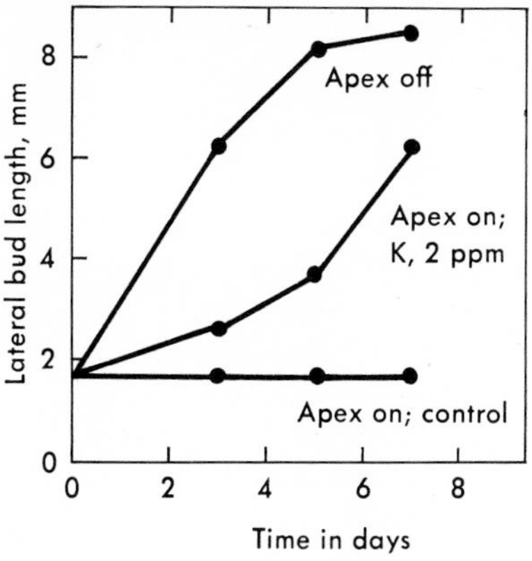

Figure 19-11 Effect of kinetin (K) on apical bud dominance in *Pisum sativum* var. Alaska. Two ppm of kinetin partially counteracted the inhibitory effect of apical bud on lateral bud growth. (After M. Wickson and K. L. Thimann. 1958. Physiol. Plantarum 11: 62.)

Other physiological effects

It is a well-known fact that the germination of lettuce seeds (*Lactuca sativa*) may be stimulated by red light and inhibited by infrared (far red) light (6). Also, the growth of bean leaf discs is sensitive to red and far red light treatment, being stimulated by red light and inhibited by far-red light treatment (15). In both of the above situations, the effect of kinetin treatment is similar to that of red light treatment (31). Only in one respect, does it differ. The stimulatory effects of kinetin are in no way inhibited by subsequent far-red treatment as in the case of red light treatment (Tables

Table 19-3 Effect of kinetin and red and far red irradiation on growth of bean leaf discs during a 48-hour growth period.[a]

Conc. of kinetin, M	*Light treatment*[b]	*Increase in diam., mm*
0	none	1.05 ± 0.04[c]
5×10^{-5}	none	2.48 ± 0.03
0	5 min red	2.58 ± 0.08
0	5 min far red	1.01 ± 0.06
0	5 min red and then 5 min far red	1.17 ± 0.07
5×10^{-5}	5 min far red	2.49 ± 0.08

[a] After C. O. Miller. 1956. Plant Physiol. 31: 318.
[b] Light treatments given at beginning of experiment.
[c] Standard error. Ten discs per treatment.

Table 19-4 Effect of kinetin and red and far-red irradiation on germination of Grand Rapids lettuce seeds during a 72-hour period.[a]

Conc. of kinetin, M	*Light treatment*[b]	*Germination, %*[c] *Expt. 1*	*Expt. 2*
0	none	8	7
5×10^{-5}	none	84	86
0	8 min red	96	96
0	5 min red and then 8 min far red	5	7
5×10^{-5}	8 min far red	86	83

[a] After C. O. Miller. 1956. Plant Physiol. 31: 318.
[b] Light treatments given 16 hours after start of experiment.
[c] Percent given as nearest whole number, 95–105 seeds per treatment.

19-3 and 19-4). Germination of seeds of white clover and carpet grass has also been observed to respond positively to kinetin treatment (48).

Although kinetin has not been isolated from plants as yet, it appears that there are, at least, kinetin-like substances present. It also is quite evident that these kinetin-like substances interact with endogenous IAA to effect an influence on the growth and development of the plant. Again, we are presented with evidence supporting the concept that the growth and development of a plant is under the influence of delicate chemical balances maintained by the presence or absence of interaction between growth regulators.

BIBLIOGRAPHY

1. Arora, N., F. Skoog, and O. N. Allen. 1959. Kinetin-induced pseudonodules on tobacco roots. Am. J. Botan. 46: 610.
2. Audus, L. J. 1959. Plant growth substances. Interscience Publishers, New York.
3. Ball, E. 1946. Development in sterile culture of stem tips and subjacent regions of *Tropaeolum majus* L. and of *Lupinus albus* L. Am. J. Botan. 33: 301.
4. Birch, A. J., R. W. Richards, and H. Smith. 1958. The biosynthesis of gibberellic acid. Proc. Chem. Soc. 192.
5. Birch, A. J., and H. Smith. 1959. The biosynthesis of terpenoid compounds in fungi. *In* Biosynthesis of terpenes and sterols. Little, Brown & Co., Boston.
6. Borthwick, H. A., S. B. Hendricks, M. W. Parker, E. H. Toole, and V. K.

Toole. 1952. A reversible photoreaction controlling seed germination. Proc. Natl. Acad. Sci. U.S. 38: 662.

7. Brian, P. W., and H. G. Hemming. 1955. The effect of gibberellic acid on shoot growth of pea seedlings. Physiol. Plant 8: 669.
8. Brian, P. W., and H. G. Hemming. 1957. A relation between the effects of gibberellic acid and indolylacetic acid on plant cell extension. Nature (London) 179: 417.
9. Brian, P. W., and H. G. Hemming. 1958. Complementary action of gibberellic acid and auxins in pea internode extension. Ann. Botan. (London) N. S. 22: 1.
10. Bukovac, M. J., and S. H. Wittwer. 1961. Biological evaluation of gibberellins A_1, A_2, A_3, and A_4 and some of their derivatives. *In* R. M. Klein (ed.), Plant growth regulation. The Iowa State University Press, Ames, Iowa. 505.
11. Caplin, S. M., and F. C. Steward. 1948. Effect of coconut milk on the growth of explants from carrot root. Science 108: 655.
12. Crane, J. C., P. E. Primer, and R. C. Campbell. 1960. Gibberellin-induced parthenocarpy in *Prunus*. Proc. Am. Soc. Hort. Sci. 75: 129.
13. Das, N. K., K. Patau, and F. Skoog. 1956. Initiation of mitosis and cell division by kinetin and indoleacetic acid in excised tobacco pith tissue. Physiol. Plant 9: 640.
14. Davison, R. M. 1960. Fruit-setting of apples using gibberellic acid. Nature 188: 681.
15. Downs, R. J. 1955. Photoreversibility of leaf and hypocotyl elongation of dark grown red kidney bean seedlings. Plant Physiol. 30: 468.
16. Fries, N. 1960. The effect of adenine and kinetin on growth and differentiation of *Lupinus*. Physiol. Plant 13: 468.
17. Galston, A. W., and D. C. McCune. 1961. An analysis of gibberellin-auxin interaction and its possible metabolic basis. *In* R. M. Klein (ed.), Plant growth regulation. The Iowa State University Press, Ames, Iowa. 611.
18. Galston, A. W., and W. K. Purves. 1960. The mechanism of action of auxin. Ann. Rev. Plant Physiol. 11: 239.
19. Glasziou, K. T. 1957. Respiration and levels of phosphate esters during kinetin-induced cell division in tobacco pith sections. Nature 179: 1083.
20. Hall, R. H., and R. S. deRopp. 1955. Formation of 6-furfurylaminopurine from DNA breakdown products. J. Am. Chem. Soc. 77: 6400.
21. Harada, H., and J. P. Nitsch. 1959. Changes in endogenous growth substances during flower development. Plant Physiol. 34: 409.
22. Harder, R., and R. Bünsow. 1956. Einfluss des Gibberellins auf die Blütenbildung bei *Kalanchoë blossfeldiana*. Naturwissenschaften 43: 544.
23. Hillman, W. S., and W. H. Purves. 1961. Does gibberellin act through an auxin-mediated mechanism? *In* R. M. Klein (ed.), Plant growth regulation. The Iowa State University Press, Ames, Iowa. 589.
24. Kato, J. 1953. Studies on the physiological effect of gibberellin. I. On the differential activity between gibberellin and auxin. Mem. Coll. Sci. Univ. Kyoto B 20: 189.

25. Kato, J. 1958. Studies on the physiological effect of gibberellin. II. On the interaction of gibberellin with auxins and growth inhibitors. Physiol. Plant 11: 10.
26. Kato, J. 1961. Physiological action of gibberellin with special reference to auxin. *In* R. M. Klein (ed.), Plant growth regulation. The Iowa State University Press, Ames, Iowa. 601.
27. Kurosawa, E. 1926. Experimental studies on the secretion of *Fusarium heterosporum* on rice plants. Trans. Nat. Hist. Soc. Formosa 16: 213.
28. Lang, A. 1957. The effect of gibberellin upon flower formation. Proc. Nat. Acad. Sci. (Washington) 43: 709.
29. Lockhart, J. A. 1961. The hormonal mechanism of growth inhibition by visible radiation. *In* R. M. Klein (ed.), Plant growth regulation. The Iowa State University Press, Ames, Iowa. 543.
30. Luckwill, L. C. 1959. Fruit growth in relation to internal and external chemical stimuli. *In* D. Rudnick (ed.), Cell, organism and milieu, 17th growth symposium. Ronald Press, New York. 223.
31. Miller, C. O. 1956. Similarity of some kinetin and red light effects. Plant Physiol. 31: 318.
32. Miller, C. O. 1961. Kinetin and related compounds in plant growth. Ann. Rev. Plant Physiol. 12: 395.
33. Miller, C. O., F. Skoog, F. S. Okumura, M. H. vonSaltza, and F. M. Strong. 1956. Isolation, structure and synthesis of kinetin, a substance promoting cell division. J. Am. Chem. Soc. 78: 1375.
34. Miller, C. O., F. Skoog, M. H. von Saltza, and F. M. Strong. 1955. Kinetin: a cell division factor from deoxyribonucleic acid. J. Am. Chem. Soc. 77: 1392.
35. Mitchell, J. W., D. P. Skaggs, and W. P. Anderson. 1951. Plant growth-stimulating hormones in immature bean seeds. Science 114: 159.
36. Mohr, H., and V. Appuhn. 1961. Zur Wechselwirkung von Licht und Gibberellinsaure. Naturwissenshaften 48: 483.
37. Mohr, H. 1962. Primary effects of light on growth. Ann. Rev. Plant Physiol. 13: 465.
38. Nickell, L. G. 1950. Effect of coconut milk on the growth in vitro of plant virus tumor tissue. Botan. Gaz. 112: 225.
39. Nitsch, J. P. 1959. Changes in endogenous growth regulating substances during flower initiation. Fourth Intern. Congr. Biochem. Pergamon Press, London 6: 141.
40. Patau, K., N. K. Das, and F. Skoog. 1957. Induction of DNA synthesis by kinetin and indoleacetic acid in excised tobacco pith tissue. Physiol. Plant 10: 949.
41. Phinney, B. O., and C. A. West. 1961. Gibberellins and plant growth. *In* W. Ruhland (ed.), Encyclopedia of plant physiology. Springer, Berlin. 14: 1185.
42. Powell, R. D., and M. M. Griffith. 1960. Some anatomical effects of kinetin and red light on disks of bean leaves. Plant Physiol. 35: 273.
43. Purves, W. K., and W. S. Hillman. 1958. Response of pea stem sections

to indoleacetic acid, gibberellic acid, and sucrose as affected by length and distance from apex. Physiol. Plant 11: 29.
44. Rebeiz, C. A., and J. C. Crane. 1961. Growth regulator-induced parthenocarpy in the Bing cherry. Proc. Am. Soc. Hort. Sci. 78: 69.
45. Sachs, R. M., and A. Lang. 1961. Shoot histogenesis and the subapical meristem: the action of gibberellic acid, amo-1618, and maleic hydrazide. *In* R. M. Klein (ed.), Plant growth regulation. The Iowa State University Press, Ames, Iowa. 521.
46. Sawada, K. 1912. Diseases of agricultural products in Japan. Formosan Agr. Rev. 36: 10, 16.
47. Sironval, C. 1961. Gibberellins, cell division, and plant flowering. *In* R. M. Klein (ed.), Plant growth regulation. The Iowa State University Press, Ames, Iowa. 521.
48. Skinner, C. G., F. D. Talbert, and W. Shive. 1958. Effect of 6-(substituted) purines and gibberellin on the rate of seed germination. Plant Physiol. 33: 190.
49. Skoog, F., and C. O. Miller. 1957. Chemical regulation of growth and organ formation in plant tissues cultured *in vivo*. *In* Biological action of growth substances. Symp. Soc. Exptl. Biol. 11: 118.
50. Strong, F. M. 1958. Topics in microbial chemistry. John Wiley & Sons, Inc., New York.
51. Stuart, N. W., and H. M. Cathey. 1961. Applied aspects of the gibberellins. Ann. Rev. Plant Physiol. 12: 369.
52. Sumiki, Y., and A. Kawarada. 1961. Relation between chemical structure and physiological activity. *In* R. M. Klein (ed.), Plant growth regulation. The Iowa State University Press, Ames, Iowa. 503.
53. Torrey, J. G. 1958. Endogenous bud and root formation by isolated roots of *Convolvulus* grown *in vitro*. Plant Physiol. 33: 258.
54. Van Overbeek, J., M. E. Conklin, and A. F. Blakeslee. 1941. Factors in coconut milk essential for growth and development of *Datura* embryos. Science 94: 350.
55. West, C. A., and B. O. Phinney. 1957. Purification and properties of gibberellin-like substances from flowering plants. Plant Physiol. 32 (suppl.): xxxii.
56. Wickson, M., and K. V. Thimann. 1958. The antagonism of auxin and kinetin in apical dominance. Physiol. Plant 11: 62.
57. Wittwer, S. H., and M. J. Bukovac. 1962. Exogenous plant growth substances affecting floral initiation and fruit set. Proc. Plant Sci. Symp. Campbell Soup Company 65.

Part SEVEN

Growth and Development

20
Photoperiodism

INTRODUCTION

Undoubtedly, even before the dawn of history, man was at least subconsciously aware of the controlling effect of light on plant growth. One can imagine that it was easily demonstrated that a plant could not grow in the dark, that light was essential. Surprisingly enough, however, this was not even suggested until 1779 when Ingenhousz recognized the importance of light in photosynthesis. Since that time, there has been slow but steady progress toward the recognition of many light-controlled processes involved in plant growth.

Prerequisite to the initiation of a plant response to light is the requirement that light be absorbed. This means a receptor of some sort (usually a pigment) has to be present and be capable of absorbing the wavelength or wavelengths of light responsible for the response. In many cases the absorbance of light by the receptor causes it to become more reactive, which in turn starts a sequence of chemical reactions, leading ultimately to a general plant response. The absorbance of light with subsequent activation of the absorbing molecule, followed by a series of chemical reactions leading to a general plant response, may be termed a *photobiological process.*

Many of the photobiological processes occurring in plants have been studied extensively by scientists, and in several cases individual constituents of these processes have been isolated and characterized. Some of the photobiological processes that have been studied in detail are *photosynthesis, chlorophyll synthesis, phototropism, photooxidation,* and *photoperiodism.* Photosynthesis, chlorophyll synthesis, phototropism, and photooxidation have all been discussed in previous chapters. We will devote our discussions in this chapter to photoperiodism.

Photoperiodism is a term that escapes precise definition. Generally, it is defined as the response of a plant to the relative lengths of light and dark periods. However, this definition can be modified in many ways. For example, the duration of the dark period is much more important than the duration of the light period. Intensity and quality of light can be modifying features in the magnitude of the response. The total quantity of light received can have an influencing effect. It is generally accepted, however, that the duration and order of sequence is most important in the initiation of a photoperiodic response. Any response, then, by a plant to the duration and order of sequence of light and dark periods may be called a *photoperiodic response.*

Plants respond to alterations of light and dark periods in a variety of ways. Flowering, vegetative growth, internode elongation, seed germination, and leaf abscission are some examples of photoperiodic responses that have been discovered in plants. Since flowering was the first photoperiodic response to be discovered and the one most extensively studied, our discussion of photoperiodism will largely be an analysis of this phenomenon.

THE FLOWERING RESPONSE

Although controlling effects of photoperiods on flowering were observed before the twentieth century, the first good experimental evidence supporting this concept was presented during the early years of this century. Tournois (42) attempted to answer the question of why hemp would flower vigorously when planted early in the spring, but would remain in a vegetative state if planted in late spring or summer. Tournois showed that if hemp is provided with short photoperiods (6 hours), it will flower, but if provided with a long photoperiod, it will remain in a vegetative state.

A study of the flowering habits of *Sempervivum* by Klebs (25) showed that flowering can be induced by artificial illumination in midwinter in a greenhouse, although the normal time of flowering for this plant is June. Klebs concluded that flowering in *Sempervivum* is controlled by the length of the photoperiod and that light serves as a catalytic factor in this respect.

The first clearly stated hypothesis on photoperiodism was given by Garner and Allard (15). For an experimental plant, they used a large-leaf mutant of the tobacco plant, which is noted for its vigorous vegetative growth and a flowering habit that differs radically from the normal tobacco plants. The mutant, Maryland Mammoth, does not flower in the field, but when brought into the greenhouse, it flowered profusely in mid-December. The following year the seeds from this plant were sown with the normal type and the pattern was repeated, the mutant remaining vegetative in the field, but when brought in the greenhouse, flowering again in December.

The next step was to subject the Maryland Mammoth tobacco plant to short day lengths during the summer by placing the plant in darkness after exposure to a day length that would be equivalent to a winter day. The mutant then was capable of flowering in the summer. In addition, it was found that the mutant can be kept in a vegetative state during the winter months by merely lengthening the days with artificial light. It is quite obvious that Maryland Mammoth only flowers under short day length conditions. Garner and Allard termed the response of Maryland Mammoth to day length photoperiodism.

Terminology

The Maryland Mammoth mutant was called a *short-day plant* because of its habit of flowering only under short-day conditions. It was soon discovered that plants vary considerably in their response to day length. In some plants long-day photoperiods induce flowering, while others appeared unresponsive, flowering under both long- and short-day conditions. Still others respond to photoperiods situated somewhere between short- and long-day lengths. The definitions given below are based on a 24-hour cycle of light and darkness.

1. A *short-day plant* flowers when the day length is less than a certain critical length. Day lengths in excess of this critical point will keep the short-day plant vegetative. The so-called critical day length differs with different species. Some examples of short-day plants are *Nicotiana tabacum* (Mary-

land Mammoth), *Xanthium pennsylvanicum* (cocklebur), and *Glycine max* (Biloxi soybean).

2. A *long-day plant* flowers after a critical day length is exceeded. Again, this critical day length differs from species to species. Some examples of long-day plants are *Spinacea oleracea* (spinach), *Beta vulgaris* (sugar beet), and *Hyoscyamus niger* (Black henbane).
3. *Day-neutral plants* flower after a period of vegetative growth, regardless of the photoperiod. Some examples of day-neutral plants are *Lycopersicum esculentum* (tomato), *Mirabilis* (four-o'clock), and certain varieties of peas (*Pisum sativum*).

Although relatively rare, there are some plants that require a long photoperiod, succeeded by a short photoperiod, to flower. Also, a relatively few plants are induced to flower when short photoperiods are followed by long photoperiods. The above plants, requiring a long-short-day sequence or a short-long-day sequence to flower, will not flower if kept under continuous short or long photoperiods.

It is important to note that the above classification is based on whether or not a plant will flower when it is subjected to a photoperiod that exceeds or is less than a critical length. The classification does not mean to imply that all short-day plants flower under photoperiods that are shorter than photoperiods inducing flowering in long-day plants. An example to amplify this point would be to compare the short-day plant *Xanthium* with the long-day plant *Hyoscyamus*. *Xanthium* has a critical day length of $15\frac{1}{2}$ hours and flowers if this critical value is not exceeded. *Hyoscyamus* has a critical day length of 11 hours and will flower when this critical value is exceeded. The significant point here is that *Xanthium,* a short-day plant, and *Hyoscyamus,* a long-day plant, will both flower if subjected to a photoperiod of 13 hours. The delimiting factor, then, is not the number of hours of light received, but when a plant will flower—before or after a critical day length.

Importance of dark period

Plants under normal conditions are subjected to a 24 hour cycle of light and darkness. Early workers on photoperiodism also used a 24 hour cycle, thus emulating the natural condition. It soon became apparent that a more sophisticated analysis of photoperiodism could be obtained by changing the normal cycle, for example, by following an 8 hour light period with an 8 hour dark period or following a 16 hour light period with a 16 hour dark period. Subjection of long and short-day plants to cycles other than 24 hours convincingly demonstrated that *flowering in plants is more of a response to the dark period than to the light.* That is, short-day plants flower when a certain critical dark period is exceeded, and long-day plants flower when the duration of the dark period is less than a critical value.

The importance of the dark period on flowering was first demonstrated by Hamner and Bonner (17) in their work with the short-day plant *Xanthium*. They show that *Xanthium* can be kept from flowering, even though on the correct photoinductive cycle, by interrupting the dark period with a brief light period (light break) (Figure 20-1). Breaking up

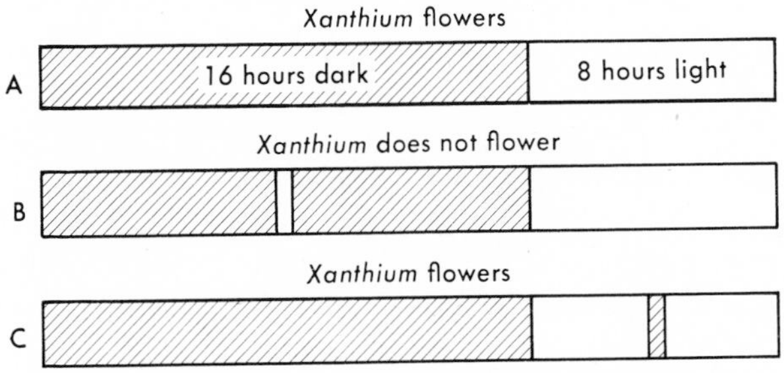

Figure 20-1 Scheme showing the importance of the dark period. A. *Xanthium* plant given a photoinductive cycle of 16 hours darkness and 8 hours light (flowers). B. *Xanthium* plant given a photoinductive cycle of 16 hours darkness and 8 hours light, the dark period being interrupted in the middle by a brief light period (plant does not flower). C. *Xanthium* plant given a photoinductive cycle of 16 hours darkness and 8 hours light, the light period being interrupted in the middle by a brief period of darkness (plant flowers).

the light period with a brief period of darkness had very little effect. In other words, the long dark period necessary for flowering in *Xanthium* was broken up into two short dark periods, thus keeping the plant in a vegetative state.

The concept that the dark period is the critical part of the photoperiodic cycle has been given considerable support by the findings of Hamner (16). Working with Biloxi soybean, a short-day plant, he found that flowering cannot be induced unless the plants receive dark periods in excess of 10 hours, while the length of the photoperiod does not matter (Figure 20-2).

Importance of photoperiod

Although the length of the photoperiod has no effect on flower initiation, it does appear to have a quantitative influence. There is an increase in

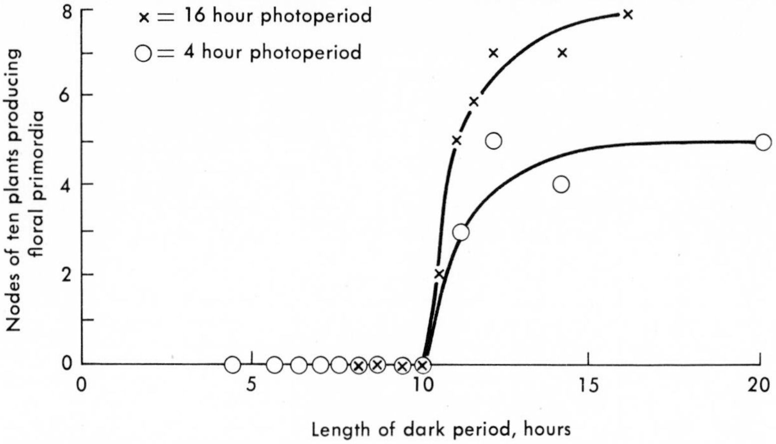

Figure 20-2 Graph showing relation between the length of dark period and the initiation of floral primordia by Biloxi soybean. (After K. C. Hamner. 1940. Botan. Gaz. 101: 658.)

number of floral primordia with increase in length of the photoperiod. It can also be seen from Figure 20-2 that increasing the dark period past 12 hours has no influence.

While the length of dark period determines actual initiation of floral primordia, the length of the light period determines the number of floral primordia initiated (16). The optimal response for the Biloxi soybean is found in a photocycle consisting of 16 hours of darkness and an 11 hour photoperiod (Figure 20-3). Photoperiods of more or less than 11 hours result in the differentiation of a smaller number of floral primordia.

As indicated in Figure 20-3, there is a quantitative response to the length of the photoperiod. With this in mind, one is confronted with the question, does the intensity of light have an influence on the number of floral primordia differentiated? The answer to this question is a very complex one. Intensity of light could have an indirect effect, such as controlling the amount of sugars flowing to meristematic regions capable of initiating floral primordia. For example, Takimoto (41) was partially successful in bringing about flowering in the dark by supplying plants with sugar solutions. In addition, the effectiveness of the photoperiod diminishes in the absence of CO_2 (43). The enhancing effect of externally supplied sugar and CO_2 certainly indicates that substrate provided by photosynthesis has some effect on the ability of the plant to produce flowers. In addition to its indirect effect through photosynthesis, the intensity of light might be of direct importance in the synthesis of some factor or hormone necessary for floral formation.

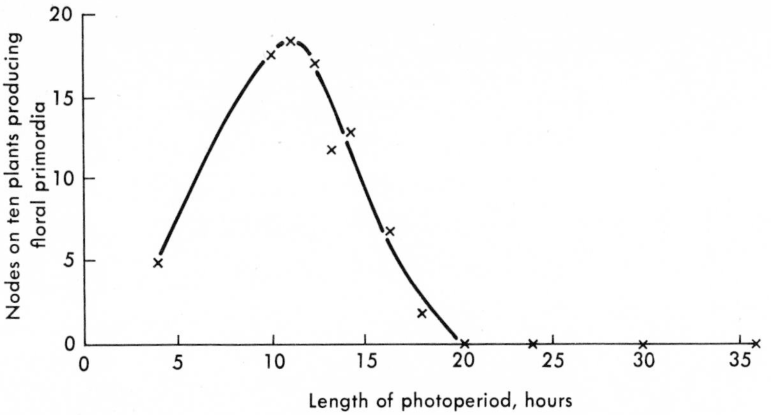

Figure 20-3 Graph showing relation between light duration and the initiation of floral primordia by Biloxi soybean. The dark period in all treatments was 16 hours. (After H. C. Hamner. 1940. Botan. Gaz. 101: 658.)

Hamner (16) studied the quantitative effect of light duration and intensity on floral initiation by Biloxi soybean on a photoinductive cycle. He found that at light intensities below 100 ft-c, no flowers are produced. Increase in light intensity increases the number of flowers produced (Figure 20-4). Of the two photoperiods used in the experiment described in Figure 20-4, the longer photoperiod produces the greater number of flowers.

Photoinductive cycles

Early workers with photoperiodism and flowering were concerned more with the number and quality of flowers obtained than the time a plant needed to be subjected to a cycle conducive to flowering in order to differentiate floral primordia. However, the number of cycles needed to induce flowering differs widely among different plant species. For example, *Xanthium pennsylvanicum* requires only one photoinductive cycle to initiate floral primordia. In contrast, *Salvia occidentalis,* a short-day plant, requires at least 17 photoinductive cycles to flower (43), and *Plantago lanceolata,* a long-day plant, needs to receive 25 photoinductive cycles for maximum floral response (22).

It must be understood that the formation of flowers by a plant is an all or nothing affair with respect to photoperiodism. Once a plant has received the minimum number of photoinductive cycles, it will flower, even if returned to noninductive cycles.

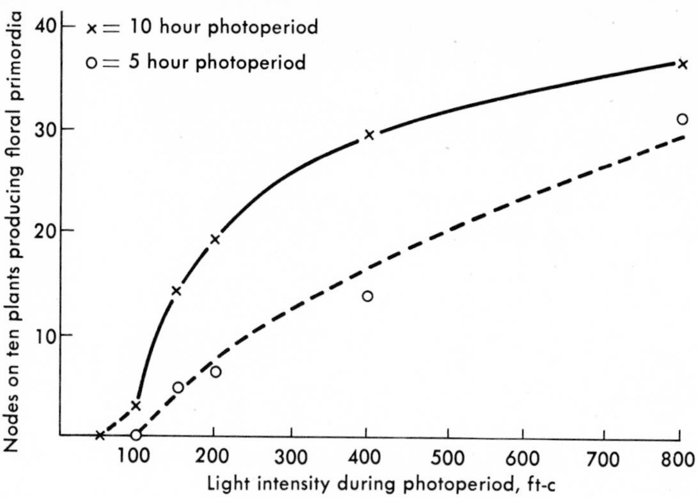

Figure 20-4 Quantitative effect of light duration and intensity on floral initiation by Biloxi soybean on a photinductive cycle. Note that no flowers are produced with light intensities under 100 ft-c and that the greater number of flowers are produced with the longer photoperiod. (After K. C. Hamner. 1940. Botan. Gaz. 101: 658.)

Partial induction may also be obtained in long-day plants. The long-day plant, *Plantago lanceolata,* needs 25 photoinductive cycles for 100% inflorescence formation. If the plant is given 10 photoinductive cycles and then subjected to a noninductive cycle, it will not flower. However, when the plant is returned to a photoinductive cycle, only 15 cycles are needed to produce 100% inflorescence(22). Similar results have been obtained by Naylor (35) and Lang and Melchers (29) with other long-day plants.

The implication is that some factor involved in the flowering response is accumulated during the inductive cycle. In some plants (e.g., *Xanthium*) enough is accumulated after only one cycle to promote flowering. In other plants more than one inductive cycle is needed. In long-day plants, the noninductive cycle does not appear to modify the effects of a previous exposure to an inductive cycle. The noninductive cycle in short-day plants, however, appears to be inhibitory. Schwabe (39) has shown this effect in several short-day plants by alternating inductive and noninductive cycles. The noninductive cycle inhibits the effect of the previous inductive cycle. Partial induction has been obtained, however, in some short-day plants (12), all of which points out the complexity of the problems involved in photoperiodism.

PERCEPTION OF THE PHOTOPERIODIC STIMULUS AND PRESENCE OF A FLORAL HORMONE

A good deal of the early work on photoperiodism was aimed at establishing which part of the plant receives the photoperiodic stimulus. The organs of the plant receiving the most attention were the leaves and buds.

Knott (26) demonstrated that in spinach, a long-day plant, the leaves are the receptors of the photoperiodic stimulus. In addition, he postulated that something is produced in the leaves in response to a photoinductive cycle and then translocated to the apical tip, causing the initiation of floral primordia.

Evidence for leaves being the organs of perception in the flowering response to photoinductive cycles is overwhelming. In many cases, giving photoinductive cycles to a single leaf, while the rest of the plant is on a noninductive cycle, is sufficient to cause flowering. For example, if a single leaf of *Xanthium* is exposed to short photoperiods, while the rest of the plant receives long photoperiods, flowers are formed (17, 32).

Grafting of photoinduced leaves from one plant to another plant on a noninductive cycle has been shown to promote flowering on the receptor plant (36, 18). Before grafting the photoinduced leaves, the receptor plants are first defoliated to eliminate any influence of the noninduced leaves.

A minimum amount of leaf tissue appears necessary for flowering to occur (23, 1). The developmental stage of the leaf is also important in regard to sensitivity to photoperiodic induction. For example, partially mature *Xanthium* leaves have been found to be most sensitive, while the very young or mature leaves are much less sensitive to photoperiodic induction (24).

Surprisingly enough, mature leaves also seem capable of neutralizing the flower-promoting effect of a photoperiodic stimulus. That is, when a photoinduced leaf or branch is grafted to a plant receiving a noninductive cycle, mature leaves present on the receptor plant antagonize progress toward the flowering response. Defoliation of the receptor plant eliminates the antagonism.

Presence of a floral hormone

The flowering factor produced in photoinduced leaves is apparently transported with relative ease in the plant. One investigator, studying the floral hormone in *Chrysanthemum,* demonstrated the diffusion of this hormone across an incomplete graft union separated by a water gap (33). However, this experiment has never been successfully repeated (34, 14). Cajlachjan, who has performed numerous experiments demonstrating the probable existence of a floral hormone, has given the name *florigen* to the, as yet, unisolated hormone (9).

Perhaps the most dramatic demonstration of the ease with which the floral hormone is translocated has been observed in two-branched *Xanthium* plants grafted in series. If the end branch of a series of plants is given a photoinductive cycle, it will cause flowering in all six plants in a chainlike reaction (see review by Naylor (37). See Figure 20-5.

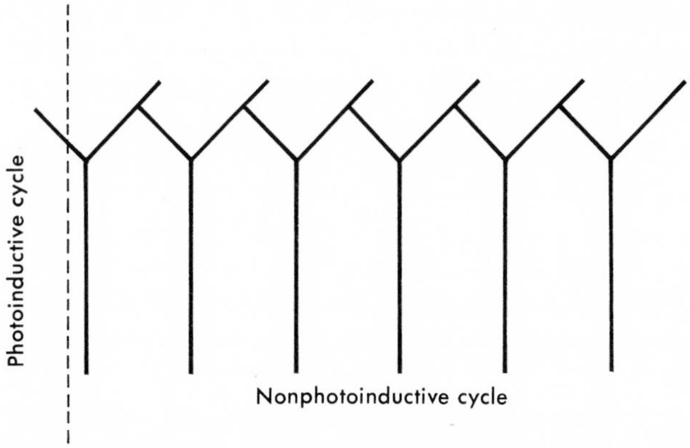

Figure 20-5 Translocation of the floral hormone. One branch of a two-branched *Xanthium* plant, grafted in series to five other *Xanthium* plants, was given a photoinductive cycle. The second branch of the first plant and the other five plants were kept on a nonphotoinductive cycle. All plants flowered.

Equally as dramatic were the experiments of Zeevaart (45), in which he grafted long-day plants to short-day plants and *vice versa.* When the long-day plant, *Sedum spectabile,* was grafted to the short-day plant, *Kalanchoe blossfeldiana,* it flowered under short-day conditions. When the latter plant was grafted to the long-day plant, it flowered under long-day conditions. In other words, these experiments demonstrated that florigen is not *species specific* and has the same properties or nearly the same properties in both long- and short-day plants. This allows for hope that florigen will some day be isolated and characterized. The economic importance of such an endeavor is immense.

Light quality and photoperiodism

As we mentioned in the introduction to this chapter, light has to be absorbed to be effective. Practically all of the early work on photoperiodism was concerned with the effects of white light on flowering, that is, the combined effects of all the wavelengths of the visible spectrum. However, it has become a customary practice in the investigation of photobiological reactions to find the wavelengths that are most effective or, in other words, to develop an action spectrum for the process. In this manner, scientists can compare the absorption spectra of known constituents of the plant with the action spectrum of a photobiological process under investigation. If the absorption spectrum of an extracted plant constituent resembles closely the action spectrum of the process, it is a strong indication of the involvement of that constituent. It is, most likely, the photoreceptor that initiates the process.

We have already seen detective work of this kind in the study of photosynthesis and auxin destruction. In photosynthesis the most effective wavelengths are found in the blue and red regions. It is in these regions that chlorophyll absorbs the most. We have also noted that the action spectrum for oat coleoptile curvature resembles closely the absorption spectrum for riboflavin. Thus, riboflavin has been suspected as the photoreceptor in auxin destruction.

This type of investigation was undertaken by a group of scientists at the U.S. Department of Agriculture, Beltsville, Maryland (5, 3, 19, 20). They were interested in determining the action spectrum for the inhibitory action of light breaks during the dark period (see page 492). Actually, the first action spectra for the control of flowering were obtained in 1946 by Parker et al. (38) from two short-day plants, *Xanthium* and Biloxi soybean. Since that time, several action spectra of this type have been measured, both for short- and long-day plants. All of these spectra appear essentially the same, suggesting a common receptor for the wavelengths of light effective in photoperiodism.

As mentioned earlier, if the long night of a photoinductive cycle for *Xanthium* is broken by a brief flash of light (light break), the plant does not flower. An action spectrum for the effectiveness of different wavelengths of light demonstrates that the most efficient wavelengths for inhibition of flowering are found between 620 and 660 mμ (orange-red) with a maximum at about 640 mμ (21). Therefore, red light is considered to be the most efficient radiation in light break reactions.

Far-red radiation when used alone has no effect as a light break factor; that is, it does not break up a long night into two short nights. However, the startling discovery was made first by Borthwick et al. (4) and then by Downs (13) that far-red radiation is capable of reversing the light break effect of red light. If a brief flash of far-red radiation follows in sequence a brief flash of red light in the middle of a long night of a photoinductive cycle for short-day plants, flowering will occur. If the far-red radiation is followed further in sequence by red light, flowering will again be inhibited. In other words, the radiation used last in the sequence will determine the response of the plant (Table 20-1).

Table 20-1 Effect of daily interruptions of the dark period with several consecutive irradiations with red (R) and far red (FR), in sequence, on flower initiation of cocklebur and soybean.[a]

Treatment	*Mean stage of floral development in cocklebur*	*Mean number of flowering nodes in Biloxi soybean*
Dark control	6.0	4.0
R	0.0	0.0
R, FR	5.6	1.6
R, FR, R	0.0	0.0
R, FR, R, FR	4.2	1.0
R, FR, R, FR, R	0.0	—
R, FR, R, FR, R, FR	2.4	0.6
R, FR, R, FR, R, FR, R	0.0	0.0
R, FR, R, FR, R, FR, R, FR	0.6	0.0

[a] R. J. Downs. 1956. Plant Physiol. 31: 279.

There is general agreement that one pigment is involved here that may exist in two forms, one red absorbing the other far-red absorbing. The two forms are photochemically interconvertible. In addition, it has been found that the far-red absorbing form will slowly convert to the red absorbing form in the dark. Bonner (2) has shown this conversion in the dark in vitro. This slow conversion to the red absorbing form is under thermal control. The pigment in question was finally isolated by the group at Beltsville and called *phytochrome* (8, 27, 40). Absorption spectra for the red and far-red absorbing forms are given in Figure 20-6.

The alternating effects of red and far-red radiation on the plant system have been summed up by Borthwick et al. (5). It appears that during the day (white light), the far-red absorbing form of phytochrome is accumulated in the plant. This form of the pigment is inhibitory to flowering in short-day plants and stimulatory to flowering in long-day plants. At the onset of a dark period, the far-red form is subjected to thermal and spontaneous decay, creating the red-absorbing form of phytochrome,

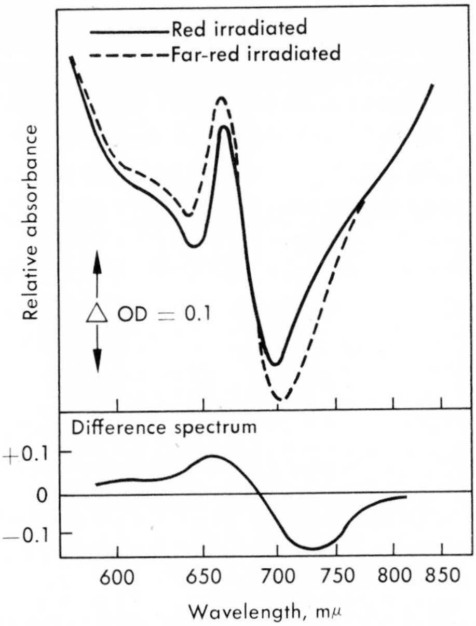

Figure 20-6 Phytochrome absorption spectrum between 580 and 850 mμ. The difference spectrum is also shown. (After W. I. Butler et al. 1959. Proc. Natl. Acad. Sci. U.S. 45: 1703.

which is stimulatory to flowering in short-day plants and inhibitory to flowering in long-day plants. The interruption of the dark period with red light will return the accumulating red-absorbing form to the far-red absorbing form of phytochrome, thus inhibiting flowering in short-day plants. If the red light break is followed by a far-red break, the red light influence is erased.

Gibberellins and the flowering response

So far in our discussion of photoperiodism and flowering, we have ignored the role of gibberellins in flowering. As mentioned in a previous chapter, the application of gibberellin to most long-day plants will cause them to flower when on a noninductive cycle. However, it is assumed that gibberellin is not a floral hormone or, at least, does not directly cause flowering. Two lines of evidence support this assumption. The stimulation of flowering by long-day induction and gibberellin induction of long-day plants appear to be different. First, in long-day induction the differentiation of floral primordia occurs simultaneously with stem elongation (31). In the gibberellin induction of flowering, stem elongation proceeds for some time before floral primordia can be observed (44, 28), suggesting that gibberellin-stimulated growth and differentiation may fulfill the needs for floral differentiation and development. This would amount to an indirect induction of flowering. Second, gibberellins have been unable to promote flowering in short-day plants on a noninductive cycle.

Whether or not gibberellins are indirectly or directly involved in the induction of flowering has not convincingly been elucidated. One investigator (6, 7) has included gibberellin in a scheme explaining photoperiodic reactions. Brian has theorized that a gibberellin-like hormone is synthesized during the photoperiod.

$$CO_2 \rightarrow \rightarrow \text{Precursor} \rightarrow \text{Gibberellin-like hormone}$$

According to Brian, the precursor may be slightly stimulatory, neutral, or antagonistic to flowering. Red light promotes the conversion of the precursor to the gibberellin-like hormone. During the dark period, there is a slow reconversion of the hormone back to the precursor. This back reaction is accelerated by far-red radiation.

If we follow this line of reasoning, then the concentration of gibberellin-like hormone in the plant is dependent upon the length of the photoperiod. If we extend ourselves a little further and associate the synthesis of florigen with the accumulation of a gibberellin-like hormone, we can then formulate a theory that includes gibberellin in the flowering response of plants.

It is assumed that a high level of gibberellin-like hormone must be maintained in long-day plants for the production of florigen. In short-day plants, this situation is reversed, a low-level of the gibberellin-like hormone being optimum for a flowering response. However, once enough florigen is produced, flowering will occur in both the long-day and short-day plant. A schematic representation of this reaction is given in Figure 20-7.

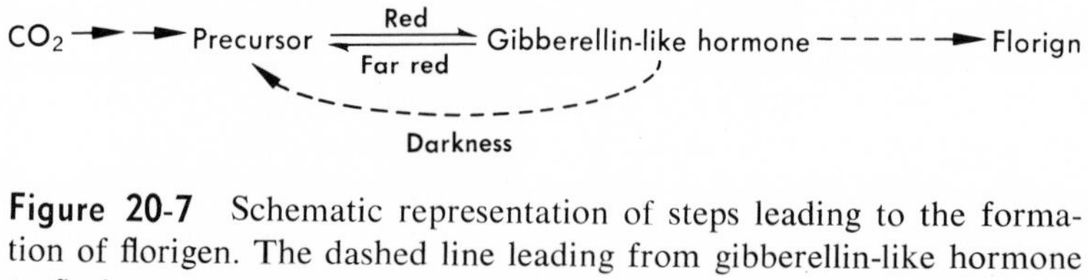

Figure 20-7 Schematic representation of steps leading to the formation of florigen. The dashed line leading from gibberellin-like hormone to florigen represents steps controlled by concentration of gibberellin-like hormone. These steps are thought to be different in long-day and short-day plants. (After A. W. Naylor. 1961. *In* W. Ruhland (ed.), Encyclopedia of plant physiology. Springer, Berlin. 16: 331.)

Actual measurements of the gibberellin levels of leaves of both short-day and long-day plants under photoinductive cycles and noninductive cycles have been made by Cajlachjan (11). His results indicate that the gibberellin content is higher under long-day conditions regardless of the class of plant used.

Cajlachjan (10) has presented a hypothesis associating gibberellin with the floral hormone in the photoperiodic response of flowering. According to him, there are two steps involved in the flowering process, the first mediated by gibberellin and the second by the flowering factor called "anthesine." Together, gibberellin and anthesine constitute the true florigen. In long-day plants on noninductive cycles, there is a sufficient amount of anthesine, but not enough gibberellin. This situation is reversed in short-day plants on noninductive cycles, gibberellin being high and anthesine low. This would account for the promotion of flowering on application of gibberellins to long-day plants on noninductive cycles. In addition, it accounts for the neutral effects of gibberellins applied to short-day plants on noninductive cycles.

SUMMARY

Since the formulation of the principle of photoperiodism in flowering by Garner and Allard in 1920, great strides have been taken toward the clarification of the several biochemical systems involved. The proper integration of these systems leads ultimately to the formation and development of the reproductive structures of the plant.

The first major step after the discovery of Garner and Allard was the understanding of the importance of the dark period. Following this step was the development of a hormone concept involved in the flowering response and the establishment of the leaf as the site of perception of the photoperiodic stimulus. The work of the Beltsville group in the discovery of a red–far-red reversible system in photoperiodism was a notable achievement. Subsequently, this group isolated the pigment (phytochrome) involved in this system. Finally, some investigators have suggested that gibberellins may be intimately associated with the photoperiodic reaction of flowering.

Although we are now provided with a pretty substantial outline of the steps leading to flowering, we are far from establishing the complete biochemical pathway. This, of course, will come with isolation and characterization of each constituent of the pathway. Finally, with the isolation of the floral hormone (florigen) and its synthesis in the laboratory, we will reap the economic harvest of a purely academic venture.

BIBLIOGRAPHY

1. Barber, H. N., and D. M. Paton. 1952. A gene-controlled flowering inhibitor in *Pisum*. Nature 169: 592.
2. Bonner, J. 1962. *In vitro* dark conversion and other properties of phytochrome. Plant Physiol. Suppl. 37: xxvii.
3. Borthwick, H. A. 1959. Photoperiodic control of flowering. *In* R. B. Withrow (ed.), Photoperiodism and related phenomena in plants and animals. American Association for the Advancement of Science. Washington, D.C. 275.
4. Borthwick, H. A., S. B. Hendricks, and M. W. Parker. 1952. The reaction controlling floral initiation. Proc. Natl. Acad. Sci. 38: 929.
5. Borthwick, H. A., S. B. Hendricks, and M. W. Parker. 1956. Photoperiodism. *In* A. Hollaender (ed.), Radiation biology. McGraw-Hill Book Co., New York. 3: 479.
6. Brian, P. W. 1958. The role of gibberellin-like hormones in regulation of plant growth and flowering. Nature (London) 181: 1122.
7. Brian, P. W. 1959. Effects of gibberellins on plant growth and development. Biol. Rev. 34: 37.
8. Butler, W. I., K. H. Norris, H. W. Siegelman, and S. B. Hendricks. 1959. Detection, assay, and preliminary purification of the pigment controlling photoresponsive development of plants. Proc. Natl. Acad. Sci. U.S. 45: 1703.
9. Cajlachjan, M. C. 1936. On the hormonal theory of plant development. Comp. Rend. (Doklady) Acad. Sci. U.S.S.R. 3: 443.
10. Cajlachjan, M. C. 1958. Hormonal factors in the flowering of plants. Fiziol. Rast. 5: 541.
11. Cajlachjan, M. C. 1961. Effect of gibberellins and derivatives of nucleic acid metabolism on plant growth and flowering. *In* R. M. Klein (ed.), Plant growth regulation. The Iowa State University Press, Ames, Iowa. 531.
12. Carr, D. J. 1955. On the nature of photoperiodic induction. III. The summation of the effects of inductive photoperiodic cycles. Physiol. Plant 8: 512.
13. Downs, R. J. 1956. Photoreversibility of flower initiation. Plant Physiol. 31: 279.
14. Galston, A. W. 1949. Transmission of the floral stimulus in soybean. Botan. Gaz. 110: 495.
15. Garner, W. W., and H. A. Allard. 1920. Effect of length of day on plant growth. J. Agr. Res. 18: 553.
16. Hamner, K. C. 1940. Interrelation of light and darkness in photoperiodic induction. Botan. Gaz. 101: 658.
17. Hamner, K. C., and J. Bonner. 1938. Photoperiodism in relation to hormones as factors in floral initiation. Botan. Gaz. 100: 388.
18. Heinze, P. H., M. W. Parker, and H. A. Borthwick. 1942. Floral initiation in Biloxi soybean as influenced by grafting. Botan. Gaz. 103: 517.

19. Hendricks, S. B. 1958. Photoperiodism. Agron. J. 50: 724.
20. Hendricks, S. B. 1959. The photoreaction and associated changes of plant photomorphogenesis. *In* R. B. Withrow (ed.), Photoperiodism and related phenomena in plants and animals. American Association for the Advancement of Science, Washington, D.C. 423.
21. Hendricks, S. B., and H. A. Borthwick. 1954. Photoperiodism in plants. Proc. Intern. Photobiol. Congr. 23.
22. Hillman, W. S. 1962. The physiology of flowering. Holt, Rinehart & Winston, New York.
23. Holdsworth, M. 1956. The concept of minimum leaf number. J. Exptl. Botan. 7: 395.
24. Khudairi, A. K., and K. C. Hamner. 1954. The relative sensitivity of *Xanthium* leaves of different ages to photoperiodic induction. Plant Physiol. 29: 251.
25. Klebs, G. 1913. Über das Verhältnis der Aussenwelt zur Entwicklung der Pflanze. S. B. Akad. Wiss. Heidelberg B 5: 1.
26. Knott, J. E. 1934. Effect of localized photoperiod on spinach. Proc. Am. Soc. Hort. Sci. (Suppl.) 31: 152.
27. Lane, H. C., H. W. Siegelman, W. L. Butler, and E. L. Firer. 1962. Extraction and assay of phytochrome from green plants. Plant Physiol. Suppl. 37: xxvii.
28. Lang, A. 1957. The effect of gibberellin upon flower formation. Proc. Natl. Acad. Sci. 43: 709.
29. Lang, A., and G. Melchers. 1947. Vernalisation and devernalisation bei einer zweijährigen Pflanze. Z. Naturf. 2b: 444.
30. Leopold, A. C., and F. S. Guernsey. 1953. Flower initiation in Alaska pea. I. Evidence as to the role of auxin. Am. J. Botan. 40: 46.
31. Lockhart, J. A. 1961. Mechanism of the photoperiodic process in higher plants. *In* W. Ruhland (ed.), Encyclopedia of plant physiology. Springer, Berlin. 16: 390.
32. Long, E. M. 1939. Photoperiodic induction as influenced by environmental factors. Botan. Gaz. 101: 168.
33. Moshkov, B. S. 1937. Blüte von Kurztags-pflanzen in kontinuierlicher Beleuchtung als Resultat von Pfropfungen. Trudy Priklad. Botan. Genetike i Selekstü A 21: 145.
34. Moshkov, B. S. 1939. Transfer of photoperiodic reaction from leaves to growing points. Comp. Rend. (Doklady) Acad. Sci. U.S.S.R. 24: 489.
35. Naylor, A. W. 1941. Effects of some environmental factors on photoperiodic induction of beet and dill. Botan. Gaz. 102: 557.
36. Naylor, A. W. 1953. Reactions of plants to photoperiod. *In* W. Loomis (ed.), Growth and development in plants. University of Iowa Press, Ames, Iowa. 144.
37. Naylor, A. W. 1961. The photoperiodic control of plant behavior. *In* W. Ruhland (ed.), Encyclopedia of plant physiology. Springer, Berlin. 16: 331.
38. Parker, M. W., S. B. Hendricks, H. A. Borthwick, and N. J. Scully. 1946.

Action spectrum for the photoperiodic control of floral initiation of short day plants. Botan. Gaz. 108: 1.

39. Schwabe, W. W. 1959. Studies of long-day inhibition in short-day plants. J. Exptl. Botan. 10: 317.
40. Siegelman, H. W., E. M. Firer, W. L. Butler, and S. B. Hendricks. 1962. Phytochrome from corn and barley seedlings. Plant Physiol. Suppl. 37: xxvii.
41. Takimoto, A. 1960. Effect of sucrose on flower initiation of *Pharbitis*. Plant Cell Physiol. (Tokyo) 1: 241.
42. Tournois, J. 1912. Influence de la lumière sur la floraison du houblon japonais et du chauvre. Comp. Rend. Acad. Sci. (Paris) 155: 297.
43. Van der Veen, R., and G. Meijer. 1959. Light and plant growth. The Macmillan Co., New York.
44. Wittwer, S. H., and M. J. Bukovac. 1957. Gibberellin effects on temperature and photoperiodic requirements for flowering of some plants. Science 126: 30.
45. Zeevaart, J. A. D. 1958. Flower formation as studied by grafting. Med. Landbouwhogeschool Wageningen 58: 1.

21
Vernalization

INTRODUCTION

Not all plants will flower when subjected to the correct photoperiod. In many plants temperature has a profound influence on the initiation and development of reproductive structures. In the annual plant, growth is started in the spring, flowers are developed in the summer, and fruit and seed produced in the fall. The influence of temperature on flowering in the case of the annual is secondary to that of light, the effect of temperature being more metabolic than catalytic.

Biennials, on the other hand, present an entirely different situation. They remain vegetative the first growing season and, after prolonged exposure to the cold temperatures of winter, flower in the following season. Without exposure to a cold treatment, the majority of these plants would remain vegetative indefinitely. However, with prolonged exposure to low temperature followed by the correct photoperiod, cold-requiring plants will flower. That a cold period is necessary was proven unequivocally when it was shown that for most biennials an "artificial" cold treatment followed by the correct photoperiod and temperature will result in flowering the first growing season. Thus, a biennial may be made to flower in the same period of time required for flowering in annuals. *Vernalization,* a term used to describe this phenomenon, has been defined by Chouard (3) as the "acquisition or acceleration of the ability to flower by a chilling treatment." However, application of the concept of vernalization without the formulation of a hypothesis has been in practice for many years (15). Growers, some instinctively and some knowingly, have recognized the need of a cold period for some plants to flower. McKinney (15), in his review of the subject of vernalization, has pointed out a report by Klippart in 1857 to the Ohio State Board of Agriculture that shows a remarkable application of the concepts of vernalization. This report, as quoted by McKinney is as follows:

> To convert winter into spring wheat nothing more is necessary than that the winter wheat should be allowed to germinate slightly in the fall or winter, but kept from vegetation by a low temperature or freezing until it can be sown in the spring. This is usually done by soaking and sprouting the seed and freezing it while in this state and keeping it frozen until the season for spring sowing has arrived. Only two things seem requisite, germination and freezing. It is probable that winter wheat sown in the fall so late as only to germinate in the earth without coming up would produce a grain which would be a spring wheat if sown in April instead of September. The experiment of converting winter wheat has met with great success. It retains many of its primitive winter wheat qualities and produces at the rate of 28 bushels per acre.

Since Klippart's report, systematic study of the influence of temperature on flowering has been pursued with earnest by numerous workers. Early work by scientists, such as Lysenko and Gessner, paved the road for the more complete understanding of the phenomenon of vernalization we have today.

VERNALIZATION AND FLOWERING

It must be emphasized that vernalization per se does not induce flowering, but merely prepares the plant for flowering. This is in contrast to photoperiodic effects on flowering, where the photoperiodic inductive cycle not only prepares the plant to flower, but also initiates flowering.

The classic experiments concerned with vernalization have been performed on *Hyoscyamus niger* (henbane) and *Secale cereale* (Petkus rye).

Therefore, we will center our discussion around the study of these two plants.

Hyoscyamus niger (henbane)

Often the ability to respond to cold treatments is genetically controlled. This is the situation with henbane, where there are annual and biennial types; the annual type flowers in one growing season, while the biennial type requires a cold winter before flowering in its second growing season. Apparently, the genetic complex necessary to initiate the chemical changes required for flowering is missing from the biennial henbane and may be substituted for by a cold treatment. Like the annual, the biennial henbane is a long-day plant, the vegetative state being maintained under short-day conditions, regardless of the temperature treatment it receives.

The biennial henbane demonstrates a qualitative response to cold treatments; that is, unless exposed to low temperatures for a certain period of time, it will remain entirely vegetative. However, after the plant has reached the rosette stage and is at least 10 days old, it may be vernalized and then flower in one growing season, provided it receives the correct photoperiod. An age of 10 days and the rosette stage appear to be necessary prerequisites for a response to cold treatment by henbane (3). Figure 21-1 shows the flowering response of a typical biennial henbane to a cold treatment. The necessity of the correct photoperiod may also be observed in Figure 21-1.

Secale cereale (Petkus winter rye)

As with henbane, there is also a spring and winter strain of Petkus rye. The spring strain is a typical annual rosette plant, flowering and fruiting in one growing season. The winter strain is a typical biennial rosette plant, staying vegetative the first growing season and then flowering and fruiting after a prolonged exposure to the cold temperatures of winter. The winter strain, when vernalized, resembles the spring strain in every way (21).

Although Petkus winter rye and henbane are cold-requiring plants, they differ in many ways in their response to cold treatments. Petkus rye may be vernalized in the seed stage (see review by Purvis (24)), while henbane has to be at least 10 days old and in the rosette stage. Unlike henbane, Petkus winter rye does not have an obligate requirement for vernalization. Under continuous light, unvernalized winter rye will "head" in 15 weeks. However, if vernalized, heading is observed in about $7\frac{1}{2}$ weeks—about the same time heading is observed in the spring variety under continuous light. Thus, in Petkus rye, vernalization serves to shorten the time to

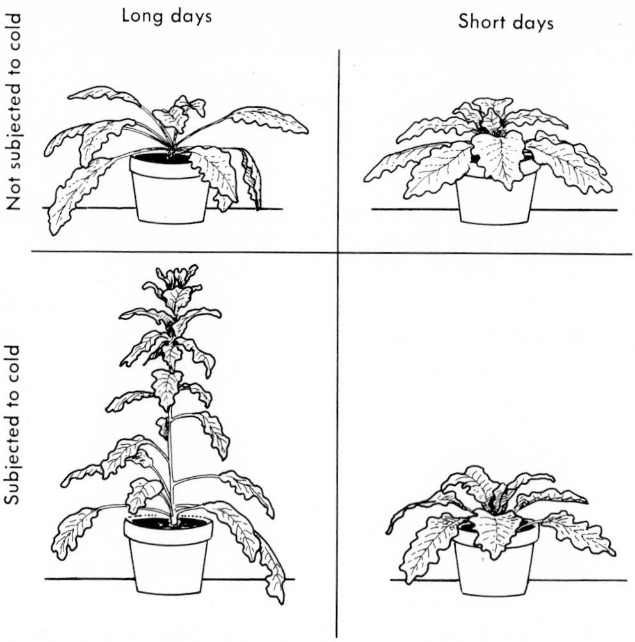

Figure 21-1 Response of the henbane, a long-day plant, to different temperature and photoperiod treatments. (Redrawn from *Principles of Plant Physiology* by James Bonner and Arthur W. Galston. Copyright by W. H. Freeman and Company, 1952. Data of G. Melchers and A. Lang. 1948. Biol. Zentr. 67: 105.)

flower and is not an absolute requirement (7). Finally, Petkus differs from henbane in that the vernalization stimulus, once received, is not transmitted across a graft union.

Purvis (24), who has contributed a great deal toward our understanding of vernalization, has worked out a theoretical scheme describing flowering in cereal plants.

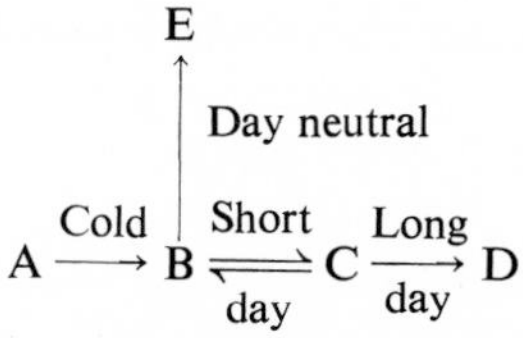

In this scheme, B is some compound that is part of a reaction system leading to flowering. This reaction system from B to D is under photoperiodic control and possibly leads to the synthesis of a floral hormone. In spring rye, B is either present in the embryo or is produced from A at normal temperatures. However, in winter rye the production of B is retarded although not completely inhibited. It accumulates at a slow rate with the growth of the plant. Exposure to low temperatures accelerates the production of B in winter rye.

Purvis gives two reasons why she believes B is accumulated even under normal temperatures. First, flowering occurs eventually under continuous light even in the absence of a cold treatment. Second, even in those species showing an obligate requirement for vernalization (e.g., henbane), once vernalized will remain as such even though the plant is subjected to a noninductive photocycle. That is, the presence of B persists until the plant is returned to an inductive photocycle and is not diluted by the vegetative growth that takes place during the time the plant is exposed to a noninductive cycle. The persistence of B has been shown in rye by Purvis (21) and in henbane by Lang and Melchers (13). In fact, it has been suggested that B, once produced by vernalization, increases without further aid from low temperatures.

The reaction from B to C to D is under photoperiodic control. The reaction from B to E (leaf forming substance) is day neutral and occurs at optimal rates when the reaction from B to C is blocked or inhibited. In the scheme by Purvis, D represents the flowering hormone, and C is an intermediate capable of initiating early stages in flower initiation. In spring rye or vernalized winter rye, there is a high accumulation of B. Under continuous light, B is only slowly converted to C, which in turn is rapidly converted to D, the flowering hormone. The continual drain of C to form D keeps the reaction B to C to D going, despite the unfavorable presence of continuous light on the reaction B to C. Eventually, D reaches a critical level and flowering ensues.

Under short-day conditions, the reaction C to D is inhibited, thus forcing the back reaction, C to B to E, to occur, keeping the plant in a vegetative state. This state will persist until the inhibited reaction C to D finally produces the critical amount of D needed for floral initiation. An analysis of this scheme will show why Petkus spring rye is a long-day plant and why the vernalized winter strain resembles it.

Some of the more important aspects of the study of vernalization in Petkus rye, henbane, and related plants are the (a) site of vernalization, (b) dependence on temperature and duration of exposure, (c) transmission of vernalization by grafting experiments, (d) age factor, (e) devernalization, and (f) substitution of gibberellin for the cold treatment. We will discuss these aspects in more detail below.

The site of vernalization

Experiments with many different cold-requiring plants, including henbane, have strongly suggested that the site of vernalization is the growing point. This has been shown with localized low temperature treatments of different plant parts in celery (6), beets (5), and chrysanthemum (27). Melchers (16, 17), as a result of grafting experiments with annual and biennial races of *Hyoscyamus niger,* has also concluded that the stem apex is the plant part that responds initially to cold treatment. Apparently, the stem tip is the site of perception of vernalization, and the stimulus is translocated to other parts of the plant. Schwabe (27) found that in chrysanthemum, keeping the apex warm and chilling the rest of the plant had negligible results with respect to flowering. In addition, Purvis (22) has shown that the dissected apices from imbibed embryos provided with sucrose and minerals can be vernalized.

That the growing tip is the only locus of perception of vernalization has been challenged by Wellensiek. He demonstrated that both isolated leaves and isolated roots of *Lunaria biennis* are capable of being vernalized (30, 31). If these isolated plants received a cold treatment, the plants regenerating from the isolated plant parts flower. Wellensiek concluded from his experiments that dividing cells are necessary for perception of vernalization, no matter what their location in the plant. Data from more recent

Table 21-1 Percentages of flowering among regenerated leaf cuttings of *Lunaria biennis*, taken from mother plants of five ages after cold treatments during five periods.[a]

Age of mother plants, weeks	*Cold treatment, weeks* 0	8	12	16	20
6	0	0	0	0	3.6
8	0	0	0	0	21.4
10	0	0	0	7.1	25.0
12	0	0	12.5	40.7	40.6
14	0	0	7.5	18.4	40.0

[a] After Wellensiek.

work by Wellensiek (32) on vernalization of isolated leaves are given in Table 21-1. Note also from Table 21-1 that the duration of cold treatment and age of the leaf are important factors in the flowering response.

Dependence on temperature and duration of exposure

Lang's (10) work with henbane illustrates the relationship between temperature and time of exposure and the influence of this relationship on the efficiency of vernalization. He exposed the cold-requiring henbane to different temperatures, ranging from 3 to 17°C for varying periods of time. The plant was then given a photoinductive cycle at 23°C until flower initiation occurred. The efficiency of the vernalization treatment was determined by the number of days to flower after treatment.

Lang found that all temperatures from 3 to 17°C are effective if the period of vernalization is 105 days. Flower initiation was observed in 8 days. However, if the vernalization period is shortened to 15 days, a separation in the effectiveness of different temperatures is observed. Under these circumstances, a temperature of 10°C during the 15 day vernalization period is the most efficient treatment, requiring 23 days to initiate flowering. If the vernalization period is extended to 42 days, the most effective temperatures are found in the range from 3 to 6°C, requiring 10 days for flower initiation. These relationships may be seen in Figure 21-2.

Hänsel (9) studied the vernalizing effect of a wide range of temperature, including temperatures below freezing, on Petkus winter rye. He found that vernalization fails at temperatures below −4°C, but from this tem-

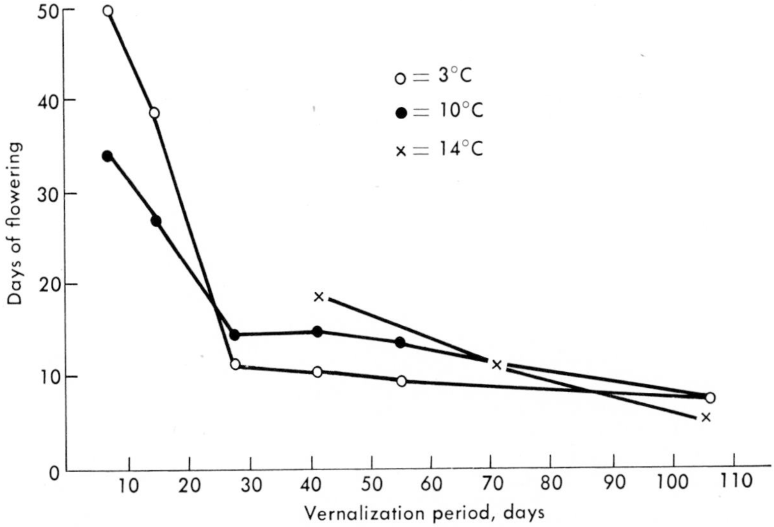

Figure 21-2 Interrelation between temperature and time of exposure in the acceleration of flowering of *Hyoscyamus niger.* (After A. Lang. 1951. Der Zuchter. 21: 241. Springer, Berlin.)

perature up to 14°C, vernalization is observed. Temperatures from 1 to 7°C are equally efficient in shortening the number of days to flowering. There is a rapid fall in the rate of vernalization when temperatures are increased from 7 to 15°C. These relationships may be seen in Figure 21-3.

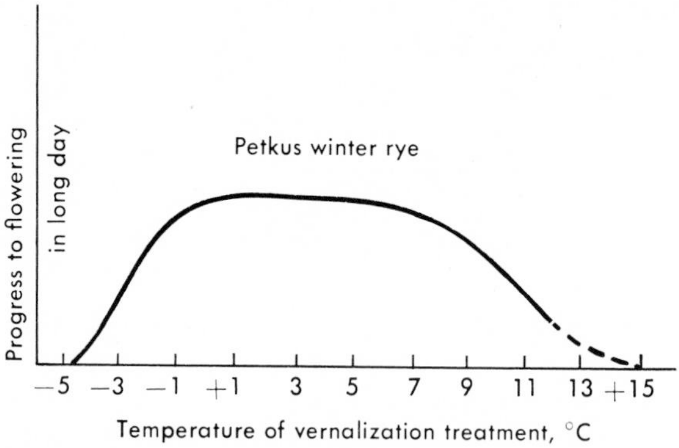

Figure 21-3 The effect of temperature on the vernalization of Petkus winter rye. (After H. Hänsel. 1953. Ann. Botan. 17: 417.)

From the above discussion and from Figures 21-2 and 21-3, it is clear that the flowering response to vernalization is dependent upon the temperature used and the duration of the vernalization period. The most efficient combination of temperature and exposure time for maximum response has to be determined for each species of plant.

Grafting experiments

The transmission of a vernalization stimulus across a graft union has been demonstrated remarkably well in *Hyoscyamus* by Melchers (16, 17). If a plant part (leaf or stem) of a vernalized henbane is grafted to an unvernalized henbane, the latter plant will flower. The question arises, is this a transmission of florigen from the donor to the receptor or a transmission of a substance produced as a result of vernalization? However, florigen has been ruled out as a result of additional experiments by Melchers and Lang (see review by Lang (11)). If an unvernalized henbane plant is grafted to a Maryland Mammoth tobacco plant, the henbane plant will flower, whether or not the tobacco plant receives a photoinductive cycle. Henbane, as the receptor in this experiment, receives a stimulus from the tobacco plant, which leads to flowering. This stimulus could not be florigen, since it is transmitted from tobacco plants on noninductive cycles as well as inductive cycles. Since the tobacco plant is not a cold-requiring plant, the stimulus or substance produced by vernalization should be present in the absence of cold treatments. Melchers (18) has named this substance *vernalin.*

The above experiments by Melchers and Lang do provide some evidence for the existence of vernalin. However, the examples of vernalization induction from donor to receptor are few in number (3). In addition, vernalin has not been extracted as yet even in crude form. Therefore, evidence for the existence of vernalin, at least in a mobile form, rests on relatively few experiments.

Age factor

One of the most noticeable aspects of the phenomenon of vernalization is the relation between the age of the plant and its response to low temperature treatments. The age at which a plant is sensitive to vernalization is quite different in different species. For example, in cereals low temperature treatments effectively vernalize the germinating seed and may even vernalize the embryos developing on the mother plant (12, 24). Shinohara (28) has reported the partial vernalization of the ripening seeds of garden peas, winter wheat and barley, Broad beans, and Minowase radish.

In contrast to these plants, there are many cold-requiring plants that require a certain period of growth before they become sensitive to low temperature treatments. We have already mentioned that the biennial strain of *Hyoscyamus niger* must be in the rosette stage and have completed at least 10 days of growth before sensitivity to vernalization may be observed. In fact, Sarkar (26) has pointed out that maximum sensitivity is not achieved until *H. niger* has completed 30 days of growth.

In still other plants, sensitivity to vernalization depends on the number of leaves produced. For example, in *Oenothera* at least six to eight leaves must be present for vernalization to be effective (2), and in Brussels sprouts, 30 leaves (29).

The term "ripeness-to-flower," first introduced by Klebs in 1913 and later used to denote the time when a plant is sensitive to photoperiod, may also be used in the study of vernalization. In cold-requiring plants the stage ripeness-to-flower is reached when the plant has fulfilled its cold requirement. The extent of vegetative growth, such as a minimal number of leaves or nodes, is used many times as a measure to determine whether or not a plant has reached the ripeness-to-flower stage.

The need for a certain amount of vegetative growth to take place suggests that the accumulation of some factor (perhaps a receptor of the vernalization stimulus) is necessary for sensitivity to be achieved. The fact that in many plants a minimal number of leaves must be present supports this concept, since the syntheses of most of the compounds found in a plant have their origin in the photosynthetic process. In those plants where seeds may be vernalized (e.g., cereals), our hypothetical substance must be already present in sufficient amounts, either donated by the mother plant or synthesized during the development of the embryo.

Study of the sensitivity to vernalization of *Arabidopis thaliana* at different stages of growth has produced some very interesting results (20). The seed of *A. thaliana* is very sensitive to vernalization. This sensitivity decreases with the development of the seedling until a relatively low sensitivity point is reached in the second week of development. With further growth of the plant, there is a marked change in sensitivity to low temperature treatments. The sensitivity of the plant now increases with age. These relationships may be seen in Figure 21-4.

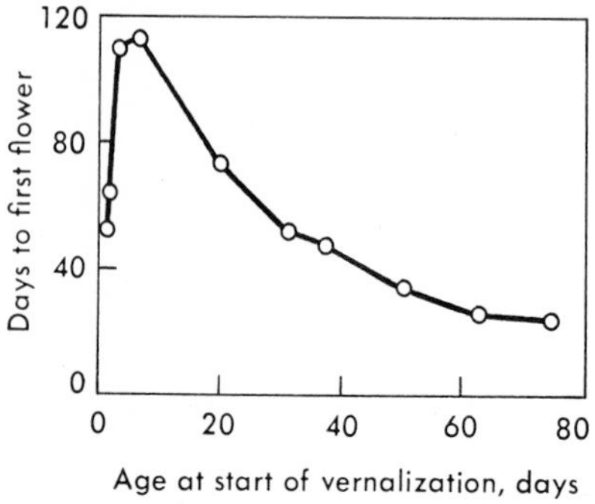

Figure 21-4 The sensitivity to vernalization of *Arabidopis thaliana* at different stages of growth. (After K. Napp-Zinn. 1960. Planta 54: 409. Springer, Berlin. Redrawn from A. C. Leopold. 1964. Plant growth and development. McGraw-Hill Book Co., New York.)

One may interpret the loss of sensitivity of *A. thaliana* in the early stages as being caused by the depletion of the stored food supply of the seed. The increase in sensitivity could be correlated with the increase in carbohydrates as a result of photosynthetic activity.

Additional evidence for the involvement of carbohydrates in the vernalization process has been provided by vernalization of Petkus winter rye embryos (24). Embryos separated from the endosperm (stored food supply) and provided sucrose and mineral nutrients will produce normal healthy plants. These embryos may also be vernalized. However, vernalization is retarded, but ultimately accomplished, if the embryos are denied a carbohydrate substrate (23). See Figure 21-5. As Purvis (23) points out, this does not necessarily mean that only sugars accelerate the vernalization process, since the less mobile carbohydrates of the embryo (e.g., hemicellulose) may be brought into use. Although not unequivocally demon-

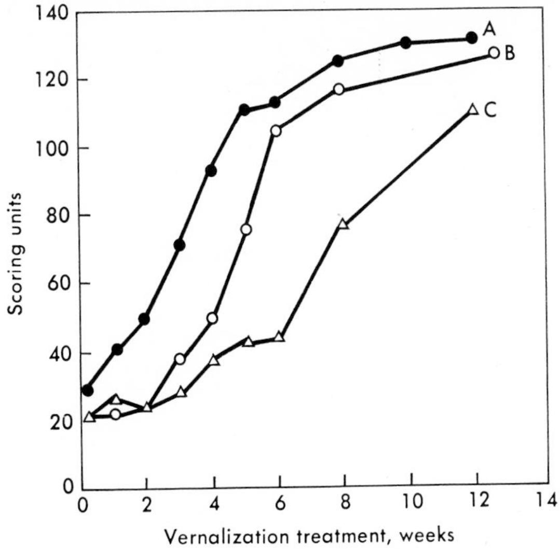

Figure 21-5 Progress of vernalization with duration of treatment. Curve A, in intact grain. Curve B, in excised embryo provided with 2% sugar. Curve C, in excised embryos without sugar supplement. (After O. N. Purvis. 1961. *In* W. Ruhland (ed.), Encyclopedia of plant physiology. Springer, Berlin. 16: 76.)

strated as yet, there appears to be a good deal of evidence supporting the concept that carbohydrates are consumed in the vernalization process and, indeed, may be essential to that process.

Devernalization

In our discussion of photoperiodism, we saw where the promotion of flowering by red light could be reversed by far-red radiation. Just as the stimulus to flower received from a burst of red light can be reversed, so too the stimulus to flower received from vernalization can also be reversed. This may be accomplished with vernalized grains of Petkus winter rye by drying the grains and storing them under dry conditions for several weeks. The grains retain the vernalized condition for 6 weeks, but by 8 weeks are almost completely devernalized (8).

The most efficient devernalizing factor, however, is high temperature. There have been many instances recorded where high temperature following vernalization has erased the effect of the low temperature treatment.

In fact, even an alteration of high temperature with low temperature during a period of vernalization weakens the vernalization response.

Early reports on the reversal of vernalization in wheat claimed that the effects of vernalization could be completely erased if followed immediately by exposure to temperatures in the neighborhood of 35°C. However, Purvis and Gregory (25) found that complete reversal in winter rye could only be accomplished after a very brief vernalization period. Increasing the duration of the vernalization treatment increases the stability of the plant toward high temperature reversal (Figure 21-6).

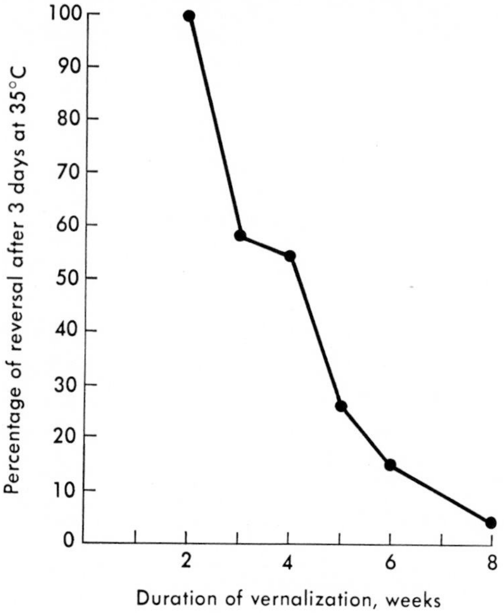

Figure 21-6 Progressive stabilization of winter rye to heat with increasing duration of vernalization treatment. (After O. N. Purvis and F. G. Gregory. 1952. Ann. Botan. 16: 1.)

In the biennial strain of *Hyoscyamus niger,* reversal of vernalization effects may also be accomplished. Exposure to high temperatures of about 35°C for a period of time will completely erase the vernalization effect (13). However, if the vernalized henbane is allowed a period of 3 to 4 days at 20°C, devernalization is not possible.

After the nullifying effects of high temperature, revernalization is possible in many plants. Low temperature treatments, for example, on devernalized winter rye, sugar beet, *Arabidopsis,* henbane, etc., will again cause the condition of vernalization.

Substitution of gibberellin for the cold treatment

In a previous chapter, we discussed the effect of gibberellin on bolting and flowering of rosette plants. We also mentioned that replacement of low temperature treatments by gibberellins is only observed among rosette plants, such as henbane. However, in rosette plants it has been suggested that gibberellin may only promote stem elongation and not flowering. In an indirect way, through stimulation of stem growth, gibberellin may promote the elaboration of factors leading to flower formation. Among the cold-requiring caulescent plants, gibberellin has failed to replace the cold requirement for flowering.

Other modifying factors in the vernalization process

One might suspect that since the vernalization process is most likely dependent upon a sequence of biochemical steps leading to the production of an active substance, the presence of water and oxygen are indispensable in the vernalization of seeds: water for activation of enzymes present in the seed, and oxygen for respiratory energy.

Water. Vernalization of dry seeds is impossible, unless the seeds have imbibed some moisture. Purvis (24) has pointed out that enough moisture must be present to initiate a small but visible degree of germination. In winter rye, she found that the water imbibed must represent 50% of the absolute dry weight for adequate vernalization.

Oxygen. Grain kept in an atmosphere of pure nitrogen, although provided with an adequate supply of water, is unresponsive to low temperature treatments (8). The oxygen requirement, although low, is absolute. Oxygen is also necessary for the vernalization of whole plants, such as henbane (see review by Chouard (3)). Apparently, respiration is a necessary factor in the vernalization process. This conclusion has received experimental support from study of the effect of respiratory inhibitors on vernalization. The response of winter wheat has been found to be considerably reduced by the use of these inhibitors (4).

SUMMARY

Our discussion of vernalization has been presented in general outline form, covering as many related topics as possible. Detailed descriptions have been confined to only those aspects fundamental to the process of vernalization, undoubtedly resulting in the overlooking of some of the less significant but, nevertheless, important investigations of this phenomenon. However, in our discussion we have recognized that some plants will not flower unless exposed to a prolonged period of cold temperature. In other plants, the requirement of low temperatures is not absolute, but if received, time to flowering is shortened. In still other plants, there is no requirement for low temperature with respect to flowering.

The fundamental factor in the vernalization process is low temperature which, however, is ineffective in the absence of oxygen, water, and adequate supplies of carbohydrates for respiratory processes. Once a plant is vernalized, it may be devernalized by high temperatures and in some cases revernalized with another exposure to cold temperatures.

As with photoperiodism, we have come a long way toward understanding the process of vernalization. The physical manipulations leading to the vernalization of a plant have been, for the most part, worked out. Biochemical investigations of the process, however, have lagged behind. Understanding of the perception of the cold temperature stimulus and the identification of the constituents involved in the sequence of reactions leading to the synthesis of the active substance are problems that need investigation. The biochemical roles of gibberellin, vernalin, and florigen need clarification. The answers to problems such as these are difficult but not impossible to arrive at. Considering the pace of modern science, we may have these answers sooner than we think.

BIBLIOGRAPHY

1. Bonner, J., and A. W. Galston. 1952. Principles of plant physiology. W. H. Freeman & Co., San Francisco.
2. Chouard, P. 1952. Les facteurs du milieu et les mécanismes régulateurs du développement des plantes horticoles. Rep. Intern. Hort. Congr. 13: 71.
3. Chouard, P. 1960. Vernalization and its relations to dormancy. Ann. Rev. Plant Physiol. 11: 191.
4. Chouard, P., and P. Poignant. 1951. Recherches préliminaires sur la vernalisation en présence d'inhibiteurs de germination et de respiration. Compt. Rend. Acad. Sci. (Paris) 23: 103.
5. Chroboczek, E. 1934. A study of some ecological factors influencing seedstalk development in beets (*Beta vulgaris* L.). Mem. Cornell Agr. Expt. Sta. 154: 1.
6. Curtis, O. F., and H. T. Chang. 1930. The relative effectiveness of temperature of the crown as contrasted with that of the rest of the plant upon flowering of celery plants. Am. J. Botan. 17: 1047.
7. Gott, M. B., F. G. Gregory, and O. N. Purvis. 1955. Studies in vernalization of cereals. XIII. Photoperiodic control of stages in flowering between initiation and ear formation in vernalized and unvernalized Petkus winter rye. Ann. Botan. (London) 19: 87.
8. Gregory, F. G., and O. N. Purvis. 1938. Studies in the vernalization of

cereals. III. The use of anaerobic conditions in the analysis of the vernalizing effect of low temperature during germination. Ann. Botan. 2: 753.

9. Hänsel, H. 1953. Vernalization of winter rye by negative temperatures and the influence of vernalization upon the lamina length of the first and second leaf in winter rye, spring barley, and winter barley. Ann. Botan. 17: 417.
10. Lang, A. 1951. Untersuchungen über das Kältebedurfnis von zweijährigem *Hyoscyamus niger*. Der Zuchter. 21: 241.
11. Lang, A. 1952. Physiology of flowering. Ann. Rev. Plant Physiol. 3: 265.
12. Lang, A. 1961. Auxins in flowering. *In* W. Ruhland (ed.), Encyclopedia of plant physiology. Springer, Berlin. 14: 909.
13. Lang, A., and G. Melchers. 1947. Vernalization und Devernalization bei einer zweijährigen Pflanze. Z. Naturf. 2b: 444.
14. Leopold, A. C. 1964. Plant growth and development. McGraw-Hill Book Co., New York.
15. McKinney, H. H. 1940. Vernalization and the growth-phase concept. Botan. Rev. 6: 25.
16. Melchers, G. 1936. Versuche zur Genetik und Entwicklungsphysiologie der Blühreife. Biol. Zbl. 56: 567.
17. Melchers, G. 1937. Die Wirkung von Genen, tiefen Temperaturen und blühenden Pfropfpartnern auf die Blühreife von *Hyoscyamus niger* L. Biol. Zbl. 57: 568.
18. Melchers, G. 1939. Die Blühhormone. Ber. Dtsch. Botan. Ges. 57: 29.
19. Melchers, G., and A. Lang. 1948. Die Physiologie der Blütenbildung. Biol. Zentr. 67: 105.
20. Napp-Zinn, K. 1960. Vernalization, Licht und Alter bei *Arabidopsis thaliana* (L.) Heynh. I. Licht und Dunkelheit wahrend Kalte-und Warmebehandlung. Planta 54: 409.
21. Purvis, O. N. 1934. An analysis of the influence of temperature during germination on the subsequent development of certain winter cereals and its relation to length of day. Ann. Botan. 48: 919.
22. Purvis, O. N. 1940. Vernalization of fragments of embryo tissue. Nature (London) 145: 462.
23. Purvis, O. N. 1947. Studies in vernalization of cereals. X. The effect of depletion of carbohydrates on the growth and vernalization response of excised embryos. Ann. Botan. 11: 269.
24. Purvis, O. N. 1961. The physiological analysis of vernalization. *In* W. Ruhland (ed.), Encyclopedia of plant physiology. Springer, Berlin. 16: 76.
25. Purvis, O. N., and F. G. Gregory. 1952. Studies in vernalization of cereals. XII. The reversibility by high temperature of the vernalized condition in Petkus winter rye. Ann. Botan. 16: 1.
26. Sarkar, S. 1958. Versuche zur Physiologie de Vernalisation. Biol. Zentralbl. 77: 1.
27. Schwabe, W. W. 1954. Factors controlling flowering in the chrysanthemum. IV. The site of vernalization and translocation of the stimulus. J. Exptl. Botan. 5: 389.

28. Shinohara, S. 1959. Genecological studies on the phasic development of flowering centering on the *Cruciferous* crops, especially on the role of vernalization on ripening seeds. Shizuoka Prefecture Agr. Expt. Sta. Tech. Bull. 6: 1.
29. Stokes, P., and K. Verkerk. 1951. Flower formation in Brussels sprouts. Mededel. Landbouwhogeschool Wageningen 50: 141.
30. Wellensiek, S. J. 1961. Leaf vernalization. Nature 192: 1097.
31. Wellensiek, S. J. 1962. Dividing cells as the locus for vernalization. Nature 195: 307.
32. Wellensiek, S. J. 1964. Dividing cells as the prerequisite for vernalization. Plant Physiol. 39: 832.

22
Dormancy

INTRODUCTION

Generally, most of us think of plant growth as a continuous process from germination to death. However, almost all plants experience sometime in their life cycle periods when growth is temporarily suspended, or at least retarded, to the point of not being visibly detectable. Interestingly enough, this situation may usually be observed in seeds and buds, plant parts associated with either the propagation of the plant or its continued development.

Growth may be suspended by some adverse condition in the environment, such as the lack of water. Seeds, for example, will not germinate under dry conditions, but will readily germinate if water is imbibed. A suspension of growth may also occur because of the concentration of some growth inhibitor, or it may be caused mechanically by the mere presence of a strong durable enclosing structure that does not allow for the expansion of growth.

The presence of membranes or seed coats impermeable to water or oxygen may also keep growth in an arrested state. Finally, many seeds and buds require special conditions of light and temperature to precede germination.

Some distinction is made between suspended growth due to a lack of some necessary external environmental factor (e.g., water) and a suspension of growth due to internal limitations, such as the presence of an inhibitor. For example, it is a well-known fact that seeds will not germinate unless water is supplied. Arrested growth because of the lack of some necessary external environmental factor is called by many *dormancy*. However, many seeds and buds are unable to grow even if provided with water because of internal limitations, a situation referred to by many as a *rest stage*. The use of these two terms is more confusing than helpful, and since the general result, *growth suspension,* is the same, there is no reason why we cannot include both situations under the general term *dormancy*.

ADVANTAGES OF DORMANCY

In temperate zones, there are large seasonal changes in temperature, ranging from near 100°F in midsummer to well below freezing in midwinter. Obviously, most plants could not survive the cold temperatures of winter in the vegetative or flowering state. Thus, in many plants seed and bud dormancy begins at the onset of winter cold, allowing the plant to pass through the winter with little or no damage. In the grain areas of the United States and Canada, for example, wild oat infestation is a serious problem because of the ability of the grains to survive the winter in a dormant state and then germinate the following spring. In contrast, the seeds of many other noxious weeds have only a brief dormant period, germinate in the fall, and are killed off during the severe winters that are common to the northern midwest areas.

The significance of dormancy among plants growing in arid regions is immediately apparent. Certainly, it is advantageous to the plant if germination and growth can be managed during the relatively brief periods of rainfall in these areas. Thus, seeds that can remain viable but dormant until sufficient water is available have a very good chance for survival. An even more bizarre example of the importance of dormancy in the adaptation of a plant to a dry region may be found in a study of the desert shrub quayule. In this plant, the chaff covering the seed contains a germination inhibitor that causes the seed to remain in a dormant state. However, with a rather strong rainfall, sufficient dilution of the inhibitor occurs to allow germination.

While talking about the advantages of dormancy, we should also mention how seed coats impermeable to water help in the persistence of a species. This type of seed coat may be found in some species of *Convolvulus* growing in arid regions. In order for these seeds to imbibe water and germinate, their seed coats must be mechanically broken. However, permeability to water gradually occurs over a long period of time. The advantage here is that never will all of the seeds germinate at one time, but only a certain number each year. Thus, it is virtually impossible for the entire species to be wiped out during the vulnerable seedling stage due to some adverse environmental condition.

Dormancy in plants is both a convenience and an inconvenience to man. The temporary dormant period experienced by many cereal grains allows for their harvest, dry storage, and ultimate use as food. Otherwise, these grains would germinate in the field and be useless to man. The ability, however, of certain weed seeds to lie dormant for many years in the soil has proved a great inconvenience. During plowing of the soil, dormancy of many of these seeds will be broken, allowing them to compete with any economic crop sown in that area. The eradication or even control of many of these weeds is almost impossible because they can never all be caught in the vulnerable seedling or vegetative state. Although some are triggered to germinate by soil disturbances caused by plowing, there are always some that remain dormant in the soil. Therefore, each year the farmer is presented with the same problem, the germination of some but not all of these weed seeds. He can only destroy those that germinate and has almost no control of those lying dormant in the soil.

SEED DORMANCY

The process of germination may be defined as that sequence of steps beginning with the uptake of water and leading to the rupture of the seed coat by the radicle (embryonic root) or the shoot. Cell divisions and enlargements in the embryo and an overall increase in metabolic activity accompany these steps. Although actual germination begins long before the rupture of the seed coat, germination is usually determined visibly by observing the protrusion of the radicle or shoot. Blockage of any one of the steps leading to germination may, and very likely will, cause a state of domancy in the seed. In our discussion of seed dormancy, we will concern ourselves with the various factors causing dormancy and the different ways of breaking dormancy.

The germination of seeds may be blocked by the absence of some external factor considered necessary for this process to occur. Thus, in the absence of water, the proper temperature, or proper mixture of gases, germination is blocked. However, many seeds may be placed in an environment considered adequate for germination and still not germinate because of some internal factor. This may be caused by a hard seed coat impermeable to water or gases or physically resistant to embryo expansion, an immature embryo, a need for after-ripening, specific light requirement, specific temperature requirements, or the presence of a substance inhibiting germination.

Hard seed coat

As mentioned above, the seed coat can cause dormancy in three ways: 1. by depriving the seed of water, 2. by depriving the seed of gases, and, 3. by mechanically restricting the growth of the embryo.

Depriving the seed of water. Many plants produce seeds with hard seed coats impermeable to water. In this respect, the Leguminosae family has by far the largest number of species (14). In addition to having hard seed coats, seeds of many members of the Leguminosae have an external waxy covering (26). Some of these seeds may be totally impermeable to water. The hardness factor in seed coats is primarily an inherited trait. However, in at least one case the hardness of a seed coat is determined by environmental conditions. Crocker (7) observed that seeds of white sweet clover are hard when they ripen during hot, dry weather, but soft when they ripen during rainy weather.

Hyde (21), in a study of some legume seeds, has described an interesting mechanism for the control of water entering the seed. In the seeds of

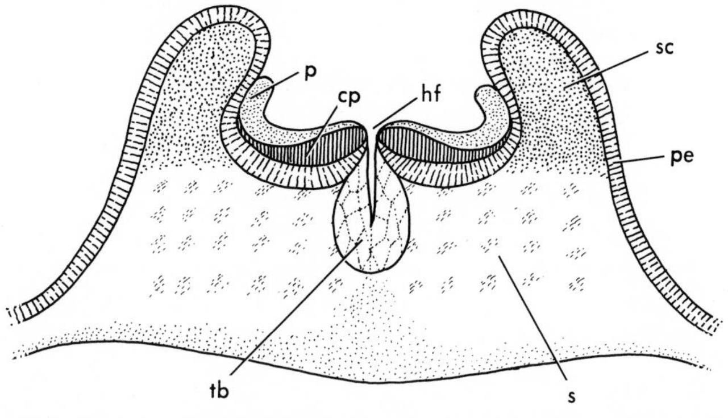

Figure 22-1 Diagrammatic illustration of the lupine tree seed, showing a transmedian section of the hilum and adjacent tissues. p, parenchyma; cp, counter-palisade; hf, hilar fissure; sc, sclerenchyma; pe, palisade epidermis; s, stellate cells; tb, tracheid bar. (After E. O. Hyde. 1954. Ann. Botan. 18: 241.)

some legumes (e.g., *Lupinus arboreus*), water enters only through the hilum. Hyde found that the absorption of water by these seeds is controlled by hygroscopic tissue composing the hilar fissure (Figure 22-1). When the relative humidity is high, this tissue swells, closing the hilar fissure to water absorption, and when the relative humidity is low, the fissure opens, allowing the seed to dry out.

That drying out of the seed is the inevitable result under these circumstances can be ascertained by measuring the moisture content of scarified and unscarified seeds of white clover after they have been subjected to different relative humidities. These seeds contain the same type of mechanism for controlling water absorption as that discussed for *Lupinus arboreus*. The moisture content of the unscarified seeds never rises when the seeds are transferred from a low to a high relative humidity and always falls when they are transferred from a high to a low relative humidity. The moisture content of the scarified seeds, in contrast, rises and falls, relative to the humidity treatments, as would be expected of a seed freely permeable to water. *Scarification* is a treatment by which the seed coat is rendered permeable to water and/or gases. The relationships discussed above are shown in Figure 22-2.

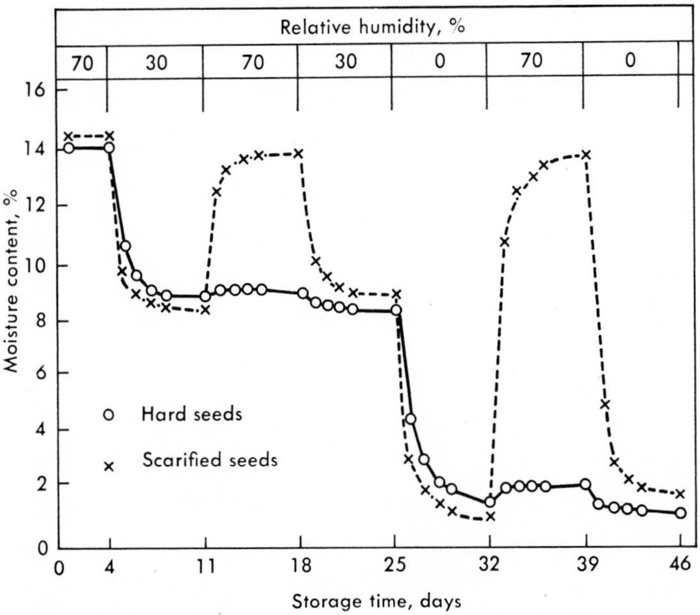

Figure 22-2 Changes in moisture content of white clover seeds transferred successively to chambers of different relative humidity. (After E. O. Hyde. 1954. Ann. Botan. 18: 241.)

Depriving the seed of gases. Strangely enough, many seeds that are permeable to water are impermeable to gases (26). The classical example of this type of impermeability may be found in the cocklebur plant (*Xanthium*). In the bur of the cocklebur plant, there are two seeds, one borne higher up in the bur, called the upper seed, and one borne lower in the bur, called the lower seed. Crocker (6) found that the seed coat of both seeds is freely permeable to water and that the lower seed will germinate under normal conditions of moisture and temperature. The upper seed will not germinate under these conditions unless the seed coat is punctured or removed. However, if the upper seed is placed under high oxygen conditions, it germinates readily. Crocker concluded that the seed coat of the upper seed limits the supply of oxygen to the embryo so that the minimum needed for germination cannot be reached. Subjection of the seed to high concentrations of oxygen overcomes this block in germination. Later work by Shull (37, 38) and Thornton (41) demonstrated the accuracy of Crocker's observations. It was clearly demonstrated by these two workers that the naked embryo of both the upper and lower seed has a much lower oxygen requirement than the intact seed, and with an increase in temperature, there is a decrease in the oxygen requirement. For the naked embryo of the upper seed, 1.5% O_2 is needed at 21°C and 0.9% O_2 at 30°C for 100% germination. When the upper seed is left intact, the oxygen requirement for germination increases considerably. Pure oxygen is needed at 21°C and 80% O_2 at 30°C to give 100% germination. Some of Thornton's data are given in Figure 22-3. It is not clear, as yet, whether

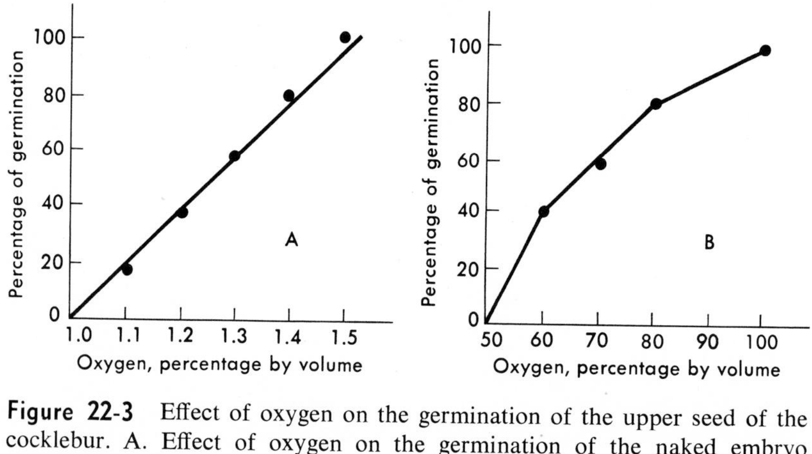

Figure 22-3 Effect of oxygen on the germination of the upper seed of the cocklebur. A. Effect of oxygen on the germination of the naked embryo (seed coat removed). B. Effect of oxygen on the germination of the intact seed. Temperature held at 21°C. Note the striking difference in oxygen requirement for germination between the naked embryo and the intact seed. (Data from N. C. Thornton. 1935. Contri. Boyce Thompson Inst. 10: 201.)

the limiting of oxygen supply by the seed coat retards metabolic activity to the point of blocking germination or the high oxygen concentrations have some other function, which promotes germination. For example, Wareing and Foda (53) have claimed that high oxygen tensions cause the oxidation of an inhibitor present in the upper seed, thus allowing germination.

Mechanically restricting the growth of the embryo. Seed coats may be freely permeable to both oxygen and water, yet still affect a dormant state in a seed. For example, the seeds of the pigweed (*Amaranthus retroflexus*) have a seed coat permeable to oxygen and water, but strong enough to resist embryo expansion (27). These seeds may sometime lie dormant but viable for many years.

Where germination is inhibited by mechanical resistance of the seed coat or impermeability of the coat to water or oxygen, dormancy may be broken by scarification. This term is used to define any treatment that renders the seed coat permeable to water and/or oxygen or weakens the seed coat so that embryo expansion is not physically retarded. Scarification may be accomplished in various ways, but may be roughly divided into two general catagories, (1) *mechanical scarification* and (2) *chemical scarification*. Mechanical scarification of hard-coated seeds is effected by any treatment of the seeds that will crack or scratch the seed coat, such as shaking the seeds with some abrasive material (e.g., sand) or scratching or nicking the coat with a knife. The cracks or scratches resulting from such treatment promote germination by decreasing the resistance of the seed coat to water and/or water absorption and to embryo expansion.

Chemical scarification is also a very effective way of breaking dormancy resulting from the seed coat. Dipping seeds into strong acids, such as sulfuric acid, or into organic solvents, such as acetone or alcohol, can break this type of dormancy. Even boiling water may be a successful treatment in this respect. As in mechanical scarification, chemical scarification breaks dormancy by weakening the seed coat.

Immature embryo

Failure of a seed to germinate may be a consequence of partial development of the embryo. Germination will occur only when embryo development is complete, and this may occur during or before the germination process (26). Dormancy due to immature embryos may be found in Orchidaceae and Ovobancheae, as well as some *Fraxinus* and *Ranunculus* species. Dormancy due to immature embryos can only be broken by allowing the embryo to complete development within the seed in an environment favorable to germination.

After-ripening

A large number of plants produce seeds that do not germinate immediately, but do so after a period of time under normal conditions for germination. A prerequisite to germination for this type of seed, then, is a period of *after-ripening*. In nature, after-ripening occurs during the period between the fall of the seed to the ground in the autumn and its germination the following spring. During this time, the seeds are covered over with debris and winter snows.

After-ripening occurs for some species during dry storage, and for others moisture and low temperatures are necessary. The latter process is called *stratification*. Natural stratification occurs when seeds shed in the fall are covered over with cold soil, debris, and snow. Man has learned to copy and improve on nature in this respect by devising a method of arti-

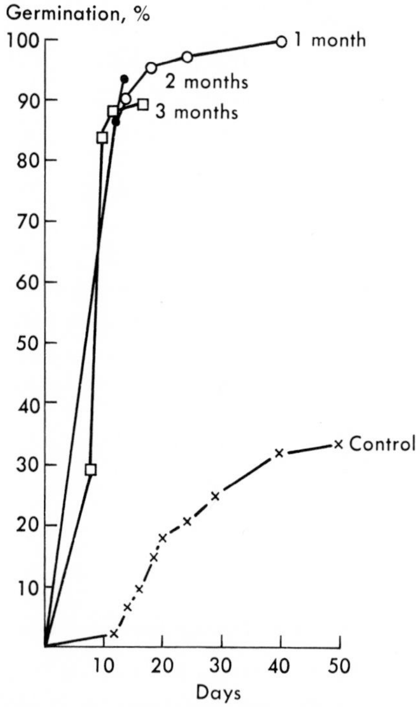

Figure 22-4 Effects of artificial stratification at 5°C for one, two, and three months on the germination of *Pinus rigida* seeds. (After W. Crocker. 1948. Growth of plants. Reinhold Publishing Corp., New York.)

ficial stratification. In artificial stratification, layers of seeds are alternated with layers of moistened sphagnum, sand, or some other appropriate material, and stored at low temperatures. The effect of artificial stratification on the germination of *Pinus rigida* may be seen in Figure 22-4.

Because many workers refer to the period of after-ripening as a dormant or rest period, the implication persists that nothing is occurring within the embryo during this time. However, many studies have demonstrated that considerable physiological activity may be observed during the so-called after-ripening or dormant period (33, 31). The effect of after-ripening time and temperature on growth of the embryonic axis of cherry seeds may be seen in Figure 22-5.

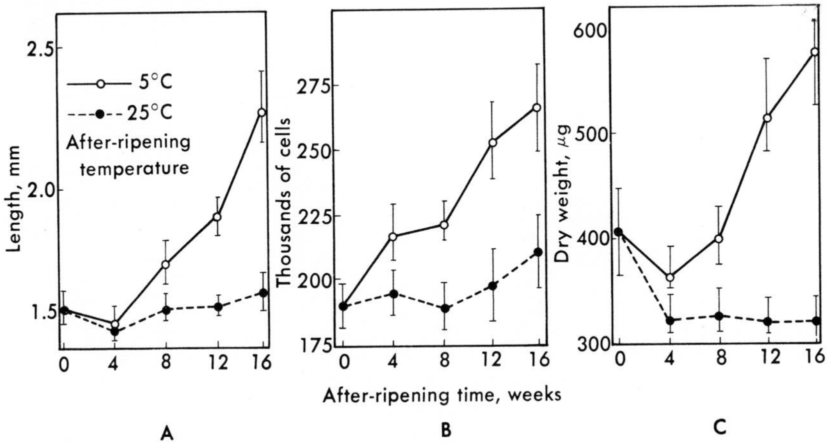

Figure 22-5 The effect of after-ripening time and temperature on growth and dry weight in the embryonic axis of cherry seeds. A. Axis length. B. Number of cells per axis. C. Dry weight per axis. The vertical lines represent the standard error, plus or minus, of the mean. (After B. M. Pollock and H. O. Olney. 1959. Plant Physiol. 34: 131.)

Specific light requirements

Seeds vary considerably in their response to light with respect to germination. Some seeds have an absolute requirement for light to germinate. In other seeds, exposure to light is inhibitory to germination and in still others, germination is associated with a photoperiodic response, that is, an alternation of light and dark periods. All this is made even more complex by the fact that temperature may interact with light in the germination of many seeds.

As in most studies where light is implicated as a catalytic agent, a search is made for the most effective wavelengths. Action spectra for the promotion and inhibition of Grand Rapids lettuce (4) and pepper grass seeds (48) have been obtained, describing red light as promotive (maximum near 660 mμ) and far-red radiation as inhibitory (maximum near 735 mμ). A series of investigations by government scientists at Beltsville, Maryland have presented convincing evidence for the existence of a pigment system absorbing in these wavelengths. The pigment is called *phytochrome*. The action spectra for the promotion and inhibition of lettuce and pepper grass seeds are shown in Figure 22-6.

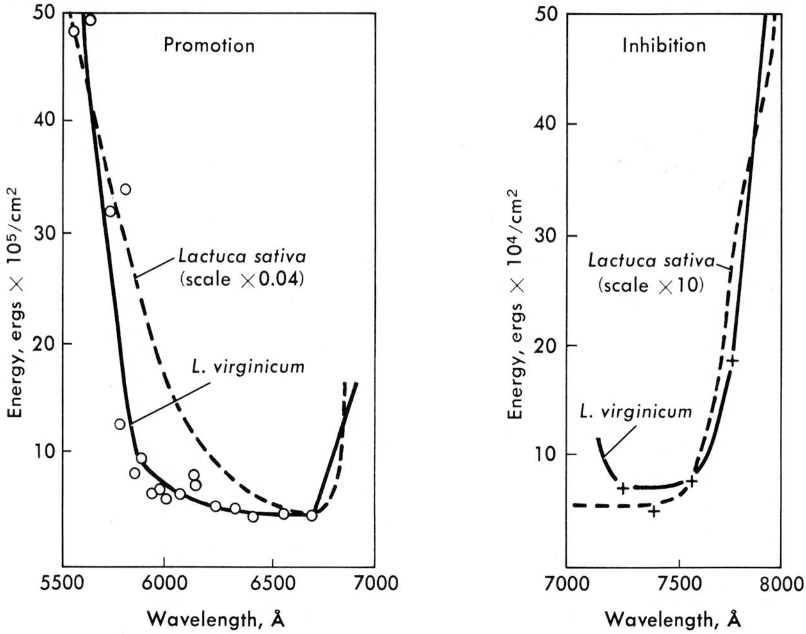

Figure 22-6 Action spectra for promotion and inhibition of germination of seeds of *Lepidium virginicum* and of *Lactuca sativa* to 50%. (After E. H. Toole et al. 1956. Ann. Rev. Plant Physiol. 7: 299. Redrawn from E. H. Toole. 1959. Am. Assoc. Advan. Sci., Washington, D. C. 55: 89.)

A detailed discussion of the effects of light on the germination of seeds is beyond the scope of this book. Since a good deal of this type of study has been done on Grand Rapids lettuce seeds, it would be to our advantage to discuss the more important findings of this work and mention other investigations only where they might supplement or detract from these findings.

Effect of imbibition. Borthwick et al. (5) found that the response to light of lettuce seeds can be modified by the amount of time the seeds are allowed to imbibe water before exposure. Red light promotion of germination increases with time of exposure up to 10 hours where a plateau is reached. However, if the seeds are allowed to imbibe for more than 20 hours, the germination response falls off. In contrast, the inhibitory effect of far red irradiation has a tendency to decrease as previous imbibition time increases up to 10 hours. In keeping with this contrast, the sensitivity of lettuce seeds to far red irradiation increases when the seeds used imbibe for more than 20 hours.

Reversible effect. The fact that promotion and inhibition of germination by red and far red irradiation is reversible was first discovered by Borthwick et al. (4). They found that red light promotion of lettuce seed germination can be reversed if far red irradiation immediately follows red light treatment. If the seeds are again treated with red light, germination will again be promoted. In other words, the system is repeatedly reversible, the last treatment determining the response of the seeds (Table 22-1).

Table 22-1 Promotion and inhibition of germination by red, R, and far red, I, irradiation. The seeds were irradiated at 26°C and then allowed to germinate at 20°C. Note reversible effect of one treatment on the other.[a]

Irradiation	*Germination, at 20°C, %*
R	70
R-I	6
R-I-R	74
R-I-R-I	6
R-I-R-I-R	76
R-I-R-I-R-I	7
R-I-R-I-R-I-R	81
R-I-R-I-R-I-R-I	7

[a] Reprinted from "Action of Light on Lettuce-seed Germination" by H. A. Borthwick, S. B. Hendricks, E. H. Toole, and V. K. Toole, *Botanical Gazette* 115: 102 by permission of The University of Chicago Press. Copyright 1954.

This same reversible effect of red–far red treatment was later found to be active in pepper grass seed (48) and, subsequently, in many other seeds. The red–far red system active in lettuce seeds is similar, and in all probability, is identical to the red–far red phytochrome system found active in the flowering of some plants, expansion of bean leaf discs, etiolation, and unfolding of the plumular hook of bean seedlings. That the red–far red reversible reaction involving the pigment phytochrome is a pure photoreaction has been demonstrated by Ikuma and Thimann (23). They demonstrated that the reaction is independent of temperature or oxygen.

Time factor. In order for good reversal of red light promotion to occur, far red irradiation should follow immediately. If far red irradiation is delayed, inhibition of germination is less marked. Toole et al. (45) found that lettuce seeds fail to respond to far red irradiation 12 hours after exposure to red light. Most likely, at this time the processes leading to germination have reached such an advanced state that reversal is impossible.

Temperature effect. As mentioned above, photocontrol of seed germination is, in many cases, interrelated with temperature. This can be seen in Table 22-2, which shows a decrease in sensitivity to light with an increase in temperature above 25°C (44). Apparently, the stimulatory conditions

Table 22-2 The effect of temperature on the photocontrol of the seed germination of two varieties of lettuce seeds after exposure to red light or darkness.[a]

Variety and germination temperature, °C	*Seeds germinating under indicated light condition, %*	
	Red	*Darkness*
White Boston		
10	99	95
15	99	78
20	98	57
25	1	0
Grand Rapids		
15	94	52
20	96	40
25	96	10
30	1	0

[a] After E. H. Toole. 1959. P. 89 *In* R. B. Withrow (ed.), Photoperiodism and related phenomena in plants and animals. American Association for the Advancement of Science, Washington, D.C. 55: 89.

for germination promoted by red light may be thermally reversed as well as being reversed by far red irradiation.

Another more complex example of temperature-light interaction may be found in the germination of pepper grass seeds (*Lepidium virginicum*). Maximum germination is achieved if the seeds are kept at a cool temperature before irradiation with red light and after being irradiated are kept at relatively high temperatures for a period of time (48). These relationships may be seen in Table 22-3.

Table 22-3 Light and temperature interaction in the germination of *Lepidium virginicum* seeds. Seeds were irradiated with red light in the region 5800–7000 Å.[a]

		Germination, %	
Temperature, °C, first 2 days	*Temperature, °C, 3rd–6th day*	*Irradiated seeds*	*Nonirradiated seeds*
15	15	37	0
25	25	41	0
15	25	92	0
25	15	32	0

[a] After E. H. Toole et al. 1955. Plant Physiol. 30: 15.

Specific temperature requirements

In discussing the various aspects of seed germination, we have mentioned several times the importance of temperature in the prolonging or breaking of dormancy. Many seeds need a period of prechilling under moist conditions before adequate germination can take place. In natural and artificial stratification, this requirement is satisfied. After the cold requirement is satisfied, the actual germination, in most situations, takes place most efficiently at about 20°C.

In some seeds, the cold requirement is modified by the age of the seed. For example, seeds of *Brassica juncea* show a definite cold requirement immediately after harvest, which decreases with age (47). Immediately after harvest, 97% of the seed germinate at temperatures of 10 or 15°C, 63% at 20°C, and only 8% at 25°C. However, after 3 weeks, 95% of the seeds germinate at 25°C. The sensitivity of seeds to high temperatures varies greatly. In some, it may persist for a long time, while in others, as in the case of *B. juncea,* sensitivity is lost in 3 weeks.

In many seeds, an alteration of temperatures gives maximum germination. In some cases, such as with *Poa pratensis,* alteration of low and high temperatures repeated several times gives the best results. We have already mentioned how a single alteration from 15° to 25°C in connection with light treatment of pepper grass seeds may significantly increase germination (Table 22-2).

As in many other seeds, low temperatures promote germination of the light-sensitive Grand Rapids lettuce seeds, and high temperatures inhibit it. At present, we know very little of the mechanism involved in low temperature promotion and high temperature inhibition of germination. However, it has been suggested that low temperatures can substitute for red light promotion of light-sensitive lettuce seeds (23). With respect to time, low temperature promotion of lettuce seed germination is much less efficient than red light promotion (Table 22-4). It should be noted from

Table 22-4 Effects of far-red light on germination of Grand Rapids lettuce seeds treated with low temperature (2°C). Irradiation with 5 min of far-red light was given at 25°C either immediately before or immediately after the cold treatment. Control seeds imbibed and were germinated at 25°C throughout, and irradiated with red or far-red light at 1.5 hours after the beginning of soaking. The percent of inhibition for far-red treatment is calculated with respect to the corresponding dark control.[a]

Treatment before final transfer to 25°C for germination	*Germination, %*	*Inhibition, %*
1 day at 2°C, then far-red	6	80
dark control	30	—
1.5 hours at 25°C, then far-red, than 1 day at 2°C	14	73
dark control	51	—
3 days at 2°C, then far-red	59	23
dark control	77	—
1.5 hours at 25°C, then far-red, then 3 days at 2°C	65	29
dark control	92	—
25°C control, 5 min red	92	—
25°C control, 5 min far-red	5	70
25°C control, dark control	17	—

[a] After H. Ikuma and K. V. Thimann. 1964. Plant Physiol. 39: 756.

Table 22-4 that far-red irradiation cannot reverse low temperature stimulation, suggesting that low temperature promotion of germination acts by a system other than that controlled by phytochrome (23).

Presence of germination inhibitors

Inhibition of germination may be caused by a great many compounds. Any compound that is toxic in general to any of the essential life processes will, of course, inhibit germination and even kill the seed if present in sufficient amounts. We are not concerned here with this type of inhibition, but with inhibition produced by natural compounds present in the seed. These compounds are often the cause of dormancy and usually act by blocking some process essential to germination. Natural germination inhibitors, however, do not reduce the viability of the seed nor produce any growth abnormalities in the seedling after germination.

Natural inhibitors are not confined to any particular part of the seed and may even be found in structures covering the seed (e.g., the glumes of oat grains contain an inhibitor). Inhibitors of germination have been found in the pulp or juice of the fruit containing the seed, seed coat, endosperm, embryo, etc. (see review by Evenari (12)). In other words, the presence of germination inhibitors is very common and widespread among plants. Some of the natural inhibitors of germination that have been identified are coumarin, parasorbic acid, ammonia, phthalids, ferulic acid, and dehydracetic acid. There are many others, but this list will suffice for our purposes. The molecular structures for five of these inhibitors are given in Figure 22-7.

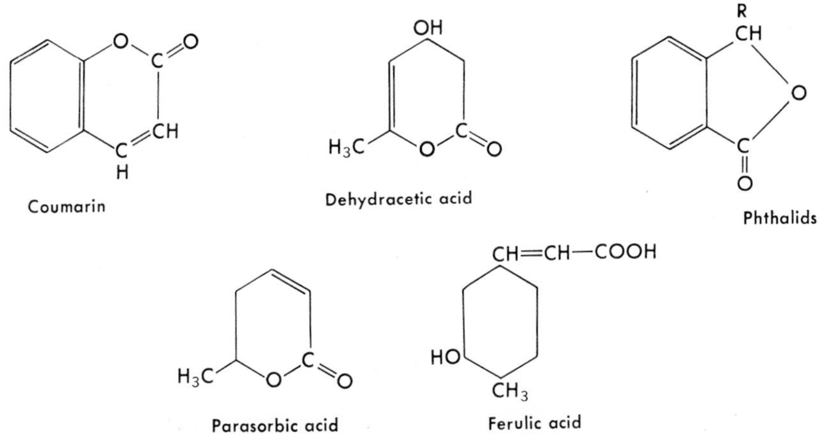

Figure 22-7 The molecular structures of five germination inhibitors: coumarin, dehydracetic acid, phthalids, parasorbic acid, and ferulic acid. (After E. H. Toole et al. 1956. Ann. Rev. Plant Physiol. 7: 299.)

Compounds stimulating germination

The promotion of germination by various compounds has been demonstrated a great number of times on many different seeds. Of the numerous promoters of germination known, the most popular and widely used are potassium nitrate (KNO_3), thiourea ($NH_2-\overset{\overset{\displaystyle S}{\|}}{C}-NH_2$), ethylene ($C_2H_4$), gibberellin, and kinetin. Thiourea, gibberellin, and kinetin are interesting in that they have, in certain instances, substituted for light requirements in light-sensitive seeds. Whether or not this is a true substitution has been disputed. Nevertheless, dark promotion of germination has been demonstrated by these compounds.

It is quite obvious from our discussion of seed germination and dormancy that there are a great many factors controlling the emergence of the embryo from the seed. Mechanical resistance of the seed coat and its permeability properties may be important factors in germination. Embryos may be immature or need a period of after-ripening, usually facilitated by low temperatures and moist conditions, before germination may occur. Certain seeds have specific light and temperature requirements, and in many cases these factors are interrelated. Finally, the inhibition and promotion of germination may be controlled by several natural and artificial compounds.

BUD DORMANCY

Before giving rise to vegetative or reproductive growth, the buds of many plant species go through a period of dormancy. A common occurrence of tree growth in temperate regions is the entrance of buds into a dormant state in late summer, and their emergence from this condition the following spring to produce new leaf and flower growth. Bud dormancy of this type may usually be broken with cold temperature treatment somewhat analogous to that given to cold-requiring seeds for germination. That is, many tree species, with buds in a dormant state, may be kept in that condition indefinitely if provided the artificial warmth of a greenhouse. However, if subjected to low temperatures (0–10°C) for a period of time and then returned to warm conditions, dormancy will be broken and growth will ensue.

Photoperiodism and bud dormancy

One is tempted to assign a role to low temperatures in inducing dormancy as well as in breaking it. However, with respect to entering dormancy, the buds of woody species respond more to day length than to cold temperatures (see review by Wareing (52)). Apparently, the shortening of the day length associated with the coming of fall and winter is an important factor in bud dormancy of woody species. Thus, Wareing (50, 51) has demonstrated that bud dormancy in woody species is a photoperiodic phenomenon, being caused by short day lengths and relieved by long day lengths.

Perception of light stimulus. In an earlier discussion, we learned that the site of perception of the photoperiodic stimulus concerned with flowering is located in the leaves. However in many cases, the condition of bud dormancy is characteristic of those woody species that lose their leaves before the onset of winter. This problem of the association of photoperiodism with bud dormancy in the absence of the usual organs of photoperiodic perception has been solved by Wareing (50). He found that the buds of *leafless* seedlings of beech (*Fagus sylvatica*) are capable of photoperiodic perception, breaking dormancy under long days and remaining dormant under day lengths of 12 hours or less (Table 22-5). The breaking of

Table 22-5 Effect of length of photoperiod on the breaking of dormancy of beech buds.[a]

Daily light period, hours	*Total number of plants*	*No. of plants breaking dormancy after 46 days*	*Time for 50% of plants to show breaking, days*
12	11	0	—
16	12	5	46
20	11	9	14
24	11	11	14

[a] After P. F. Waring. 1953. Physiol. Plant. 6: 692.

dormancy of beech buds may be accomplished in the absence of a low temperature treatment.

Not in every case of bud dormancy is the bud the organ of photoperiodic perception. For example, in actively growing seedlings of *Acer pseudoplatanus* and *Robinia pseudacacia,* the photoperiodic perception is primarily mediated through the mature leaves (51).

As in the flowering response, the response of buds to photoperiodism is actually controlled by the length of the dark period, rather than the day length. Thus, Wareing (50) found that although buds of *Fagus sylvatica* remain dormant under short light periods, alternation of short light periods with short dark periods breaks dormancy. He also demonstrated how an interruption of a long dark period, which would normally keep buds in a dormant state, by a light break of 1 hour is sufficient to break dormancy.

Dormancy-inducing hormone

The evidence is strong that in bud dormancy the organs of photoperiodic perception are the leaves and buds. Since dormancy sets in after the photoperiodic stimulus has been received, a reasonable assumption would be that reception of the stimulus causes certain changes leading to the production of a dormancy-inducing hormone. The first suggestion that bud dormancy in woody plants is controlled by growth-inhibiting substances produced in the bud was advanced by Hemberg (16, 17). Hemberg based his suggestion on the fact that the endogenous growth inhibitor level increases with dormancy and decreases with release of dormancy. Since Hemberg's work, several studies have been made on different woody species correlating the level of endogenous inhibitors with induction and release of dormancy (20, 3, 32). And in agreement with our earlier discussion on the role of photoperiodism in bud dormancy, short day induction of bud dormancy has been shown in some species to be paralleled with increased levels of inhibitors in buds and leaves (29, 32, 36).

In all of the above studies, actual induction of bud dormancy in a vigorously growing seedling by application of extracts from the leaves of that species had not been accomplished. This next step, however, was demonstrated by Eagles and Wareing (11). They found that when a partially purified methanol extract of birch leaves is applied to the leaves of birch seedlings on a photoperiod usually used to maintain spring growth, growth is arrested and bud dormancy sets in. They also found that the effect of the extracted inhibitor can be overcome by gibberellic acid. This last discovery was not too surprising, since gibberellin is known to overcome bud dormancy of many tree species. However, this fact implies that endogenous gibberellin may be involved in the regulation of bud dormancy. The cold treatment required by many buds to break dormancy may be a means of bringing endogenous gibberellin to the level needed to break dormancy. The fact that higher concentrations of gibberellin-like substances have been found in bolted cold-requiring plants, as compared to the nonbolted form (13, 30), supports the above supposition that the level of endogenous gibberellin is raised as a result of low temperatures. Thus, bud dormancy in woody species may be regulated by some balance or ratio between a dormancy-inducing hormone and gibberellins. Eagles and Wareing (11) have proposed that the term *dormin* be used for substances that appear to function as endogenous dormancy inducers. The relationships discussed above are given in Figure 22-8.

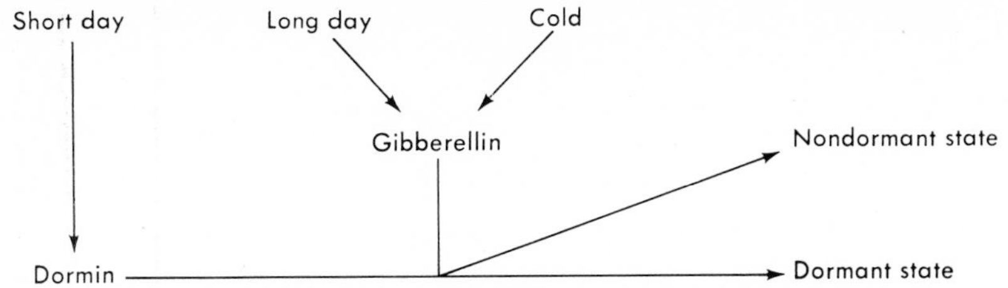

Figure 22-8 Diagrammatic representation of those factors leading to the inducement and release of bud dormancy in woody species.

Dormancy of the potato tuber

Potato bud dormancy is a good example of bud dormancy in a nonwoody or herbacious plant. The potato tuber is a modified, fleshy underground stem, containing several buds in localities commonly referred to as "eyes." If the newly formed potato tuber is placed under conditions favorable to growth, sprouting will not take place. That this is not due to apical dominance, which is prevalent in potatoes, is demonstrated by the persistence of the dormant state in the individual buds separated from the tuber. Dry storage at 35°C or moist storage 20°C have been found to eliminate potato bud dormancy, low temperatures apparently having no effect (43).

GROWTH-INHIBITING SUBSTANCES

In a series of studies on potato bud dormancy, Hemberg (15, 16, 17, 18) demonstrated that substances extracted from potato peels of dormant tubers are capable of counteracting the effect of IAA in the *Avena* curvature test. The group of inhibitors extracted by Hemberg were made up of acid and neutral substances. The acid inhibitors could not be detected at termination of dormancy (19). Paper chromatographic analysis showed that the acid inhibitor present in potato peels of dormant potatoes is *inhibitor-β* (2, 49), a complex of organic compounds first identified by Bennet-Clark and Kefford (1) from paper chromatograms of plant extracts. It is interesting to note that inhibitor-β has recently been extracted from dormant buds of the silver maple (24).

A correlation has been shown between increase and decrease of inhibitor-β with respect to onset and release of potato bud dormancy, and inhibitor-β has been extracted from the dormant buds of at least one woody species. However, inhibitor-β cannot be compared to "dormin" extracted by Eagles and Wareing. In no study has it been demonstrated that inhibitor-β could induce dormancy in a nondormant potato or a vigorously growing seedling of some woody species.

Compounds breaking bud dormancy

The regulation of dormancy release has academic as well as practical importance. Controlling the time of release of dormancy by artificial manipulation of the environment, or by the use of active compounds, many times will reveal some of the mechanisms involved in dormancy, thus contributing to our understanding of the overall process. The release of dormancy by some artificial means often aids the farmer in an economic way. For example, the release of potato bud dormancy of newly harvested tubers will allow some growers to produce a second crop. This, of course, would depend on the length of the growing season. Some of the chemicals found useful in the release of dormancy are ethylenechlorohydrin, thiourea, and gibberellin.

Ethylenechlorohydrin ($ClCH_2CH_2OH$). A thorough study of the dormancy-breaking abilities of many different compounds by Denny (8, 9) brought into prominence one especially active compound, ethylenechlorohydrin. This compound proved highly effective in inducing sprouting in dormant potato tubers with the added attraction of having a wide safety margin between active and toxic dosages. In addition, ethylenechlorohydrin proved to be very successful in breaking bud dormancy of fruit trees when applied in vapor form.

Several metabolic changes may take place as a result of ethylenechlorohydrin application. A study of its effect on dormant potato tubers showed that there is a rise in respiration, catalase and peroxidase activity, sucrose, and glutathione. There is a drop in H^+ ion and citric acid concentrations. Most likely, citric acid is being utilized as a substate in respiration, and its decrease in content decreases the H^+ ion concentration (7). These relationships may be seen in Figure 22-9.

Thiourea (NH_2CSNH_2). Although not as effective as ethylenechlorohydrin, thiourea has proved effective in forcing sprouting in dormant potato tubers. Thiourea has an unusual effect in that it may cause the growth of several bud primordia in one "eye." As many as eight sprouts have been observed growing from one eye (7). In contrast, ethylenechlorohydrin causes the growth of only one sprout in each eye. It is interesting to note that reduced oxygen pressures have an effect somewhat similar to thiourea, causing multiple sprouting (42).

Gibberellin. A special case can be made for gibberellin acting as a bud dormancy breaker. In contrast to ethylenechlorohydrin and thiourea, it is a natural compound and may be involved as a controlling factor in the overall process of bud dormancy (see Figure 22-8). In earlier discussions, we learned that gibberellin has a profound influence on dormant shoots and seeds, promoting the growth of both when applied. One would logically

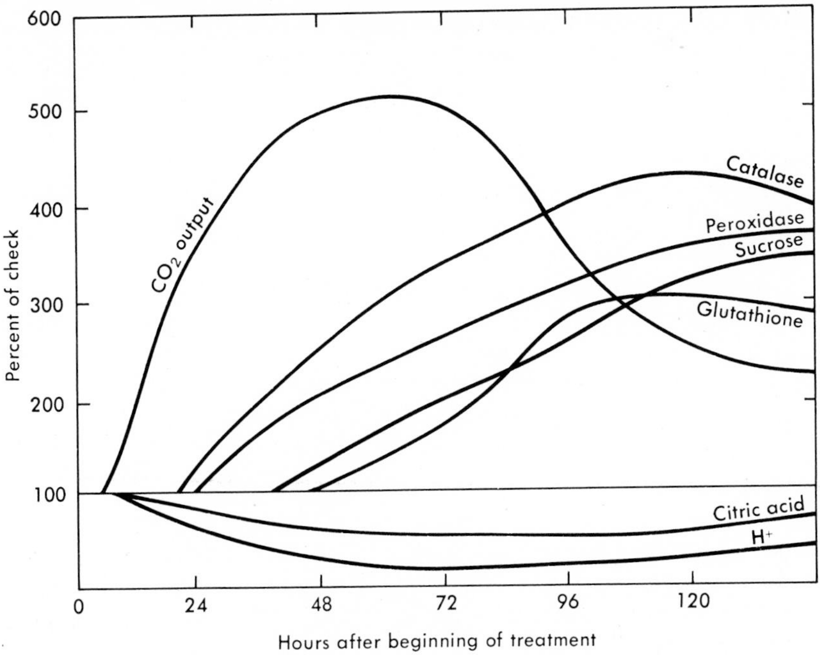

Figure 22-9 Effect of ethylenechlorhydrin on the metabolism of potato tubers (Data of L. P. Miller et al. 1936. Contri. Boyce Thompson Inst. 8: 41. Redrawn from W. Crocker. 1948. Growth of plants. Reinhold Publishing Corp., New York.)

assume that gibberellin would also be capable of breaking bud dormancy. This was eventually demonstrated with excellent success on dormant potato tubers (34, 35) and on dormant peach buds (10). Generally in those plants requiring a low temperature period to break dormancy, gibberellin will substitute for the cold treatment and force the release of dormancy (Figure 22-10).

Figure 22-10 Effect of the application of gibberellin on the breaking of bud dormancy of Elberta peach. Buds were treated in March after 164 hours below 8°C. (Data of C. W. Donaho and D. R. Walker. 1957. Science 126: 1178. Redrawn from A. C. Leopold. 1964. Plant growth and development. McGraw-Hill Book Co., New York.)

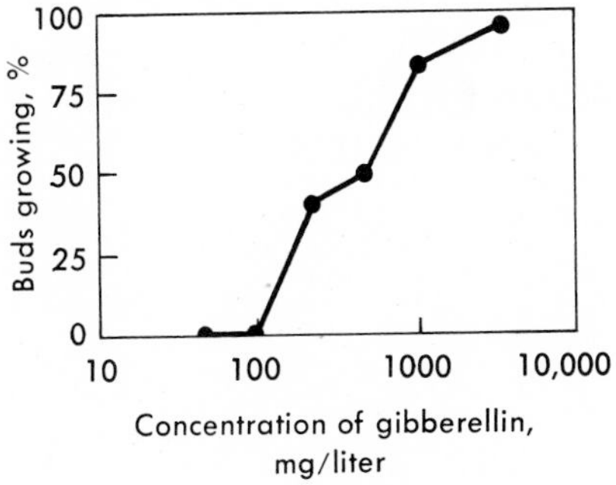

Much work has been done on the effect of gibberellin on potato bud dormancy. Gibberellin can induce sprouting of potato tubers still on the plant (25) and in harvested tubers at any time in their dormant period. Therefore, the induction of sprouting by gibberellin may be accomplished anywhere from the beginning of tuber enlargement to the end of the dormant period (40). The remarkable ability of gibberellin to induce sprouting when applied as a spray to potato plants 4, 2, and 1 week before harvest can be seen in Table 22-6.

As mentioned before, endogenous gibberellins may play a major role in the control of dormancy. This assumption has been given major support

Table 22-6 Percentage of sprouted tubers at harvest from plants that received preharvest foliar sprays of gibberellin at 4, 2, and 1 week before harvest.[a]

Gibberellin, mg/liter	*Tubers sprouted at harvest, %*		
	4 weeks	*2 weeks*	*1 week*
0	0.0	1.4	0.2
10	3.0	1.5	1.5
50	58.3	18.0	0.4
100	75.6	34.3	2.1
500	83.6	50.0	5.8

[a] After L. F. Lippert et al. 1958. Plant Physiol. 33: 132.

in several recent studies. For example, in 1959 it was reported that gibberellin-like substances are present in potato tubers and that higher levels can be detected in sprouting tubers than in newly harvested tubers (39). Subsequently, Smith and Rappaport (40) reported that the concentration of endogenous gibberellin remains low during the dormant period, but rises thirtyfold after sprouting begins (Figure 22-11).

SUMMARY

Bud dormancy is a common phenomenon found in a wide variety of plant species. It is essentially a protective process, allowing the very delicate meristems to survive through the cold temperatures of winter without undue harm.

Since the recognition of dormancy as a plant process, immense progress has been made by man toward an understanding of this phenomenon. He has learned to control it by application of chemicals or by artificially ma-

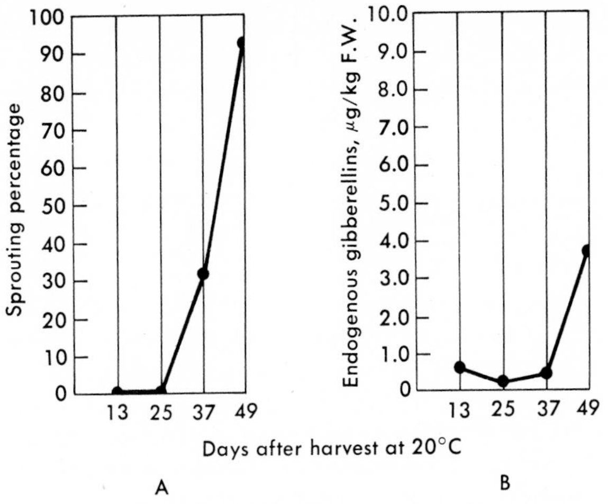

Figure 22-11 Relation between sprouting Red Pontiac potato tubers (A) and level of endogenous gibberellins in potato peels and buds during and after-rest (B). (After O. E. Smith and L. Rappaport. 1961. *In* R. F. Gould (ed.), Gibberellins. Am. Chem. Soc. 28: 42.)

nipulating the environment so that inducement or release of dormancy can be predicted. The individual steps leading to dormancy are slowly being uncovered in a general way at the moment, but with future promise of complete analysis. As in many other plant processes, it appears that the process of dormancy is controlled by natural growth regulators, among which gibberellins, kinins, and IAA have been implicated.

BIBLIOGRAPHY

1. Bennet-Clark, T. A., and N. P. Kefford. 1953. Chromatography of the growth substances in plant extracts. Nature 171: 645.
2. Blommaert, K. L. J. 1954. Growth and inhibiting substances in relation to the rest-period of the potato tuber. Nature 174: 970.
3. Blommaert, K. L. J. 1955. The significance of auxins and growth inhibiting substances in relation to winter dormancy of the peach. Dept. Agr. South Africa Sci. Bull. 368: 1.
4. Borthwick, H. A., S. B. Hendricks, M. W. Parker, E. H. Toole, and V. K. Toole. 1952. A reversible photoreaction controlling seed germination. Proc. Natl. Acad. Sci. U.S. 38: 662.
5. Borthwick, H. A., S. B. Hendricks, E. H. Toole, and V. K. Toole. 1954. Action of light on lettuce-seed germination. Botan. Gaz. 115: 205.

6. Crocker, W. 1906. Role of seed coats in delayed germination. Botan. Gaz. 42: 265.
7. Crocker, W. 1948. Growth of plants. Reinhold Publishing Corp., New York.
8. Denny, F. E. 1926. Hastening the sprouting of dormant potato tubers. Am. J. Botan. 13: 118.
9. Denny, F. E. 1926. Effect of thiourea upon bud inhibition and apical dominance of potato. Botan. Gaz. 81: 297.
10. Donaho, C. W. and D. R. Walker. 1957. Effect of gibberellic acid on breaking of the rest period in Elberta peach. Science 126: 1178.
11. Eagles, C. F., and P. F. Wareing. 1963. Dormancy regulators in woody plants. Experimental induction of dormancy in *Betula pubescens.* Nature 199: 874.
12. Evenari, M. 1949. Germination inhibitors. Botan. Rev. 15: 153.
13. Harada, H., and J. P. Nitsch. 1959. Changes in endogenous growth substances during flower development. Plant Physiol. 34: 409.
14. Harrington, G. T. 1916. Agricultural value of impermeable seeds. J. Agr. Res. 6: 761.
15. Hemberg, T. 1947. Studies of auxins and growth-inhibiting substances in the potato tuber and their significance with regard to its rest period. Acta Hort. Berg. 14: 133.
16. Hemberg, T. The significance of growth-inhibiting substances and auxins for the rest period of the potato tuber. Physiol. Plant 2: 24.
17. Hemberg, T. 1949. Growth-inhibiting substances in terminal buds of *Fraxinus.* Physiol. Plant 2: 37.
18. Hemberg, T. 1950. The effect of glutathione on the growth-inhibiting substances in resting potato tubers. Physiol. Plant 3: 17.
19. Hemberg, T. 1952. The significance of the acid growth-inhibiting substances for the rest period of the potato tuber. Physiol. Plant 5: 115.
20. Hendershott, C. H., and L. F. Bailey. 1955. Growth inhibiting substances in dormant flower buds of peach. Proc. Am. Soc. Hort. Sci. 65: 85.
21. Hyde, E. O. 1954. The function of the hilum in some Papilionaceae in relation to the ripening of the seed and permeability of the testa. Ann. Botan. (London) 18: 241.
22. Ikuma, H., and K. V. Thimann. 1960. Action of gibberellic acid on lettuce seed germination. Plant Physiol. 35: 557.
23. Ikuma, H., and K. V. Thimann. 1964. Analysis of germination processes of lettuce seed by means of temperature and anaerobiosis. Plant Physiol. 39: 756.
24. Lane, F. E., and L. F. Bailey. 1964. Isolation and characterization studies on the β-inhibitor in dormant buds of the silver maple, *Acer saccharinum* L. Physiol. Plant 17: 91.
25. Lippert, L. F., L. Rappaport, and H. Timm. 1958. Systematic induction of sprouting in white potatoes by foliar applications of gibberellin. Plant Physiol. 33: 132.

26. Mayer, A. M., and A. Poljakoff-Mayber. 1963. The germination of seeds. The Macmillan Co., New York.
27. Meyer, B. S., and D. B. Anderson. 1952. Plant physiology. D. Van Nostrand Co., Princeton, N. J.
28. Miller, L. P., J. D. Guthrie, and F. E. Denny. 1936. Induced changes in respiration rates and time relations in the changes in internal factors. Contri. Boyce Thompson Inst. 8: 41.
29. Nitsch, J. P. 1957. Growth responses of woody plants to photoperiodic stimuli. Proc. Am. Soc. Hort. Sci. 70: 512.
30. Nitsch, J. P. 1959. Changes in endogenous growth regulating substances during flower initiation. Fourth Intern. Congr. Biochem. Pergamon Press, London. 6: 141.
31. Olney, H. O., and B. M. Pollock. 1960. Studies of rest period. II Nitrogen and phosphorus changes in embryonic organs of after-ripening cherry seed. Plant Physiol. 35: 970.
32. Phillips, I. D. J., and P. F. Wareing. 1958. Effect of photoperiodic conditions on the level of growth inhibitors in *Acer pseudoplatanus*. Naturwiss. 13: 317.
33. Pollock, B. M., and H. O. Olney. 1959. Studies of the rest period. I. Growth, translocation, and respiratory changes in the embryonic organs of the after-ripening cherry seed. Plant Physiol. 34: 131.
34. Rappaport, L., L. F. Lippert, and H. Timm. 1957. Sprouting, plant growth, and tuber formation as affected by chemical treatment of white potato seed pieces. I. Breaking dormancy with gibberellic acid. Am. Potato J. 34: 254.
35. Rappaport, L., H. Timm, and L. Lippert. 1958. Gibberellin on white potatoes. Calif. Agr. 12: 4, 14.
36. Robinson, P. M., P. F. Wareing, and T. H. Thomas. 1963. Dormancy regulators in woody plants. Isolation of the inhibitor varying with photoperiod in *Acer pseudoplatanus*. Nature 199: 875.
37. Shull, C. A. 1911. The oxygen minimum and the germination of *Xanthium* seeds. Botan. Gaz. 52: 453.
38. Shull, C. A. 1914. The role of oxygen in germination. Botan. Gaz. 57: 64.
39. Smith, O. E., and L. Rappaport. 1959. Abstracts, Meeting Am. Soc. Plant Physiol., AAAS Meeting, San Diego, Calif.
40. Smith, O. E., and L. Rappaport. 1961. Endogenous gibberellins in resting and sprouting potato tubers. *In* R. F. Gould (ed.), Gibberellins. Am. Chem. Soc. 28: 42.
41. Thorton, N. C. 1935. Factors influencing germination and development of dormancy in cocklebur seeds. Contri. Boyce Thompson Inst. 7: 477.
42. Thornton, N. C. 1939. Carbon dioxide storage. XIII. Relationship of oxygen to carbon dioxide in breaking dormancy of potato tubers. Contri. Boyce Thompson Inst. 10: 201.
43. Thornton, N. C. 1953. Dormancy *In* W. E. Loomis (ed.), Growth and differentiation in plants. The Iowa State University Press, Ames, Iowa. 137.
44. Toole, E. H. 1959. Effect of light on the germination of seeds. *In* R. B.

Withrow (ed.), Photoperiodism and related phenomena in plants and animals. Am. Assoc. Advan. Sci., Washington, D. C. 55: 89.
45. Toole, E. H., H. A. Borthwick, S. B. Hendricks, and V. K. Toole. 1953. Physiological studies of the effects of light and temperature on seed germination. Proc. Intern. Seed Testing Assoc. 18(2): 267.
46. Toole, E. H., S. B. Hendricks, H. A. Borthwick, and V. K. Toole. 1956. Physiology of seed germination. Ann. Rev. Plant Physiol. 7: 299.
47. Toole, E. H., and V. K. Toole. 1939. Proc. Intern. Seed Testing Assoc. 11: 51.
48. Toole, E. H., V. K. Toole, H. A. Borthwick, and S. B. Hendricks. 1955. Photocontrol of *Lepidium* seed germination. Plant Physiol. 30:15.
49. Varga, M., and L. Ferenczy. 1956. Effect of "rindite" on the development of the growth substances in potato tubers. Nature 178: 1075.
50. Wareing, P. F. 1953. Growth studies in woody species. V. Photoperiodism in dormant buds of *Fagus sylvatica*. Physiol. Plant 6: 692.
51. Wareing, P. F. 1954. Growth studies in woody species. VI. The locus of photoperiodic perception in relation to dormancy. Physiol. Plant 7: 261.
52. Wareing, P. F. 1956. Photoperiodism in woody plants. Ann. Rev. Plant Physiol. 7: 191.
53. Wareing, P. F., and H. A. Foda. 1957. Growth inhibitors and dormancy in *Xanthium* seed. Physiol. Plant 10: 266.

Author index

Numbers in *italic* indicate bibliographic references.

Subject index